California Wildlife:
Conservation Challenges

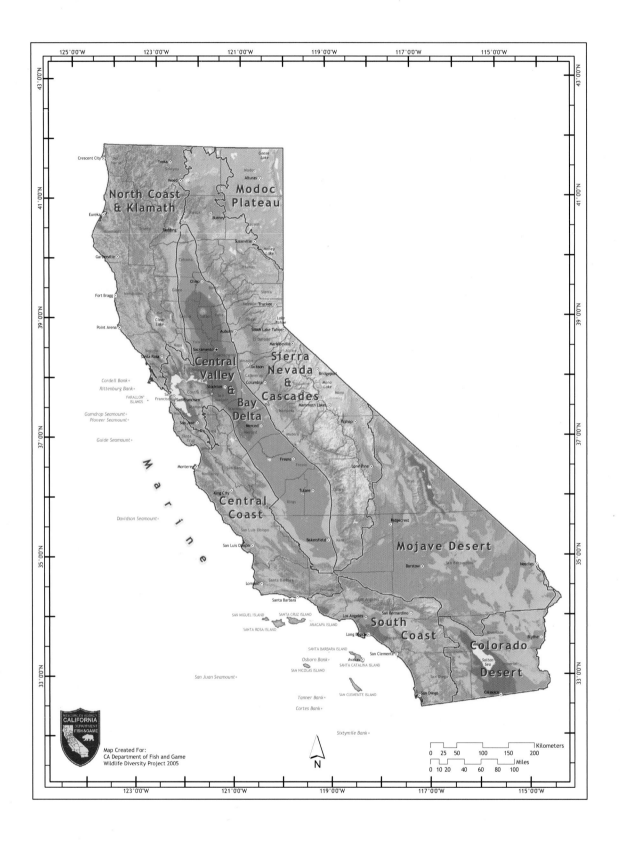

North Coast
& Klamath

Modoc
Plateau

Central
Valley
&
Bay
Delta

Sierra
Nevada
&
Cascades

M a r i n e

Central
Coast

Mojave Desert

South
Coast

Colorado
Desert

Crescent City
Yreka
Weed
Eureka
Garberville
Fort Bragg
Point Arena
Santa Rosa
Sacramento
Stockton
San Francisco
San Jose
Santa Cruz
Monterey
King City
San Luis Obispo
Lompoc
Santa Barbara
Los Angeles
Long Beach
San Diego

Alturas
Burney
Redding
Susanville
Honey Lake
Chico
Truckee
South Lake Tahoe
Auburn
Markleeville
Jackson
Columbia
Bridgeport
Mammoth Lakes
Merced
Fresno
Bishop
Tulare
Lone Pine
Bakersfield
Ridgecrest
Barstow
San Bernardino
Needles
Riverside
Blythe
Avalon
San Clemente
Calexico

Goose Lake
Modoc
Lassen
Plumas
Nevada
Mono Lake

Cordell Bank*
Rittenburg Bank*
FARALLON ISLANDS
Gumdrop Seamount*
Pioneer Seamount*
Guide Seamount*
Davidson Seamount*

SAN MIGUEL ISLAND
SANTA CRUZ ISLAND
SANTA ROSA ISLAND
ANACAPA ISLAND
SANTA BARBARA ISLAND
Osborn Bank*
SAN NICOLAS ISLAND
SANTA CATALINA ISLAND
San Juan Seamount*
SAN CLEMENTE ISLAND
Tanner Bank*
Cortes Bank*
Sixtymile Bank*

Salton Sea

N

RESOURCES AGENCY
CALIFORNIA
DEPARTMENT
FISH&GAME

Map Created For:
CA Department of Fish and Game
Wildlife Diversity Project 2005

Kilometers
0 25 50   100   150   200

Miles
0 10 20   40   60   80   100

California Wildlife: Conservation Challenges

California's Wildlife Action Plan

Prepared by the UC Davis Wildlife Health Center

David Bunn
Andrea Mummert
Marc Hoshovsky
Kirsten Gilardi
Sandra Shanks

California Department of Fish and Game

Design: Alison Kent Cover design: Nancy Ottum

Photo credits: David Bunn, Brandon Cole, Gerald and Buff Corsi/California Academy of Sciences, Mark Cortright, Everette Denney, Jeff Dye, William Flaxington, Global Forest Service, Richard Hall, Jeremy Howell, Paul Ippolito, Sean Lema, Deborah Leonard, Jim Little, Karen McClymonds, Peter Moyle, Pacific Biodiversity Institute, Tim Palmer, Will Richardson, Steve Sosensky, Don Stehsel

Cover photos: Tananarive Aubert, David M. Davies, Tony Dunn, Jeff Dye, Deborah Leonard, Karen McClymonds, Tim Palmer, Daniel Pierce, Harris Shiffman, Don Stehsel

GIS and cartography: Roxie Anderson

California Department of Fish and Game, 1416 Ninth Street (12th floor), Sacramento, CA 95814

ISBN: 978-0-9722291-2-4

Library of Congress Control Number: on file

This work was prepared by the Wildlife Health Center, School of Veterinary Medicine, University of California, Davis, One Shields Avenue, Davis, CA 95616
www.wildlifehealthcenter.org

This work is available online at www.dfg.ca.gov/habitats/wdp/

This book is dedicated to the inhabitants of California.

Contents

Foreword

From its rocky shores to fruitful Central Valley to snow-capped Sierra, California is rich in environmental diversity. Similarly, California's wildlife is as diverse as it is abundant.

The people of our great state have long been leaders in restoring and preserving wildlife and have fought hard to maintain clean water, clean air, and suitable habitats for all species.

I commend the Department of Fish and Game and its partners in producing *California Wildlife: Conservation Challenges.* Identifying and addressing the complex issues of resource conservation and responsible use ensures that California's vital resources will be sustained for this generation and the next.

Mike Chrisman
California Secretary for Resources

Preface

California is both the most populous and the most biologically diverse state in the nation. We enjoy more intricate landscapes, varieties of waters, and intriguing species than can be found anywhere in the country. We also experience environmental stressors and resource conservation challenges that are unparalleled. With rapid population growth and its accompanying developmental pressures, the demands on our state's natural resources are greater than ever.

The diversity of California's resources and the complexities of sustaining them emphasize the need for a collaborative approach to conservation, and the state wildlife action plan, *California Wildlife: Conservation Challenges,* is a tool for this purpose. The plan was developed in consultation with wildlife professionals, stakeholders, and the public, and specifically focuses on stressors affecting wildlife and the additional actions needed to maintain wildlife diversity and abundance in the future. It offers a straightforward discussion of the difficult issues we face in every region of California, both by describing the effects of a stressor or group of stressors on ecosystems, and considering the actions necessary to mitigate these impacts.

The Department of Fish and Game is responsible for managing the state's wildlife resources for their ecological value and enjoyment by the public. Federal, state and local agencies, nongovernmental organizations, private landowners, and numerous other stakeholders also engage in hundreds of conservation efforts throughout the state. I am pleased and encouraged that many of the issues identified in this plan are already being considered and addressed effectively through innovative adaptive management plans and restoration projects. We will continue to encourage the involvement of and collaboration with wildlife professionals, stakeholders, and the public in developing and implementing the necessary conservation strategies recommended in the plan.

A healthy, sustained environment is necessary for all species. Just as we all have a stake in the vitality of California's resources, we all have a responsibility to ensure they are protected and conserved now and into the future. Actively managing public and private lands to mitigate the impacts of human activities on native habitats; maintain wildlife corridors and habitat connectivity; safeguard surface and groundwater quality;

impede the establishment of invasive species; and employ beneficial fire management practices requires engagement by every Californian.

Working together to implement the recommendations of *California Wildlife: Conservation Challenges,* Californians can ensure that the wildlife diversity we enjoy today will be here for our children and grandchildren to appreciate and enjoy into the future.

L. Ryan Broddrick, Director
California Department of Fish and Game

Acknowledgments

Developing *California Wildlife: Conservation Challenges,* California's Wildlife Action Plan, was a partnership between the California Department of Fish and Game and the Wildlife Health Center at the University of California, Davis. The Wildlife Health Center managed scoping meetings, expert consultations, and conservation workshops, and prepared the report. Fish and Game provided guidance, technical analyses, and critical review and editing.

Fish and Game Director Ryan Broddrick provided clear direction and strong support for the Wildlife Action Plan development. Deputy directors Banky Curtis, Diana Jacobs, and Sonke Mastrup provided constructive review. Ron Rempel, former deputy director of the Habitat Conservation Division, Sandra Morey, former branch chief of the Habitat Conservation Planning Branch, and Dale Steele, program manager, Species Conservation and Recovery Program, served as Fish and Game's coordinating contacts and advisers, in addition to commenting on drafts.

Members of the Fish and Game Statewide Review Team were Chuck Armor, Glenn Black, Betsy Bolster, Richard Callas, John Carlson, Larry Eng, Becky Jones, Don Koch, Frank Hall, Chris Hayes, Eric Larson, Eric Loft, Darlene McGriff, Becky Miller, Dale Mitchell, Sandra Morey, Kimberly Nicol, Gail Presley, Robert Schaefer, Jeff Single, John Siperek, Kent Smith, Dale Steele, Terri Stewart, Mark Stopher, Dee Sudduth, John Ugoretz, and Carl Wilcox.

Jonna Mazet and Walter Boyce, co-directors of the UC Davis Wildlife Health Center, provided guidance and advice for the project.

The following individuals made up the team that developed and produced the Wildlife Action Plan: Project manager and co-author David Bunn; co-authors Andrea Mummert, Kirsten Gilardi, Marc Hoshovsky, and Sandra Shanks; GIS specialist and cartographer Roxie Anderson; species and habitat data analysts and wildlife species matrix developers Sandra Shanks and Kiffanie Stahle; wildlife monitoring survey analyst Ken Kriese; editor Barbara Anderson; designer and production editor Alison Kent; cover designer Nancy Ottum; web developer Phillip Deák; administrative support Kathy Collins, Brenda Barnes, Lavonne Hull, Kathy Meares, Alexia Retallack, and Sherri Smith; workshop facilitators Will Murray, Shelli

Bischoff, and Leni Wilsmann; workshop organizers Tricia Dunlap, Joe Caves, and Leslie Friedman-Johnson.

Reviewing and updating species information, updating and creating new species range maps, and development of the Wildlife Species Matrix were supervised by Fish and Game's Habitat and Data Analysis Branch, led by Branch Chief Tom Lupo. Joe Carboni, Darlene McGriff, Kevin Hunting, Monica Parisi, and Roxanne Bittman all provided technical assistance and contributed to the project. This team also provided technical review of the GIS maps in the report.

Eric Loft contributed to the discussion of resource assessment. Gail Presley reviewed the Natural Community Conservation Plans and authored the conservation planning section. Chris Stermer provided guidance and assistance with evaluation of GIS data sets and production of GIS maps.

Numerous individuals from local, state, and federal agencies and private conservation organizations provided invaluable input concerning species, ecosystems, habitats, stressors, conservation challenges, and solutions for the regions of the state. The following regional experts provided critical input and/or detailed review of early drafts, greatly enhancing the final Wildlife Action Plan:

Mojave Desert: Jeff Aardahl, Keith Axelson, Kristin Berry, Thomas Bilhorn, Glenn Black, Kirby Brill, Bill Christian, Norman Caoulette, Clarence Everly, John Hamill, Linda Hanson, Ed Hastey, Rebecca Jones, Todd Keeler-Wolf, Larry LaPre, Phil Leitner, Jeffrey E. Lovich, Neil Lynn, Jim Moore, Daniel R. Patterson, Gail Presley, Randy Scott, Paul Spitler, Dale Steele, Larry Whalon

Colorado Desert: Tom Anderson, Doug Barnum, Cameron Barrows, Glenn Black, Betsy Bolster, Walter Boyce, Dan Cooper, Jack Crayon, Dick Crowe, Kim Delfino, Lester Dillard, Howard Gross, Chris Hayes, Bryn Jones, Jeanine Jones, Tom Kirk, Chris Knauf, Eddy Konno, Leon Lesicka, Julia Levin, Kimberly Nicol, Jennifer Pitt, Chris Schonam, Paul Smith, Willadeena Thomas

South Coast: Bill Berry, Monica Bond, Trish Chapman, Robert Fisher, Mary Larson, Steve Loe, Claudia Luke, Becky Miller, Scott Morrison, Kristeen Penrod, Gail Presley, Ken Quigley, Dan Silver, Wayne Spencer, Terri Stewart, Camm C. Swift, Bill Tippets, Susan Wynn

Central Coast: Jo Ann Baumgartner, Betsy Bolster, Liz Clark, Paul Collins, Robin Cox, Bob Curry, Bruce Delgado, Julie Delgado, Erin Duffy, Chris Fischer, Deb Hillyard, Dennis Kearns, Jeff Kuyper, Jennifer Moonijan, Gary Page, Gary Patton, Katie Perry, Richard Rayburn, Kevin Shaffer, Gary Shallcross, Bob Stafford, Sam Sweet, Terry Watt, Jim Weigand, Carl Wilcox, Scott Wilson

North Coast–Klamath: John Alexander, Brian Barr, Cathy Bleier, Randy Brown, Richard Callas, Max Creasy, Dominick DellaSala, Lowell Diller, Scott Downie, Diana Jacobs, Karen Kovacs, Bob McAllister, Wendy Millet, Mark Moore, Gail Newton, John O. Sawyer Jr., Kevin Schaffer, John Siperek, Jack Williams, Peter Yolles

Modoc Plateau: Don Armentrout, Vern Bleich, Richard Callas, Mary Flores, Frank Hall, Todd Keeler-Wolf, Aaron Holmes, Bill Laudenslayer, Eric Loft, John Menke, Richard Miller, Peter Moyle, Melissa Nelson, K.C. Pasero, Tom Rickman, Paul Roush, Bob Schaeffer, Richard Shinn, John Siperek, David Smith, Sydney Smith, Brian Woodbridge, Marty Yamagiwa

Sierra Nevada and Cascades: Don Armentrout, Sam Blankenship, Vern C. Bleich, Louis Blumberg, Walter Boyce, Susan Britting, John Buckley, David Burton, Richard Callas, Laura Colton, Clu Cotter, Frank Davis, Brett Furnas, Dave Graber, Sacha Heath, Carolyn Hunsaker, Kathryn Purcell, Roland Knapp, William Laudenslayer, Eric Loft, Francis Mangels, Mary Ann McCrary, Paul McFarland, Jim McKinney, Curtis Milliron, Peter Moyle, Kevin O'Conner, Steve Parmenter, Tom Rickman, Ken Roby, Jeff Single, John Siperek, David O. Smith, Stan Stephens, Peter Stine, Robb Tibstra

Central Valley and Bay-Delta: Chuck Armor, Randy Baxter, Roger Bloom, Betsy Bolster, Laurie Briden, Julie Brown, Jay Chamberlin, Ann Chrisney, Joshua Collins, Pat Coulston, Steve Edmondson, Kevin Fleming, Greg Gerstenberg, Geoffrey Geupel, Dan Gifford, Armand Gonzales, Rob Hansen, Wayne Harrison, Rob Holbrook, Diana Jacobs, Doug Johnson, Steve Juarez, Patrick Kelly, Wim Kimmerer, Eric Kleinfelter, Tim Kroeker, Alice Low, Jenny Marr, Dennis McEwan, Dale Mitchell, Peter Moyle, Mike Mulligan, Terry Palmisano, Scott Phillips, Rick Rayburn, Larry Saslaw, David Schaub, Michelle Selmon, Bob Shaffer, Jeff Single, John Takekawa, Curt Uptain, Frank Wernette, Roy Woodward, Dawit Zeleke, Dave Zezulak

Marine Region: James Allen, Larry Allen, Mike Beck, Dennis Bedford, Mary Bergen, Steve Crooke, Gary Davis, Paul Dayton, Kate Faulkner, Rod Fujita, Zeke Grader, Mary Gleason, Edwin Grosholz, Pete Haaker, Sean Hastings, Burr Henneman, Konstantin Karpov, Brenna Langabeer, Karen Martin, Sarah McWilliams, James Moore, Dave Parker, Mitchell Perdue, Paul Reilly, Sam Schuchat, Ian Tanaguchi, John Ugoretz, Marija Vojkovich, Anne Walton, Guang-yu Wang, Michael Weber, Pamela Yochem

David Bunn
October 31, 2005, and May 31, 2007

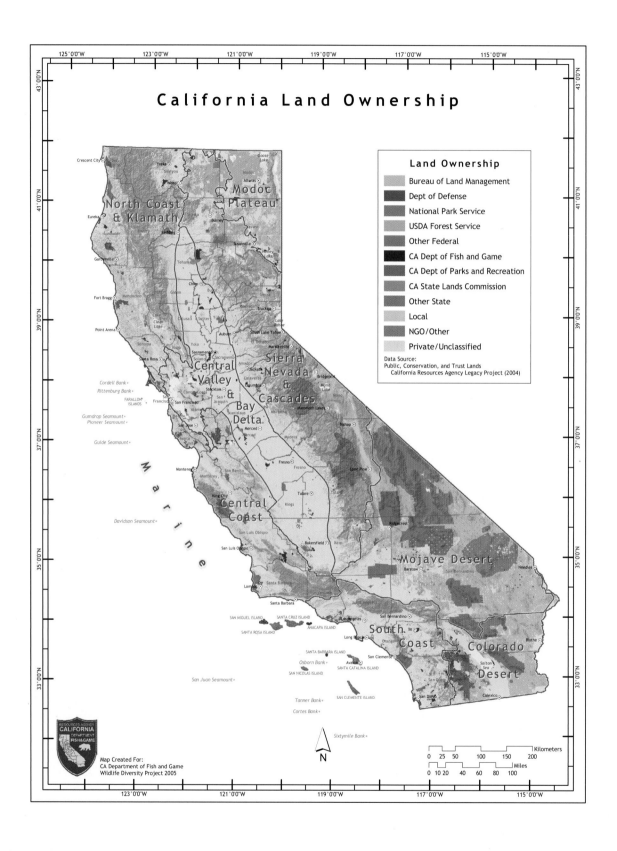

California Land Ownership

Land Ownership

- Bureau of Land Management
- Dept of Defense
- National Park Service
- USDA Forest Service
- Other Federal
- CA Dept of Fish and Game
- CA Dept of Parks and Recreation
- CA State Lands Commission
- Other State
- Local
- NGO/Other
- Private/Unclassified

Data Source:
Public, Conservation, and Trust Lands
California Resources Agency Legacy Project (2004)

North Coast & Klamath

Modoc Plateau

Central Valley & Bay Delta

Sierra Nevada & Cascades

Central Coast

Mojave Desert

South Coast

Colorado Desert

Marine

Map Created For:
CA Department of Fish and Game
Wildlife Diversity Project 2005

N

Kilometers
0 25 50   100   150   200

Miles
0 10 20   40   60   80   100

Executive Summary ~~~~~~~~~~~~~~~~~~~~~~~~~~~~~

In 2000, Congress enacted the State Wildlife Grants Program to support state programs that broadly benefit wildlife and habitats but particularly "species of greatest conservation need." As a requirement for receiving funding under this program, state wildlife agencies were to have submitted a Wildlife Action Plan (comprehensive wildlife conservation strategy) to the U.S. Fish and Wildlife Service in 2005. The California Department of Fish and Game (Fish and Game), working in partnership with the Wildlife Health Center, University of California, Davis, directed the development of this report, *California Wildlife: Conservation Challenges*, the state's Wildlife Action Plan, and associated Web publications.

California Wildlife: Conservation Challenges is directed at answering three primary questions:

- What are the species and habitats of greatest conservation need?
- What are the major stressors affecting California's native wildlife and habitats?
- What are the actions needed to restore and conserve California's wildlife, thereby reducing the likelihood that more species will approach the condition of threatened or endangered?

California's Natural Diversity

California is the wildlife state. Its diverse topography and climate have given rise to a remarkable diversity of habitats and a correspondingly diverse array of both plant and animal species. California has more species than any other state in the United States and also has the greatest number of endemic species—species that occur nowhere else in the world (CDFG 2003). Wildlife provides significant economic benefits to the state through recreation, tourism, and commercial harvest. Many of the places where wildlife thrives are often the same as those valued for recreation and other human activities. By learning what threatens the state's wildlife and the steps that can be taken to reduce those threats, California's residents have the opportunity to become more active stewards of this precious resource, ensuring that the Golden State remains the wildlife state for generations to come.

Species at Risk

One of the elements of developing a wildlife action plan is to identify and compile information on species of wildlife, including low and declining populations, that are indicative of the diversity and health of the state's wildlife. Fish and Game has chosen to use the Special Animals List, which it maintains and updates within the California Natural Diversity Database (CNDDB). This list is also referred to as the list of "species at risk" or "special status species," and it includes vertebrates and invertebrates. The special status species are diverse, and they inhabit the varied ecosystems across the state. Many of the special status species have been identified as **species of special concern*** due to their low or declining numbers.

Included in the associated Web publication of this report is the Wildlife Species Matrix consisting of all wildlife **taxa** (species and subspecies) on the California Department of Fish and Game's Special Animals List. This special status species list includes 140 birds, 127 mammals, 102 fishes, 43 reptiles, 40 amphibians, and 365 invertebrates. Of these, 13 birds, 69 mammals, 19 reptiles, 22 amphibians, 46 fish, and 312 invertebrates are endemic to the state; these taxa are indicated in the matrix with an asterisk.

Threats to Wildlife Diversity in California

The regional chapters describe the problems and threats that may adversely affect wildlife and their habitats (see map facing page 1 for regional divisions). These threats are termed "stressors." In each region of the state, there are multiple stressors to wildlife and habitats, operating alone and in combination. A number of these stressors are common to the entire state or to several different regions. The scope and effects of the most widespread stressors are briefly described on the facing page. More in-depth discussion of these stressors and their roles in each region can be found in the regional chapters.

*   Terms in boldface are defined in the glossary.

Major Wildlife Stressors Identified by Region

Mojave Desert

- Multiple uses conflicting with wildlife on public lands
- Growth and development
- Groundwater overdrafting and loss of riparian habitat
- Inappropriate off-road vehicle use
- Excessive livestock grazing
- Excessive burro and horse grazing
- Invasive plants
- Military land management conflicts
- Mining operations

Colorado Desert

- Water management conflicts and water transfer impacts
- Inappropriate off-road vehicle use
- Loss and degradation of dune habitats
  - Disruption of sand transport processes
  - Invasive plant species
  - Inappropriate off-road vehicle use
- Growth and development
- Invasive species

South Coast

- Growth and development
- Water management conflicts and degradation of aquatic ecosystems
- Invasive species
- Altered fire regimes
- Recreational pressures

Central Coast

- Growth and development
- Intensive agriculture
- Excessive livestock grazing
- Water management conflicts and degradation of aquatic ecosystems
- Recreational pressures
- Invasive species

North Coast–Klamath

- Water management conflicts
- Instream gravel mining
- Forest management conflicts
- Altered fire regimes
- Agriculture and urban development
- Excessive livestock grazing
- Invasive species

Modoc Plateau

- Excessive livestock grazing
- Excessive feral horse grazing
- Altered fire regimes
- Western juniper expansion
- Invasive plants
- Forest management conflicts
- Water management conflicts and degradation of aquatic ecosystems

Sierra Nevada and Cascades

Stressors affecting upland habitats

- Growth and land development
- Forest management conflicts
- Altered fire regimes
- Excessive livestock grazing
- Invasive plants
- Recreational pressures
- Climate change

Stressors affecting aquatic and riparian habitats

- Water diversions and dams
- Watershed fragmentation and fish barriers
- Hydropower project operations
- Excessive livestock grazing
- Water diversion from the Owens Valley
- Introduced non-native fish

Central Valley and Bay-Delta

- Growth and development (including urban, residential, and agricultural)
- Water management conflicts and reduced water for wildlife
- Water pollution
- Invasive species
- Climate change

Marine Region

- Overfishing
- Degradation of marine habitat
- Invasive species
- Pollution
- Human disturbance

Growth and development, water management conflicts, **invasive** species, and climate change each have major consequences for species, **ecosystems**, and **habitats** in every region of the state.

A number of other stressors also recur in multiple regions. Excessive livestock grazing, either in sensitive habitats or grazing of too many animals or for too long a grazing period, significantly affects wildlife habitats in the Mojave Desert, Central Coast, North Coast–Klamath, Modoc Plateau, and Sierra Nevada and Cascades regions. Forest management conflicts represent a major stressor in the North Coast–Klamath, Modoc Plateau, and Sierra Nevada and Cascades regions. Altered **fire regimes** were identified as major stressors in the South Coast, North Coast–Klamath, Modoc Plateau, and Sierra Nevada and Cascades regions. Pollution and urban or agricultural runoff were identified as major stressors in the South Coast, Central Coast, Central Valley and Bay-Delta, and Marine regions. Recreational pressures and human disturbance are issues in the Mojave Desert, Colorado Desert, South Coast, Central Coast, Sierra Nevada and Cascades, and Marine regions.

The stressors that affect wildlife, and the conservation actions needed to address them and restore and conserve ecosystems and wildlife populations, were analyzed in each region of the state. While some stressors are significant in only a few regions, others are pervasive across the state. Similarly, some conservation actions are important for a few regions, while other conservation actions are needed throughout the state or are more appropriately implemented through a statewide program. This chapter describes recommended statewide conservation actions.

Recommended Statewide Conservation Actions

Conservation actions were considered for each region, based on the stressors and circumstances in each. Statewide conservation actions are those actions that are important across most or all regions. The following are recommended statewide conservation actions:

a. The state should develop policies and incentives to facilitate better integration of wildlife conservation considerations into local and regional planning and land-use decision-making.

b. Permitting agencies, county planners, and land management agencies should work to ensure that infrastructure development projects are designed and sited to avoid harmful effects on sensitive species and habitats.

c. The state should develop policies and incentives to better integrate wildlife conservation into state and regional transportation planning. Wildlife considerations need to be incorporated early in the transportation planning process.

d. State and federal agencies should work with cities and counties to secure sensitive habitats and key habitat linkages.

e. State and local agencies should allocate sufficient water for ecosystem uses and wildlife needs when planning for and meeting regional water supply needs.

f. Federal, state, and local agencies should provide greater resources and coordinate efforts to control existing occurrences of invasive species and to prevent new introductions.

g. Federal, state, and local agencies and nongovernmental conservation organizations, working with private landowners and public land managers, should expand efforts to restore and conserve riparian communities.

h. Federal, state, and local agencies and nongovernmental organizations, working with private landowners, should expand efforts to implement agricultural and rangeland management practices that are compatible with wildlife and habitat conservation.

i. In their conservation planning and ecosystem restoration work, state and federal wildlife agencies and land managers should consider the most current projections regarding the effects of global warming.

j. Both state and federal governments should give greater priority to wildlife and natural resources conservation education.

k. The state should strengthen its capacity to implement conservation actions and to assist local agencies and landowners with planning and implementation of wildlife and habitat restoration and conservation efforts.

Recommended Region-Specific Conservation Actions

Implementing the statewide conservation actions and the region-specific conservation actions is necessary to restore and conserve ecosystems and wildlife populations. **For fuller discussion of recommended region-specific conservation actions, see Section 4 in each of the regional chapters.**

Mojave Desert Region

a. Improve stewardship on federally managed lands to protect wildlife diversity.

b. Stabilize groundwater levels and recharge depleted sub-basins of the Mojave River Basin, restoring groundwater to levels that support riparian habitat.

c. Stabilize groundwater levels and secure wet habitats in the Amargosa River Basin. This action will help protect the endangered Amargosa vole and the Amargosa pupfish, among other species.

d. Provide maximum federal and state protection for remaining riparian, spring, seep, and wetland habitats, and restore degraded riparian, spring, seep, and wetland areas.

e. The Bureau of Land Management should improve, and, upon approval, implement the West Mojave Plan with conservation measures to address all special status species and to maintain wildlife diversity.

f. Reduce off-road vehicle damage to wildlife habitats.

g. Federal, state, and local agencies should provide greater resources and coordinate efforts to eradicate or control existing occurrences of invasive species and to prevent new introductions.

h. Fully implement the recovery plans for the Mojave tui chub, Amargosa vole, and Inyo California towhee.

i. Fish and Game, BLM, and the three military bases that support the Mohave ground squirrel should develop a collaborative conservation and recovery strategy for the Mohave ground squirrel so that federal listing is not necessary.

Colorado Desert Region

a. Federal, state, and local agencies, along with nongovernmental conservation organizations, should work together to reach agreement upon and fund a restoration plan for the Salton Sea.

b. Federal and state wildlife agencies should work to ensure that environmental impacts resulting from water transfers (both those permitted under the Quantification Settlement Agreement [QSA] and any future transfers) are mitigated and that the related habitat conservation plans are fully implemented.

c. Federal and state wildlife agencies, water management agencies, and nongovernmental conservation organizations should develop and invest in restoration and protection efforts for the Salton Sea, the Colorado River delta, and other regional wildlife habitats.

d. Wildlife agency staff developing the Imperial Valley Habitat Conservation Plan, working with Imperial County planners and nongovernmental conservation organizations, should identify and protect critical avian habitats in southern Imperial County.

e. The Bureau of Land Management, working with state and federal wildlife agencies and nongovernmental conservation organizations, should protect and restore biologically significant habitats in the Algodones Dunes.

f. State and federal agencies and nongovernmental partners should collaborate to develop a comprehensive Southern California Outdoor Recreation Program (for the South Coast and Colorado Desert regions) to provide recreational opportunities and access that do not conflict with wildlife habitat needs. Areas for intensive recreational access and off-road vehicle use should be developed on the least-sensitive public lands in order to direct pressures away from sensitive habitats.

g. Federal, state, and local agencies and nongovernmental conservation organizations should work to protect and restore biologically significant habitats in the Coachella Valley.

h. Nongovernmental conservation organizations should continue to work to protect important wildlife habitat areas.

i. Permitting agencies, county and local planners, and land management agencies should work to ensure that infrastructure development projects are designed and sited to avoid harmful effects on sensitive species and habitats.

j. Federal, state, and local agencies should work with nongovernmental organizations to provide greater resources to eradicate or control and to limit introductions of invasive species in the region.

South Coast Region

a. Wildlife agencies and local governments should work to improve the development and implementation of regional Natural Community Conservation Plans (NCCPs), which is the primary process to conserve habitat and species in the region's rapidly urbanizing areas.

b. Wildlife agencies should establish regional goals for species and habitat protection and work with city, county, and state agency land-use planning processes to accomplish those goals.

c. Federal, state, local agencies, and private conservancies should safeguard and build upon Camp Pendleton's contribution to the regional network of conservation lands. Similarly, protect habitats on lands adjacent to the Marine Corps Air Station Miramar.

d. To address regional habitat fragmentation, federal, state, and local agencies, along with nongovernmental conservation organizations, should support the protection of the priority wildlands linkages identified by the South Coast Missing Linkages project.

e. Federal, state, and local agencies, along with nongovernmental conservation organizations, should protect and restore the best remaining examples of coastal wetlands that provide important wildlife habitat.

f. Public agencies and nongovernmental conservation organizations should invest in efforts to protect and restore the best remaining regional examples of ecologically intact river systems.

g. Federal, state, and local agencies should provide greater resources and coordinate efforts to eradicate or control existing occurrences of invasive species and to prevent new introductions.

h. Federal, state, and local public agencies should sufficiently protect sensitive species and important wildlife habitats on their lands and should be adequately funded and staffed to do so.

i. Federal and state agencies and nongovernmental partners should collaborate to institute appropriate fire management policies and practices to restore the ecological integrity of the region's ecosystems while minimizing loss of property and life.

j. The state should coordinate the development of a model ordinance and building codes for new or expanding communities in fire-adapted landscapes to make those communities more fire compatible and reduce the state's liability for fire suppression.

k. State and federal wildlife agencies, the U.S. Forest Service, state and county parks, BLM, and nongovernmental partners should collaborate to develop a comprehensive Southern California Outdoor Recreation Program to provide recreational opportunities and access that do not conflict with wildlife habitat needs.

Central Coast Region

a. Wildlife agencies should establish regional goals for species and habitat protection and work with city, county, and state agency land-use planning processes to accomplish those goals.

b. Federal, state, and local agencies, along with nongovernmental organizations, should work with private landowners and land managers to implement agricultural and rangeland management practices that are compatible with wildlife and habitat conservation.

c. Federal, state, and local agencies, along with nongovernmental organizations, should work with private landowners to both continue and develop programs that help keep grazing-land uses profitable.

d. Federal, state, and local agencies, along with nongovernmental conservation organizations, should work to protect large, relatively unfragmented habitat areas, wildlife corridors, and underprotected ecological community types.

e. Federal, state, and local public agencies should sufficiently protect sensitive species and important wildlife habitats on their lands.

f. Federal, state, and local agencies should work to restore fish passage in aquatic systems important for anadromous and wide-ranging fish populations.

g. State and local agencies should allocate sufficient water for ecosystem uses when planning for and meeting regional water supply needs. Providing adequate water for wildlife and instream uses is particularly important in systems that support sensitive species or important habitat areas.

h. State and federal agencies should work to protect and restore biologically significant regional river systems.

i. Federal, state, and local agencies should provide greater resources and coordinate efforts to control existing occurrences of invasive species and prevent new introductions.

North Coast–Klamath Region

a. For regional river systems where insufficient or altered flow regimes limit populations of salmon, steelhead, and other sensitive aquatic species, federal and state agencies and other stakeholders should work to increase instream flows and to replicate natural seasonal flow regimes.

b. Federal, state, and local agencies and private landowners should work to restore fish passage in aquatic systems important for anadromous and wide-ranging fish populations.

c. Through the Federal Energy Regulatory Commission (FERC) relicensing process, the state should pursue changes in operations of hydropower projects to provide more water for aquatic species and ecosystems and require that flows be managed to approximate natural flow regime.

d. Fish and Game should continue fisheries restoration and watershed assessment efforts.

e. Fish and Game should work to complete and implement recovery strategies and plans for listed species and develop and implement statewide or regionwide recovery plans to benefit multiple species.

f. Where historical or active gravel mining has had substantial effects on river systems that are important for sensitive aquatic species, federal, state, and local agencies should continue monitoring and restoration efforts to minimize the negative effects of mining. Active mining operations should employ the most ecologically sensitive practices possible.

g. Public forest lands should be managed to maintain healthy ecosystems and wildlife diversity. State and federal forest and wildlife managers should work cooperatively to develop a vision for future forest conditions.

h. On public lands, post-fire and post-harvest treatments and forest management should be designed to achieve the principles listed in Action g, above.

i. Federal and state agencies should work to understand the natural fire regimes of different ecosystems and how the ecological role of wildfire can be replicated with prescribed fire and other forest management practices.

j. State and federal forest and wildlife managers should work cooperatively with private landowners and timber companies to develop timber-harvest cumulative-impact standards for watersheds in the North Coast–Klamath Region to protect ecosystem health and wildlife habitat.

k. State and federal agencies should work with private forestry operators and landowners to implement forest management practices that are compatible with wildlife and habitat conservation.

l. The state should coordinate the development of a model ordinance and building codes for new or expanding communities in fire-adapted landscapes to make those communities more fire compatible and reduce the state's liability for fire suppression.

m. Federal, state, and local agencies and nongovernmental organizations should work with regional landowners to develop and implement agricultural and rangeland management practices that are compatible with wildlife and habitat conservation.

n. Federal, state, and local agencies should provide greater resources and coordinate efforts to eradicate or control existing occurrences of invasive species and to prevent new introductions.

o. Federal, state, and local agencies, nongovernmental conservation organizations, and private landowners should protect and restore underprotected and sensitive habitat types such as riparian forests and coastal dunes.

Modoc Plateau Region

a. Federal land management agencies should more effectively manage forest, shrub, aspen, meadow, and riparian habitat to enhance ecosystems and conditions for wildlife.

b. Federal land management agencies should implement modifications to grazing management on public lands that are conducive to recovery of key habitats for restoring and conserving wildlife.

c. The Bureau of Land Management should update the Resource Management Plans (RMPs) to include provisions to restore and conserve wildlife diversity.

d. Feral horse numbers should be maintained at levels that meet the constraints imposed by law, and funds should be provided for BLM and the Forest Service to meet the standards in place for the protection of meadows and riparian areas.

e. The Cooperative Sagebrush Steppe Restoration Initiative and the National Resource Conservation Service (NRCS) should design juniper-removal projects to benefit wildlife diversity and ecosystem health.

f. Public forest lands should be managed to maintain healthy ecosystems and wildlife diversity, including thinning to restore diverse habitats and reduce the risk of catastrophic wildfire. State and federal forest managers and wildlife agencies should work cooperatively to develop a vision for the future forest condition.

g. Regarding forest management conservation actions, see Conservation Actions d, e, f, and g in Chapter 13, Sierra Nevada and Cascades Region.

h. Land management and wildlife agencies and conservation nongovernmental organizations should develop an aquatic multispecies conservation plan for the Pit River watershed.

Sierra Nevada and Cascades Region

a. The state should provide scientific and planning assistance and financial incentives to local governments to develop and implement regional multispecies conservation plans for all of the rapidly developing areas of the Sierra Nevada and Cascades.

b. The Sierra Nevada Conservancy should develop a program, closely coordinated with federal, state, and local wildlife conservation planning efforts, that prioritizes areas for acquisition and easements based on the needs of wildlife.

c. In areas where substantial development is projected, the state and federal land management and wildlife agencies should identify and protect from development those critical wildlife migration or dispersal corridors that cross ownership boundaries and county jurisdictions.

d. Public forest lands should be managed to maintain healthy ecosystems and wildlife diversity, including thinning to restore diverse habitats and reduce the risk of catastrophic wildfire. State and federal forest managers and wildlife agencies should work cooperatively to develop a vision for the future forest condition.

e. On public lands, post-fire and post-harvest treatments and forest management should be designed to achieve the principles listed in Action d.

f. State and federal forest managers and state and federal wildlife managers should cooperatively develop timber-harvest cumulative-impact standards for each watershed or group of adjacent watersheds of the Sierra, Cascades, and Modoc regions to protect aquatic ecosystems and conserve wildlife habitat.

g. The California Resources Agency should coordinate the development of a model ordinance and building codes for new or expanding communities in fire-adapted landscapes to make those communities more fire compatible and reduce the state's liability for fire suppression.

h. Federal, state, and local agencies and fire-safe councils should work cooperatively to expand the use of prescribed fire and natural-burn programs.

i. State and federal wildlife agencies and federal land managers should jointly develop and implement grazing strategies for the Sierra Nevada and Cascades Region to reduce or eliminate livestock grazing on sensitive habitats to restore the condition of meadow, riparian, aspen, and aquatic habitats.

j. Federal, state, and local agencies should provide greater resources and coordinate efforts to eradicate or control existing occurrences of invasive species and to prevent new introductions.

k. In their conservation planning and ecosystem restoration work, state and federal wildlife agencies and land managers should consider the most current projections regarding the effects of global warming.

l. Fish and Game should be allocated the resources to monitor and enforce the distribution of sensitive fish and other aquatic species populations and to engage effectively in water-rights decision processes, water diversion issues, land-management planning, and conservation planning actions to restore and enhance aquatic systems.

m. Through the Federal Energy Regulatory Commission relicensing process, the state should pursue changes in operations of hydropower projects that will provide more water for wildlife, mandate that water flows be managed as close to natural flow regimes as possible, and ensure that the new license agreements provide the best possible conditions for ecosystems and wildlife.

n. The state, Inyo County, and the city of Los Angeles should fully implement the Lower Owens River Project (LORP), restoring riparian and aquatic habitat along 62 miles of the lower Owens River.

o. The city of Los Angeles should reach long-term agreement with Inyo County and the state to use shallow flooding to control dust on the Owens Lake lakebed.

p. Fish and Game should establish trout-free sub-basins and lakes across the high Sierra and Cascades to restore amphibians and other native species while concurrently improving trout fisheries in other lakes.

q. Fish and Game and the U.S. Fish and Wildlife Service should seek an agreement with the Los Angeles Department of Water and Power (LADWP) to establish Owens pupfish and Owens tui chub in springs and creeks of the Owens Valley on LADWP lands as part of a strategy to recover these two endangered fish and ensure their long-term survival.

Central Valley and Bay-Delta Region

a. The California Resources Agency, Fish and Game, the U.S. Fish and Wildlife Service, public land managing agencies, and local governments need to develop multicounty regional habitat conservation and restoration plans.

b. While numerous private landowners are leaders in conservation, Fish and Game, the U.S. Fish and Wildlife Service, the USDA Natural Resources Conservation Service, and local resource conservation districts need to improve conservation and restoration on private lands by assisting private landowners.

c. Public land managers need to continue improving wildlife habitat for a variety of species on public lands.

d. Public agencies and private organizations need to work with the San Francisco Bay Joint Venture to protect and restore tidal habitats and baylands in San Francisco Bay.

e. Public agencies and private organizations need to collaboratively protect and restore habitat connectivity along major rivers in the Central Valley.

f. Public agencies and private organizations need to collaboratively protect and restore upland linkages among protected areas in the San Joaquin Valley.

g. Public agencies and private organizations need to collaboratively protect and restore lowland linkages in San Francisco Bay.

h. Public agencies and private organizations need to collaboratively protect upland linkages and reduce the risk of habitat isolation in the eastern and northern San Francisco Bay area.

i. Water management agencies need to secure dependable and adequate amounts and quality of water for wildlife.

j. Water management agencies need to reestablish and maintain more natural river flows, flooding patterns, water temperatures, and salinity conditions to support wildlife species and habitats.

k. Water management agencies need to restore gravel supply in sediment-starved rivers downstream of reservoirs to maintain functional riverine habitats.

l. Public agencies and private organizations should protect, restore, and improve water-dependent habitats (including wetland, riparian, and estuarine) throughout the region. Design of these actions should factor in the likely effects of accelerated climate change.

m. Water management agencies, state and federal wildlife agencies, and other public agencies and private organizations need to collaboratively improve fish passage by removing or modifying barriers to upstream habitat.

n. To support healthy aquatic ecosystems, public agencies and private organizations, in collaboration with the California Bay-Delta Authority, need to improve and maintain water quality in the major river systems of this region.

o. Regional water quality boards, in collaboration with other public agencies and private organizations, need to improve and maintain water quality in streams and tidal waters of San Francisco Bay.

p. Fish and Game should expand funding and coordinate efforts to prevent the establishment of invasive species and to reduce the damage caused by established invasive species.

q. State and federal agencies should expand law enforcement funding and staffing and coordinate efforts to enforce regulations to prevent the degradation of rivers and streams and to detect, prevent and take actions to protect water quality.

Marine Region

a. The state should fully implement the Marine Life Management Act to ensure that marine fisheries and the marine ecosystem are managed sustainably.

b. The state should move forward in implementing the Marine Life Protection Act by establishing a network of marine protected areas.

c. The state should secure Tidelands Revenues for implementation of the California Ocean Protection Act.

d. The state should increase efforts to restore coastal watersheds.

e. The state should adopt a "no net loss" policy for critical marine habitat.

f. The federal and state resource agencies should expand efforts to eradicate introduced predators from all seabird colonies.

g. The state should systematically review and monitor the distribution and abundance of nonharvested marine fish and invertebrates.

h. Federal and state resource agencies and institutions should foster and facilitate interstate collaborative research on marine species whose ranges cross jurisdictional boundaries.

Monitoring and Adaptive Management

Natural communities, ecosystems, species population dynamics, and the effects of stressors on the environment are inherently complex. Wildlife and resource managers often are called upon to implement conservation strategies or actions based upon limited scientific information and despite considerable uncertainties. Adaptive management is a key element of implementing effective conservation programs. Adaptive management combines data from monitoring species and natural systems with new information from management and targeted studies to continually assess the effectiveness of, and adjust and improve, conservation actions.

Some conservation actions recommended in this Wildlife Action Plan may be assessed adequately simply by monitoring a few environmental variables. At the other extreme, a regional multispecies conservation effort requires a major long-term comprehensive monitoring program. Chapter 5 summarizes current monitoring programs and addresses the steps and considerations needed to design a monitoring program in an adaptive management context. Chapter 5 also provides a process for establishing the monitoring program for each recommended conservation action.

Strengthening California's Conservation Capabilities

California needs to strengthen its wildlife resource assessment and conservation planning capabilities. The state also needs to dedicate greater and more reliable funding for wildlife conservation. These three conservation elements are addressed in Chapter 6.

Development of the Wildlife Action Plan

Project staff conducted regional reviews, organized scoping meetings and workshops, gathered digital data sets and prepared GIS maps, compiled information regarding over 800 species at risk and prepared associated range maps, and surveyed wildlife research and monitoring efforts throughout the state. Based on this work, the project staff prepared this report and its affiliated Web publications (available on the Web at http://www.dfg.ca.gov/habitats/wdp/index.html).

California Wildlife:
Conservation Challenges

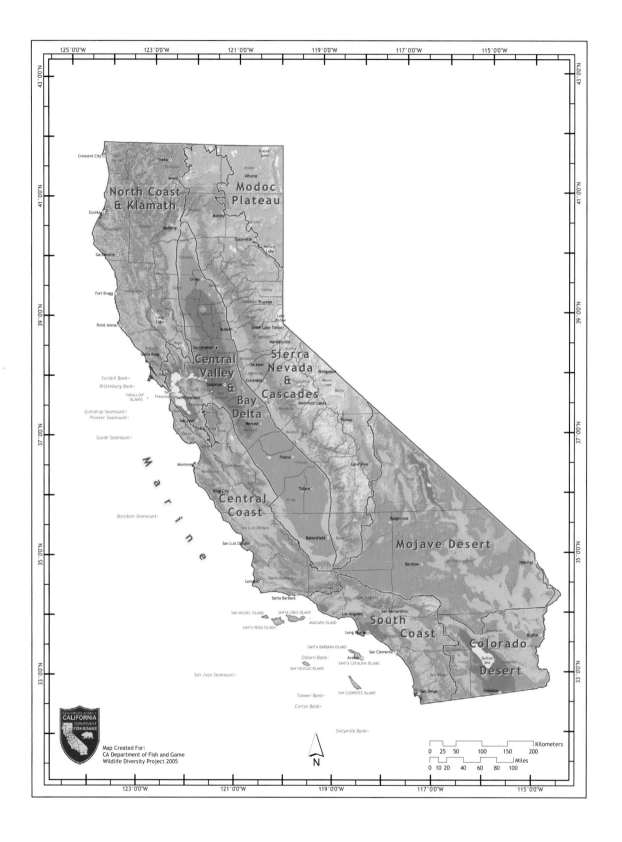

125°0'0"W   123°0'0"W   121°0'0"W   119°0'0"W   117°0'0"W   115°0'0"W

43°0'0"N

41°0'0"N

39°0'0"N

37°0'0"N

35°0'0"N

33°0'0"N

Crescent City

Yreka
Weed
Modoc
Alturas

North Coast & Klamath

Modoc Plateau

Eureka
Burney
Redding
Garberville

Fort Bragg
Chico

Point Arena
Clear Lake
Truckee

Susanville
Honey Lake

Auburn
South Lake Tahoe

Santa Rosa
Sacramento
Markleeville

Central Valley & Bay Delta
Jackson
Stockton
Columbia
Bridgeport
Mono Lake

Sierra Nevada & Cascades

Cordell Bank
Rittenburg Bank
FARALLON ISLANDS
San Francisco

Gumdrop Seamount
Pioneer Seamount
San Jose
Merced
Mammoth Lakes

Guide Seamount
Bishop

Monterey
Fresno

Marine
King City
Lone Pine

Central Coast
Tulare

Davidson Seamount
Ridgecrest
San Luis Obispo

Bakersfield
Kern

Mojave Desert
Lompoc
Santa Barbara
Barstow
San Bernardino
Needles

Santa Barbara

SAN MIGUEL ISLAND   SANTA CRUZ ISLAND
SANTA ROSA ISLAND   ANACAPA ISLAND
Los Angeles
San Bernardino

Long Beach
South Coast
Riverside
Blythe

SANTA BARBARA ISLAND
Osborn Bank
SAN NICOLAS ISLAND
SANTA CATALINA ISLAND
San Clemente
Avalon

Colorado Desert
Salton Sea

San Juan Seamount
San Diego

Tanner Bank
SAN CLEMENTE ISLAND
San Diego
Calexico

Cortes Bank

Sixtymile Bank

RESOURCES AGENCY
CALIFORNIA
DEPARTMENT
FISH & GAME

Map Created For:
CA Department of Fish and Game
Wildlife Diversity Project 2005

N

Kilometers
0 25 50 100 150 200

Miles
0 10 20 40 60 80 100

Introduction

I n 2000, Congress enacted the State Wildlife Grants Program to support state programs that broadly benefit wildlife and habitats but particularly "species of greatest conservation need." As a requirement for receiving funding under this program, state wildlife agencies submitted a Wildlife Action Plan (a comprehensive wildlife conservation strategy) to the U.S. Fish and Wildlife Service no later than October 2005. The California Department of Fish and Game (Fish and Game), working in partnership with the Plan development team at the University of California, Davis, directed the development of this report, *California Wildlife: Conservation Challenges* (the comprehensive wildlife conservation strategy) and associated Web publications.

California Wildlife: Conservation Challenges is directed at answering three primary questions:

- What are the species and habitats of greatest conservation need?
- What are the major stressors affecting California's native wildlife and habitats?
- What are the actions needed to restore and conserve California's wildlife, thereby reducing the likelihood that more species will approach the condition of threatened or endangered?

Fish and Game's Public Trust Responsibility for California Wildlife

Fish and Game has public trust responsibility and jurisdiction over the conservation, protection, and management of fish, wildlife, native plants, and habitat necessary for biologically sustainable populations of those species. That includes the authority to designate and manage threatened or endangered native animals and to establish game refuges, ecological reserves, and other natural areas.

As the state's trustee agency for fish and wildlife resources, the department is responsible for providing biological expertise to review and comment upon environmental documents and impacts arising from development and other project activities as they are considered under the California Environmental Quality Act (Fish and Game Code 1802). ("A trustee agency" is a state agency having jurisdiction by law over natural resources that may be affected by a project and that are held in trust for the people of the state of California.)

Fish and Game responsibilities also include:

- Conducting wildlife resource assessments, wildlife and habitat research and monitoring, conservation planning, and wildlife management.

- Serving as lead agency for the development of Natural Community Conservation Plans.

- Collecting scientific data, conducting analyses, and developing regulations to provide hunting and fishing opportunities for the public, activities required by statute, providing considerable public benefit and contributing substantially to the state's economy.

- Serving as the principal public contact for wildlife issues in all counties and communities.

- Educating the public on wildlife conservation and wildlife public safety issues.

- Providing technical advisers for species and habitat conservation planning efforts and evaluating lands considered for acquisition for benefit of wildlife resources.

- Advising local governments, various commissions, and working groups regarding biological, technical, and conservation issues.

- Serving as the lead agency charged with resolving livestock depredation problems and other wildlife conflicts, an increasing challenge due to growth and development in rural communities and natural areas and expansion of agricultural activities.

- Participating in the development of strategies to manage wildlife disease and responding to potential outbreaks of disease (adenovirus, duck viral enteritis, botulism, chronic wasting disease, etc.).

Audience

Conserving wildlife in California requires the efforts of law enforcement, biologists, land managers, research scientists, water resource experts, city and county planners, landowners, developers, educators, policy-makers, and many others. Generally, this report is written with this broad audience in mind. However, certain portions of this report may be more useful for certain audiences than others. In particular, the Wildlife Species Matrix, which is described in Chapter 2 (and available on the Web at http://www.dfg.ca.gov/habitats/wdp/matrix_search.asp), was prepared more specifically for biologists and conservation planners. Much of this report is a discussion of biological or ecological information and issues. An effort was made to present issues concisely using common terminology for a general audience. Where technical terms or concepts are used, they are defined or they are in **bold face** and may be found in the Glossary.

Tone

A significant portion of this report discusses how problems, threats, or stressors negatively affect wildlife species and habitats. This is inherently a negative topic. There are hundreds of positive examples of private organizations, landowners, and public agencies working to solve problems affecting wildlife and to restore degraded habitats. But this report is specifically focused on stressors affecting wildlife and what additional actions are needed to maintain wildlife diversity in the future. The issues are presented in a straightforward style, describing effects of a stressor or group of stressors on habitats, ecosystems, or species. For example, the report is direct about how growth and development are replacing and fragmenting wildlife habitats. The directness of the report should not be interpreted as a lack of appreciation for the legitimacy and benefits of activities and projects that also affect wildlife. Residential and commercial development, agricultural operations, diversions of state waters, and recreational activities are all necessary and important. However, the report does recommend changes in human activities, such as improving conservation planning, to reduce the impact of development on important habitats.

Regional, Habitat, and Multispecies Approach

The California Wildlife Action Plan approaches conservation issues and needs from a regional landscape, habitat, and ecosystem level, rather than taking a species-by-species approach. This is consistent with current conservation biology science and recommendations of conservation practitioners. For example, in California, since the early 1990s, federal, state, and local agencies have collaborated to develop Natural Community Conservation Plans (NCCPs) that protect habitat areas important to numerous species within a region. (See further discussion of NCCPs in Chapter 6.) In 2000, California enacted amendments to the NCCP statutes, reconfirming the state's endorsement of broad regional-scale approaches to wildlife conservation. Nongovernmental conservation organizations, such as The Nature Conservancy, are encouraging broad approaches to conservation, developing projects that benefit not just individual species but the full complement of species that make up ecological communities.

In the sections on species at risk in the regional chapters, two or three species at risk are discussed to illustrate how stressors or threats affect species and to highlight conservation challenges and opportunities. These species discussions are not intended to imply that conservation should have a single-species approach, although recovery of some species requires very species-specific actions.

Defining Regions for the California Wildlife Strategy

From the deserts to high mountains to the coast, California is geographically extensive, with great diversity of climate, topography, and ecology. State and federal wildlife and land-management agencies have divided the state into practical management jurisdictions based roughly on distribution of biological resources but also on the necessity of creating manageable areas. California's Biodiversity Council has designated regions based on these agency management jurisdictions combined with ecological features of the landscape. The Plan development team took an approach similar to that of the Biodiversity Council, with some adjustments.

Regarding Plants and Plant Communities

California Wildlife: Conservation Challenges is focused on wildlife (vertebrates and invertebrates) and the habitats and ecosystems that sustain them. Obviously, plants and plant communities are integral components of habitats and ecosystems. However, it is beyond the scope of this report to review individual plants or plant communities. But as components of habitats, plants are discussed indirectly throughout the report. Plants or plant communities are integral to topics about stressors such as invasive plants and as affected habitats that are important for maintaining wildlife diversity. Habitat descriptions include mention of important dominant or characteristic plants.

Identifying Major Stressors and Conservation Actions

The major regional stressors were identified through regional stakeholder workshops, Fish and Game scoping meetings, consultations with 20 to 30 resource experts in each region, and through review of major conservation planning documents. There was very little disagreement among those participating regarding the major stressors affecting wildlife. A few stressors that may be considered major are not addressed in this report. If the stressor is not within the jurisdiction of or likely to be affected by the work of wildlife- and natural resources management agencies or organizations, this report may not have addressed it. For example, air pollution is certainly a stressor affecting soils in the Mojave Desert and forest ecosystems in the Sierra Nevada, but solutions to air pollution will most likely be motivated by human health considerations in urban areas rather than any management consideration regarding wildlife resources. Thus, this report does not highlight air pollution as a stressor.

The conservation actions to address the effects of the major stressors were developed through the sets of workshops, scoping meetings, expert consultations, and document reviews noted above. Several conservation issues particularly important for maintaining wildlife diversity were prominent statewide. For these topics, the Plan development team organized seven day-long conservation-action workshops. The results of the conservation action workshops can be found at http://www.dfg.ca.gov/habitats/wdp. Development of the conservation actions also received input from the Fish and Game Statewide Review Team and from 45 outside expert reviewers.

Coordinating Implementation of Conservation Actions and Updating *California Wildlife: Conservation Challenges*

The Director of the Department of Fish and Game will establish a Conservation Strategy Special Project Team to coordinate, facilitate, and monitor the implementation of conservation actions recommended in this plan. The Special Project Team will work with other agencies, nongovernmental organizations, local governments, and landowner interests to encourage partnerships for conservation and to improve planning and project coordination. The Special Project Team will also monitor and evaluate progress of the conservation actions and prepare a biennial progress report on their implementation. In addition, Fish and Game will continue to routinely update information regarding special status species. Additional work relevant to the Plan and implementation updates will be made available on the Web at http://www.dfg.ca.gov/habitats/wdp. It is the goal of Fish and Game to assess the status of stressors and update conservation actions appropriately and amend *California Wildlife: Conservation Challenges* every five to 10 years.

Overview of the Report

Part I discusses statewide issues. Chapter 1, California's Natural Diversity, is an overview of the extraordinary diversity of plant and animal species of the state. Chapter 2, Species at Risk in California, summarizes the special status species and endemic species statewide. The components of the Wildlife Species Matrix, a Web publication, are also defined. Chapter 3, Threats to Wildlife Diversity, summarizes the major threats to wildlife across the state. Chapter 4 presents recommended statewide conservation actions. Chapter 5 discusses the importance of monitoring and adaptive management, current monitoring efforts, and monitoring for effectiveness of conservation actions. Chapter 6 addresses the conservation capabilities of the state. Resource assessment and conservation planning are two key functions the state provides for conservation of wildlife. Sections 1 and 2 of Chapter 6 address the status of these functions and the limited capabilities of Fish and Game to provide them. All of the state's conservation efforts are constrained by funding, and many of the recommendations of this report will not be implemented without greater investment in conservation. Section 3 of Chapter 6 looks at Fish and Game's challenge to fund the implementation of expanding wildlife stewardship mandates.

Part II of the report contains a chapter on each of the nine regions. Each chapter addresses species at risk, stressors affecting wildlife and habitats, and conservation actions. (See the Introduction to Part II for an overview of the content of the sections of the regional chapters.)

California Wildlife: Conservation Challenges is also available on the Web at http://www.dfg.ca.gov/habitats/wdp/ in English and Spanish. The report's affiliated Web publications are also available at this Web site.

Part I

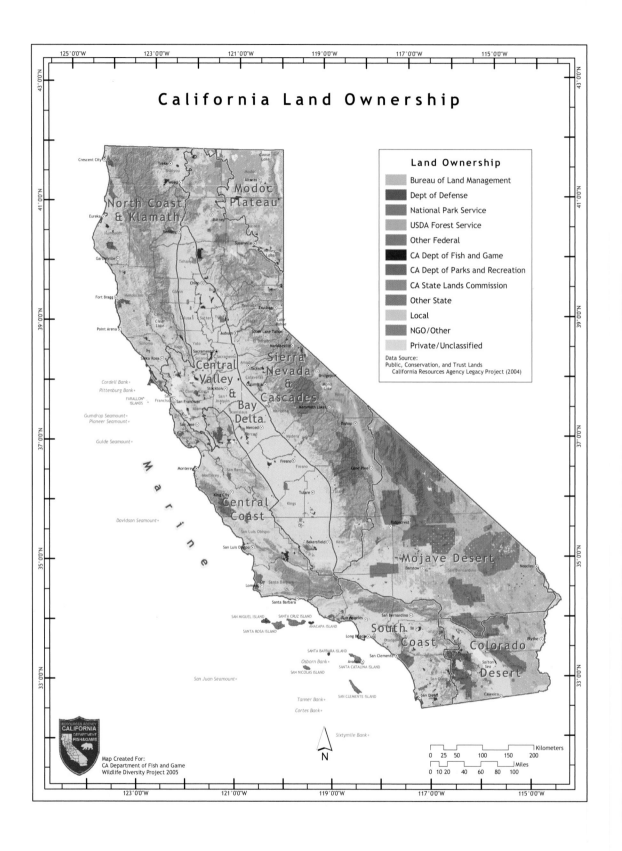

California Land Ownership

Land Ownership

- Bureau of Land Management
- Dept of Defense
- National Park Service
- USDA Forest Service
- Other Federal
- CA Dept of Fish and Game
- CA Dept of Parks and Recreation
- CA State Lands Commission
- Other State
- Local
- NGO/Other
- Private/Unclassified

Data Source:
Public, Conservation, and Trust Lands
California Resources Agency Legacy Project (2004)

Map Created For:
CA Department of Fish and Game
Wildlife Diversity Project 2005

Kilometers
0 25 50   100   150   200

Miles
0 10 20   40   60   80   100

N

1   *California's Natural Diversity* ∼∼∼

California is the wildlife state. Its varied topography and climate have given rise to a remarkable diversity of habitats and a correspondingly diverse array of both plant and animal species. California has more species than any other state in the United States and also has the greatest number of **endemic** species, those that occur nowhere else in the world (CDFG 2003).

Wildlife provides significant economic benefits to the state through recreation, tourism, commercial harvest, and ecological services such as pollination. Many of the places where wildlife thrive are often the same as those valued for recreation and other human activities. By learning what threatens the state's wildlife and the steps that can be taken to reduce those threats, California's residents have the opportunity to become more active stewards of this precious resource, ensuring that the Golden State remains the wildlife state for generations to come.

∼∼∼

From the shores of the Pacific to the crest of the Sierra Nevada, California's topography is unparalleled. Within 80 miles of one another lie the highest and lowest points in the lower 48 states—Mount Whitney at 14,495 feet and Death Valley at 282 feet below sea level. Geological and climatic forces have shaped the state's topography and soils. Glaciation, sedimentary and volcanic deposits, movement along fault zones, the uplift of subterranean rock and sediment layers, and gradual erosion have created unique topographical features and a mosaic of bedrock and soil types.

The state's geography and topography have created distinct local climates. North to south, the state extends for over 500 miles, bridging the temperate rainforests in the Pacific Northwest and the subtropical arid deserts of Mexico. Many parts of the state experience Mediterranean weather patterns, with cool, wet winters and hot, dry summers. Along the northern coast there is abundant precipitation, and ocean air produces foggy, moist conditions. High mountains have cool conditions, with a deep winter snow pack. Desert conditions exist in the rain shadow of the mountain ranges.

This exceptional variation in landscape features, latitudinal range, geological substrates and soils, and climatic conditions supports alpine meadows, desert scrub, coastal wetlands, sandy beaches, dunes and bluffs, oak woodlands, diverse grasslands, moist redwood forests, spring-fed lakes, and freshwater streams, rivers, and marshes.

Plant Diversity

California leads the nation in numbers of native and endemic plant species. Its 5,047 native plant species represent 32 percent of all vascular plants in the United States (CDFG 2003, Jepson Flora Project 2002). Nearly one-third of the state's plant species are endemic (Stein et al. 2000), and California has been recognized as one of 34 global hotspots for plant diversity (Conservation International 2005).

The state's native flora include many unusual species. The giant sequoia, an ancient species that has survived from the Tertiary Age, is one of the most massive living organisms known. Coastal redwoods are the tallest trees in the world, reaching as high as 321 feet, taller than a 30-story building (CDF et al. 2005, Faber 1997). A bristlecone pine in California's White Mountains, called Methuselah, at 4,767 years of age, has lived 1,000 years longer than any other known tree (Vasek and Thorne 1988). California is home to the smallest flowering plant in existence, the pond-dwelling water-meal, less than one-tenth of an inch across. The state also supports nine species of carnivorous plants, including sundews, butterworts, and the California pitcher plant. Numerous species have adapted to grow on serpentine soils that are low in calcium, high in magnesium, and full of chromium, nickel, and other metals toxic to other plant species. Closed-cone conifer species, such as pygmy cypress and some chaparral plants, need hot fires to complete their life cycles (Faber 1997).

California contains examples of most of the major biological provinces, or biomes, in North America, including grassland, shrubland, deciduous forest, coniferous forest, tundra (alpine), mountains, deserts, rainforest (temperate), marine, estuarine, and freshwater habitats. Each of these biomes contains many different types of plant communities, such as redwood forests, vernal pool wetlands, or blue oak woodlands. Altogether, the state supports 81 types of forests, 107 types of shrublands, and 52 types dominated by herbaceous plants, in addition to 27 other types of vegetation (Sawyer and Keeler-Wolf 1995). Some of California's plant species and communities, such as mixed conifer forests, chamise chaparral, and creosote scrub, are widespread. Others are highly restricted in their distributions, such as unique stands of Crucifixion-thorn, Gowen cypress, Hinds walnut, and Torrey pine.

Some parts of the state are particularly rich in plant species diversity. Areas with the greatest number of plant species are the Klamath and inner North Coast ranges, the high Sierra Nevada, the San Diego region, and the San Bernardino Mountains. Other regions with considerable plant diversity are the outer North and Central Coast Ranges, the Cascade Range, the Sierra Nevada foothills, and the western Transverse Range (CDFG 2004).

Wildlife Diversity

California has a high number of animal species, representing large portions of wildlife species nationwide. The state's diverse natural communities provide a wide variety of habitat conditions for wildlife. The state's wildlife species include 84 species of reptiles (30 percent of the total number found in the United States); 51 species of amphibians (22 percent of U.S. species); 67 species of freshwater fish (8 percent of U.S. species); 433 species of birds (47 percent of U.S. species); and 197 mammal species (47 percent of U.S. species) (CDFG 2003). Seventeen species of mammals, 17 species of amphibians, and 20 species of freshwater fish live here and nowhere else.

The state has remarkable native fauna, including the largest bird in North America, the California condor (Poole and Gill 2002), the coast horned lizard that squirts blood from its eyes as a defense mechanism (Stebbins 2003), the tailed frog, which is among the most primitive living frog species (Ford and Cannatella 1993), and the once-endangered California gray whale. The wildlife state is home to 31 species of lungless salamanders, 29 species of colubrid snakes, 31 species of tyrant flycatchers, 17 species of woodpeckers, 27 subspecies of squirrels and chipmunks, 14 different species of kangaroo rats, and 12 species of shrews.

Animal species are not equally distributed across the state. Some of California's natural communities are particularly rich in wildlife species, supporting hundreds of species each. Twenty-four habitats—including valley foothill riparian, mixed conifer, freshwater wetlands, mixed chaparral, and grasslands in the state—support more than 150 terrestrial animal species each (CDFG 2005a). Oak woodlands also are among the most biological diverse communities in the state, supporting 5,000 species of insects, more than 330 species of amphibians, reptiles, birds and mammals, and several thousand plant species (CDFG 2003).

Other community types may be especially important to a particular species or species group. California's rocky offshore islands typically support a limited number of species but are nonetheless important habitat for those species that depend on them for nesting; the islands host some of the largest breeding colonies of seabirds in the U.S. The Farallon Islands, for example, are home to 12 colonies, including the largest colonies of Western gulls and Brandt's cormorant in the world and one of the largest ashy storm-petrel colonies (PRBO 2004).

California's species display a variety of life history patterns, illustrating the many ways wildlife can make a living across a wide variety of habitats. Some of California's wildlife species are habitat specialists, adapted to the vegetation, forage resources, landscape features, or climate of a particular natural community and are found almost exclusively in these communities. As with plant species, some wildlife species are not only dependent on a certain habitat type but are also restricted to a very small geographic range, perhaps occurring at only one site in the world.

The valley elderberry longhorn beetle, for example, eats and reproduces only on the elderberry bush found in Central Valley riparian habitats (USFWS 1984). The marbled murrelet, a seabird, spends most of its life swimming and foraging in the ocean but flies inland to nest, where it relies almost entirely on the branches of old-growth redwood and Douglas-fir trees to provide wide nesting platforms (USFWS 1997). The willow flycatcher is dependent on willow thickets for feeding, cover, and reproduction (CDFG 2005b); the endangered salt marsh harvest mouse prefers pickleweed stands for cover and reproduction (CDFG 2005b); and bank swallows nest in natural river banks (CDFG 2005b). There are also numerous examples of animals that forage primarily on one or very few plant species. The red tree vole lives in Northern California coastal fog forests and eats only the soft inner tissue of Douglas-fir or grand fir needles (Williams 1996); pinyon jays seek pinyon, ponderosa, or Jeffrey pine seeds (CDFG 1988-1990); the chisel-toothed kangaroo rat of the northeastern Great Basin is largely dependent entirely on a particular species of saltbush (*Atriplex confertifolia*) (CDFG 1988–1990); and larval geometrid moths of the genus *Drepanulatrix* eat only leaves of *Ceanothus* species (Rindle 1949).

Some of California's unique wildlife species are adapted to survive in harsh, inhospitable environments. Unique taxa of native pupfish are adapted to salty warm waters of isolated desert pools and creeks. In the Central Valley, seasonal vernal pools evaporate quickly in the hot, dry summer conditions, leaving behind cracked and baking dry ground. Invertebrates such as fairy shrimp species are adapted to this cycle, producing a tough casing that allows their eggs to remain dormant in desiccated conditions, only to emerge when rains refill pools the following summer (USFWS 2004). Kangaroo rat species that inhabit the eastern Modoc plateau, the Colorado Desert, and southern San Joaquin Valley are all well suited for extremely dry conditions (Williams et al 1998). They have specialized kidneys that enable them to excrete solid urine, conserving water and allowing them to survive for long periods without drinking. The alpine chipmunk lives in the Sierra Nevada, typically at elevations greater than 9,000 feet, where the ground is covered with a snow pack from 5 to 10 feet deep for nearly five months of each year. It survives by storing adequate seeds and other food resources during the summer months to sustain it through the winter (DFG 2005a).

Some species are also restricted to a very small geographical area. This can occur when a species is strongly associated with a habitat that is naturally limited in extent or that has grown scarce (usually because of human alteration of the landscape) or when a new subspecies has evolved as a result of being isolated from other populations of the same species by geological or climatic changes. The desert slender salamander (state and federally listed as endangered), for example, is known only from two populations in the Santa Rosa Mountains in Riverside County. The species is a relic of cooler, moister climate regimes but now is restricted to canyon areas that provide cliffs and rock crevices where there is continuous water seepage (CDFG 2005b). The Mount Hermon June beetle and Zayante band-winged grasshopper (both federally endangered) are restricted to small outcrops of sandstone and limestone soils derived from marine sediments, known as Zayante sandhills habitat, in the Santa Cruz mountains (USFWS 1998). The island fox, the world's smallest grey fox (state listed as threatened), occurs only on the six largest Channel Islands off the coast of Santa Barbara and Ventura counties (CDFG 2005b). There are many other examples of species with very limited ranges in California, including invertebrates limited to a particular group of vernal pools and invertebrates, reptiles, and amphibians restricted to particular desert dune or spring systems.

Conversely, other species are habitat generalists, able to survive in many different conditions and to make use of many resources to meet their needs for survival. And, while some entire species' populations are restricted to small areas, there are also wildlife species that are notable for their ability to travel widely or for the large home range occupied by just one individual or family of the species.

Herds of mule deer and pronghorn, for instance, can cross distances of more than 100 miles traveling between their summer and winter ranges in northeastern California. The California bighorn sheep summers in the high elevations of the Sierra Nevada (up to 14,000 feet) and migrates to lower-elevation sagebrush-steppe habitat (below 5,000–6,000 feet) to escape deep winter snows (Zeiner et al. 1990). Some predators, like the mountain lion and fisher, may cover thousands of acres when hunting; much larger areas are required to sustain entire populations (CDFG 1998).

Many of California's bird species also travel substantial distances over the course of their seasonal migrations. Birds that spend their summers in the upper mountainous elevations, such as the yellow-rumped warbler and cedar waxwing, descend tens or hundreds of miles during the wintertime to forage in the milder climates in the Central Valley or along the coast. Long-distance migrating birds, including numerous species of swallows, terns, hawks, shorebirds and songbirds, forage or nest seasonally in California. The golden-crowned sparrow uses California as a winter home and spends summer months far to the north. The Swainson's hawk migrates between California and the tropics.

Functioning Ecological Communities

The long-term conservation of animal species depends on healthy, functioning ecological systems. These systems, in turn, depend on a wide variety of plant and animal species that have important ecological roles.

The Role of Plants

Plants are essential for maintaining a healthy environment for both wildlife and humans. They provide a host of ecological services, maintaining soil, water, and air and controlling destructive biological invaders. As primary producers in ecosystems, green plants transform solar energy into living matter, which is utilized as sources of food, shelter, and habitat structure by other species, including humans.

Plants build soil, absorb runoff from winter storms, help recharge underground aquifers, and reduce erosion. A rich diversity of plant species is also essential for recovery from environmental disturbances like flooding, fires, drought, and mudslides. A catastrophic fire can reduce a forested area to a relatively barren state, and plants that can tolerate bright sun and water stress typically are the first to re-establish there. These species increase shade and retention of soil moisture, creating conditions that allow other plants to become established. Over time, given the right conditions, vegetation similar to the original, pre-fire forest may return.

A dramatic example of what can happen when plant life is removed is illustrated by the hydraulic mining that occurred in California during the late 19th century, which removed the vegetation of entire watersheds across the Sierra Nevada. Lacking its protective cover of plants, the ground was laid bare to winter storms; rapidly increasing runoff eroded deep gullies and removed valuable topsoil. Downstream, farmers in the Central Valley suffered devastating floods that buried houses and entire farms under 15 to 30 feet of sediment (Holliday 1999). The damage was so extensive that, even now, 130 years after such mining was outlawed, some parts of the Sierra Nevada are still recovering.

Plants absorb chemicals from the surrounding environment and thus are natural filters of pollutants from the soil and water. Plants are used in bioremediation of coal mine and industrial wastes (Missouri Botanical Garden 2005). Wetlands are so successful at cleaning water that some cities use them as part of their municipal water treatment process (City of Arcata 2005). Healthy populations of native plants also control the spread of insects, diseases, and damaging invasive plants.

Plants provide the basic physical structure for most animal habitats. For example, in the canopy of an oak forest, birds use branches for nesting, and invertebrates use twigs and bark for laying eggs. Birds such as flycatchers and raptors use exposed branches to launch aerial attacks on flying prey. Below the canopy, animals use trunk cavities for nesting and hiding, even after the tree itself has long since died. Woodpeckers and other animals probe the tree's bark for insects to eat. At least 60 bird species use cavities in trees for nesting and cover. Woodpeckers, sapsuckers, and flickers may also use trees as granaries for storing acorns and other seeds for later use (Scott et al. 1977). In the **understory**, shrubs provide cover from predators, particularly for more vulnerable young animals. The litter layer on the ground retains moisture that allows invertebrates and amphibians to survive the dry season. Below ground, the extensive root network of mature oaks enables mammals and insects to burrow into the soil for dens and other shelter.

The Role of Wildlife

Wildlife species are important components of functioning ecosystems and for the survival of plant species. Animal species depend on one another, often as part of the food web, and they create or maintain habitat conditions for one another. For example, in the Central Valley, California ground squirrel burrows provide shelter for other species, including the California tiger salamander and burrowing owl (CDFG 2005a). Beavers are well-known dam builders, creating small wetlands used by a host of other animals.

Some animal species are integral to sustaining the life history of plants, playing an important role in pollination, seed dispersal, and decomposition. The yucca moth is the sole pollinator of chaparral yucca in San Diego County, and the yucca seeds are the sole food source for the moth larvae (Cox 1981). Solitary bees pollinate vernal pool plants. These bees nest in holes in the uplands and emerge in the spring at the precise time their food sources, vernal pool plants such as *Downingia* and *Limnanthes* species, are flowering (Thorp 2005). Birds and small mammals can also help disperse plant seeds as they eat or collect and transport them. For example, kangaroo rats and most herbivorous rodents harvest and store grass and herb seeds for later use; often, these seeds germinate, forming new plant populations. Worms, millipedes, and other invertebrates are responsible for conversion of plant matter detritus into soil, needed for both plant and animal life.

The Wildlife State at Risk

While California has exceptional plant and wildlife diversity as described in this chapter, many of the species populations that make up that diversity are stressed by extraordinary development pressures and economic activities. Chapter 2 identifies the hundreds of wildlife species at risk, and Chapter 3 describes the major stressors affecting those species and their habitats.

2   Species at Risk ～～～～～～～～～～～～～～～～～

One of the elements in developing a wildlife action plan is identifying and compiling information on species of wildlife, including low and declining populations that are indicative of the diversity and health of the state's wildlife. Fish and Game has chosen to use the **Special Animals List,** which it maintains and updates within the California Natural Diversity Database (CNDDB). This list is also referred to as the list of **species at risk** or **special status species,** and it includes vertebrates and invertebrates. The special status species are diverse, and they inhabit the varied ecosystems across the state. Many of the special status species have been identified as **species of special concern** due to their low or declining numbers.

The associated Web publication of this report includes the Wildlife Species Matrix, consisting of all wildlife species and subspecies on the California Department of Fish and Game's Special Animals List.

As described elsewhere in this report, a number of stressors are putting wildlife and habitats at risk; the greatest stressors now facing the state's natural communities and wildlife are those related to human activity. Among these, growth and development, water management conflicts, invasive species, and climate change each have major consequences for species, ecosystems, and habitats throughout the state. A number of other stressors also negatively affect species and habitats in many regions. As a result of these stressors, many wildlife and plant species are declining and are rare, or in some cases, extinct or at risk of extinction.

Plants at Risk

While the Wildlife Action Plan is focused on wildlife and its habitats, plant species are also at risk, as described here. Many of California's plant communities are threatened by rapid urban growth and development, particularly in the Sierra foothills, the Central Valley, the San Francisco Bay Area, and the South Coast Region. Examples of plant communities in the path of urban expansion include valley oak woodland, native perennial grasslands, and coastal sage scrub. Additionally, forest communities, including mixed evergreen and conifer forests, are increasingly being fragmented by rural residential development. Highly water-dependent plant communities, including riparian areas, wetlands, and vernal pools, are also at risk. These communities not only suffer from the pressure of land conversion but are also subject to changes in water availability due to water management actions, water quality issues, and excessive livestock grazing.

California has more plant species at risk (nearly 1,700 species, or 31 percent of its total flora) than any other state in the nation (Stein 2002). At least 13 of California's plant taxa are now extinct in the wild, and at least 18 other plant taxa are presumed extinct (i.e., they have not been seen for at least 20 years, although suitable habitat still exists) (CDFG 2005b). Some of these at-risk species have been listed under either state or federal endangered species acts. California hosts 186 plants federally listed as endangered, the highest number in the country after Hawaii (with 273 species). California also has 222 state-listed plants (with some of these species also occurring on the federal list) (CDFG 2005b, USFWS 2005).

Wildlife at Risk

Among wildlife species, those with limited distributions and those that are restricted to particular habitat types face formidable challenges if the habitats or resources upon which they depend are lost or degraded. Wide-ranging and migratory species also face unique threats because they are vulnerable to habitat fragmentation and because it can be difficult for conservation managers to secure the protection of widely separated habitat areas.

According to conservation status rankings developed by **Natural Heritage** programs across the United States, 23 percent of at-risk amphibian species in the United States are found in California, 29 percent of at-risk reptiles, 19 percent of at-risk birds, 41 percent of at-risk mammals, and 10 percent of at-risk freshwater fishes. In terms of overall biological diversity (including both plants and animals), California ranks second among the states for the percent of its species that are at risk (Stein et al. 2000).

More than half of California's vertebrate wildlife (a total of 455 species) are at risk and listed on the Department of Fish and Game's Special Animals List. The state also has 369 invertebrate species at risk. At least seven species or subspecies of California vertebrates and 16 total animal species are known to have become extinct in the last 150 years. Eight species of vertebrates and a number of species of invertebrates have become completely **extirpated** and four bird species no longer breed in the state (TNC 1987).

Fish and Game maintains and updates the Special Animals List in the California Natural Diversity Database (CNDDB). This list is also referred to as the list of species at risk or special status species, and it includes vertebrates and invertebrates. The special status species are diverse and inhabit the varied ecosystems across the state. Many of the special status species have been identified as species of special concern due to their low or declining numbers.

The CNDDB program has been inventorying the state's rare and declining species since 1979. The Special Animals List is updated regularly and currently contains more than 800 **taxa**. The current list is available at http://www.dfg.ca.gov/bdb/html/animals.html.

Species and subspecies are included in the Special Animals List if they fall into one or more of the following categories:

- Officially listed or proposed for listing under the state and/or federal Endangered Species Acts.

- State or federal candidate for possible listing.

- Taxa that meet the criteria for listing, even if not currently included on any list, as described in Section 15380 of the *California Environmental Quality Act Guidelines.*

- Taxa considered by Fish and Game to be a Species of Special Concern (SSC).

- Taxa that are biologically rare, very restricted in distribution, declining throughout their range, or have a critical, vulnerable stage in their life cycle that warrants monitoring.

- Populations in California that may be on the periphery of a taxon's range but are threatened with extirpation in California.

- Taxa closely associated with a habitat that is declining in California at an alarming rate (e.g., wetlands, riparian, old growth forests, desert aquatic systems, native grasslands, vernal pools.)

- Taxa designated as special status, sensitive, or declining species by other state or federal agencies or non-governmental organizations (NGOs).

The Plan development team updated information for the nearly 800 special status species statewide by conducting literature searches for each species on the Special Animals List; entering new-occurrence information from journal articles; consulting species experts for opinions regarding the inclusion of additional rare or threatened species; and entering data from the California Natural Diversity Database backlog of field survey forms and reports. The information was then used to develop a matrix, the Wildlife Species Matrix, that includes information about those 800 species. The regional species and habitat information is described below with instructions on how to access it on the Web.

(For a description of other species and habitat databases and information available at Fish and Game, see Appendix D.)

Regional Chapters

The Species at Risk sections of the regional chapters summarize the numbers of species, endemic species, and species at risk associated with the region (DFG Special Animals List). Appendix D describes the criteria for inclusion on the Special Animals List. Details regarding the special status species, compiled in the Wildlife Species Matrix, are available on the Web at http://www.dfg.ca.gov/habitats/wdp/matrix_search.asp. The Wildlife Species Matrix lists the species at risk and provides the rarity ranking status, associated habitat, population trends, and range maps.

Each Species at Risk section also features two or three species to illustrate how various activities negatively affect species in the region. The regional chapters also discuss the major stressors affecting wildlife and habitat. Regional habitat condition is described in the context of the major stressors; e.g., degraded, altered habitat resulting from population growth and development. Habitat extent can be determined by consulting online maps provided by the California Wildlife Habitat Relationship System, described below. Finally, the regional sections present specific conservation actions to restore and conserve habitats and wildlife.

Wildlife Species Matrix

Included in the associated Web publication of this report is the Wildlife Species Matrix, consisting of all wildlife taxa (species and subspecies) on the California Department of Fish and Game's Special Animals List. This special status species list includes 140 birds, 127 mammals, 102 fishes, 43 reptiles, 40 amphibians, and 365 invertebrates. Of these, 13 birds, 69 mammals, 19 reptiles, 22 amphibians, 46 fish, and 312 invertebrates are endemic to the state; these taxa are indicated in the matrix with an asterisk. The matrix can be sorted by taxa names and by region. For each taxon, the matrix gives the following information:

Rarity Ranking Status—the CNDDB status column combines **NatureServe's** Global Ranking, which indicates a taxon's relative rarity globally (G), with the state rarity ranking (S), which is assigned by Fish and Game:

G/S5: Secure; common and widespread

G/S4: Apparently secure; uncommon but not rare

G/S3: Vulnerable; at moderate risk of extinction due to a restricted range, relatively few populations (often 80 or fewer), recent and widespread declines, or other factors

G/S2: Imperiled: at high risk of extinction due to very restricted range, very few populations (often 20 or fewer), steep declines, or other factors

G/S1: Critically imperiled: at very high risk of extinction due to extreme rarity (often five or fewer populations), very steep declines, or other factors

G/SH: Possibly extinct

G/SX: Presumed extinct

Descriptions of other ranking systems included in the Wildlife Species Matrix are included in the introduction to Fish and Game's Special Animals List, available online at http://www.dfg.ca.gov/bdb/pdfs/SPAnimals.pdf.

Habitat association—A descriptive habitat association is given, which is based on the Wildlife and Habitat Relationship Database's list of 60 habitat types found within the state. When too little habitat information is available, the association is marked as "Insufficient data for habitat determination"; when a large number of habitats is used, the phrase "Wide variety of habitats" appears. Habitat associations were determined by using ArcMap to query the California Wildlife Habitat Relationship Database by individual habitat types for taxa occurrences in the California Natural Diversity Database.

Population trends—By definition, rare species are infrequently encountered. For certain well-studied, regularly surveyed groups such as birds and fishes, population trends are available from various sources and have been noted in the matrix as declining, stable, or increasing. For many taxa in the matrix, particularly invertebrates and small mammals, lack of data precludes meaningful population trend estimates; for these, the trend is listed as unknown.

Range maps—The current range of a species within California (where available) can be viewed by using the range map access button. These range maps appear at a statewide scale, unless the species' limited distribution merits a different scale. The range maps were developed using one of two different protocols. The more recent maps were created after development of a standardized mapping approach that considers current data and scale and incorporates a peer review process. They are designed to produce an accurate and standardized depiction of a species' range in California. More information on how current maps were created and the process that will be employed to revise the older California Wildlife Habitat Relationship (CWHR) maps is available on the Web at http://www.dfg.ca.gov/bdb/index.html. Advantages of a standardized approach that incorporates current occurrence data and a peer review process are: 1) using standardized features supports the underlying assumption that these range polygons can be used as data for spatial analysis; 2) the process of map preparation follows the scientific principles of repeatability and the use of fully described methods; and 3) they can be used as a baseline against which future range trends can be measured. Some older maps were created for the CWHR project in the late 1980s and are based solely on professional judgment. These maps were hand-drawn on letter-sized paper without the benefit of supporting data. They were not intended as a rigorous or precise definition of a species range in California and were created in support of a wildlife-habitat relationship modeling system. Until revised, these maps represent the best available range information for these species.

Current species-level range maps for fish were produced by the University of California, Davis, Information Center for the Environment, in conjunction with Dr. Peter Moyle and his graduate student Paul Randall as part of the Hexagon Project conducted by The Nature Conservancy in 1998. Digital data from 10 different fish databases and GIS layers containing California hydrology and California state boundaries were projected on paper maps (roughly 11 inches by 17 inches). Polygons were then hand-drawn on these paper maps and digitized using ARC/INFO GIS software. The resulting polygons are accurate at a scale of roughly 1:1,000,000. For more information about this project or to see additional maps produced, please visit http://ice.ucdavis.edu/aquadiv/fishcovs/fishmaps.html.

3 Threats to Wildlife Diversity in California

The regional chapters describe the problems and threats that may adversely affect wildlife and their habitats. These threats are termed "stressors." In each region of the state, there are multiple stressors to wildlife and habitats, operating alone and in combination. A number of these stressors are common to the entire state or to several different regions. The scope and effects of the most widespread stressors are briefly described below. More in-depth discussion of these stressors and their roles in each region can be found in the regional chapters.

Growth and development, water management conflicts, **invasive** species, and climate change each have major consequences for species, **ecosystems**, and **habitats** in every region of the state.

Growth and Development

Statewide, California's population grew by 49 percent between 1970 and 1990 and again by nearly 14 percent—adding over 4 million residents—between 1990 and 2000 (CDOF 2005). Increasing needs for housing, services, transportation, and other infrastructure place ever-greater demands on the state's land, water, and other natural resources. Without conservation planning, growth and development can eliminate important habitats and fragment and decrease the quality of remaining natural areas. With the exception of the Modoc Plateau, development represents a substantial stressor for species and habitats across the state.

In the South Coast, for example, nearly 40 percent of the region's land has been converted to urban and suburban use (CDF 2002). Some habitat types have been reduced to a small fraction of their historical extent; **vernal pool** habitats have been reduced to less than 5 percent of their historical extent (USFWS 1998g) and coastal sage scrub to about 18 percent (Pollak 2001a). Populations of species that depend upon these habitats have declined significantly.

In other parts of the state, growth and development threats have increased tremendously in recent decades. The Sierra Nevada, for instance, underwent population growth of 130 percent between 1970 and 1990, and future growth in the region is expected to continue to exceed the state average (SNEP 1996, Duane 1998). Most of this growth is low-density, single-home and commercial development that lacks the benefit of regional conservation planning. The Central Valley and the **Inland Empire** also continue to develop at a rapid pace.

Water Management Conflicts

Across all regions of the state, limited water resources are managed to meet water and power supply needs and to accommodate residential and agricultural land use. Water management activities include the operation of dams and diversions, development and operation of irrigation canal systems, extraction of groundwater, and construction of flood-control projects such as levees and channelization. These activities can reduce the amount of water available for fish and wildlife, obstruct fish passage, and result in numerous other habitat alterations. In all regions of the state, **aquatic** and **riparian** habitats support rich biological communities, including many **special status species**, and degradation of these habitats represents a serious threat to the state's biological heritage.

The highly controlled water resources of the Central Valley and Bay-Delta region exemplify many of these water management issues. Dams are located on all but one of the major rivers flowing into the Central Valley, more than 2,600 miles of rivers are constrained by levees or bank protection, and up to 70 percent of the region's freshwater flows are diverted (DWR 2005b, Steere and Schaefer 2001). As a result of these alterations, natural riverine habitat is lost, and fish migration routes are disrupted. In many regions of the state, diversions and groundwater pumping deplete river basins to the point where river reaches regularly dry up or are diminished to such low flows that native species cannot survive; this has occurred in such rivers as the Carmel River on the Central Coast (CDFG 1996), the Colorado River in the Colorado Desert (Pitt 2001), the Mojave River in the Mojave Desert (CDFG 2004e), and the Scott and Shasta rivers in the North Coast–Klamath Region (CDFG 2004g).

Invasive Species

Since the arrival of the first European settlers in California, non-native species have been introduced both unintentionally and purposefully to the state. At present, more than 1,000 introduced plant species (Barbour et al. 1993) and more than 110 non-native fish and wildlife species inhabit California (Grenfell et al. 2003, Moyle 2002). Among these non-native species, those that disrupt or alter native ecological communities and have negative consequences for native species and habitats are considered to be invasive.

In many habitats, invasive plants outcompete native species for light, water, and soil. These plants may also offer inferior habitat and nutritional values for native animal species and sometimes alter ecosystem processes, such as natural **fire regimes.** Invasive animals out-compete, prey upon, or disturb the habitat of native wildlife and may spread diseases.

The invasive riparian plants arundo and tamarisk, which are pervasive throughout the central and southern portions of the state, illustrate the scale of habitat disruption that can be caused by invasive vegetation. Both species displace native riparian vegetation and provide inferior habitat for wildlife. Other highly aggressive plants include starthistle and medusa-head, both of which invade grasslands and scrub habitats across the state. Control of these aggressive plant species adds a substantial work burden to the management of natural lands.

Invasive species are also a major concern in the Marine Region, where discharged ballast water and other sources can introduce marine organisms carried from a ship's home port. San Francisco Bay ranks as one of the most-invaded bodies of water in the world, and estimates are that a new species unintentionally becomes established in San Francisco Bay every 14 weeks (SFEI 2004). Among the invasive marine species introduced to California's coastal waters are the Asian clam and European green crab, which have caused declines in phyto-plankton and Dungeness crab populations, respectively (Grosholz 2002, Grosholz et al. 2000).

Climate Change

Climate change will affect ecological communities and wildlife species throughout California. Current climate models predict overall temperature increases of between 4 degrees and 10.5 degrees Fahrenheit by the end of the century, accompanied by hotter, drier summers and warmer, wetter winters (Hayhoe et al. 2004, Schneider and Kuntz-Duriseti 2002, Turman 2002).

Rising temperatures and altered precipitation patterns will result in changes in plant com-munities and reduced habitat suitability for some wildlife species. Some communities and species may shift to higher elevations or latitudes, but this will become ever more challenging as remaining natural areas shrink and the gaps between habitats grow. Throughout the state, drier summers may also increase fire frequency and intensity. Climate change effects will be especially disruptive in the Sierra Nevada and Cascades and Central Valley and Bay-Delta regions.

In the Sierra Nevada, warmer temperatures will reduce the annual snowpack and result in earlier snowmelt. Spring and summer streamflows are projected to decline by as much as 25 percent by 2050 and 55 percent by the end of the century (duVair 2003). With warmer temperatures, alpine and subalpine communities may also be greatly reduced.

In the Bay-Delta region, soil erosion has caused farmlands to subside to elevations below sea level. These areas are protected by levees, but rising sea levels could overstress levees and water pumping systems, resulting in flooding and failure of water-conveyance system (Mount and Twiss 2005).

Other Widespread Stressors

A number of other stressors also recur in multiple regions. Excessive livestock grazing, either in sensitive habitats or grazing of too many animals or for too long a grazing period, significantly affects wildlife habitats in the Mojave Desert, Central Coast, North Coast–Klamath, Modoc Plateau, and Sierra Nevada and Cascades regions. Forest management conflicts are major stressors in the North Coast–Klamath, Modoc Plateau, and Sierra Nevada and Cascades regions. Altered fire regimes were identified as major stressors in the South Coast, North Coast–Klamath, Modoc Plateau, and Sierra Nevada and Cascades regions. Pollution and urban or agricultural runoff were identified as major stressors in the South Coast, Central Coast, Central Valley and Bay-Delta, and Marine regions. Recreational pressures and human disturbance are issues in the Mojave Desert, Colorado Desert, South Coast, Central Coast, Sierra Nevada and Cascades, and Marine regions.

Major Wildlife Stressors Identified by Region

Mojave Desert

- Multiple uses conflicting with wildlife on public lands
- Growth and development
- Groundwater overdrafting and loss of riparian habitat
- Inappropriate off-road vehicle use
- Excessive livestock grazing
- Excessive burro and horse grazing
- Invasive plants
- Military land management conflicts
- Mining operations

Colorado Desert

- Water management conflicts and water transfer impacts
- Inappropriate off-road vehicle use
- Loss and degradation of dune habitats
  - Disruption of sand transport processes
  - Invasive plant species
  - Inappropriate off-road vehicle use
- Growth and development
- Invasive species

South Coast

- Growth and development
- Water management conflicts and degradation of aquatic ecosystems
- Invasive species
- Altered fire regimes
- Recreational pressures

Central Coast

- Growth and development
- Intensive agriculture
- Excessive livestock grazing
- Water management conflicts and degradation of aquatic ecosystems
- Recreational pressures
- Invasive species

North Coast–Klamath

- Water management conflicts
- Instream gravel mining
- Forest management conflicts
- Altered fire regimes
- Agriculture and urban development
- Excessive livestock grazing
- Invasive species

Modoc Plateau

- Excessive livestock grazing
- Excessive feral horse grazing
- Altered fire regimes
- Western juniper expansion
- Invasive plants
- Forest management conflicts
- Water management conflicts and degradation of aquatic ecosystems

Sierra Nevada and Cascades

Stressors affecting upland habitats

- Growth and land development
- Forest management conflicts
- Altered fire regimes
- Excessive livestock grazing
- Invasive plants
- Recreational pressures
- Climate change

Stressors affecting aquatic and riparian habitats

- Water diversions and dams
- Watershed fragmentation and fish barriers
- Hydropower project operations
- Excessive livestock grazing
- Water diversion from the Owens Valley
- Introduced non-native fish

Central Valley and Bay-Delta

- Growth and development (including urban, residential, and agricultural)
- Water management conflicts and reduced water for wildlife
- Water pollution
- Invasive species
- Climate change

Marine Region

- Overfishing
- Degradation of marine habitat
- Invasive species
- Pollution
- Human disturbance

4   *Statewide Conservation Actions*

The stressors that affect wildlife, and the conservation actions needed to address them and restore and conserve ecosystems and wildlife populations, were analyzed in each region of the state. While some stressors are significant in only a few regions, others are pervasive across the state. Similarly, some conservation actions are important for a few regions, while other conservation actions are needed throughout the state or are more appropriately implemented through a statewide program.

Recommended Statewide Conservation Actions

Conservation actions were considered for each region, based on the stressors and circumstances of the regions. Statewide conservation actions are those actions that are important across most or all regions. The following are recommended statewide conservation actions:

a. **The state should develop policies and incentives to facilitate better integration of wildlife conservation considerations into local and regional planning and land-use decision-making.**

- Wildlife agencies should establish regional goals for species and habitat protection and work with city, county, and state agency land-use planning processes to accomplish them.

- The state should expand Fish and Game's capacity to assist local and regional agencies with conservation planning and implementation.

See also the Conservation Planning section in Chapter 6.

b. **Permitting agencies, county planners, and land management agencies should work to ensure that infrastructure development projects are designed and sited to avoid harmful effects on sensitive species and habitats.**

Wherever possible, infrastructure development projects should be sited near existing urban areas and development corridors and away from areas that are relatively undeveloped or with significant biological resources.

c. **The state should develop policies and incentives to better integrate wildlife conservation into state and regional transportation planning. Wildlife considerations need to be incorporated early in the transportation planning process.**

   • Transportation systems and corridors should be retrofitted to better accommodate wildlife.

   • Stewardship of existing transportation facilities should include better consideration of wildlife needs.

d. **State and federal agencies should work with cities and counties to secure sensitive habitats and key habitat linkages.**

   • State and federal wildlife agencies, working with nongovernmental organizations, should inventory and evaluate sensitive wildlife habitat and key habitat linkage areas.

   • Public land managers should protect wildlife habitat linkages on public lands.

   • Lead planning agencies should incorporate habitat linkages and other identified key habitats into conservation plans. Regional conservation plans should include adaptive management provisions to accommodate protecting important wildlife linkages as they are identified.

   • The state should partner with federal and local land managers, land trusts, and conservancies to prioritize and secure, through purchase, swaps, or easements, important habitat linkages and other priority sites that are not now protected.

e. **State and local agencies should allocate sufficient water for ecosystem uses and wildlife needs when planning for and meeting regional water supply needs.**

   • Incorporate water-for-wildlife considerations into regional integrated water planning.

   • Develop water budgets for individual watersheds, assessing and accounting for available water resources, groundwater recharge goals, aquatic species' flow requirements, and current and forecasted water supply needs. Create water use-and-supply plans that do not overdraft groundwater and that provide suitable groundwater and surface water flows for aquatic species.

   • Establish and implement minimum flows and flow requirements that mimic, as closely as possible, natural seasonal high- and low-flow patterns.

   • Secure long-term contracts for water for instream flows and for wetlands.

- Preserve or purchase lands with water rights and lease or acquire water rights from willing sellers to protect instream flows. Conservation interests should look for opportunities to protect lands that both preserve instream flows and support other sensitive resources.

- Assess and catalog existing water diversions and monitor compliance with permitted water rights. Remove unauthorized diversions. Use diversion structures that allow water diversion only when minimum flow requirements are met.

f. **Federal, state, and local agencies should provide greater resources and coordinate efforts to eradicate or control existing occurrences of invasive species and to prevent new introductions.**

- Work in cooperation with private organizations, pest control councils, coordinated weed management areas, and conservation organizations and agencies to develop and implement prevention, eradication, and control programs for invasive species.

- Develop a rapid response capacity to identify and eradicate invasive species, with a rapid response team and emergency fund to tackle new invasions (possibly modeled after the Office of Spill Prevention and Response program). Cooperative Weed Management Areas groups, watershed groups, and resource conservation districts could be part of the rapid response team.

- Increase research and monitoring of exotic species that compete with, predate, or parasitize sensitive native species or degrade important habitats.

- Update and publish watch lists of highly invasive species and maps of occurrences of invasive species.

- Engage key stakeholders and the public in ways they can reduce the threat to native wildlife posed by invasive species.

- Adopt agency policies and encourage the use of weed-free materials in restoration projects, erosion control, post-fire seeding and other land management projects.

g. **Federal, state, and local agencies and nongovernmental conservation organizations, working with private landowners and public land managers, should expand efforts to restore and conserve riparian communities.**

- Redesign flood control strategies and infrastructure to allow the restoration of riparian communities. Elements of riparian conservation involve restoring more natural flow regimes, accommodating over-bank flooding, enlarging levee set-backs, and removing **riprap** in some areas.

- Elevate as a conservation priority and increase funding for restoration and conservation of riparian communities.

- Enhance programs and incentives to assist ranchers, farmers, and other landowners to restore and conserve riparian communities.

h. Federal, state, tribal, and local agencies and nongovernmental organizations, working with private landowners, should expand efforts to implement agricultural and rangeland management practices that are compatible with wildlife and habitat conservation.

- Use existing programs (particularly Natural Resources Conservation Service programs) that provide funding and technical expertise for such practices. Public agencies, including Fish and Game, should assist landowners in navigating the permitting processes necessary to receive assistance under these programs. Nongovernmental organization partners should include groups such as the California Rangeland Trust, the California Cattlemen's Associations, the Community Alliance with Family Farmers, the Elkhorn Slough Foundation, and local land trusts.

- Expand partnerships among regional water quality control boards and interests from the agricultural industry to implement management practices that protect environmental quality.

- Support and develop certification and labeling programs that increase the market value of agricultural and livestock products produced using ecologically sustainable management practices, such as protection of riparian areas, efficient use of water, reduced application of agricultural chemicals, promotion of oak regeneration, and control of invasive species. Develop guidance documents and technical consultation processes for implementation of these management practices, as well as processes for field inspections and certification.

- Encourage livestock operators with grazing leases on public lands to institute ecologically sustainable grazing practices. Incentive systems should be established to reduce costs for operators who follow such practices.

- Work with private landowners to retire crop lands that are marginally productive but ecologically important for wildlife.

See also Appendix G, Information Sources for Wildlife and Habitat Conservation on Private Lands.

i. In their conservation planning and ecosystem restoration work, state and federal wildlife agencies and land managers should consider the most current projections of the effects of global warming.

Global warming is expected to have major consequences for ecosystems and wildlife populations throughout the state. Projected changes are important factors to consider when planning long-term conservation or restoration projects.

j. **The state and federal governments should give greater priority to wildlife and natural resources conservation education.**

Conservation efforts will be less successful if the public does not appreciate the state's wildlife resources or understand the conservation challenges facing the most biologically diverse state in the nation. The state should:

- Encourage wildlife conservation education in formal education, particularly in grades K–12.
- Expand efforts to connect Californians to the state's natural resources through expanded formal and nonformal education programs in outdoor settings.
- Devote greater resources to enhancing education regarding conservation of wildlife and natural resources in the urban population.
- Educate the public about the need for sound water management policy and large-scale conservation planning that support a diverse and sustainable fish and wildlife resource.
- Educate the public on ways to avoid wildlife-human conflicts.

k. **The state should strengthen its capacity to implement conservation actions and to assist local agencies and landowners with planning and implementation of wildlife and habitat restoration and conservation efforts.**

See also Chapter 6, Strengthening California's Conservation Capabilities.

l. **Working with the Department of Defense, the state and conservation organizations should expand efforts to secure important wildlife habitat that also serves as development buffer zones around military bases and training grounds.**

A collaborative effort of the Department of Defense, the Nature Conservancy, the Wildlife Conservation Board, and the California Resources Agency has funded the establishment of a wildlands buffer around La Posta Navy Mountain Warfare Training Center east of San Diego. A similar effort is being made to secure important wildlife habitat around Camp Pendleton in the South Coast Region. There are numerous areas around bases across the state where it is in the interest of conservation and military operations to establish wildland buffers.

m. **Permitting agencies, county and local planners, and land management agencies should work to ensure that infrastructure development projects are designed and sited to avoid harmful effects on sensitive species and habitats.**

As demands for roads, power, water, and waste disposal sites grow, efforts should be made to update and upgrade existing infrastructure to meet those needs. For example, rather than developing additional wind farms, existing wind farms can be updated to produce more electricity per windmill, and transmission lines can be upgraded to higher-voltage lines to avoid the need for new utility corridors across undeveloped lands.

Wherever possible, infrastructure development projects should be sited near existing urban areas and development corridors and away from areas that are relatively undeveloped or with significant biological resources.

If new landfill facilities are built in the region, permitting agencies should work with project developers to ensure that all possible measures are taken to prevent environmental impacts, such as using closed-top landfill pits and reliably sealed liners to prevent water and soil contamination.

n. To address habitat fragmentation and avoid the loss of key wildlife corridors, federal, state and local agencies, along with nongovernmental organizations, should support scientific studies to identify key wildlife habitat linkages throughout the state.

The South Coast Missing Linkages Project has identified key wildlife corridors in South Coast Region. A similar effort is needed in each region of the state.

o. The state should provide scientific and planning assistance and financial incentives to local governments to develop and implement regional multispecies conservation plans for all of the rapidly developing areas.

p. While numerous private landowners are leaders in conservation, Fish and Game, the U.S. Fish and Wildlife Service, the USDA Natural Resources Conservation Service, and local resource conservation districts need to expand efforts to improve conservation and restoration on private lands by assisting private landowners.

q. State and federal government should give greater priority to funding and staffing of wildlife and natural resource law enforcement efforts.

Effective conservation requires law enforcement, which is a basic and essential element of resource protection. State and federal agencies should:

- Review law enforcement staffing levels and deployment and encourage increased staff to provide adequate protection.
- Develop greater resources to enhance law enforcement's ability to maintain officers in the field through operating-budget augmentations, salary improvements, and equipment purchases.

Recommended Region-Specific Conservation Actions

Implementing the statewide conservation actions and the region-specific conservation actions is necessary to restore and conserve ecosystems and wildlife populations. For the recommended region-specific conservation actions, see Section 4 in each of the regional chapters.

Conservation Action Workshops

In the course of the regional reviews of stressors affecting wildlife and habitats and the actions needed to restore and conserve wildlife diversity, several key issues surfaced repeatedly. In spring 2005, the Plan development team convened workshops to identify challenges and opportunities regarding several of these key issues and to develop recommendations for action. Summaries of the workshop results and recommendations may be found on the Web at http://www.dfg.ca.gov/habitats/wdp/.

5 Monitoring California's Conservation Actions

Monitoring and Adaptive Management

Natural communities, ecosystems, species population dynamics, and the effects of stressors on the environment are inherently complex. Wildlife and resource managers often are called upon to implement conservation strategies or actions based upon limited scientific information and with considerable uncertainties. Adaptive management is a key element in implementing effective conservation programs. Adaptive management combines data from monitoring species and natural systems with new information from management and targeted studies to continually assess the effectiveness of, adjust, and improve conservation actions.

Some conservation actions recommended in this Wildlife Action Plan may be assessed adequately simply by monitoring a few environmental variables. At the other extreme, a regional multispecies conservation effort requires a major long-term comprehensive monitoring program. The steps and considerations needed to design a monitoring program in an adaptive management context are summarized below. This information is a guide to designing a program to measure the success of the conservation actions of this wildlife plan and will be useful to consider, whether developing a major regional conservation plan or a very limited conservation project.

Designing a Monitoring Program to Support Adaptive Management

All of the information in this section regarding monitoring and adaptive management is adapted from a guidance document developed collaboratively by the California Department of Fish and Game, the U.S. Geological Survey, and the U.S. Fish and Wildlife Service. For a full discussion of monitoring for effectiveness of regional conservation planning, see the entire document: Atkinson, A.J., P.C. Trenham, R.N. Fisher, S.A. Hathaway, B.S. Johnson, S.G. Torres, and Y.C. Moore. 2004. Designing monitoring programs in an adaptive management context for regional multiple species conservation plans. U.S. Geological Survey Technical Report. USGS Western Ecological Research Center, Sacramento, Calif. 69 pages. (Available at http://www.dfg.ca.gov/nccp/pups/monframewk10-04.pdf)

Monitoring species, habitat, and natural communities to assess the success of conservation efforts involves, at a minimum, effectiveness monitoring and targeted studies.

Effectiveness monitoring evaluates the success of the conservation action or conservation plan in meeting its stated biological objectives (Noss and Cooperrider 1994). Typical effectiveness monitoring measures:

- Status and trends of resources (e.g., quantitative data on priority species, biodiversity, vegetative structure)
- Status and trends of known pressures (e.g., invasive species, contaminants, disturbance)
- Effects of management actions on resources and known pressures (e.g., density of invasive plants measured before and then 1 to 5 years after herbicide treatment)

Targeted studies are a special subset of effectiveness monitoring. Targeted studies increase the effectiveness of monitoring and management by improving knowledge about the ecological system and about management techniques. Targeted studies are short-term studies rather than long-term monitoring; they typically include resolving critical uncertainties and improving knowledge of natural systems under management and applying experimental management treatments.

Adaptive management openly acknowledges our uncertainty about how ecological systems function and how they respond to management actions. Adaptive management involves monitoring, targeted studies, and applying management activities as experimental treatments. The results feed back into decision-making, reducing uncertainty and improving the effectiveness of the program through time (Walters 1986; Noss et al. 1997; Nyberg 1998; Wilhere 2002).

Foundational scientific principles and the best available empirical information inform both the conservation goals and the strategy for implementing conservation plans. Ideally, this process includes the following steps: identify the conservation goals, create a simple conceptual model of how the ecosystem functions or of a species life history (such models can also help to define the goals), and use the conceptual model(s) to identify a conservation strategy, followed by an implementation approach involving management activities and monitoring.

Conceptual models summarize our current understanding of ecosystem or community function or species life history, clarifying likely responses to management actions and pressures (i.e., stressors, causes of change). Problem-focused conceptual models that link program objectives to causes of change and to management activities are particularly helpful to adaptive management and provide a key bridge from the conservation strategy to management and monitoring.

Assumptions upon which the proposed conservation strategy and management program are based can be tested through monitoring and with targeted studies and experimental management. Monitoring, which measures ecosystem condition and responses of the ecosystem to both intentional (management actions) and natural perturbations, is a critical piece of the adaptive management feedback loop. Ideally, monitoring can identify problems early, so that corrective management action can be taken as soon as it is needed. Conversely, targeted studies (at small spatial scales or in pilot studies) may be more appropriately used to resolve critical questions regarding ecosystem functioning or management applications.

The results from monitoring and targeted studies are evaluated and used to update goals and conceptual models and to revise the conservation strategy and implementation (management) program, as well as the monitoring methodology and even foundational scientific knowledge.

Steps to Create a Monitoring Program

Below are specific guidelines and recommendations for constructing a functional and scientifically defensible monitoring program. There is no one best approach for managing and monitoring any system; however, following these steps will produce a monitoring program based on the best available science. Although originally tailored to monitoring programs that fulfill specific requirements of regional conservation plans in California, the approach should be applicable to monitoring design for other programs. It integrates monitoring of specific priority species with monitoring ecological integrity and incorporates an adaptive management approach. Design and creation of a monitoring program is a nine-step process:

1. Identify the conservation goals and objectives.

2. Identify the scope of the monitoring program.

3. Compile information relevant to monitoring program design.

4. Strategically divide the system and prioritize for monitoring program development.

5. Develop simple management-oriented conceptual models.

6. Identify monitoring recommendations and critical uncertainties.

7. Determine strategy for implementing monitoring.

8. Develop data quality assurance, data management, analysis, and reporting strategies.

9. Complete the adaptive management loop by ensuring effective feedback to decision-making.

In practical application, the steps in this process may overlap. At each step, it is likely that information or insights will surface that can inform and improve the products of earlier steps.

The program should clearly document its decisions and seek input and review from scientists, managers, and stakeholders throughout the process. Developing high-quality monitoring programs requires creativity as well as sufficient information on which to build a sound foundation. To keep the process as transparent as possible and for future reference, detailed records should be kept of important decisions and the rationale behind them. Because science benefits from peer review and an open and unbiased process, review should be sought early and regularly and should include some scientists completely independent of the local program.

1. Identify the conservation goals and objectives

To evaluate the success of any conservation program, clearly stated goals and objectives are essential. For every element the monitoring program needs to evaluate, there should be a specific stated goal and/or objective. The goals and objectives should ideally be:

- Easily understandable
- Biologically meaningful
- Measurable
- Feasible, both financially and scientifically
- Written with a level of detail consistent with level of current knowledge
- Compatible with goals and objectives for all covered species and habitats
- Compatible with goals and objectives for neighboring conservation lands (e.g., conservation plan reserve networks, state parks, ecological reserves)

Specific goals and objectives make the design and implementation of the monitoring program easier. Vague goals and objectives consume staff time, because monitoring program designers have to interpret the initial intention.

2. Identify the scope of the monitoring program

This step identifies the scope and boundaries of what the monitoring program intends to evaluate and identifies any requirements, constraints, and opportunities that should be accommodated in the program's design. Identification of the following elements of scope will facilitate the program design in subsequent steps:

- Geographic scope
- Land ownership and constraints
- Audiences/users of monitoring program information
- Spatial scales of focus
- Relevant time scales—biological and programmatic
- Available resources and opportunities

3. Compile information relevant to monitoring program design

Monitoring program designers should assemble information for developing conceptual models (see Step 5), information on existing monitoring programs, and existing data on species, habitats, and other environmental factors. Relevant information may come from a wide variety of sources. Note potential biases and limitations when evaluating the usefulness of information sources.

4. Strategically divide the system and set priorities

Designing effective monitoring and adaptive management programs requires a clear strategy for identifying the most important system elements to monitor and the critical uncertainties to address. This strategy should realistically meet the need for tracking individual species and other smaller scale elements while taking a systems approach, as is increasingly recommended by scientists (e.g., Ives and Cardinale 2004).

5. Develop simple management-oriented conceptual models

Once the vast array of plan components has been organized into a smaller number of species groups, natural community assemblages, and landscape-level issues, the next step is conceptual model development. Monitoring and adaptive management program design are significantly improved by use of conceptual models (National Research Council 1990; Margoluis, et al. 1998; CALFED Bay-Delta Program 2000a, 2000b; Elzinga, et al. 2001; Stevens and Gold 2003; Noon 2003; Ogden, et al. 2003; RECOVER 2004).

There are many different types of conceptual models in use. See full discussion of conceptual models in "Designing monitoring programs in an adaptive management context for regional multiple species conservation plans" (Atkinson, A.J., et al. 2004).

6. Determine what to monitor, and identify critical uncertainties

Once draft conceptual models have been assembled, the program can select which attributes of the system to monitor, determine the specific monitoring objectives and appropriate monitoring variables for each attribute, and identify critical uncertainties requiring targeted study. The program should also assess the suite of monitoring and research opportunities from a program-wide viewpoint, identifying any remaining gaps and eliminating unnecessary redundancies. Although outside review of the conceptual models is helpful, the program need not wait to receive such review before moving forward with Step 6 (see Tables 1–4 regarding monitoring variables).

7. Develop a strategy for implementing monitoring

Once the monitoring variables and critical uncertainties have been identified, they should be prioritized and organized into a workplan that includes anticipated monitoring and adaptive management tasks and timelines. The workplan should include:

- Good monitoring protocols
- Prioritized monitoring and research questions
- Monitoring and research categorized by the level of effort required
- A plan for coordination with existing monitoring programs

8. Develop data quality assurance and data management, analysis, and reporting strategies

A new monitoring program must not underestimate the importance and cost of data handling, analysis, and reporting. Monitoring information is "wasted if it is not analyzed correctly, archived well, reported in a timely manner, or communicated appropriately" (Gibbs et al. 1999). The program should invest in a good data management program. The National Park Service Inventory and Monitoring Program recommends that at least 30 percent of monitoring funds go to data management and reporting (National Park Service Inventory and Monitoring Program 2004).

Good data management maximizes the utility of the data, making it available for queries by managers and scientists addressing new issues and research questions while also providing information for the long-term monitoring program. Data generated by monitoring programs has vast potential value beyond its initial intended uses. Maintaining access to raw data, coupled with metadata describing data collection methods, greatly increases data value and utility.

A well-designed data management system also improves the level of quality assurance in the program and provides strong incentives to all program participants to standardize and coordinate protocols. The state of California is developing a multitaxa, multilevel integrated data management system for monitoring data collected throughout the state that will allow powerful queries by species, study type, habitat, or geography.

9. Complete the adaptive management loop by ensuring effective feedback to decision-making

An efficient decision support system that feeds information efficiently back into decision-making requires both initial planning and adjustment over time. Ensuring that the monitoring results appropriately influence management requires consistent effort from assigned staff who have adequate funding and a consistent attitude of getting quality information out to be evaluated, peer-reviewed, and into the hands of decision-makers in a timely fashion. Such a decision support system serves the entire conservation program.

Table 5.1: Characteristics of Good Monitoring Variables
(Adapted from Margoluis et al. 1998; Gibbs et al. 1999; Pawley 2000; Bisbal 2001; Carolyn Marn, pers. comm.).

Relevant to management

Relevant to program goals and objectives; can assess program performance
Relevant to adaptive management process
Appropriate spatial scale
Appropriate temporal scale

Scientifically defensible

Biologically pertinent; reflects status and dynamics of system under management
Sufficient scientific basis, supported by published scientific findings or conceptual models

Statistically powerful and interpretable

Directly related to the ecosystem component it is intended to represent or is an acceptable surrogate
Sensitive to changes in the ecosystem component it represents
Indicates cause of change as well as existence of change
Timely; relevant to management timeframe
Anticipatory; serves as an early warning of change
Responsive across necessary range of stress; i.e., provides continuous assessment over wide range of stress (does not level off) or complements other monitoring variables to achieve necessary range
Known statistical properties, with baseline data, reference, or benchmark available

Measurable and feasible

Technically feasible; measurable using standard methodologies
Accurate and precise, with low observer variability and bias
Cost effective
Low impact to system being monitored
Low risk to field personnel

Coordinated with existing programs and data sets

Compatible with already existing monitoring programs' data collection or could be modified to be so
If data exist, they are obtainable, preferably as long-term data sets

Easily understood

Simple, direct
Communicable; easily interpreted and explained
Documented; methodology supported by complete standard operating procedures

Table 5.2. Species-level monitoring variables. Variables are listed in order of increasing level of investment and data resolution.
(Adapted from Sierra Nevada Framework (USFS 2001))

Presence in study area

Some species may be hypothesized to have been extirpated from part or all of a study area. The first priority for these species will be detection.

Habitat as surrogate

Depending on the priority level of a species and the expected pressures, habitat extent, distribution, and condition may be used as a surrogate for monitoring the species directly. However, a great deal of uncertainty exists in doing so, and the assumptions involved should be clearly documented and reassessed periodically. Typically there are insufficient data to allow confident monitoring of populations via habitat.

Number of populations

Number and location of populations can be a useful metric for rare plants and animals, especially when the coefficient of variation in the number of individuals per population is very high.

Distribution (range)

Distribution data consist of changes in locations of species occurrence across a region. Changes can occur around edges of species range, in association with pressures, or with appearance or disappearance of populations. Boundary mapping is sometimes used to measure change.

Occupancy

Target value is typically the proportion of sampling units occupied by the species. A species may maintain the same distribution, while the proportion of occupied habitat changes. When the detection probability of a protocol is less than one, better estimates are achieved using proportion of area occupied (PAO) statistics that use repeat visits to estimate the detection probability.

Relative abundance

Relative abundance is an index of abundance derived using a specific protocol. Catch per unit effort, timed surveys, timed bird point counts, and transect surveys are all different indices of relative abundance. Results derived using different protocols are not directly comparable.

Population size or absolute abundance

Population size is a direct estimate of the number of individuals. For very rare species, an absolute count (census) of the population size is possible. Where a complete census is not possible, methods such as mark/recapture and line-distance sampling provide estimates of absolute abundance.

Apparent recruitment

A qualitative or semi-quantitative measure of key stage classes for species, often including an assessment of the proportion of the population appearing to be composed of juveniles (USFS 2001).

Reproductive success

Reproductive success can be measured a variety of ways, depending on the species and sampling method. Reproductive success is most often pursued for bird species, where the number of eggs and fledglings can be readily enumerated to calculate number of young produced per adult. It is also described for some taxa in terms of the proportion of females reproducing. However, an index of the number of young produced per adult or breeding pair can be derived for most species (USFS 2001).

Table 5.2. Species-level monitoring variables, cont.

Population structure and dynamics

Many measures of population growth and structure are available for use in monitoring. They range from individual attributes of a population (e.g., age ratios, sex ratio) to derived rates of change (e.g., mortality rates, fecundity rates, growth rates) (USFS 2001) to population genetic structure.

Population condition (in association with other monitoring)

A sample of individuals is captured or otherwise inspected and their condition determined relative to issues (e.g., tissue contamination index, parasite loads, symptoms of disease). The proportion showing signs of impaired condition is then used to monitor population condition.

Table 5.3, below, shows examples of the types of monitoring variables often suggested as indicators of natural community assemblage condition. Such examples are for illustration purposes only and are not what would necessarily be chosen to monitor for a specific program. Programs should not skip the steps of model development and identifying testable questions. Some monitoring variables require research, such as identifying which species are "stress-sensitive species" vs. "stress-tolerant species." In general, before adopting any indicator, field verification and fine-tuning in the system of interest is required. Definitions are not provided for each suggested measure, but key references have been cited where possible.

Table 5.3: Natural community assemblage monitoring variables

Community composition variables

Where protection of biological diversity is a goal, community-level monitoring is needed to evaluate success. This topic has been addressed in detail in the scientific literature, but ultimately the approach taken will depend on the goals of the conservation program.

- Native species richness—estimate of the number of species in an area (Krebs 1999).
- Measures of similarity and association based on species presence or abundance can be used to compare community composition with a baseline condition or reference site (Krebs 1999; Morrison et al. 2001).
- Presence, abundance, biomass, capture rate, or proportional capture rate of
    ◊ guilds or functional groups (e.g., in songbirds: ground gleaners, foliage gleaners, aerial hawkers; in planktonic communities: phytoplankton, microzooplankton, mesozooplankton).
    ◊ key species; e.g., focal species (keystone, umbrella, and/or engineer species (Noon 2003)), at-risk species (legally protected species and otherwise sensitive species (Noon 2003)), community indicator species, habitat indicator species, economic species, pest species (Goals Project 1999).
    ◊ stress-sensitive versus tolerant species; e.g., species that do poorly in urban environments versus those that adapt well
    ◊ native versus non-native species.
- Index of Biotic Integrity (IBI): Using reference systems of known condition or integrity, a diversity-based index of biotic integrity is developed. This IBI can then be used to assess the condition of other systems based on a diversity-based score (Noss et al. 1997; National Research Council 2000).

Table 5.3: Natural community assemblage monitoring variables, cont.

Vegetation structure and function variables

In many systems, wildlife and plants of interest are critically dependent on local vegetation structure. Monitoring vegetation may provide early indication of changes that are known or hypothesized to be detrimental; e.g., weeds or community succession.

- Estimation of absolute and relative abundance (or cover) of native and non-native species using standard vegetation survey methods. This is the most time- and labor-intensive approach to vegetation monitoring.
- Shrubland vegetation structure metrics (percent cover, canopy height, percent shrub cover, percent tree cover, percent grass and forb cover, percent of specific vegetation series species, patchiness of vegetation cover, soil type, litter depth).
- Forest vegetation structure metrics: frequency distribution of seral stages (age classes) for each community type and across all types; woody stem density in various size (dbh) classes; average, range and diversity of tree ages or sizes in stand; tree species diversity; productivity; canopy density and size and dispersion of canopy openings; foliage-height profiles; abundance and density of key structural features (e.g., snags and downed logs); crown condition; physical damage to trees (Noss et al. 1997; National Research Council 2000).
- Photo plots: Photos taken from fixed reference points can provide a qualitative and sometimes a quantitative assessment of changes in the environment (MacDonald and Smart, 1992). Photos should be recorded at the same time of year, in the same direction, etc.

Ecological function

Although conceptually attractive, monitoring general ecological function is rare unless there is an obvious connection to issues of value to humans.

Terrestrial
- Energetics/productivity—biomass, carbon storage, net primary production, productivity (National Research Council 2000). Productivity is more clearly of interest in extraction systems such as working forests.
- Fires and other disturbances—frequency, return interval or rotation period of fires or other disturbances, location and areal extent, will influence the diversity, abundance and distribution of vegetative communities and associated wildlife (Noss et al. 1997).
- Soil stability and erosive resistance, slumping—early successional species may require landslides.
- Weather (precipitation, high-low-average temperature, humidity, evapotranspiration index).
Aquatic
- Streams/rivers—stream flow and stage (height), stream flow hydrographs, frequency and extent of floodplain inundation
- Channel migration, bank and channel stability and erosive resistance, stream cross-sectional area
- Water quality—water clarity/turbidity, conductivity, temperature, pH, dissolved oxygen, organic carbon, nutrients, contaminants
- Biological oxygen demand (BOD)
- Sediment quality—composition and grain size, total organic carbon, nitrogen, sulfides, pH, contaminants

In Table 5.4, below, examples are provided of variables that might be used to monitor landscape-level issues that affect multiple natural community assemblages or otherwise cross-cutting issues. Such examples are for illustration purposes only and are not what would necessarily be chosen to monitor for a specific program. Programs should not skip the steps of model development and identifying testable questions.

Table 5.4. Landscape-level monitoring variables

Extent and distribution of habitats across landscape

- Extent, distribution and location of protected lands and land uses (natural, agricultural, disturbed, urban, military, etc.).
- Extent and distribution of natural communities and natural community assemblages.
- Extent of core habitat (e.g., >500 m from roads or development), because many species of concern do not survive or reproduce well when subject to disturbance or other edge effects (Noss et al. 1997; Rutledge 2003).

Fragmentation, connectivity, measures of patch characteristics and dispersion

- Patch characteristics and dispersion measures—interpatch distance (mean, median, range) for various natural community assemblages; patch density; number of patches; patch size frequency distribution; nearest neighbor (Noss et al. 1997; Rutledge 2003).
- Road density inside reserves and in total planning area (Noss et al. 1997).
- Studies to assess animal movement across barriers or through hypothesized corridors. Use radio tracking or marked animals, or possibly develop genetic markers to assess gene flow indirectly.

Invasive species

- Range, rate of spread, distribution, and size of populations of key nonindigenous plant species (e.g., *Arundo donax*, *Tamarisk* spp., perennial pepperweed, purple loosestrife, water hyacinth, ice-plant, yellow starthistle, pampas grass, non-native annual grasses) and non-native fauna (e.g. fire ants, Argentine ants, bullfrogs, African clawed frogs, crayfish, non-native fish, non-native foxes, non-native turtles, feral cats and dogs).
- Detection of new species at common introduction points (e.g., plant nurseries for fire ants, trails for yellow starthistle, international shipyards for aquatic organisms in estuaries).
- Maintain information clearinghouse to report new invasive species established in region and provide information on invasive species status, ecology, and control methods.

Large-scale or widely distributed pressures

- Fires and other disturbances—frequency, return interval, or rotation period of fires or other disturbances, location, and areal extent (Noss et al. 1997).
- Location and severity of potential pressures on system (e.g., dams and impoundments, water diversions, sources and distribution of contaminants).
- Intensity of human recreation use or other land uses (e.g., livestock stocking rates).

Current Monitoring Efforts

Numerous existing programs of Fish and Game and other agencies, conservation organizations, and research institutions are monitoring wildlife resources across the state in terrestrial, aquatic, and marine environments. These programs monitor at the regional, natural community, ecosystem function, and species levels. In 2005, the Fish and Game Resource Assessment Program, as part of the development of this plan, conducted an initial survey of wildlife monitoring projects and programs throughout the state. The survey was designed to provide a summary of current wildlife monitoring efforts in California and to facilitate communication among different individuals, organizations, and agencies. More than 400 monitoring efforts were identified, and basic information including location, project purpose, and lead organization were categorized into a comprehensive Wildlife Monitoring Survey. Survey results may be viewed and queried on the California Wildlife Action Plan Web site at http://www.dfg.ca.gov/habitats/wdp/project_search.asp.

Geographically the third-largest state in the nation, California is also the most biodiverse. Given its extensive area, the diversity of species, and the numbers of special-status species, the job of monitoring and assessing California's native wildlife statewide is enormous. There are scores of biologists associated with various public and private institutions studying wildlife and wildlife issues.

Surveying wildlife assessment work across the state involves contacting hundreds of researchers and institutions. For this survey, attempts were made to contact biologists at 20 federal, state, and local agencies or branches, including the U.S. Department of the Interior, the U.S. Department of Agriculture, the U.S. Department of Defense, the California Department of Fish and Game, State Parks, Department of Forestry and Fire Protection, Department of Water Resources, and Bay-Delta Authority.

There are 10 campuses within the University of California system, 21 campuses within the California State University system, 25 private colleges and universities, and 103 community colleges that have biological science departments and natural reserves with faculty who may be actively engaged in wildlife research. In addition, there are numerous local biologists employed by city and county governments, nonprofit groups and foundations, and private consulting firms who may be actively involved in wildlife research or may coordinate wildlife monitoring programs. Since research or monitoring projects that actually involve handling wild animals must have a permit (more than 2,700 scientific collecting permits to individuals from more than 800 different organizations were issued in 2004 by Fish and Game's License and Revenue Branch), they provided a source of information to identify monitoring programs statewide. This initial survey identified only a portion of the wildlife monitoring and resource assessment activities in California.

Examples of the current monitoring programs in California at the regional, natural community, ecosystem function, and species levels are described below.

Examples of Regional Level Monitoring
Western Riverside County MSHCP Biological Monitoring Program
(Resource Assessment Program, Fish and Game)

In 2003, the Department began developing a long-term monitoring program to determine the status and trend of 146 sensitive plant and animal species within the western Riverside County MSHCP conservation area. The goal of the monitoring program is to implement a multiple species approach that 1) targets the 146 covered species and associated plant and animal communities, 2) provides data on whether the biological objectives of the MSHCP are being met, and 3) provides data to the adaptive management program. The monitoring program is implemented in two phases. The inventory phase, carried out during the first five years of the permit, focuses on mapping vegetation communities, gathering and synthesizing existing species information, conducting field surveys for selected species, and testing a community-based approach. The long-term monitoring phase will employ a multiple species sampling strategy that is developed based on the information gathered during the inventory phase. The Department is leading the first five- to eight-year inventory phase that will be followed by long-term monitoring.

See http://www.dfg.ca.gov/habitats/RAP/project_summaries_expand_all.html

Coastal Watershed Assessments Planning and Assessment Program

The Coastal Watershed Planning and Assessment Program (CWPAP) is a Fish and Game program conducting fishery-based watershed assessments along the length of the California coast. Assessment basins are chosen as study areas based upon the nature of the socio-economic and natural resource problems within them. The Fish and Game Coho Recovery Plan and Steelhead Recovery Plan are useful in selecting basins, as well. CWPAP has developed assessment methods, protocols, and report outlines. The program's work is intended to provide answers to the following six guiding assessment questions at the basin, subbasin, and tributary scales in coastal watersheds:

- What are the history and trends of the size, distribution, and relative health and diversity of salmonid populations?
- What are the current salmonid habitat conditions; how do these conditions compare to desired conditions?
- What are the impacts of geologic, vegetative, fluvial, and other natural processes on watershed and stream conditions?
- How has land use affected these natural processes and conditions?
- Based upon these conditions, trends, and relationships, are there elements that could be considered to be limiting factors for salmon and steelhead production?
- What watershed management and habitat improvement activities would most likely lead toward more desirable conditions in a timely, cost-effective manner?

One of the products of the CWPAP is to determine monitoring needs to support adaptive management.

Bay-Delta Interagency Ecological Program

The Interagency Ecological Program's monitoring element encompasses both biological and physical parameters. It does so by utilizing the combined resources and expertise of the various member agencies to provide a clearer understanding of the many factors that affect the health of the San Francisco Bay/Estuary ecosystem. Results from the monitoring program may be found at www.delta.dfg.ca.gov or at the IEP database (www.iep.ca.gov). Components of the monitoring program include:

- Fall Midwater Trawl—Annual survey to determine the abundance and distribution of juvenile and early-adult pelagic fishes in the San Francisco Estuary and lower Sacramento and San Joaquin rivers.
- Summer Townet Survey—Annual survey to determine the abundance and distribution of late-stage larvae and juvenile pelagic fishes in the San Francisco Estuary and lower Sacramento and San Joaquin rivers.
- 20 mm Survey—Annual survey to determine the abundance and distribution of late-stage larvae and early juvenile pelagic fishes in the San Francisco Estuary and lower Sacramento and San Joaquin rivers. Data are reported on a near real-time basis (within one day of collection) and are used to guide State Water Project and Central Valley Project operation decisions during the spring.
- Larval Fish Survey—Annual survey to determine the abundance and distribution of late-stage larvae and early juvenile pelagic fishes in the San Francisco Estuary and lower Sacramento and San Joaquin rivers.
- Spring Kodiak Trawl—Long-term survey of small adult pelagic fishes, principally delta and longfin smelt, in the San Francisco Estuary and lower Sacramento and San Joaquin rivers.

- Delta Outflow/San Francisco Study—Survey of juvenile and early-adult pelagic fishes, shrimp, and crabs in the San Francisco Estuary and lower Sacramento and San Joaquin rivers.

- Delta Resident Fishes Survey—Electrofishing survey of inshore and near-shore fishes in the upper San Francisco Estuary and lower Sacramento and San Joaquin rivers.

- Adult Striped Bass Population Estimates—Gill-net and **fyke**-net-based mark and recapture effort for striped bass (>18 inches) in the lower Sacramento and San Joaquin rivers. All tagged fish are aged from scales. Information from associated creel census is used to estimate harvest rate, mortality rates, and population estimates for all age groups.

- Adult Sturgeon Population Estimates—Trammel-net-based mark-and-recapture effort for adult white sturgeon that takes place in September and October. Typically, tagging has been done two out of every five years. Currently, it is now being done annually and the time expanded to start in August to facilitate the tagging of green sturgeon. Adult sturgeon are collected using boat-deployed trammel nets in San Pablo and Suisun bays. Information is used to estimate harvest rate, mortality rates, and population estimates for all age groups.

- Ecosystem Monitoring Program (EMP)—This program provides necessary information for compliance with flow-related water quality standards. The EMP also provides information on a wide range of chemical, physical, and biological baseline variables. Discrete water quality stations are sampled monthly using a research vessel and a laboratory van. Several constituents are also measured continuously at eight stations. In addition, the EMP collects and analyzes benthos, phytoplankton, and zooplankton samples.

- CVP and SWP Fish Salvage Reporting—Survey of fish collected at the State Water Project Skinner Fish Facility and the Central Valley Project Tracy facility. Fish are collected as part of the diversion of water from the estuary to CVP and SWP customers. See www.delta.dfg.ca.gov and www.iep.ca.gov

Examples of Natural Community Level Monitoring
Montane Meadow Monitoring Program
(Resource Assessment Program, Fish and Game)

In 2001, Fish and Game initiated a community approach to assessing montane meadows in the Sierra Nevada, recognizing the importance of such communities to many wildlife species of concern. In part, recognition of the importance of these systems through the U.S. Forest Service's Sierra Nevada Framework and the congressionally mandated Sierra Nevada Ecosystem Project spurred the initiation of this three-phase program. The first phase has been to develop a high-resolution map product of the distribution of montane meadows in the Sierra Nevada. Specific umbrella wildlife species, such as the willow flycatcher and great gray owl, where population status and dynamics reflect the condition and quality of montane meadow systems, are also being surveyed as potential indicator or umbrella species in anticipation of a long-term monitoring strategy. Numerous other wildlife species are also being surveyed in these communities using remote camera stations, visual encounter surveys, focal point counts, and trapping. Because of their typical close association as habitats, the program also is working to map and identify the condition of quaking aspen communities in a collaborative effort with the U.S. Forest Service and Bureau of Land Management.

See http://www.dfg.ca.gov/habitats/RAP/project_summaries_expand_all.html

Landscape Habitat and Wildlife Monitoring Program
(Department of Fish and Game, Region 1)

This program monitors habitats and wildlife at plots throughout the Klamath, Southern Cascades, and Modoc ecoregions. The objective is to describe baseline conditions and assess trends with respect to habitat conditions and wildlife populations at the landscape scale. Information gathered from this monitoring project is used to inform management decisions. To date, 335 plots have been monitored over four years. Through various methods, including breeding bird surveys, small mammal trapping, and baited camera stations, more than 160 species of birds and mammals have been identified at these plots.

Channel Islands Marine Protected Areas Monitoring

The Channel Island Marine Protected Areas (CIMPA) monitoring plan (CDFG 2004) includes both biological and socioeconomic components. Data are collected both inside the MPA and in adjacent areas outside the MPA to detect differences in the indicator parameters. The plan cites values from the literature concerning expected changes in density and size for a variety of species.

The CIMPA monitoring plan objectives are to determine:

- Changes in abundance, size, biomass, and spawning biomass of species
- Species composition as it relates to ecosystem function
- Habitat changes as they relate to physical alteration (e.g., trawling) and secondary impacts of biological community changes (e.g., habitat-forming algae)
- Amount of spillover
- Changes in catch per unit effort and total catch

Biological monitoring activities have been separated into four general habitat/ecosystem categories: shallow subtidal; deep subtidal; intertidal; and seabirds and marine mammals. The monitoring categories have been prioritized based on the expected level of impact that marine protected areas will have on the species or habitats, the need for new monitoring activities, the feasibility of determining changes, and the relative level of previous consumptive use.

See http://www.dfg.ca.gov/mrd/channel_islands/monitoring.html

Examples of Ecosystem Function Level Monitoring
Multi-Agency Fish Barrier Monitoring and Fish Passage Assessment

In recognition of the importance of California's once-abundant salmon and steelhead populations, the State Coastal Conservancy, in collaboration with the California Department of Fish and Game and the Pacific States Marine Fisheries Commission, have initiated an inventory of existing barriers to fish passage throughout the state. The inventory is to be used to identify barriers suitable for removal or modification to restore habitat connectivity, spawning, and riparian conditions for salmon and steelhead and to enhance aquatic and riparian habitat.

The Passage Assessment Database (PAD) is an ongoing map-based inventory of known and potential barriers to anadromous fish in California, compiled and maintained through a cooperative interagency agreement. The PAD compiles currently available fish passage information from many different sources, allows past and future barrier assessments to be standardized and stored in one place, and enables the analysis of cumulative effects of passage barriers in the context of overall watershed health. The database is set up to capture basic information about each potential barrier. It is designed to be flexible. As the database grows, other modules may be added to increase data detail and complexity.

See http://www.calfish.org/DesktopDefault.aspx?tabId=69

Meadow Status and Trend Monitoring
(Pacific Southwest Research Station, USFS)

The focus of the meadow monitoring program was to determine the ecological condition of montane meadows within the Sierra Nevada Forest Plan Amendment study area. The study surveyed a random selection of herbaceous meadows. The program arose out of concerns raised in the Sierra Nevada Ecosystem Project Final Report about the ecological condition of aquatic, riparian, and meadow ecosystems. Meadows in the sample area are distributed across a broad range of elevations and include remote meadows that are seldom visited as well as meadows with recreation and grazing activities and roads. Data collection included plant species composition, nested rooted frequency, ground cover, and soil hydrologic characteristics in a more holistic approach to ecosystem functioning than has been done in past studies.

See http://www.fs.fed.us/psw/topics/wildlife/

Monitoring the Responses of Sensitive Herpetofauna to Manipulated Flow Regimes and Salmonid-focused Habitat Modifications Along the Mainstem Trinity River
(Pacific Southwest Research Station, USFS)

The western pond turtle and foothill yellow-legged frog have been impacted by the construction and operation of dams on the mainstem of the Trinity River. Responses of these sensitive herpetofauna to manipulated flow regimes and salmonid-focused habitat modifications are monitored and management recommendations are offered based on monitoring findings.

See http://www.fs.fed.us/psw/

Examples of Species Level Monitoring
Statewide Swainson's Hawk Survey/Monitoring Program and Study of Crop/Habitat Foraging Value
(Resource Assessment Program, Fish and Game)

Based on two years (2005 and 2006) of intensive statewide surveying to establish a baseline, the intent of this program is to institute an objective statewide monitoring program and implement key applied research studies to enhance our understanding of the Swainson's hawk and its habitat relationships. A long-term monitoring strategy will be designed after the 2006 field season to objectively monitor and track Swainson's hawk population at a large regional (Central Valley) scale. The purpose of the five-year study program on crop/habitat value is to develop more accurate models of the relationship between Swainson's hawk use of agricultural crops and native habitats and to specifically develop a foraging value for the various land-cover types. This information can then be used for conservation, management, and planning efforts to benefit the species to the extent possible.

See http://www.dfg.ca.gov/habitats/RAP/project_summaries_expand_all.html

Marbled Murrelet Research Projects
(Pacific Southwest Research Station, USFS)

One of the primary goals of the USFS Pacific Southwest Research Station's bird monitoring research has been to conduct research on habitat relationships of birds associated with forest ecosystems. The station began its research on the marbled murrelet in 1987, after the USGS identified the species in old-growth forests where it was conducting research on other forest birds. This seabird has the unique strategy of utilizing both the marine and terrestrial environments by foraging at sea and nesting in the old-growth forests. Over the past 100 years, the murrelet population has been in decline and, in 1992, was listed as threatened under the federal Endangered Species Act. The Research Station's research has provided valuable information for the Marbled Murrelet Recovery Team on the species status and habitat requirements. The Research Station also has provided research and expertise to the Northwest Forest Plan since 1992 to inform resource management decisions.

See http://www.fs.fed.us/psw/topics/wildlife/birdmon/mamu/

Aquatic Amphibian and Reptile Surveys
(Bureau of Land Management)

Aquatic amphibians are good indicators of the health of aquatic systems (Hall 1980). Through monitoring the trends in the abundance of foothill yellow-legged frogs, BLM is able to make management decisions that provide for high-quality, low-impact OHV recreation and travel while conserving frog populations. BLM staff at the Hollister Field Office developed a monitoring protocol for the foothill yellow-legged frogs in 2001. Surveys for yellow-legged frogs occur inside 10 100-meter-long by 1-meter wide transects at OHV crossings and 10 identically shaped transects away from OHV crossings. BLM samples streams in accordance with a standardized protocol for surveying aquatic amphibians (Fellers and Freel, 1995). The project surveys creeks in the Hollister area that potentially support populations of foothill yellow-legged frog, western pond turtle and two-striped garter snake. Annual monitoring is conducted at a subset of transect sites.

Marine Invasive Species Monitoring Program
(Office of Spill Prevention and Response, Fish and Game)

The Ballast Water Management Act of 1999 established a multi-agency program to prevent the introduction and spread of non-indigenous aquatic species (NAS) from the ballast of ships into the state waters of California. This program was designed to control ballast introductions and determine the current level of species invasions while researching alternatives to the present control strategies. Under this program, Fish and Game was required to study the extent of non-native species introductions into the coastal waters of the state. To fulfill this requirement, the Department's Office of Spill Prevention and Response (OSPR) initiated several baseline field surveys of ports and bays along the California coast and a literature survey of records of non-indigenous species (NIS).

OSPR's first survey (in 2000) targeted California's seven major harbor areas from Humboldt Bay to San Diego Harbor, and most of the smaller ports and bays along the entire coast, from Crescent City, near the Oregon border, to Mission Bay in San Diego. The survey and literature searches revealed that all areas of the California coast have experienced some level of invasion by species not native to California. Researchers have found a total of 397 non-native organisms in California's marine, estuarine, and tidal freshwater environments. An additional 339 organisms were classified as "cryptogenic," meaning that it was not obvious whether they were native or introduced but were likely introduced, as they have not been identified previously.

See http://www.dfg.ca.gov/ospr/organizational/scientific/exotic/MISMP.htm

Monitoring Effectiveness of Conservation Actions

While current regional, natural community, ecosystem function, and species monitoring efforts are adequate to assess the progress of some of the recommended conservation actions, in most cases, additional monitoring efforts are needed.

The lead agency, organization, or collaborative partners implementing a conservation action should review what information and monitoring are required to assess progress and to support adaptive management. Answering the five questions below will help design the effectiveness assessment for a conservation action.

1. What questions need to be answered to assess effectiveness or progress of the conservation action?

See Assessment Questions for each conservation action in Appendix J. The lead agency or collaborators should review these questions and reach agreement on a complete list of those that are relevant.

2. What is the monitoring level and what are the information or monitoring requirements needed to answer the assessment questions?

The level of monitoring needed depends on the nature of the goals and objectives of the conservation action. If the goal is to recover one species, then monitoring that species may be all that is required. However, if the goal is to restore natural communities over a large landscape, such as sagebrush communities on the Modoc Plateau, monitoring will be at a more comprehensive level. Monitoring levels are identified for each conservation action in Appendix J (see Table 5.5, Monitoring Levels). The lead agency or collaborators should design a monitoring program to gather the information required to assess success of the conservation action. Regional, natural community, ecosystem function, or otherwise complex monitoring programs should be based on a thorough review of the monitoring and adaptive management needs based on a process such as the guidance offered in Section 1. Then, the monitoring requirements should be listed.

3. What current monitoring programs provide information that helps to answer the assessment questions?

As described in the previous section, there are hundreds of wildlife monitoring efforts in California. Current relevant monitoring programs may be identified by:

- Searching the Wildlife Monitoring Survey at http://www.dfg.ca.gov/habitats/wdp/project_ search.asp. The monitoring programs may be searched by region, project purpose, and lead organization.
- Contacting the monitoring and research units of the potential collaborators listed in Appendix J. Many of the listed collaborator's Web sites have links to other organizations conducting research or monitoring in their region.
- Reviewing the current literature regarding relevant species and natural systems.

4. What additional monitoring efforts are needed to answer the assessment questions?

Compare identified monitoring requirements with current monitoring efforts to determine the need for additional monitoring.

5. What organizations or collaborators are appropriate to implement the additional monitoring requirements?

An initial list of potential collaborators is given with each conservation action in Appendix J. This list is only a starting point. By reviewing the Web links provided on the Web sites of the potential collaborators, other collaborators may be found, including nongovernmental conservation organizations, university science centers, and local conservation programs.

Monitoring Level

The conservation actions recommended in this plan vary in management level, geographic scale, and complexity. Some may be implemented through regional multi-agency collaborative efforts, while others may be implemented by a single program within a state department. Some conservation actions are focused on a small geographical area, while others apply to a large region of the state, if not the entire state. Some conservation actions affect a specific environmental characteristic, whereas other actions relate to the dynamics of natural communities.

Assessing the effectiveness of a conservation action requires matching the level of monitoring to the nature of the conservation action. Some actions warrant monitoring at multiple levels. Monitoring levels relevant to the recommended conservation actions are identified in Appendix J. The monitoring levels range from management level to species level, as defined in Table 5.5.

Table 5.5: Monitoring Levels

Management

Involves a management or budget action to ultimately benefit conservation programs and projects. For example, among the conservation actions is a recommendation to strengthen the state's capacity to assist local governments with conservation planning and implementation.

Regional

Involves monitoring the full complexity of a geographical area that may encompass several watersheds, numerous natural communities, a diversity of species populations and ecological systems. The Wildlife Action Plan divided the state into nine large regions for analysis. However, regional-level assessment may apply to geographically smaller areas, such as the areas within a Natural Community Conservation Plan in Southern California.

Natural Community

Involves monitoring the community of native plants and animals, many of which are interdependent, in a given ecosystem. Often named for the principal type of vegetation in the community; for example, "coastal sage scrub community" or "blue oak woodland community."

Ecosystem Function

Involves monitoring the operational role of ecosystem components, structure, and processes.

Habitat Linkages

Involves monitoring pathways of natural habitat occurring within larger developed areas or converted lands. The habitat linkage areas attract wildlife and act as safe passages for wildlife between neighboring natural areas. Linkages are often along creek riparian zones that run through cropped fields or urban areas.

Species

Involves monitoring species, populations of species, or groups of species. Species are often monitored as part of recovery programs and as one of numerous "covered species" of a habitat conservation plan.

Collaborative Monitoring Efforts

Collaborative monitoring programs involving multiple agencies, nongovernmental organizations, landowners, or university researchers have several benefits. Multiple collaborators are collectively more likely to have knowledge of all current monitoring programs. The broader expertise and perspectives of collaborators will contribute to design of monitoring programs that yield better information. In addition, through the collaborative process, monitoring protocols will be more compatible and the monitoring results are likely to be more broadly disseminated for informing conservation decisions. Collaborative efforts with farmers and ranchers are important to monitor wildlife resources on private lands, which constitute about half the state. The Wildlife Action Plan encourages collaborative efforts to implement most of the recommended conservation actions.

6   *Strengthening California's Conservation Capabilities*

Resource Assessment

Resource assessment, the monitoring and study of wildlife populations, habitats, and ecosystems, has long been recognized as a fundamental requirement for effective conservation, restoration, and management. It was noted in a 1926 edition of *California Fish and Game* that "the best insurance that the state can take out . . . is to see that facilities for study and investigation are enlarged upon. The lack of biological data is, without a doubt, one of the greatest single factors in retarding development of a larger conservation program."

All aspects of wildlife management, particularly efforts to restore species at risk, depend on biological information. The increasing stresses on wildlife resources, including the loss, degradation, and fragmentation of habitats, effects of water diversions, and proliferation of invasive species, have further increased the need to assess the status and trends of wildlife species and ecosystems in California.

At present, Fish and Game can assess only a fraction of the species and habitats throughout the state, and wildlife managers often must make decisions and recommendations with limited information. To effectively monitor species populations and ecological trends, Fish and Game needs an expanded, comprehensive, statewide program that coordinates wildlife assessment activities.

The Role of Resource Assessment in Wildlife Conservation

State and federal wildlife agencies, nongovernmental conservation organizations, biological consultants, and private landowners use information gathered from field monitoring of wildlife populations and environmental indicators to make conservation decisions. Such resource assessment information is used to:

- **Support wildlife and environmental recommendations and regulatory decisions.** To reduce environmental impacts of various land uses, state and federal wildlife regulatory agencies require changes in development projects, recommend changes in timber harvest plans, and determine the appropriate conditions under which to issue permits to **take** endangered species and to permit activities in rivers and streams and wetlands.

- **Design habitat restoration projects and effective mitigation for development.** Conservation of many species at risk involves restoring aquatic and terrestrial habitats. Resource assessment provides the information needed to design successful habitat restoration or mitigation projects.

- **Prepare multispecies regional conservation plans.** Designing conservation plans at the regional scale, including appropriate wildland reserves, involves compiling ecological information on dozens of species and on the aquatic and terrestrial ecosystems. Long-term information is needed to indicate trends of species populations and natural communities and rates of change and the responses of ecosystems and wildlife to stressors. The implementation of these conservation plans also requires monitoring to assess if conservation goals are met and whether plan adjustments are needed.

- **Prepare management plans for public lands to restore and maintain wildlife habitat.** The U.S. Forest Service, BLM, California State Parks, the National Park Service, Fish and Game, and other local agencies and districts evaluate available biological information to prepare resource management plans for public lands.

Elements of Resources Assessment

Resource assessment involves several important functions to guide field research, to manage data, and to make that information available to wildlife managers and conservation project managers. These functions include:

- **Prioritizing field research and wildlife monitoring projects.** It is neither practical nor economical to inventory all species and habitats in every geographic area of California. One function of a resource assessment program should be to coordinate the development of resource assessment priorities among the various public and private efforts.

- **Designing efficient resource assessment strategies.** A resource assessment program should also design and implement analytical approaches and monitoring strategies that gather the most useful information in the most efficient manner. Well-designed field monitoring and research use methods that generate results that then may be broadly applied to assist various conservation efforts.

- **Facilitating collaboration among wildlife biologists, plant ecologists, range specialists, hydrologists, and numerous other technical disciplines to achieve more comprehensive assessments.** These broader assessments provide more complete information regarding the status and trends of natural communities and ecosystems.

- **Standardizing data collection and management protocols.** Numerous state and federal natural resources agencies, private landowners and firms, and dozens of academic and research institutions are involved in monitoring wildlife and ecosystems in the state, and each agency usually conducts field research to support its specific management needs. Consulting firms conduct wildlife and natural resource surveys to support CEQA documentation for projects. Ideally, the field data collected by these various organizations in a particular region of the state could be assembled like pieces of a puzzle that would then provide a more comprehensive understanding of wildlife populations and ecosystems. However, different objectives, data-collection protocols, or scales are often employed, and the data collected by one institution is not comparable to data collected by another. A resource assessment program should facilitate implementation of standard procedures and protocol for the numerous kinds of wildlife and ecosystem assessments and data management.

- **Compiling and organizing data and information.** Research and monitoring of wildlife and natural communities generate a tremendous volume of data. It is a significant management task to organize this information to make it available for researchers and public and private wildlife- and land managers. Data management involves designing common formats and protocols, developing programs to manage databases, providing access to the information, and facilitating the sharing of wildlife and ecosystem information by land managers, wildlife managers and researchers, private landowners, and others involved in making conservation decisions.

Fish and Game's Resource Assessment Efforts

Fish and Game has conducted various wildlife resource assessment functions for decades. However, over the last 30 years, the resource assessment activities of the department have been significantly reduced. Budget reductions have reduced the department's field research capabilities, and field biologist positions have gradually become primarily desk positions to process, evaluate, and prepare environmental documentation to meet the requirements of CEQA, CESA, streambed alteration agreements, and other laws.

In the past, Fish and Game had a greater field research presence, often publishing results in articles in the department's own scientific journal, *California Fish and Game*, in Administrative Reports, and in other scientific journals. Larger studies on fish species were published in the *Fish Bulletin* series. Fish and Game used to maintain technical libraries, including a Marine Information Technical Center in Long Beach. These libraries and information centers were closed in the last decade due in part to the anticipation that this kind of wildlife and technical information would become available electronically. However, today, Fish and Game scientists have very limited access to the scientific literature now available electronically by subscription.

Nevertheless, Fish and Game continues to maintain several resource assessment functions. Several units of the department design and conduct projects to inventory and monitor wildlife populations or ecosystem indicators. The Habitat Conservation and Planning Branch, the Central Valley Bay Delta Branch, the Native Anadromous Fish and Watershed Restoration Branch, the Wildlife and Fisheries Program Branch, the Department's Marine Region, and the Scientific Branch of the Office of Spill Prevention and Response are all engaged in some field studies.

Fish and Game continues to manage species and habitat data, particularly information regarding species at risk. The department develops data management protocols and serves as a hub for the collection and management of resource assessment data. The department manages the California Natural Diversity Database, the Vegetation Classification and Mapping Program, the Biogeographic Information and Observation System, and the California Wildlife Habitat Relationships information system. Fish and Game also compiles information on and evaluates the status of threatened and endangered species and species of special concern and produces status reports on those species.

In recent years, Fish and Game has assigned several existing staff to build a resource assessment program (RAP) to develop and implement a long-term strategic program to inventory, monitor, and assess priority species and natural communities. RAP is intended to enhance consistency of field monitoring products, improve coordination among biological disciplines, and ensure that specific monitoring programs and activities throughout the state are focused on obtaining important and useful information for resource managers and for the public. In 2005, RAP initiated a survey of wildlife assessment and monitoring efforts statewide. The survey was designed to provide a summary of current wildlife monitoring efforts in California, identify resource assessment gaps and needs, and facilitate communication among different individuals, organizations, and agencies.

RAP has begun assisting outside organizations and researchers to manage data and is reaching out to other agencies and institutions to help coordinate wildlife resource assessment work. To date, collaborative agreements have been initiated with the Wildlife Health Center at UC Davis, the Center for Conservation Biology at UC Riverside, the UC White Mountain Research Station, and the U.S. Geological Survey–Western Ecological

Research Center to assist Fish and Game to develop and implement resource assessment and monitoring strategies. One objective of these collaborations is to generate interest among academic institutions in addressing applied research questions that are relevant to various conservation efforts.

Among state agencies, Fish and Game works with the departments of Parks and Recreation, Forestry and Fire Protection, Water Resources, and Transportation on resource assessment projects. RAP is coordinating with Parks and Recreation's Inventory, Mapping, and Assessment Program (IMAP) to achieve consistency in plant and animal surveys.

The Fire and Resource Assessment Program (FRAP) of the Department of Forestry and Fire Protection and the USDA Forest Service coordinate land-cover mapping and monitoring within California. This program generates data that describe the extent and condition of various land-cover types and are used by the Fish and Game to model wildlife habitats.

Key federal agencies, including the U.S. Fish and Wildlife Service, the National Marine Fisheries Service, the U.S. Geological Survey, the National Park Service, the Bureau of Land Management, and the U.S. Forest Service, are important collaborators in developing monitoring programs for California wildlife and habitats. Coordination with the U.S. Fish and Wildlife Service on resource assessment occurs through recovery efforts for threatened and endangered species, Natural Community Conservation Planning, and other large-scale conservation planning efforts. Species and habitat monitoring of areas covered under conservation plans is a priority for resource assessment. The U.S. Forest Service has recently identified priority species to monitor to inform their land management decisions. RAP is implementing efforts to survey and then monitor several of these species, including the willow flycatcher, great gray owl, and various amphibian species.

Half of the state's lands are privately owned. Fish and Game works to develop cooperative relationships with private landowners and local governments to monitor species and habitats on private and municipal lands.

California's Need for an Expanded Resource Assessment Capability

Despite the efforts and collaborations described above, there are large gaps in resource assessment, and very little is known about many species populations in California. While Fish and Game, other state and federal agencies, universities, and private landowners are involved in resource assessment activities, very limited funding is available for field studies to gather basic biological information. Many of the state's programs described above have only a few staff statewide. Fish and Game's various field programs can assess only a small selection of habitats across the state. Consequently, wildlife managers and conservation planners must routinely make decisions with limited information about the status of species or ecosystems. Conservation efforts to maintain wildlife diversity would be more effective if the state strengthened its capacity to conduct and coordinate resource assessment.

Conservation Planning[*]

Land-use and development decisions are made primarily at the local and regional level on a project-by-project basis, often without adequate protections for important habitats and wildlife populations. Some state and federal programs provide incentives to encourage local project decisions to better accommodate the needs of wildlife conservation. However, those incentives are often limited compared to other economic considerations.

Private land in California comprises approximately 51 percent of the state, and many endangered or declining species are dependent on habitat on private lands for their survival. Fifty-eight counties and some 470 incorporated cities are the primary land use decision-making bodies for undeveloped private wildlands of the state, regulating land use via planning and zoning regulations, subdivision controls, and building permits. Maintaining wildlife diversity and reversing the trend of declining species depend on integrating conservation and habitat restoration into local land-use decisions.

Because existing state and federal laws were not designed to maintain essential habitats and abundant wildlife, a new policy framework is needed to prevent the loss of key habitats and to halt the decline of species at risk. The California Environmental Quality Act (CEQA), the California Endangered Species Act (CESA), and the federal Endangered Species Act (ESA) are the preeminent laws for minimizing the effects of development on wildlife and habitats; several other resource-protection laws require permits for activities on such specific habitats as forest lands, wetlands, and streams and rivers.

Since 1970, CEQA has required local governments to analyze the environmental effects of proposed development projects and to consider such projects through a public process. While the city or county is typically the lead agency over the environmental review, Fish and Game provides recommendations for avoiding, minimizing, and mitigating project effects on habitats, ecosystems, and wildlife, offering information about wildlife resources and giving guidance on how a project can be modified to protect sensitive habitats. Fish and Game's recommended changes to proposed projects are advisory. Fish and Game lacks the staff to comment on many projects, and local projects are often approved without review by a biologist employed by Fish and Game or a local agency.

CEQA mandates that local General Plans contain a conservation and open space element. However, the conservation elements usually do not contain an adequate assessment of what

[*] This section on Conservation Planning was authored by Gail Presley, Habitat Conservation Planning Branch, California Department of Fish and Game.

resources need to be protected to conserve wildlife, and conservation measures mentioned in General Plans are often not implemented.

The CESA and ESA were not crafted to provide a conservation framework to maintain abundant wildlife populations nor to protect sensitive habitats and healthy ecosystems. Rather, CESA and ESA are policies of last resort to protect species approaching extinction. CESA states that "… it is the policy of the state to conserve, protect, restore, and enhance any endangered species or any threatened species and its habitat and … to acquire lands for habitat for these species." The state and federal endangered species acts do not provide adequate protection for a species until it is in desperate shape. If the loss of habitat is the cause of the species decline, by the time the species qualifies for listing, recovery is challenging because it would likely require extensive and expensive habitat restoration.

The local project-by-project approval of new development, without measures to address cumulative effects of projects over time and across the region, leads to the slow dismantling and fragmentation of important wildlife habitats, migratory corridors, and ecosystems. A development decision may appear to have negligible consequences for wildlife populations if it is destroying a small percent of the remaining habitat or wildlands in the project area. But, over time, the percentages add up, and habitat shrinks. Without the benefit of a regional conservation analysis, a land-use decision may develop a small patch of land that forever blocks an important regional wildlife migratory corridor or degrades a key ecosystem component important to wildlife diversity in the broader region. Without a thorough understanding of wildlife populations and their associations with plant communities, it is difficult to evaluate the wildlife-related consequences of project alternatives.

Despite the broad array of environmental laws, none is adequately designed to proactively conserve ecosystems and habitats necessary to sustain healthy wildlife populations. Lacking adequate incentives, scientific expertise, financial resources, and legal mandates, most local governments do not manage their jurisdictions for the long-term conservation of wildlife.

California's Regional Multispecies Conservation Program

Having recognized the detrimental consequences of the local project-by-project approach to development approval, California over the last 15 years has implemented a voluntary multispecies regional approach to wildlife habitat conservation. The California Natural Community Conservation Planning Program (NCCP), administered by Fish and Game, takes a regional, multispecies approach to planning for the protection and perpetuation of biological diversity. A Natural Community Conservation Plan provides regional protection for plants, animals, and their habitats, while allowing compatible and appropriate economic activity. The NCCP standard goes beyond mitigating for the effects of development to providing for the recovery of sensitive species in the plan area and conserving other species in the area.

The NCCP approach or similar regional multispecies approaches to conservation planning are essential to conserve habitats and ecosystems at a scale necessary to ensure long-term survival of species. (See "Multispecies Conservation Planning Efforts," below.)

Private lands with important habitat value are identified in an NCCP through the planning process and integrated into a scientifically validated system of reserves, including corridors and linkages with other natural lands, to be managed for the long-term conservation of species. The number of species covered by NCCPs ranges from 12 (Palos Verdes Peninsula) to 146 (Western Riverside Multi-Species Habitat Conservation Plan). NCCPs range in size from 8,559 acres (Palos Verdes Peninsula) to 1.2 million acres (Western Riverside MSHCP).

Creating a conservation plan involves a diverse array of stakeholders who represent their interests in a negotiated process. The process also provides opportunities for participation by the general public. In a typical conservation plan, a local lead agency (either city or county) coordinates a collaborative planning process. Working with landowners, development interests, environmental organizations, and other interested parties, the local agency oversees the numerous activities that constitute the development of a conservation plan, including collecting ecological data; designing a reserve system; identifying proposed development; creating a monitoring and adaptive management program for the reserve lands; and determining funding for implementation. The state and federal wildlife agencies (Fish and Game, the U.S. Fish and Wildlife Service, and, where appropriate, NOAA Fisheries) are relied upon during all of these activities to provide the necessary support, direction, scientific expertise, and guidance to the conservation planning participants.

The desired result of this process is a comprehensive plan that provides for species conservation and management and, at the same time, approves development in areas that are less critical for wildlife. Under an approved NCCP, wildlife agencies may issue permits to authorize the take of species under the federal Endangered Species Act and NCCP Act. Species whose conservation and management are provided by the plan are called "covered" species. The NCCP Act gives Fish and Game the authority to permit take of any covered species (whether or not it is listed as threatened or endangered under the California

Endangered Species Act). This authority provides an incentive to local applicants to cover certain species not currently listed, eliminating the need to reapply for additional permits should those species become listed in the future. Covering nonlisted species requires that those species be treated as if they were listed and can mean the protection of additional habitats, core areas, linkages, ecological processes, and improved reserve configurations that bolster the overall conservation strategy.

NCCP planning has expanded to 11 counties statewide, but Fish and Game does not have sufficient staff to provide the scientific assistance and planning required by these important and complex conservation efforts. Conservation of wildlife in many areas of the state will require a greater state commitment of scientific and planning resources in combination with incentives for local governments to collaborate in both planning and implementing regional conservation plans.

The wildlife agencies have embraced the benefits of regional conservation planning as the most effective conservation tool we currently possess. The alternative would be to process hundreds of individual permits for projects that would cause take of threatened or endangered species—an impossible workload, and one that would not address wildlife concerns at the ecosystem scale. Thus, even when these agencies know their staffing levels are inadequate, they encourage local jurisdictions to consider creating comprehensive plans to address all their sensitive wildlife issues. But counties and cities often become frustrated because these same staffing limitations constrain state and federal wildlife agencies from providing the needed conservation planning assistance in a timely manner.

NCCP Implementation Commitments

The higher conservation standard of NCCP embodies both the concept and the Legislature's intent that the public share responsibility for a portion of the cost of conservation. In most of the NCCPs approved to date, the state and the federal government have agreed to contribute acres to the reserve system and assist with management and monitoring, either in the form of grants to local partners or as land the agencies, themselves, hold. For example, state and federal agencies agreed to contribute 13,500 acres to the San Diego MSCP reserve system and 50,000 acres to the Western Riverside MSHCP reserve system. These agencies also agreed to conduct ecological monitoring and implement adaptive management to meet the plan standards on lands they acquire and hold.

As more plans near completion, local entities expect a similar level of state and federal contribution. The agencies, however, insist that the plans incorporate language stating that their commitments are subject to availability of budgeted funds. It is hoped that the state and federal funding streams will continue at levels sufficient to meet the needs of the plans. Without these contributions, most local governments would not be able to provide funding sufficient to implement agreed-upon plans.

Inherent in these commitments are the wildlife-agency staff positions that will be needed during implementation. Wildlife agency staff will continue to be involved in the land-use planning process, coordinating with local partners on plan implementation, monitoring program compliance, assessing land acquisition priorities, applying for grant funds, and participating in ecological monitoring and adaptive management. Over time, planning efforts will continue, while the implementation workload will increase.

Integrating Conservation of Wildlife into Local Land-Use Decisions

Developing NCCPs is one approach to regional multispecies and ecosystem conservation. However, over the next few decades, most development decisions will continue to be made outside the NCCP framework. Thus, conserving wildlife on private wildlands will require better integration of wildlife and habitat conservation into existing local land-use decision processes. New incentives and financial support for conservation, combined with regional analyses and coordination, are needed to bring about local land-use decisions that maintain habitats and ecosystems critical for maintaining wildlife diversity at the regional and state-wide level.

Numerous species and species group conservation strategies have been initiated, covering greater sage-grouse, burrowing owl, tricolored blackbird, bats, major bird groups, Southern California fishes, and other species. Consideration of these important conservation strategy documents needs to be integrated into local land-use planning processes as well.

Because the role of local land-use decisions in conserving wildlife is so important, the Wildlife Diversity Project held two one-day workshops (in Davis and Riverside) to discuss the barriers and opportunities for integrating wildlife conservation into local land-use decisions. The workshops developed recommendations for improving conservation efforts at the local and regional level.

Funding for Wildlife Conservation

Existing conservation programs and many of the conservation actions recommended in this report require additional funding. Halting the slide of species toward endangered species status will require new research, expanded conservation planning and management, greatly increased species assessment and monitoring, and major habitat restoration projects. But success or failure to conserve California's wildlife may well hinge on the level of funding dedicated to wildlife conservation and restoration programs over the next few decades.

The California Department of Fish and Game is the state's lead agency charged with conserving and restoring wildlife and ecosystems, responsibilities that have expanded and become more complex over the last three decades. Responding to the increasing problems affecting species and habitats, state policy-makers have enacted new wildlife conservation and environmental protection mandates. But lacking a broad-based reliable funding mechanism, Fish and Game is hard-pressed to implement many of these conservation programs, even at modest levels. Resource assessment, conservation planning, and dozens of tasks necessary to conserve wildlife species at risk are severely underfunded.

Expanding Responsibilities and Demands for Wildlife Conservation

The problem of inadequate funding for wildlife conservation has been 30 years in the making. In light of the growing stresses on wildlife, Fish and Game has appropriately evolved from primarily managing fishing and hunting programs to serving as the public trust steward for all wildlife, habitat, and ecosystems, while continuing to manage fishing and hunting programs. With the enactment of more than 20 conservation programs since 1968, Fish and Game's wildlife and wildlands stewardship role has expanded dramatically. Many of these measures have mandated major new workloads for Fish and Game without providing sufficient funding. (See Mandated Responsibilities of Fish and Game Since 1968, below.)

Increased Demands on Conservation Agencies by Growth and Development

Rapid growth and development, water diversions from creeks and rivers, invasions of exotic species, growth in off-road vehicle recreation, and numerous other activities that affect wildlife have demanded additional efforts of wildlife scientists and conservation managers.

With expanding development, California's unique habitats are shrinking. Maintaining healthy populations of species on fragmented and smaller areas of habitat requires more intensive management, environmental review, conservation planning, monitoring, mitigation project design, and habitat restoration work. Accompanying growth and development is an increasing demand by the public for recreational access to public land, waterways, and ocean resources and greater pressure to develop wildlands that now provide key wildlife habitat, all of which involves more work for state wildlife managers.

In addition to already existing conservation programs, in recent years, dozens of major new projects and programs have increased demands on Fish and Game. They include the Bay-Delta Restoration and CALFED Programs, implementation of the Marine Life Management Act and the Marine Life Protection Act, Headwaters Forest management and monitoring, Natural Community Conservation Planning in Southern California and elsewhere, habitat conservation planning, relicensing of hydropower projects, Salton Sea restoration, Yolo Basin Wildlife Area planning and management, the bighorn sheep recovery project, the Lower Colorado River Habitat Conservation Plan, and environmental review of the expansion of San Francisco International Airport, to name only a few.

Resources Needed for Regional Planning

Constant conflicts between development projects and protection of endangered species have led conservation scientists, stakeholders, and Fish and Game to recognize the value of regional planning for habitat conservation and protecting biodiversity. The goals of these broader proactive approaches to conservation are to identify and protect key habitats and designate areas more appropriate for development well in advance of planning for individual projects in a region. Fish and Game serves numerous important functions in these broader conservation efforts, providing:

- Biological data on individual species, which is then used to develop multispecies conservation plans, recovery programs, and restoration projects;
- Habitat quality and resource assessments, used to identify the most important lands for supporting multiple species;
- Planning and design expertise for conservation planning projects;
- Design of appropriate mitigation measures for effects of development on natural resources;
- Facilitation in bringing diverse stakeholders to the table and assisting them in developing conservation strategies at the local government level; and
- Monitoring implementation of conservation plans and mitigation projects.

These responsibilities are not in lieu of work at the species level. It is the species-level research and management, and particularly implementation of the California Endangered Species Act, that trigger efforts that evolve into the broader conservation planning efforts.

Wildlife Conservation Funding Crisis—Recognized But Not Solved

The fiscal difficulties of Fish and Game have been repeatedly acknowledged by the Legislature but not solved. The Legislature described the problem in statute in 1978, 1990, and 1992, as noted in Fish and Game Code sections below:

> **Section 710.** The Legislature finds and declares that the department has in the past not been properly funded … This lack of funding has prevented proper planning and manpower allocation. The lack of funding has required the department to restrict warden enforcement and to defer essential repairs to fish hatcheries and other facilities. The lack of secure funding for fish and wildlife activities other than sport and commercial fishing and hunting activities has resulted in inadequate non-game fish and wildlife protection programs. (Added to statutes in 1978.)

> **Section 710.5.** The Legislature finds and declares that the department continues to not be properly funded. While revenues have been declining, the department's responsibilities have been expanding into numerous new areas. The existing limitations on the expenditure of department revenues have resulted in its inability to effectively provide all of the programs and activities required under this code and to manage the wildlife resources held in trust by the department for the people of the state. (Added to statutes in 1990.)

> **Section 710.7** … The department continues to face serious funding instability due to revenue declines from traditional user fees and taxes and the addition of new program responsibilities. (Added to statutes in 1992.)

The fiscal situation has worsened in recent years. Since 2001, the state budget crisis has compounded the funding challenges at Fish and Game. Wildlife and marine conservation programs, which are the primary beneficiaries of the limited General Fund dollars, have suffered dramatic budget cuts. General Fund support for Fish and Game dropped from $84 million in 2000 to $37 million in 2005.

Wildlife Conservation Program Needs

Fishing and hunting programs and related conservation efforts have specific dedicated funding derived from licenses, fees, and taxes on outdoor equipment. The public-trust duties of Fish and Game and its conservation programs that broadly benefit species, habitats, and ecosystems warrant funding from all Californians. Conservation-related activities that should be supported by broad-based funding may be described within the following four categories:

Science and Planning

Managing and conducting resource assessment

Implementing ecological research that supports conservation and management

Developing regional conservation plans

Wildlife Conservation and Habitat Restoration

Implementing conservation and recovery plans and projects

Designing, implementing, and monitoring habitat restoration projects

Developing conservation and recovery strategies and plans

Enforcement for Wildlife, Wildlands, and Marine Resources

Expanding wildlife and marine enforcement staff, salaries, and resources

Developing an investigator class of wildlife enforcement staff

Wildlife Conservation Education and Service

Educating the public on wildlife conservation issues

Providing interpretive information and public services related to outdoor activities

Wildlife Lands Management Needs

State and federal wildlife and land management agencies and some state policy-makers have expressed great concern for the lack of resources for wildlife conservation, restoration, and enforcement on public lands. The needs for operation and maintenance of lands managed by Fish and Game are discussed below. The U.S. Fish and Wildlife Service, BLM, the Forest Service, the National Park Service, and California State Parks have similar challenges to fund the restoration and management of wildlife areas, parks, and other wildlands.

Fish and Game manages wildlife areas, ecological reserves, and wildlands specifically for the benefit of wildlife and important habitats. These lands are a cross section of California's remarkable natural diversity of animals, plants, habitat types, and ecosystems. Some of the state's finest-quality wildlife habitats are represented in these holdings. But acreage of lands managed by Fish and Game has quadrupled in the last 25 years, from 250,000 acres in 1980 to 1 million acres today, and funding to manage these lands has not kept pace. Major bond acts and some appropriations have funded acquisition of new lands for wildlife, but there is not a corresponding source of funding to maintain, restore, and manage these lands. Land management entails providing site security, managing public health and safety on the lands, managing wildlife and natural resources, maintaining infrastructure, and managing recreation and other uses.

The consequences of neglecting lands are many:

- An area that is not secure or regularly inspected invites trespass by individuals and livestock and encroachment by such adjoining land uses as agricultural operations and off-road vehicles. Trespassing often involves vandalism and dumping. The result is degradation of the land, and the state is seen as a bad neighbor.

- Without management, wildlife values of the lands are also compromised. The habitat is degraded if invasive species are not controlled, fire is not managed, and ecosystems functions are not maintained.

- Lacking restoration efforts and/or management, many acquired lands do not meet the habitat goals for which they were purchased.

- Many lands have major public-use and education potential that cannot be realized without staff resources.

State wildlife lands have been acquired for specific conservation or recreation goals. Managing lands for their intended purpose requires staff and resources. Depending on the intended purposes of the land and the habitat values, Fish and Game's Lands and Facilities Branch estimates annual land operating management costs for many wildlife areas to range from $16 to $100 per acre. Local agencies estimate land operating and management costs to be significantly higher. In 2005, maintenance, restoration, and management of Fish and Game's wildlife areas and ecological reserves were supported, on average, at the level of $13 per acre and one staff person per 10,000 acres. Many lands were operated at $1 per acre, with no dedicated staff (DFG Lands and Facilities Information Sheet).

New Funding Options

California is not unique in its difficulties with establishing an adequate and reliable revenue source for its wildlife conservation department. Numerous other state wildlife departments that have also evolved from fishing and hunting management organizations to expanded conservation organizations are also struggling to secure additional and more reliable funding.

Federal funding accounts for 23 percent of Fish and Game's budget. Federal funds are provided through several programs, including the U.S. Fish and Wildlife Service's programs pursuant to Section 6 of the Endangered Species Act, the federal State Wildlife Grants Program, programs pursuant to the Sport Fish and Wildlife Restoration Acts, wetlands grant programs of the U.S. Environmental Protection Agency and U.S. Forest Service, and grant programs provided pursuant to the Clean Water Act.

Most state wildlife departments, in addition to receiving federal funding, are funded by a combination of user fees; a few tap into general sales-tax revenues. State wildlife department funding mechanisms include nonconsumptive user fees, state lottery revenue, general sales tax, vehicle license plate fees, real estate transfer fees, tax check-offs, and natural resource extraction surcharges.

California's Environmental License Plate Fund Program generates funds for environmental and natural resources departments. However, these funds are usually appropriated to Fish and Game in lieu of General Fund dollars rather than to augment the base budget. In California, some of the better-funded resource departments and water agencies have funded a Fish and Game position to ensure certain wildlife-related services are provided.

Arkansas and Missouri have two of the better-funded state wildlife programs. Both of these states have constitutional mandates that devote a percentage of general sales tax dollars to wildlife conservation. In 1976, Missouri enacted a constitutional amendment that raised the sales tax by one-eighth of a cent, generating about $70 million annually for wildlife management and conservation projects. In 1996, Arkansas enacted a similar constitutional amendment, which yields about $20 million annually for wildlife programs.

In 1991, the California Legislative Analyst's Office identified several user or impact fees that have a connection to wildlife and might be assessed to fund Fish and Game. They are:

- **Motor-vehicle and highway impact fees**—Vehicles and the highways affect wildlife in several significant ways. Road kills account for substantial mortality of many species, including deer, owls, and snakes. More deer are killed by collisions with vehicles than by hunting. Habitat is eliminated and fragmented by roads and highways. Oil and other chemicals from roads pollute aquatic ecosystems. And invasive species are often introduced along highways. Impact fees could be assessed as an increase in sales tax on vehicles sales, or a flat-rate surcharge could be attached to vehicle registration fees. Assessing an additional $1 per vehicle registration would generate approximately $26 million. Another option is a surtax on vehicle fuels. The California Constitution allows gasoline tax dollars to be used for environmental mitigation related to construction and operation of roads and highways.

- **Nonpoint source discharge fees**—Pollution from diverse sources runs off into wetlands and aquatic ecosystems. Those who create nonpoint source discharges could be assessed a fee to mitigate wildlife conservation impacts.

- **Water use fees**—Water diversions from rivers, streams, and the Delta significantly affect fish, amphibians, and aquatic life. To mitigate these effects, the Legislature could impose a water-use fee on each acre-foot of water to fund wildlife conservation. A penny per acre-foot would generate about $220,000.

- **Wastewater discharge fees**—Pollution from industrial point sources degrades fish and aquatic life. Dischargers currently pay a fee that funds the State Water Resources Control Board's water quality regulatory program.

- **Recreational fees or taxes**—Currently, only hunting and fishing recreational users pay annual fees for a license. Additional user fees could be assessed for other wildlife-related user activities, including birding, diving, and whale-watching.

- **Mining fees**—Gravel- and open pit mining affects wildlife. For example, gravel mining from streambeds degrades salmon spawning grounds and degrades aquatic habitat. To fund wildlife conservation mitigation, a fee could be charged per volume of material removed.

Broad-based fees or taxes, such as a flat-tax surcharge on annual state income tax, a parcel tax or parcel transfer fee, or a percent of sales tax, are in line with the policy that wildlife is a public trust resource and the responsibility of all Californians. If California followed the Missouri and Arkansas examples and enacted a one-eighth of a percent surcharge on sales tax, it would generate about $650 million for wildlife conservation and management of natural resources.

Other Multispecies Conservation Planning Efforts

In addition to NCCPs, conservation planning is under way in a variety of other forms throughout the state, including Habitat Conservation Plans, recovery plans, species-group plans (including Joint Ventures), restoration plans, watershed plans, river management, and land-use or habitat management plans. The following is a brief introduction to each of these types of plans. More information can be found in Appendix C.

Habitat Conservation Plans (HCPs) are long-term agreements between the U.S. Fish and Wildlife Service (FWS) and an applicant (private landowner or nonfederal public land manager). They are designed to offset any harmful effects a proposed activity might have on federally listed threatened and endangered species.

Recovery plans are FWS documents prepared for one or more federally listed species that detail the specific tasks needed for recovery. These plans provide a blueprint for private, federal, and state agencies to cooperate in conserving specific species and their ecosystems.

Species-group plans address the conservation needs of related species. Two broad initiatives in this regard are the North American Bird Conservation Initiative and the Marine Life Protection Act Initiative. There are also planning efforts regarding other species groups and subgroups, including amphibians, reptiles, and bats.

The North American Bird Conservation Initiative is a conservation effort across the continent that brings together public and private organizations to focus on bird conservation. This initiative integrates both national and regional bird conservation plans as well as habitat Joint Ventures. National bird plans provide recommendations for conserving water birds, shorebirds, seabirds, and land birds across the country. Regional plans in California provide actions that are more specific for southern Pacific shorebirds, California Current marine birds, and bird habitats in riparian areas, coniferous forest, coastal scrub, grassland, oak woodland, shrub steppe, and the Sierra Nevada. These plans provide status and life history information, assess conservation needs, and recommend conservation actions.

Habitat Joint Ventures are regionally based coalitions of public and private organizations that integrate multiple bird conservation plans with a specific geographical area. California hosts all or part of six Joint Ventures (California Riparian, Central Valley, Intermountain West, Pacific Coast, San Francisco Bay, and Sonoran), with a seventh one (California Current) under development for the marine region.

The Marine Life Protection Act Initiative is also a multispecies- and habitat-focused effort. It is a cooperative public-private partnership of the California Resources Agency, Fish and Game, and a nongovernmental organization to expand, fund, and manage a system of marine protected areas along the California coast.

Continued on next page

Other Multispecies Conservation Planning Efforts, cont.

Habitat restoration plans range in scope from a few acres to CALFED's Ecosystem Restoration Program that covers much of the Central Valley and San Francisco Bay Area. These efforts aim to restore natural resource conditions that have been damaged, including revegetating riparian habitat, reducing erosion, improving water quality, restoring fish passage or habitat, and removing invasive species. Hundreds of restoration planning efforts are currently under way throughout the state.

Watershed plans and river management plans include wildlife conservation and restoration as an important element. Watershed plans usually focus on smaller drainage areas than do river plans. Both types are typically very collaborative in nature, involving many different stakeholders. Watershed plans integrate habitat conservation with other natural resource concerns, such as water quality, water supply, flood control, recreational use, erosion, and fire management. These plans are typically nonregulatory documents, although some are designed to meet water quality standards under the Clean Water Act (total maximum daily load (TMDL) standards).

Land use plans, whether developed by local government or public land managing agencies, also have wildlife conservation as major feature. Local land use plans include city or county General Plans. Large public land managers, such as the U.S. Forest Service, Bureau of Land Management, or Department of Defense, have land and resource plans that can cover 1 million acres or more. Smaller land managing agencies, such as the California Departments of Fish and Game and Parks and Recreation, also develop habitat and recreation management plans for lands they manage.

Although these land use plans play an important role in integrating a variety of land and natural resource issues, they typically do not address wildlife issues that spread onto neighboring lands beyond the set administrative boundaries.

NCCP Program Accomplishments

The first two NCCPs were approved in 1996 and 1997; these were the Orange County Central Coastal Natural Community Conservation Plan and the San Diego Multiple Species Conservation Program (covering southwestern San Diego County).

By the end of the 1990s, nine NCCPs were under way in San Diego, Orange, Riverside, Los Angeles, and San Bernardino counties.

In August 2000, a programmatic NCCP was approved for the massive CALFED Bay-Delta Program covering water infrastructure and habitat restoration projects throughout the Sacramento–San Joaquin Delta, San Francisco Bay, and Central Valley.

In July 2004, the Western Riverside Multiple Species Habitat Conservation Plan, covering 1.2 million acres and 146 species, was approved.

By early 2005, five Northern California regional conservation planning efforts signed NCCP planning agreements, and three others were in early discussion.

The first "working landscape" NCCP is being developed by the Mendocino Redwood Company to address timber harvest.

NCCP will be the approach used to resolve Colorado River water transfer issues for the Salton Sea Ecosystem Restoration Project.

Today, there are 31 active NCCPs of varying scope and complexity; 10 others have been approved. Eleven counties are participating in NCCP planning.

State and Federal Entities Involved in NCCP Development

Because each NCCP plan is uniquely designed to fit the issues, ecology, and politics of the region it covers, a list of other state and federal entities that could be involved varies with each plan. The following is representative of how some state entities have participated.

NCCP Participation by State Agencies

California Resources Agency–The umbrella agency over Fish and Game and other resource departments, the Resources Agency was instrumental in launching the NCCP program and providing political support in the program's formative years.

Wildlife Conservation Board (WCB)–The land acquisition entity for Fish and Game, the WCB acquires habitat lands at the request of Fish and Game to support NCCPs and other programs. WCB staff participate in the Southern California NCCP management meetings to assist with coordination of land acquisition.

State Conservancies–There are several state-sanctioned conservancies whose missions are to protect natural habitats in specified geographic areas. The conservancies often receive earmarked funding from land acquisition bond acts. They work with the Wildlife Conservation Board and Fish and Game to acquire lands to meet the reserve design of approved NCCPs.

Department of Parks and Recreation–Some NCCPs have state parks within their borders that are managed to protect natural biodiversity. As appropriate, state parks can be included in the reserve design to assist with conservation of species, natural communities, and ecological processes.

Universities–Scientists from California's universities are instrumental in creating a solid scientific foundation for the plans. University faculty members often serve as science advisers throughout plan development and implementation. They also carry out targeted studies in the plan areas to resolve critical uncertainties and improve knowledge of natural ecological systems, and they apply experimental management treatments to support monitoring and adaptive management.

Caltrans–The California Dept. of Transportation oversees all highway construction and improvement projects. Existing and future highways can have significant effects on reserve design and species, and Caltrans will likely need take authority to construct road projects. It is important that Caltrans be involved in NCCP planning.

NCCP Participation by Federal Agencies

USFWS–The U.S. Fish and Wildlife Service is the lead federal partner in the development of an NCCP. The USFWS issues permits in conjunction with an NCCP when federally listed threatened or endangered species are covered by a plan.

USGS–The Biological Resources Division of the U.S. Geological Survey participates in implementing NCCP plans in Southern California by coordinating ecosystem monitoring and conducting targeted studies.

Continued on next page

NCCP Participation by Federal Agencies, cont.

BLM–The U.S. Bureau of Land Management has significant landholdings in California. BLM coordinates new acquisitions to fulfill reserve design goals of NCCPs.

Army Corps of Engineers–The Corps of Engineers is consulted when a plan affects wetlands. In this case, plan participants work through a parallel wetland permitting process with the Corps of Engineers, so that projects covered by the NCCP may also have a streamlined wetland permitting process.

Mandated Responsibilities of Fish and Game Since 1968

Major conservation mandates enacted by the Legislature or by Initiative include:

1968–Fish and Game Management Policy Authorizes Fish and Game to establish ecological reserves to protect specialized habitat types and dependent species for the benefit of the general public and for research. Establishing ecological reserves involves evaluating potential land acquisitions, assessing fish and wildlife values, preparation of management plans, management and maintenance of lands, monitoring species and habitats, and providing public services at selected ecological reserves.

1969–Porter-Cologne Water Quality Control Act Establishes the basic authority of the state and regional water quality boards. Fish and Game's duties include water quality investigations, water quality monitoring, and lab work performed under agreement with state and regional water quality boards.

1970–California Environmental Quality Act (CEQA) Requires the review of projects and activities that affect the environment. Fish and Game's work includes reviewing environmental documents and providing comments to lead agencies on the potential effects of projects and activities, recommending mitigation measures to reduce or offset the impact of projects and activities, and monitoring compliance with mitigation requirements. Also, Fish and Game must conduct the environmental review of wildlife area management plans and hunting and fishing regulations.

1970–Conservation of Aquatic Resources Authorizes Fish and Game to manage aquatic resources, which includes resource assessment, developing sport and commercial fishing regulations, monitoring fish harvest rates, and managing of aquaculture.

1974–Conservation of Wildlife Resources Requires Fish and Game, as trustee for fish and wildlife resources, to consult with lead and responsible agencies and provide biological expertise to review and comment upon environmental documents and impacts arising from projects activities, per CEQA.

Continued on next page

Mandated Responsibilities of Fish and Game Since 1968, cont.

1976–Fish and Wildlife Conservation Policy Requires Fish and Game to regulate projects or activities that affect streams and lakes. Fish and Game's duties include reviewing proposed projects, working with project proponents to minimize or offset negative effects on natural resources, developing written agreements, and monitoring implementation of projects.

1977–Native Plant Protection Act Requires Fish and Game to establish criteria for determining if a native plant species is rare or endangered and to enforce laws protecting those plants. Authorizes Fish and Game to conduct botanical research and field investigations and hold hearings to determine conservation measures needed to protect native plants. Authorizes Fish and Game to develop regulations (for adoption by the Commission) to protect plants.

1981–Significant Natural Areas Establishes the Significant Natural Areas Program and requires Fish and Game to maintain a natural resources data management system (Natural Diversity Database–NDDB); consult with federal, state, and local governments and interest groups; report on those natural areas deemed to be most significant; and seek ways to protect and conserve those areas. Work includes gathering, validating, and updating information to be included in the NDDB and maintaining and improving the NDDB system (both hardware and software).

1982–Streamflow Protection Standards Requires Fish and Game to identify and list those streams and watercourses for which minimum flow levels need to be established to assure the continued viability of fish and wildlife resources. Also requires Fish and Game to prepare proposed streamflow requirements for those listed waters. Work includes streamflow studies and consultation with various federal, state, and local governments and other interested parties.

1984–California Endangered Species Act Under this act, the Fish and Game Commission determines whether a species should be listed as threatened or endangered. Fish and Game evaluates petitions for listing or delisting; prepares status reports to the Fish and Game Commission; controls and authorizes the take of listed species pursuant to specific terms through permits, agreements, and memoranda of understanding; develops and implements species recovery plans; and enforces the protections for listed species. Fish and Game also works with the agriculture industry to minimize incidental and accidental take of endangered species.

1985–Fisheries Restoration Pursuant to this act, Fish and Game administers a program to fund restoration projects, consults with various agencies and groups in selecting projects to be funded, and conducts pre-project and post-project evaluations.

1988–Salmon, Steelhead Trout, and Anadromous Fisheries Program Act Requires Fish and Game to develop a program to increase natural production of salmon and steelhead and to consult with various groups and agencies in developing the program.

Continued on next page

Mandated Responsibilities of Fish and Game Since 1968, cont.

1988–Wildlife and Natural Areas Conservation Program Funds Fish and Game and the Wildlife Conservation Board to acquire, enhance, restore, and protect land and water resources for the conservation of important habitats. (Enacted by Prop. 70.)

1990–California Wildlife Protection Act Created the Habitat Conservation Fund and directs the use of those funds. (Enacted by Prop. 117.)

1990–Inland Wetlands Conservation Program Administered by the Wildlife Conservation Board, this program implements the Central Valley Habitat Joint Venture. Fish and Game assists the board with the implementation of the program, including acquisition and restoration of wetlands.

1991–Natural Community Conservation Planning Act Authorizes Fish and Game to enter into agreements for developing and implementing regional multispecies conservation plans. Work includes consultation with organizations and governmental agencies; determining standards and guidelines; gathering and using public input; monitoring and reporting; establishing and working with advisory groups; and conducting surveys and resource assessment activities.

1998–Marine Life Management Act Requires Fish and Game and the Fish and Game Commission to manage marine fisheries through the development and implementation of fishery management plans. The act requires that Fish and Game proactively maintain sustainable fisheries and healthy marine ecosystems. The Act requires the department to involve stakeholders in the development of marine management plans and to use the best available science.

1999–Marine Life Protection Act Requires Fish and Game to develop a master plan for modification of existing and designation of new marine protected areas for adoption by the Fish and Game Commission. The Act includes public input and scientific peer review during the planning process.

Part II
Regions

~~~~~~

Mojave Desert Region

Colorado Desert Region

South Coast Region

Central Coast Region

North Coast–Klamath Region

Modoc Plateau Region

Sierra Nevada and Cascades Region

Central Valley and Bay-Delta Region

Marine Region

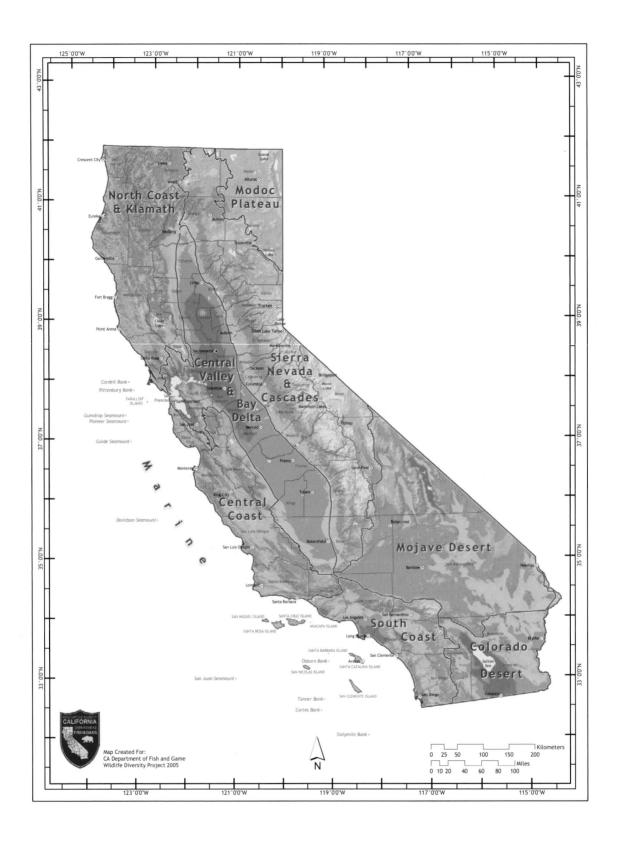

Introduction to the Regions ~~~~~

The plan development team reviewed major threats to wildlife and habitats and examined conservation needs on a regional level. The team divided the state into nine regions:

- Mojave Desert
- Colorado Desert
- South Coast
- Central Coast
- North Coast–Klamath
- Modoc Plateau
- Sierra Nevada and Cascades
- Central Valley and Bay-Delta
- Marine

These regional divisions were based on the state's physiographic characteristics (i.e., watersheds and vegetation communities) coupled with consideration of wildlife- and natural resources management areas of responsibility. The regional approach facilitated the discussion of habitats, ecosystems, and conservation issues at a scale appropriate for conservation planning and compatible with resource management jurisdictions and decision-making authorities.

For example, the Sierra Nevada and Cascades ranges are discussed under one region, the Sierra Nevada–Cascades, because these ranges are contiguous, and a large proportion of the land in these regions is federally managed pursuant to similar management policies and documents, such as the Forest Service's Sierra Nevada Forest Plan. The Central Valley was grouped with the Bay-Delta region because the jurisdictional area of the California Bay-Delta Authority program (Authority) encompasses both regions. Water management issues form the crux of many habitat issues in both the Central Valley and Bay-Delta, and the Authority has a lead role in coordinating state and federal agencies' efforts to protect and restore ecosystems and improve water quality across the region.

A map of each region is included at the beginning of each regional chapter, and the regional chapters include the following standard sections:

Overview

This introductory section provides a general description of the region's physical landscape, land ownership, terrestrial and aquatic resources, and species and habitats within the region. The overview may also give a brief account of some of the region's major conservation challenges and trends for species and habitats.

Species at Risk

The wildlife **species at risk** (also referred to as Fish and Game's **Special Animals List** or special status species) and **endemic** species are summarized by species group, and the Web reference is provided for the Wildlife Species Matrix, where information may be found regarding all special-status species, their distribution, and habitat associations. The matrix may be sorted by region and provides a link to detailed information for each species, where available.

While each species is not discussed in detail, this section does feature two or three special status species to illustrate how various activities and habitat changes have affected wildlife in the region. These individual species discussions also illustrate needs and opportunities for conservation and habitat restoration.

Stressors Affecting Wildlife and Habitats

This section describes the major stressors or threats that adversely affect wildlife, habitats, and ecosystems. Many of the activities and projects identified as stressors to wildlife provide important benefits in meeting the housing, transportation, recreation, and sustenance needs of California's residents. In identifying such activities among the regional stressors, it is not this report's intention to suggest that these activities do not provide important societal functions and services. Rather, the purpose is to clearly describe the effects of the stressors on wildlife and habitats.

Conservation Actions to Restore and Conserve Wildlife

This section describes important conservation actions for maintaining wildlife diversity. Included are suggested programs and initiatives, recommendations for improving or expanding current programs, and needs for support and funding. Also identified are the venues or lead agencies through which these conservation actions would likely be taken. The conservation actions are based on consultations with regional experts, results of conservation-action workshops, and review of major resource conservation and planning documents.

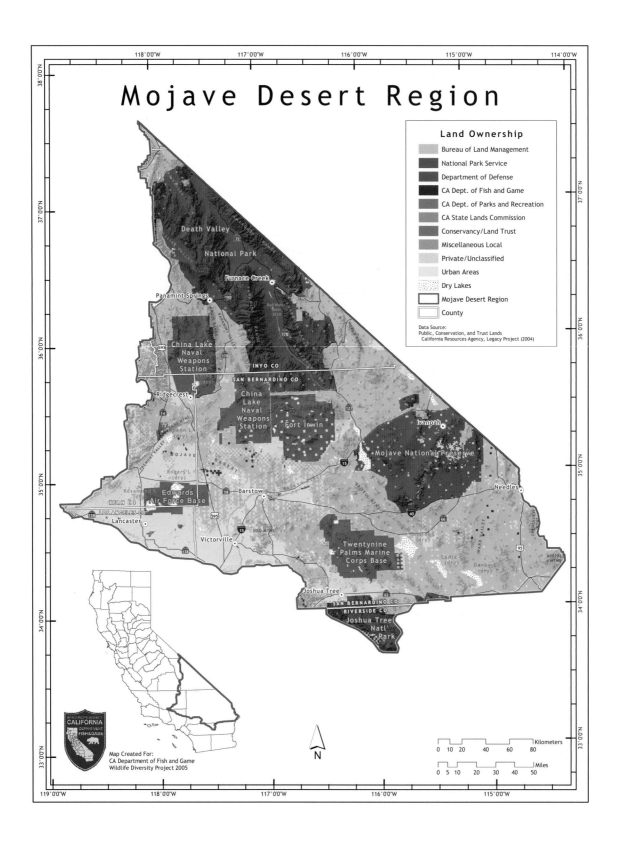

Mojave Desert Region

Land Ownership

- Bureau of Land Management
- National Park Service
- Department of Defense
- CA Dept. of Fish and Game
- CA Dept. of Parks and Recreation
- CA State Lands Commission
- Conservancy/Land Trust
- Miscellaneous Local
- Private/Unclassified
- Urban Areas
- Dry Lakes
- Mojave Desert Region
- County

Data Source:
Public, Conservation, and Trust Lands
California Resources Agency, Legacy Project (2004)

Death Valley National Park

Furnace Creek

Panamint Springs

China Lake Naval Weapons Station

Ridgecrest

INYO CO

SAN BERNARDINO CO

China Lake Naval Weapons Station

Fort Irwin

Ivanpah

Mojave National Preserve

Needles

KERN CO

LOS ANGELES CO

Rogers L. (dry)

Rosamond

Edwards Air Force Base

Lancaster

Barstow

Victorville

Twentynine Palms Marine Corps Base

Joshua Tree

SAN BERNARDINO CO

RIVERSIDE CO

Joshua Tree Nat'l Park

CALIFORNIA
DEPARTMENT
FISH & GAME

N

Map Created For:
CA Department of Fish and Game
Wildlife Diversity Project 2005

0 10 20 40 60 80 Kilometers

0 5 10 20 30 40 50 Miles

7   *Mojave Desert Region*

The vast Mojave Desert's more than 32 million acres extend into four states: California, Nevada, Arizona, and Utah. Within California, the Mojave Region's 20 million acres cover one-fifth of the state, spanning an area larger than the counties of San Diego, Orange, Los Angeles, Imperial, Riverside, Ventura, Santa Barbara, and San Luis Obispo combined.

About 80 percent of the Mojave Desert in California is managed by federal agencies, each of which has differing sets of missions that often expand beyond wildlife conservation. The Bureau of Land Management (BLM), the largest land manager of the region, oversees 8 million acres, or 41 percent, of the federally owned sector. The National Park Service manages the Mojave National Preserve and Death Valley and Joshua Tree national parks, which account for another 26 percent of the region. The Department of Defense manages five military bases that cover about 13 percent of the region. State Parks and Fish and Game wildlife areas account for just 0.32 percent of the region. About 18 percent of the region belongs to private landowners or municipalities (CRA 1998, 2004).

Lying in the rain shadow of the southern Sierra Nevada and Southern California's Transverse and Peninsular Ranges, the dry Mojave landscape is highlighted by dramatic geologic features, encompassing peaks, cliffs, canyons, dry washes, sand dunes, and large playas. Variations in elevation and soil composition and different orientations to the wind and sun, along with desert springs, moist seeps, and two major riparian corridors, provide isolated microclimates and ecosystems throughout the region. The harsh yet diverse environment of the Mojave has facilitated the evolution of numerous **endemic** and specially adapted species of plants and wildlife on islands of unique habitat in a sea of creosote bushes, the most widespread plant community of the state.

From 282 feet below sea level in Death Valley to altitudes of 11,000 feet in the Panamint Mountains, the range of habitats supports 130 different **plant alliances**. However, the landscape is mostly a moderately high plateau at elevations between 2,000 and 3,000 feet. The common habitats of the region are creosote bush scrub, desert saltbush, Joshua tree scrub, desert wash, alkali scrub, and juniper-pinyon woodlands. Although limited in area, springs, seeps, perennial streams of the Panamint Range's Surprise Canyon and Cottonwood Creek, along with the Amargosa and Mojave rivers, are vital wet habitats supporting wildlife diversity in the region.

Hidden Desert Wildlife

On a typical hot-day's drive through the Mojave Desert, the casual observer may not experience or appreciate the wildlife, which seek shelter and shade to avoid the heat of the day. At dusk, desert horned lizards shake loose from the sandy soil crust to snatch unsuspecting ants. Kangaroo rats with tufted tails emerge from burrows beneath shrubs. Common nighthawks engage in aerial acrobatics. The shudder of the male nighthawk's wings makes a loud whooshing "hoooov" sound as it pulls out of its display dive in the otherwise silent desert dusk. Coyotes begin their hunts, often loping along ridgelines, scanning the desert for cottontail rabbits and ground squirrels, while bats weave in the darkening sky above, scooping up flying insects.

The crescendo of songbird melodies breaks the desert quiet again just before dawn. Sparrows, wrens, and towhees dart among the brush, foraging in the relatively cool morning. Songbirds, shorebirds, wading birds, kingfishers, waterfowl, owls, and hawks inhabit the riparian habitats of the Mojave and Amargosa rivers and desert spring habitats of meandering water, willows, and cottonwoods. The traffic of nocturnal mammals, bobcat, coyotes, skunks, and voles leaves paw prints in sandy soils.

The Mojave Desert is home to extraordinary plants and wildlife. The Joshua tree, barrel and prickly pear cacti, and pinyon pine highlight the desert landscape, home to prairie falcons, burrowing owls, desert tortoises, rosy boas, desert horned lizards, collared and leopard lizards, Mohave ground squirrels, kangaroo rats, Mojave River and Amargosa voles, bobcats, kit foxes, mountain lions, and bighorn sheep.

It is the vastness of the Mojave Desert that has given some the impression that it is a wasteland that can endure unlimited adverse impacts to its species, habitats, and ecosystems. Thirty years ago, however, the fragile nature of the desert was well recognized.

> "The vast natural resources of the California desert are today severely threatened by the extent of adverse human intrusion, combined with the natural fragility of the desert ecosystem."
>
> —*The Fragile Balance: Environmental Problems of the California Desert*
>   (Ginsberg et al. 1976)

> "The impact of accelerated human and vehicle activity cannot be overstated. Careless mining operations and improper grazing practices have scarred the land. Unplanned construction and road-building have played a destructive game of tic-tac-toe across the desert's face. Excessive and uncontrolled recreational use are undermining the concept of multiple use and removing the desert from the dwindling list of sanctuaries for many rare and endangered species."
>
> —U.S. Senator Alan Cranston, preface to *Fragile Balance,* 1976

> "The California desert environment is a total ecosystem that is extremely fragile, easily scarred, and slowly healed . . . and its resources, including certain rare and endangered species of wildlife, plants, and fishes, and numerous archeological and historic sites, are seriously threatened by air pollution, inadequate Federal management authority, and pressures of increased use, particularly recreational use, which are certain to intensify because of the rapidly growing population of Southern California."
>
> —Federal Land Policy and Management Act of 1976, Title VI

Since the enactment of the Federal Land Policy and Management Act, the major threats to wildlife populations continue, and new threats have emerged. Wildlife species are at risk, and ecosystems are degraded from the cumulative impact of urban growth, off-highway vehicle activity that adds thousands of miles of dirt roads and trails, cattle and sheep grazing, overdrawn groundwater, illegal harvest or illegal commercialization, and dominance of invasive plants. These activities, events, and conditions have and are continuing to fragment the landscape, degrade wildlife habitat, and disrupt desert ecosystems. Only with sufficiently large protected ecosystems and coordinated, strategic, and well-funded conservation actions will wildlife recovery be achieved.

Numerous public agencies, private organizations, and landowners are involved in wildlife conservation efforts in the Mojave. Since the early 1980s, private conservation organizations such as the Conservation Fund, The Nature Conservancy, and Preserving Wild California have protected thousands of acres of essential habitat for the Mojave Desert's unique plants and animals. Since 1994, the Desert Managers Group (DMG), an interagency group, has served the role of coordinating desert conservation, visitor services, public outreach, and public safety in the region. Initially representing state and federal land management, recreation and wildlife agencies, and the Department of Defense, in 2005 the DMG expanded to include participants from the desert counties. Fish and Game participates in and contributes funds to the DMG. The DMG provides an important regionwide forum for facilitation of conservation efforts. It is involved in identifying research needs, conservation planning, restoration projects, and conservation programs and helps to secure funding for these efforts.

Species at Risk

The Plan development team updated vertebrate and invertebrate species information in the California Natural Diversity Database (CNDDB) during 2004–2006. The following regional summary of numbers of wildlife species, endemic species, and species at risk is derived from the updated CNDDB.

While the Mojave Desert supports a great diversity of wildlife, accumulated degradation of the desert wildlands over the last several decades has caused many desert species to decline in numbers and distribution, and thus they have been identified as species at risk.

There are 439 vertebrate species that inhabit the Mojave Desert Region at some point in their life cycle, including 252 birds, 101 mammals, 57 reptiles, 10 amphibians, and 19 fish. Of the total vertebrate species that inhabit this region, 69 bird **taxa**, 38 mammalian taxa, 15 reptilian taxa, four amphibian taxa, and nine fish taxa are included on the **Special Animals List.** Of these, 14 are endemic to the Mojave Desert Region, one is endemic to California but introduced to this region, and 15 other species found here are endemic to California but not restricted to this region (Table 7.1).

Table 7.1: State-Endemic Special Status Vertebrates of the Mojave Desert Region

	Anniella pulchra pulchra	Silvery legless lizard
*	*Aphelocoma californica cana*	Eagle Mountain scrub-jay
	Batrachoseps campi	Inyo Mountains slender salamander
	Batrachoseps robustus	Kern Plateau salamander
*	*Bufo exsul*	Black toad
	Charina umbratica	Southern rubber boa
	Cyprinodon nevadensis amargosae	Amargosa pupfish
*	*Cyprinodon nevadensis nevadensis*	Saratoga Springs pupfish
*	*Cyprinodon nevadensis shoshone*	Shoshone pupfish
*	*Cyprinodon salinus milleri*	Cottonball Marsh pupfish
*	*Cyprinodon salinus salinus*	Salt Creek pupfish
*	*Dipodomys merriami collinus*	Earthquake Merriam's kangaroo rat
	Dipodomys panamintinus argusensis	Argus Mountains kangaroo rat
*	*Dipodomys panamintinus anamintinus*	Panamint kangaroo rat
	Elgaria (=Gerrhonotus) panamintinus	Panamint alligator lizard
*	*Gila bicolor mohavensis*	Mohave tui chub
+	*Gila orcutti*	Arroyo chub
	Gopherus agassizii	Desert tortoise
*	*Microtus californicus mohavensis*	Mohave River vole
*	*Microtus californicus scirpensis*	Amargosa vole
	Microtus californicus vallicola	Owens Valley vole
	Onychomys torridus tularensis	Tulare grasshopper mouse
	Perognathus alticolus inexpectatus	Tehachapi pocket mouse
	Perognathus inornatus inornatus	San Joaquin pocket mouse
*	*Perognathus longimembris salinensis*	No common name
	Perognathus parvus xanthonotus	Yellow-eared pocket mouse
*	*Pipilo crissalis eremophilus*	Inyo California towhee
	Rhinichthys osculus ssp. 2	Owens speckled dace
	Spermophilus mohavensis	Mohave ground squirrel
*	*Tamias panamintinus acrus*	Kingston Mountain chipmunk
	Tamias speciosus speciosus	Lodgepole chipmunk

* denotes taxon is endemic to region
+ denotes taxon is endemic to California but introduced in this region

The number of arthropod species is so great, and they are so poorly known taxonomically, that it is presently impossible to accurately estimate the total number of invertebrate species occurring in the state. In the Mojave Desert Region, however, 29 invertebrate taxa are included on the Special Animals List, including 19 arthropod taxa and 10 mollusk taxa. Of these, 22 are endemic to the Mojave Desert Region, and six other taxa found here are endemic to California but not restricted to this region (Table 7.2).

Table 7.2: State-Endemic Special Status Invertebrates of the Mojave Desert Region

*	*Agabus rumppi*	Death Valley agabus diving beetle
*	*Ambrysus funebris*	Nevares Spring naucorid bug
*	*Ammopelmatus kelsoensis*	Kelso Jerusalem cricket
*	*Assiminea infima*	Badwater snail
*	*Belostoma saratogae*	Saratoga Springs belostoman bug
	Certaochrysis menkei	Menke's chrysidid wasp
	Eremarionta morongoana	Morongo (=Colorado) desertsnail
*	*Eremarionta rowelli bakerensis*	Baker's desertsnail
*	*Fontelicella sp*	Deep Springs fontelicella
*	*Glaresis arenata*	Kelso Dunes scarab glaresis beetle
*	*Helminthoglypta mohaveana*	Victorville shoulderband
	Helminthoglypta taylori	Westfork shoulderband
*	*Hubbardia shoshonensis*	Shoshone Cave whip-scorpion
*	*Ipnobius robustus*	Robust tryonia
*	*Macrobaenetes kelsoensis*	Kelso giant sand treader cricket
*	*Miloderes nelsoni*	Nelson's miloderes weevil
	Myrmosula pacifica	Antioch multilid wasp
*	*Paranomada californica*	Californian paranomada cuckoo bee
*	*Pelocoris biimpressus shoshone*	Amargosa naucorid bug
*	*Plebulina emigdionis*	San Emigdio blue butterfly
*	*Polyphylla anteronivea*	Saline Valley snow-front june beetle
*	*Polyphylla erratica*	Death Valley june beetle
	Psychomastix deserticola	Desert monkey grasshopper
	Pyrgulopsis wongi	Wong's springsnail
*	*Rhopalolemma robertsi*	Roberts' cuckoo bee
*	*Trigonoscuta brunnotesselata*	Brown tassel trigonoscuta weevil
*	*Tryonia margae*	Grapevine Springs elongate tryonia
*	*Tryonia rowlandsi*	Grapevine Springs squat tryonia

* denotes taxon is endemic to region

The Wildlife Species Matrix, including data on listing status, habitat association, and population trend for each vertebrate and invertebrate species included on the Special Animals List, is available on the Web at http://www.dfg.ca.gov/habitats/wdp/matrix_search.asp. For vertebrates, the matrix also includes links to species-level range maps. Additionally, a link to the California Department of Fish and Game's online Field Survey Form is available to assist in reporting positive sightings of species on the Special Animals List to the California Natural Diversity Database (CNDDB).

Three Species at Risk

Note: *The following discussion of three species at risk illustrates how stressors or threats affect species and highlights conservation challenges and opportunities. These species discussions are not intended to imply that conservation should have a single-species approach.*

These three species are highlighted to illustrate how various stressors affect them and their habitats and the challenges of conservation. Some of the species in trouble are like the wide-ranging desert tortoise, suffering from the compounded effects of numerous factors. The Amargosa vole, while affected by several human activities, is at risk due to the loss of grasslands and wet habitat along the Amargosa River corridor. The Mohave ground squirrel is at risk because numerous stressors degrade essential habitat within its limited range.

Desert Tortoise

The desert tortoise is the flagship species of the Mojave Desert. The wide-ranging and long-lived tortoise is a herbivore with a diversified diet, occurring in numerous vegetation communities and habitats across the Mojave and Sonoran deserts. The Mojave tortoise population was state listed as threatened in 1989 and federally listed as threatened in 1990. Desert tortoise populations have declined dramatically in the last 25

years. In some areas of occupied habitat, tortoise density has dropped by 50 percent to 90 percent; near some desert towns, they have been almost completely extirpated (Berry 1999, 2003, Jones 2005 pers. comm.).

More than 20 stressors affecting tortoise populations have been identified, and the cause of their decline has been the cumulative impact of human-related activities. Habitat degradation and fragmentation, the increase in exotic plant species, increased fire, collection for pets

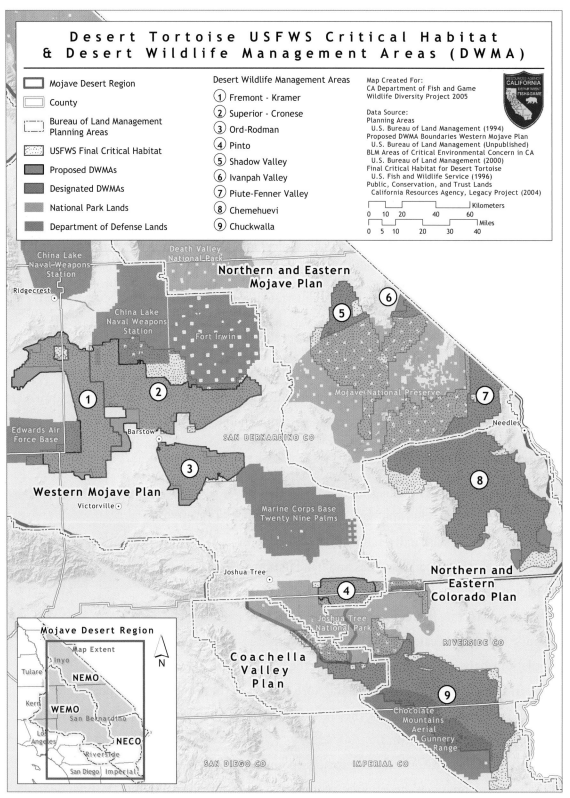

Fig. 7.1: Desert Tortoise critical habitat

Desert Wildlife Management Areas (DWMAs) are the central component of the strategy to protect and recover the desert tortoise.

or food, shooting, crushing by off-road and military vehicles, disease, predation by dogs and by human-induced expanded raven populations, agricultural activities, development of roads, utility corridors, and residential communities have all taken their toll on the tortoise and its habitat (BLM 2005b, DMG 2004, Doak et al. 1994, USFWS 1999).

The explosion of the raven population in the desert illustrates how indirect effects of human activities can disrupt ecological balances. Ravens are both predators and scavengers. They have been described as "bears with wings," because they become pests that feed on human-produced garbage. Ravens proliferate near garbage dumps, sewage ponds, agricultural areas, and along roads, all of which provide unnaturally abundant food, water, perches, and nest sites. Common ravens increased by 1,500 percent in the Mojave Desert between 1968 and 1988 (Boarman and Berry 1995). Ravens consume juvenile tortoises and likely prey upon other less-studied native reptiles. Estimates of tortoise mortality in localized areas due to raven predation range from 9 percent to 72 percent (BLM 2005b, Liebezeit and George 2002).

The life history of the tortoise dictates that even under very favorable conditions, its population may grow at a rate of only 1 percent to 2 percent annually, making recovery very slow. Even with the stressors significantly reduced, it would require 200 years for tortoise numbers to increase from 10 to 80 animals per square mile (USFWS 1994b).

The central strategy for saving the tortoise, pursuant to the 1994 Recovery Plan, has been the establishment of Desert Wildlife Management Areas (DWMAs), designed to provide special protection for the tortoise and other wildlife. The Recovery Plan described the special management actions to be implemented in each DWMA to protect and recover the desert tortoise. However, most of the special management actions have not been implemented or have been only partially implemented. The recovery plan recommended tortoise barrier fencing be installed within the DWMAs where tortoises are prevalent to keep them from being killed on major highways and roads. In the Joshua Tree DWMA that lies nearly entirely within lands managed by the National Park Service, barrier fencing has not yet been installed to protect tortoises. The recovery plan also called for reducing raven numbers in DWMAs to reduce predation on young tortoises, but this has been hindered by legal challenges. The recovery plan called for eliminating livestock grazing to reduce the degradation of tortoise habitat. With the exception of several cattle leases that have been bought out by the U.S. Army as part of the Fort Irwin expansion mitigation and by the Desert Tortoise Preserve Committee, cattle grazing continues on lands within the DWMAs and on desert tortoise critical habitat in the western Mojave. Another action to protect tortoises that has yet to be implemented is to construct fences in key areas to keep free-roaming dogs out. (Berry 2004 pers. comm., DMG 2002b, Jones 2004 pers. comm., RI 2002b, USFWS 1994b).

In 2004, the desert Tortoise Recovery Plan Assessment Committee, a team of experts assembled by the U.S. Fish and Wildlife Service, completed a report evaluating the science and implementation of the 1994 Recovery Plan. The committee found that the recovery effort over the last decade was unsuccessful, primarily because the plan was only partially implemented. Desert tortoise populations continue to decline, most clearly so in the West Mojave Recovery Unit. The committee concluded that recovery of the tortoise requires additional research on the animal's demography and population dynamics. The inability to implement the original recovery plan is also due to the lack of coordinated and rangewide tracking of implementation (Tracy et al. 2004, USFWS 2004).

The U.S. Fish and Wildlife Service has established a new desert tortoise recovery office and recovery implementation work groups. The Desert Manager's Group is providing coordination of federal, state, and local agencies to assist with desert tortoise recovery and management of natural resources.

Amargosa Vole

Everette Denney

The Amargosa vole has evolved in isolated grasslands and wetland and riparian habitat along segments of the Amargosa River. It is entirely dependent on the future of the wetlands and riparian habitat along the river. Marshes occupied by the vole are separated by desert habitat, limiting its dispersal (CDFG 2005b).

Conversion of wetlands to farmland, diversion of surface water, groundwater pumping that lowers the water table, and the invasion of exotic vegetation have reduced wildlife habitat along the river corridor. As the native grasslands and riparian communities along the Amargosa River have declined, so has its resident vole. The Amargosa vole was state listed and federally listed as endangered in the early 1980s. The increase in groundwater pumping required for the projected growth of upstream Nevada communities threatens to dry up the last vestiges of the voles' habitat, leading to its extinction.

The U.S. Fish and Wildlife Service completed a recovery plan for the vole in 1997. The plan indicated that protection of the wetland habitat along the Amargosa River and maintaining the water sources for these wetlands is critical to the vole's survival (USFWS 1997a). The Northern and Eastern Mojave Desert Management Plan (NEMO), approved in 2002, emphasizes protection for the watershed of the Amargosa River and identifies five areas along the river that are important for conserving the vole. The NEMO also recommends that segments of the Amargosa River be considered for addition to the National Wild and Scenic River system. Conservation of the Amargosa vole will require protecting important habitats and preventing groundwater overdrafting in the Amargosa River watershed in California and Nevada.

Mohave Ground Squirrel

Endemic to the western Mojave Desert, the Mohave ground squirrel is especially adapted to the hot, dry desert. It is active in spring and early summer, when it forages on leaves and seeds of native plants. In years of good plant forage due to adequate winter rains, the squirrel will produce young. However, in drier years the squirrel foregoes reproduction and instead stores fat for its long dormancy period from mid-summer through February. The squirrel's desert survival adaptations, long seasonal inactive periods, and the skipping of reproduction in drier years make it very difficult for biologists to conduct studies of its distribution and abundance.

Habitat loss and fragmentation due to urban and agricultural development and habitat degradation from livestock grazing, military training activities, off-road vehicle recreation, and invasive grasses are all stressors of the Mohave ground squirrel populations (BLM 2005b, CDFG 2005). (See Fig. 7.2, showing Mohave ground squirrel sightings.) Livestock grazing from February to June coincides with the squirrel's active period. Sheep and cattle consume some of the same plants that are important forage and cover for squirrels (CDFG 2005b).

The degradation and loss of its habitat in its limited range led to its listing as a threatened species under the California Endangered Species Act in 1971. Over the last two decades, a decline in biologists' trapping success has raised concern that the species is still declining (BLM 2005b, Brooks and Pyke 2001). In 1995 the U.S. Fish and Wildlife Service concluded that not enough is known about the squirrel to warrant listing it as threatened or endangered under the federal Endangered Species Act.

Recent field studies have helped to clarify the status and conservation needs of the Mohave ground squirrel. Four core areas have been identified that still support viable populations. These areas make up less than 10 percent of the species range and are widely separated, leading to concerns regarding habitat fragmentation and genetic isolation. Two of these core areas are on military installations where conservation action is necessarily limited because the species is not federally listed. The Mohave ground squirrel appears to be largely absent from the southern portion of its range and has a very patchy, low-density distribution elsewhere apart from the four known core areas. Potential connections between certain core areas are threatened by changes in land use that contribute to habitat loss and degradation. The present status of the Mohave ground squirrel appears precarious, and current conservation measures are not adequate to ensure its recovery (Leitner 2005 pers. comm.).

Major Stressors Affecting Wildlife and Habitats

- Multiple uses conflicting with wildlife on public lands
- Growth and development
- Groundwater overdrafting and loss of riparian habitat
- Inappropriate off-road vehicle use
- Excessive livestock grazing
- Excessive burro and horse grazing
- Invasive plants
- Military lands management conflicts
- Mining operations

Multiple Uses Conflicting with Wildlife on Public Lands

With four-fifths of California's Mojave region under federal stewardship, the prevailing assumption by local governments is that federal lands provide adequate habitat to maintain wildlife, and that the private and municipal lands are available to be developed. However, the habitats required to sustain wildlife diversity do not correspond to the regional political boundaries. For example, most riparian and spring habitats, critical for wildlife, are on privately owned lands. Their protection depends on both cooperative and incentive-based approaches, as well as the enforcement of state and federal wetlands regulations, and, in the case of the Mojave River, the implementation of the adjudicated water rights agreement. Nevertheless, the Northern and Eastern Mojave Desert Management Plan (NEMO), the Desert Tortoise Recovery Plan, and the proposed West Mojave Plan (WMP) rely principally on federal lands management for maintaining healthy wildlife populations.

Federal policy dictates that BLM manage its lands to accommodate multiple uses. Many of these uses conflict with wildlife conservation, damaging the fragile desert habitats. (See Fig. 7.2,

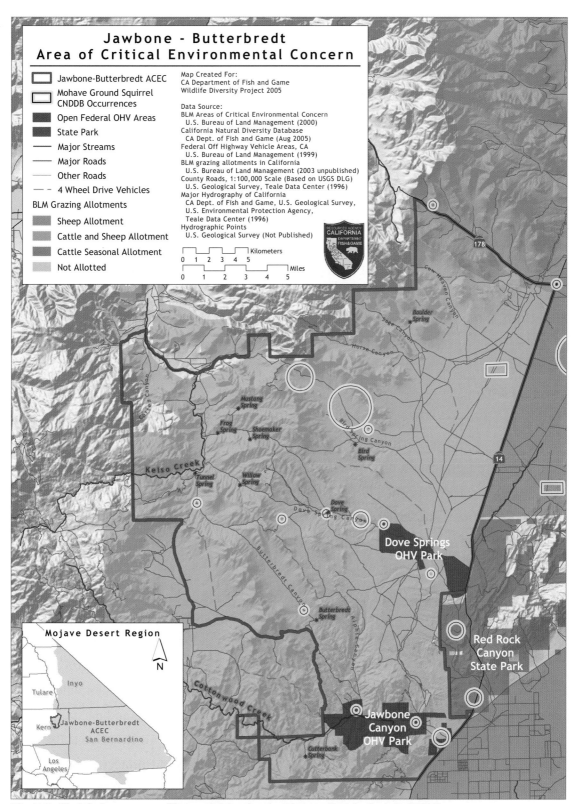

Fig 7.2: Multiple-use conflicts within the Jawbone-Butterbredt ACEC

The Jawbone-Butterbredt Area of Critical of Environmental Concern is an example of an area where accommodating multiple land-uses causes degradation of wildlife resources. In this case, there are off-road areas and livestock grazing allotments overlapping or adjacent to riparian and other sensitive habitats. Circled areas indicate Mohave ground squirrel sites.

Multiple-Use Conflicts within the Jawbone-Butterbredt ACEC.) The Federal Land Policy and Management Act of 1976 broadened BLM's purposes to include preserving public lands in their wild condition and required BLM to prepare a comprehensive long-range plan for the California Desert Conservation Area, which covers both the Mojave and Colorado Desert regions. Among the goals of the plan, completed in 1980, was for BLM to maintain environmental quality and to protect endangered and threatened species of plants and wildlife while accommodating grazing, mining, and recreational activities. However, some land uses that degrade habitat are incompatible with restoring habitat and conserving species (Lovich and Bainbridge 1999, Tracy et al. 2004, USGAO 1989, 1991a, 1991b).

The California Desert Conservation Area (CDCA) Plan set out to protect wildlife and sensitive habitats primarily by establishing Areas of Critical Environmental Concern (ACEC), various wildlife habitat management areas, and large units of limited use. Enforcing grazing and off-road vehicle restrictions was a high priority within these areas. ACECs were intended to be specially managed areas with specific goals, such as protecting and enhancing wildlife (BLM 1980). However, ACECs with special wildlife values are difficult to monitor and enforce without substantially greater staff resources. Restrictions to protect these areas are often violated by off-road vehicles and livestock intrusions, damaging habitat. And multiple uses, such as off-road vehicle use, livestock grazing, mining, and public utilities, have eroded and continue to erode the condition of wildlife resources in many of the ACECs that have been in existence since their designation in 1980. Invasive plant species have also degraded the habitat within ACECs (Aardahl 2005 pers. comm., USGAO 1991b). Without adequate conservation, management, and enforcement resources devoted to wildlife stewardship, BLM has been unable to protect these areas or implement adequate restoration projects and invasive species control programs to restore ecosystems and habitat values.

The CDCA Plan is undergoing a 20-year update through amendments divided among six area plans. Two plans cover the Mojave Desert: the Northern and Eastern Mojave Desert Management Plan (NEMO) and the proposed West Mojave Plan. The NEMO, approved in December 2002, established additional areas containing special protections for wildlife, including a determination that Surprise Canyon, Cottonwood Creek, and parts of the Amargosa River were eligible for designation under the Wild and Scenic Rivers Act. Two Desert Wildlife Management Areas (DWMAs) were designated for the protection of the desert tortoise, and ACECs were established to protect additional portions of the Amargosa River riparian habitat. The plans also call for reducing cattle and burro numbers in sensitive habitats. While there has been a major effort to reduce burro numbers, resources have yet to be allocated to implement and enforce the other major provisions of NEMO and to provide prescribed protection levels of the Desert Wildlife Management Areas (BLM 2002, 2005b).

The latest version of the West Mojave Plan was released by BLM in spring 2006. Successful wildlife stewardship in the western Mojave planning area will require even greater conservation and enforcement resources than those in the northern and eastern Mojave, due to the more intensive development, recreation pressures, and other habitat-damaging land uses of the western Mojave. Rapid and full implementation of the Mojave area plans is necessary to prevent further degradation of wildlife habitat and the decline of wildlife populations.

Growth and Development

Within the Mojave Desert region, the west Mojave has the greatest land area with the fewest protections for maintaining wildlife diversity (TNC 2000b). The western Mojave has experienced tremendous growth over the last 20 years, and that trend is expected to continue. (See Fig. 7.3, Projected Development.) Collectively, the 11 incorporated cities of the western Mojave grew by 25 percent in the last decade, about double the statewide growth rate, and the region's population is expected to grow from 733,000 in 2000 to 1.5 million in 2036. Existing local government General Plans provide for residential growth in the western Mojave to reach a population of 5 million (BLM 2005b, Hunter et al. 2003). Significant growth is not anticipated in the eastern Mojave of California, where there is little infrastructure (BLM 2002b). But growth across the California-Nevada state border, in Pahrump and Las Vegas, will likely have increasing effects on the groundwater of California's eastern Mojave Desert.

In the western Mojave, sprawling development replaces and fragments desert habitat. Growing communities require additional rights-of-way for power lines, pipelines, and roads, further fragmenting habitat. This pattern and density of growth dramatically increases the severity of development's effects on wildlife (Hunter et al. 2003).

Development also increases pressure to overdraw groundwater. Groundwater levels began dropping as a result of overdrafting in the 1950s, drying up riverbeds, springs, and seeps and diminishing riparian ecosystems that depend on flowing water and saturated soils. The new water demands of rapid growth also reduce the options for recharging and restoring groundwater levels.

For more than a decade, federal, state, and local wildlife- and land-management agencies have worked to develop a multispecies regional conservation plan for the rapidly growing

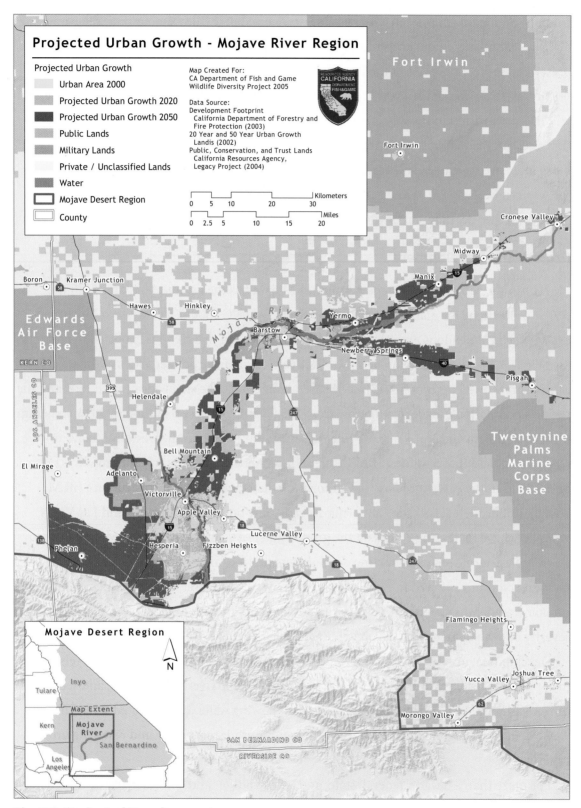

Fig. 7.3: Projected Development
The rapid growth in the Mojave River basin is fragmenting habitat and increasing demands on groundwater resources.

western Mojave. Its purpose is to conserve and protect the threatened desert tortoise and Mohave ground squirrel and nearly 50 other sensitive plants and animals and the natural communities of which they are a part, while accommodating anticipated rapid growth and development in the region (BLM 2005b). The challenge of developing the Plan is to design scientifically supported conservation measures and land-use restrictions that will ensure the long-term survival of all native species. The West Mojave Plan, as currently proposed, envisions that the conservation of species would occur primarily on existing public lands managed by BLM. A very limited amount of additional private lands within the proposed conservation area would be purchased or protected, in conjunction with facilitating development and expansion of desert cities and communities. This is not consistent with the other Southern California regional conservation planning efforts, because it will provide BLM funding to be used for conservation of species on lands they already manage rather than securing protection of species on important lands that are at risk of being developed (Morey 2003, 2005).

Groundwater Overdrafting and Loss of Riparian Habitat

Scattered riparian and spring ecosystems are the oases that serve as habitat for 75 percent of desert wildlife species, allowing them to exist and make use of the vast adjacent dry habitats. The Mojave River and the Amargosa River corridors are the major arteries of life for the Mojave Desert region, providing vital habitat for wildlife.

Surface water flows the length of the Mojave on average only once every 6 to 10 years. Perennial surface water had existed at three reaches of the river, in the Victorville-Helendale corridor, at Camp Cady east of Barstow, and in Afton Canyon. In the Victorville area, perennial surface water now exists at the Fish and Game–managed regional park and downstream in the Oro Grande area. Both owe their existence to some degree of discharges from adjacent water users—the Mojave Narrows Fish Hatchery and the Victor Valley Water Reclamation Authority. Local pumping has so lowered the water table at Camp Cady that no natural surface water has existed since the early 1990s. The record storm of early 2005, along with the purchase of water rights immediately upstream, may allow return of seeps and small ponds. Local faults and underlying clay layers create the conditions for the riparian corridor in the Victorville area as well as Camp Cady. However, local heavy pumping endangers these areas (Bilhorn 2005 pers. comm., CDFG 2004e, MWA 2004).

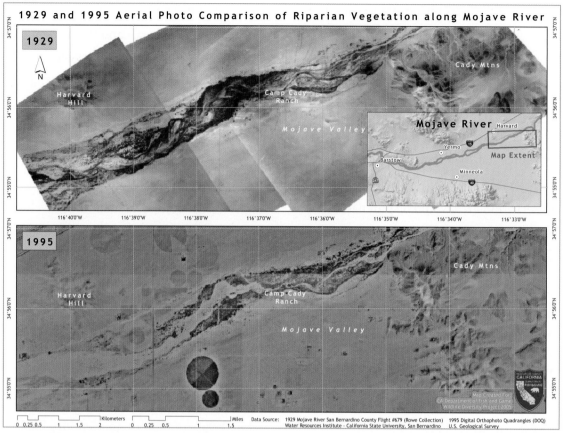

Fig 7.4: Riparian Vegetation Comparisons
The 1995 aerial photograph compared to the 1929 aerial photograph shows the dramatic decline in riparian vegetation along the Mojave River corridor. This riparian habitat decline is largely attributed to the receding groundwater levels.

Groundwater pumping for agricultural, industrial, and domestic uses in the Mojave Desert has lowered groundwater levels. Throughout the Mojave River basin, springs and riparian areas have dried up, causing water-stressed cottonwoods, willows, and mesquite to perish. In some areas, where groundwater levels dropped 7–10 feet, more than 50 percent of the cottonwood trees have perished. (See Fig. 7.4, Riparian Vegetation Comparisons.) Where the water table has dropped by 20 feet beneath the Mojave River, 95 percent of has died. Many of the remaining areas of the riparian corridor are dominated by tamarisk (saltcedar), an exotic plant that invades areas where the native riparian habitat is stressed. Tamarisk roots can reach deeper for water, causing groundwater to recede farther (Lines 1996b and 1999b, Smith 1999).

Development and demand for water have grown dramatically in the region. While natural inflows to the basin during the last decade have exceeded the long-term average, studies indicate that groundwater levels have continued to drop. The human population in the Mojave region is expected to double over the next 30 years. Pressure to further overdraft groundwater in the Mojave basin will be intense, as the projected annual water deficit for the area will reach 60,000–80,000 acre-feet (AF) by the year 2020. The drafting of groundwater would be about double the average annual natural recharge of the aquifer (MWA 2004).

The 1995 court adjudication of water rights in the Mojave Basin, resolving conflicts among 1,000 groundwater pumpers, has provided a framework for managing and controlling groundwater production. The adjudication also established the Biological Resource Trust Fund, a $1 million revolving fund, which currently receives 65 cents (a figure that is indexed to inflation) per acre-foot of pumped water to support mitigation of damaged riparian habitat where agreed-upon groundwater levels have not been reached. However, this fund is not adequate to fully mitigate for declining riparian habitat. Today, groundwater levels along some sections of the Mojave River have receded below the safe levels as defined in the adjudication, and riparian habitat continues to decline (CDFG 2004e).

Stabilizing and increasing groundwater levels, in part by recharging overdrafted sub-basins, are essential to maintaining riparian habitats, allowing riparian-dependent wildlife to return to several sections of the Mojave River and adjacent streambeds. The Mojave Water Agency (MWA) has developed a plan to recharge the groundwater basin that would require importing about 59,000 AF of water per year by 2020 to maintain groundwater at levels that would support riparian habitats along the river and its tributaries. Recharging the region will likely require increasing water purchases from the State Water Project and other outside sources.

Groundwater overdrafting also imperils the Amargosa River basin riparian habitat and wetlands, and groundwater pumping in the Amargosa Valley and in the upstream watershed is expected to increase. Increasing water use by expanding residential communities is projected in the upper basin region of Amargosa Valley and Pahrump, Nev. Ten thousand new homes have already been approved for construction in the community of Pahrump. In addition, the city of Las Vegas also is seeking to tap into the groundwater basins of the surrounding rural areas in Nye County, Nev. The Pahrump Valley is itself short of water for predicted local growth and is among the areas being examined to export water to Las Vegas (Christian 2005 pers. comm., Moyle 2002). If the Amargosa River Basin is overdrafted, wildlife diversity will decline in Ash Meadows, the Amargosa Canyon, and in Death Valley National Park as the Amargosa riparian corridor withers.

Inappropriate Off-Road Vehicle Use

Desert plant communities of the Mojave Desert are thousands of years old, and much of the long-lived vegetation established roots several hundred to several thousand years before the first European explorers set foot on the West Coast (Koehler et al. 2005, Van Devender 1999, Vasek 1995, Vasek and Barbour 1988). Limited by available moisture, plants grow slowly over decades. Soil structure and the biological soil crust upon which plants and animals depend were created by processes over millennia (Belnap 2002, Boarman and Berry 1995, Cody 2000, Haley and Bainbridge 1999, Lovich and Bainbridge 1999). Unique species of mammals, reptiles, and birds have evolved in association with these ancient habitats.

The impacts of off-road vehicles on these fragile desert landscapes have been described by scientists and resource managers for more than 30 years (Stebbins et al. 1978, Webb and Wilshire 1983). The 1980 California Desert Conservation Area Plan referred to off-road vehicles as the "most pervasive management issue in the area." Along with direct collisions with desert tortoises and other wildlife and the crushing of animal burrows, off-road vehicles compact soils, induce erosion, spread invasive plant species, and denude the landscape of vegetation. Off-road driving or riding has essentially a nonrestorable impact on some desert habitat; damaged soils and perennial vegetation are not likely to recover for several hundred years or more (Haley and Bainbridge 1999). Revegetation efforts on disturbed upland areas of the Mojave are expensive and have had little success.

The number of off-road vehicle registrations in California has more than doubled since 1980, and the rapid growth of the numbers of off-highway vehicle recreationists continues. In addition to resident recreationists, the Mojave Desert attracts 2 million off-road vehicle visitors annually. While the vast majority of motorcyclists and all-terrain vehicle riders are responsibly recreating at designated off-road vehicle parks or on designated trails and roads on public lands, many others are carving new trails across threatened desert tortoise and Mohave ground squirrel habitat, often across sensitive habitats in closed portions of designated Areas of Critical Environmental Concern (ACEC). For example, BLM closed the 18,000-acre West Rand ACEC to off-road vehicle use in 2002 due to extensive damage to critical habitat for the desert tortoise. However, off-road vehicle users have routinely violated the closure (DMG 2002b).

While desert planning efforts attempt to minimize off-road vehicle damage to natural resources by designating open, limited use, and closed areas, damage to natural resources continues. The lack of public education regarding the rules and road networks, lack of ad-

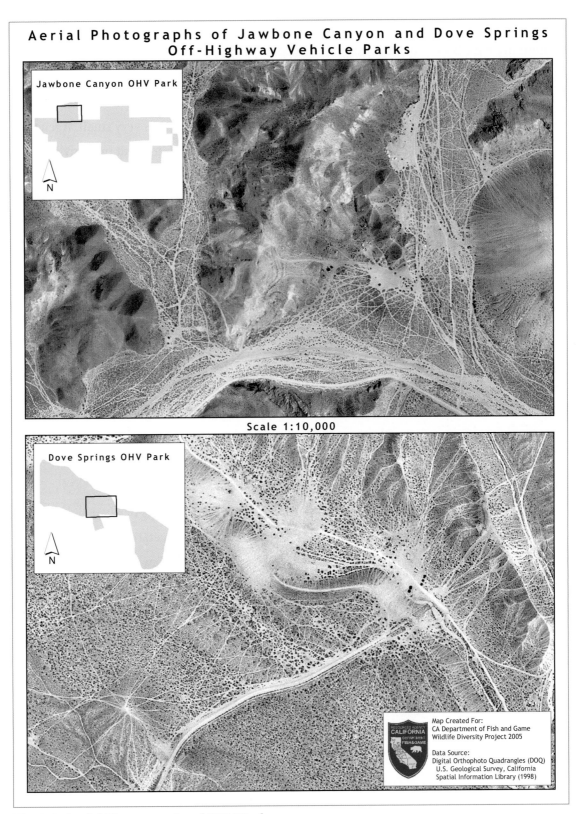

Aerial Photographs of Jawbone Canyon and Dove Springs Off-Highway Vehicle Parks

Jawbone Canyon OHV Park

N

Scale 1:10,000

Dove Springs OHV Park

N

Map Created For:
CA Department of Fish and Game
Wildlife Diversity Project 2005

Data Source:
Digital Orthophoto Quadrangles (DOQ)
U.S. Geological Survey, California
Spatial Information Library (1998)

Fig. 7.5: Aerial Photographs of OHV Parks
Off-road vehicle tracks can clearly be seen. Some tracks continue out of the OHV Park and into Areas of Critical Environmental Concern (ACEC).

equate enforcement staff, and outright defiance by a small segment of the off-road vehicle community have thwarted efforts to protect wildlife and vegetation, including areas around desert springs and other sensitive sites.

Only two or three BLM rangers per 1 million acres are assigned to patrol the Mojave Desert, so the risk of receiving a citation for riding in restricted areas is very small. Agencies in the region have posted signs indicating where vehicles are prohibited, but in many areas this is futile. BLM concluded in the June 2003 Decision Record for the Western Mojave Desert Off-Road Vehicle Designation Project:

> "The least effective short-term action taken in the Ord Mountains was signing the closed route network. Not only did this effort consume a great deal of staff time; in addition, signs were removed almost as quickly as they were put up. The need to resign routes placed additional demands on scarce staff time and material."

The Decision Record also revealed that BLM was unable to keep off-road vehicles out of sensitive areas. The frequent destruction of signs led BLM to sign the open route network and to cease signing the closed areas, reasoning that people are less likely to destroy "open area" signs than "closed area" signs. While this saves signs, this policy makes it difficult to inform recreationists where off-road vehicle activities are prohibited, providing less protection for important habitats. Even though the route-designation decision for the western Mojave area was signed by BLM in June 2003, the route designations have not been implemented (Aardahl 2005 pers. comm.).

Sensitive habitats are particularly at risk where off-road vehicle parks or open areas are located on lands adjacent to those habitats. For example, riparian vegetation in the Jawbone-Butterbredt ACEC is routinely crossed by vehicles straying from the Jawbone and Dove Spring Canyon off-highway vehicle open areas (See Aerial Photographs of Jawbone Canyon and Dove Springs Off-Highway Vehicle Parks, Fig. 7.5). The El Mirage and the Spangler Hills off-highway vehicle open areas are contiguous to the Fremont-Kramer Desert Wildlife Management Area (DMG 2002b).

Excessive Livestock Grazing

Excessive livestock grazing has altered ecosystems across the Mojave. Grazing has been particularly detrimental to the wetland and riparian habitats important for maintaining wildlife diversity in the desert, denuding and eroding fragile soils around rivers, springs, and seeps and polluting scarce surface water. Livestock reshape streambeds and trample and consume vegetation and seedlings of native trees and shrubs, preventing regeneration.

Grazing has also altered the desert scrub ecosystems, reducing preferred native shrubs and herbaceous plants that support the desert tortoise and other reptiles, the Mohave ground squirrel, and other small mammals, birds, and butterflies (Avery 1999). Heavy grazing also facilitates the spread of cheatgrass and other invasive annual grasses, replacing native grasses, herbs, and perennial shrubs, further diminishing habitat conditions for wildlife (Barbour et al. 1993). In turn, fires are more frequent where invasive annual grasses are abundant, preventing the natural restoration of native vegetation and further disturbing habitat for native wildlife.

Since 1994, nearly 60,000 **Animal Unit Months** (AUMs) for cattle have been approved by BLM on 3.5 million acres of the Mojave Desert region spread across 25 allotments (USFWS 1994c). (An animal unit month is defined as the amount of forage required to sustain one cow and calf or one horse or five sheep for one month.) In some portions of the Mojave, livestock grazing has been reduced to lessen impacts on the desert tortoise and other wildlife. Since 1991, BLM has prohibited domestic sheep grazing on 800,000 acres of desert tortoise critical habitat and has implemented seasonal restrictions on cattle grazing in some allotments to protect tortoises (USGAO 2002). The National Park Service has dramatically reduced grazing in the Mojave National Preserve. Sheep grazing has been halted in tortoise habitat of San Bernardino County, based on agreement among scientists and resource agencies that sheep grazing significantly degraded feed and habitat for the threatened desert tortoise. However, sheep and cattle continue to graze in wildlife habitats, including desert tortoise habitat, in the western Mojave areas within Inyo and Kern Counties (DMG 2002b). Cattle graze within ACECs and in areas designated as critical habitat for the desert tortoise, and they continue to degrade riparian habitats vital to numerous birds and mammals (BLM 2005b).

Excessive Burro and Horse Grazing

The 1971 Wild Free-Roaming Horses and Burros Act requires BLM to manage wild free-roaming horses and burros "in a manner designed to achieve and maintain a thriving natural ecological balance on public lands." The bureau is also required to remove horses and burros where overpopulation exists "in order to restore a thriving ecological balance to the range."

Although they have inhabited the West since the end of the 16th century, burros and horses have likely grazed the California desert in significant numbers since they were released by settlers and miners in the 1800s (Beever 2003, McKnight 1958). Descendents of wild asses from northeastern Africa, burros are well-adapted to the desert environment, and they readily propagate in Mojave Desert habitats where water and forage occur. Horses, although less adapted to the desert, have established herds in a few areas. BLM established appropriate management levels (AMLs) for burro and horse herds in the Mojave Desert pursuant to the amended California Desert Plan of 1980. The levels were mostly established in the 1980s, based on the range capacity for grazing rather than on limits that would protect wildlife habitat and sensitive plant and animal species.

The AMLs for burro and horse numbers are often greatly exceeded. Between 1981 and 1987, 18,700 burros were removed from the desert, but, since 1987, efforts to control burros have been limited due to lack of funding. Today there are 13 burro- and a few horse-herd areas in the Mojave region. Burro numbers exceed the AML in five of the 13 herd areas. In one management area, there are 280 horses where the AML is 168 horses (BLM 2004b).

Excessive burro numbers have led to overgrazing and degradation of desert resources. Riparian habitats associated with seeps and springs are often denuded and trampled by burros and horses. Water quality at seeps and springs frequented by burros or horses is usually poor due to accumulated sediment, urine, and feces. Feral burros and horses, exotic animals in the desert, place additional stress on the natural ecological balance of sensitive desert habitats (Aardahl 2005 pers. comm., La Pre 2004 pers. comm.).

Invasive Plants

Numerous exotic non-native plants have altered plant communities across large areas of the Mojave Desert, outcompeting native species and degrading upland and riparian habitats for native wildlife. Invasive annual grasses and **forbs** have displaced native plants, often greatly diminishing the native forage for the desert tortoise, lizards, birds, and small mammals. These exotic grasses and forbs now dominate plant communities throughout the region. In desert tortoise critical habitat of the western Mojave, exotic plants account for more than 60 percent of the annual vegetative biomass (Berry 1999, Brooks and Matchett 2002, DeFalco and Brooks 1999). Some invasive plants, such as Saharan mustard, continue to spread across the region.

The abundance of exotic forbs and annual grasses (particularly *Schismus barbaratis, S. arabicus,* and *Bromus madritenus rubens*) increases the fuel and continuity of fuels, facilitating more-frequent and hotter fires. This destroys the less-fire-intolerant native plants and facilitates other exotic plants that thrive in disturbed areas, further transforming the plant communities (Brooks and Matchett 2002, Brooks and Pyke 2001, D'Antonio 2000).

Imported tamarisk, a plant of inferior habitat value for native wildlife, has replaced native cottonwoods and willows in much of the riparian habitat of the Mojave River and of other watercourses in the region. A 1995 survey found that tamarisk dominated half of the 10,000 acres of riparian habitat along the Mojave River (Holmes et al. 2001, Lines 1999a). The leaves of tamarisk concentrate and shed salts, degrading soil conditions for native plants (Smith 1999). Tamarisk is more drought tolerant than native cottonwood trees and willows. In areas where groundwater levels are receding, tamarisk outcompetes water-stressed native plants (Cleverly et al. 1997, Lovich 2000).

Various local, state, and federal agencies have implemented projects to remove and control tamarisk. However, the priority areas for tamarisk removal and habitat restoration do not correspond to jurisdictional boundaries. The Desert Managers Group is coordinating a regional response to restoring riparian habitats invaded by tamarisk and is seeking funding for the regional effort (DMG 2004).

In 2002, local, state, and federal agencies signed the Mojave Weed Management Area (WMA) Memorandum of Understanding (MOU), which spells out a coordinated planning effort to prevent, control, and eradicate weeds and to educate the public about weed control in the region (DMG 2002a). The MOU identifies a priority list of species to control in the Mojave. Implementation of the Mojave WMA plan is limited by available funding.

Table 7.3: Mojave Weed Management Area Target Species

Ailanthus altissima	Tree of Heaven
Alhagi camelorum	Camel thorn
Arundo donax	Giant reed
Brassica tournefortii	Sahara mustard
Bromus madritensis	Red brome
Centaurea solstitialis	Yellow starthistle
Halogeton glomeratus	Halogeton
Linaria dalmatic	Dalmation toadflax
Pennisetium setaceum	Fountain grass
Salsola tragus	Russian thistle
Solanum elaegnifolium	White horsenettle
Tamarix ramosissima	Tamarisk (saltcedar)
Tribulus terrestris	Puncture vine

Military Land Management Conflicts

Military training activities utilize large areas of the Mojave landscape. Bases and training centers occupy 2.6 million acres, or 13 percent, of the land area. Some of the most degraded lands and some of the most pristine habitats are on lands managed by the Department of Defense. In areas of the U.S. Army's National Training Center at Fort Irwin and the Marine Corps Air Ground Combat Center at Twentynine Palms, where warfare is practiced with heavy tracked armored vehicles, significant tracts are nearly denuded of plants, and the soils are hard packed. However, in other areas of Fort Irwin, Edwards Air Force Base, and China Lake Naval Air Weapons Station (NAWS) there exist some of the best representative habitats of the desert region, protected from public access and destructive land uses. There is no formal protection for these quality habitats; thus, as the military's mission evolves, base operations may change, with consequences for the remaining good habitat areas (Jones 2004 pers. comm., Lynn 2005 pers. comm.).

Military bases and operations affect wildlife habitat in two ways: Construction of base facilities and support communities eliminates and fragments wildlife habitats, much like other development, and field training, with tank maneuvers and air-to-ground bombing, can damage habitat (Lovich and Bainbridge 1999, USFWS 1994c).

Expanding base infrastructure and areas of heavy use would cause the additional loss of important habitat for the desert tortoise and other species. Fort Irwin, for example, has annexed an additional 110,000 acres to expand its training area, causing the loss of desert tortoise and Mohave ground squirrel habitat. Mitigation for this base expansion will involve relocating hundreds of tortoises, buying out and retiring the cattle-grazing permits on other lands to improve conditions for these species, and acquiring private land that is critical habitat for the desert tortoise (LaRue 2000, Lynn 2005 pers. comm.).

Federal law requires the military to prepare and implement an Integrated Natural Resources Management Plan (INRMP) for each military installation to address the management and conservation of wildlife habitats and species. Significant funding is allocated to implement these plans and, in particular, implement the plan provisions to address threatened and endangered species. State and federal wildlife agencies are consulted in the development of the INRMPs. However, their input is only advisory, and their recommendations regarding actions to protect species may or may not be incorporated into the plans.

Department of Defense conservation staff are actively involved in cooperative efforts with state and federal agencies and some nongovernment organizations to conduct wildlife research and to implement conservation projects. For example, Edwards Air Force Base has installed fencing to protect critical desert tortoise habitat and has cleaned up tortoise hazards by plugging 42 old mine shafts and wells. On China Lake NAWS there is one of the few remaining populations of Mohave tui chub, and that station's staff monitor the population. The military is a member of the Desert Managers Group and is an important partner, engaged in research, conservation, and restoration (DMG 2002a, 2002b, 2002c, 2005).

Mining Operations

Mineral commodities extracted from the Mojave Desert include lead, zinc, gold, silver, copper, sand, gravel, limestone, gypsum, sodium, and borates. The desert also provides minerals from evaporative deposits that are used in filtration systems, chemical refining, ceramics, and drilling muds. In 1990, nearly 40 percent of the gold extracted in California came from the Mojave Desert. Gold mining continues to be important in the region. In the West Mojave, there are 160 authorized mining plans, with operations at about 25 mines at any one time. Most active mines are on fewer than 10 acres each (BLM 2003a, Lovich and Bainbridge 1999, Schoenherr 1992).

On BLM-managed lands, approved mining operation plans are required if a project will remove 1,000 tons of material, five acres are disturbed, or the mining activity is proposed on lands classified as multiple-use areas, Areas of Critical Environmental Concern, endangered species critical habitat, national wilderness preservation system lands, national monument, or other protected sites. Mining plans may include approval for disposing of mine wastes on public lands.

Mining has harsh environmental impacts in localized areas scattered across the Mojave Desert. At thousands of mine sites in the desert, mining roads, tailing mounds, pits, ore piles, and chemical runoff scar the natural landscape. Pit mining and dry-lakebed mineral projects are sources of chemical-laden dust that drifts, depositing it over large land areas. Uncovered mine leachate ponds are a hazard for waterfowl, shorebirds, bats, and other species. Cyanide-heap leaching of gold recovery operations has the potential to kill a variety of wildlife if not properly managed. Also, renewed earth-moving and mining operations around old mine sites can destroy important bat roosts.

Conservation Actions to Restore and Conserve Wildlife

In addition to the recommended regional actions described below, see the recommended statewide conservation actions as given in Chapter 4 and action "b" in the Colorado Desert chapter related to the Lower Colorado River Multi-Species Conservation Plan.

a. Improve stewardship on federally managed lands to protect wildlife diversity.

- Congress should allocate significantly greater staff and resources to BLM for implementation of wildlife conservation activities, habitat restoration, and enforcement of off-road vehicle and grazing restrictions.

- Congress should fund BLM and its partner federal and state agencies to fully implement the Desert Tortoise Recovery Plan and the wildlife protection provisions of the Northern and Eastern amendments to the CDCA Plan (including the special protections for the Ivanpah-Shadow and Piute Eldorado DWMAs and for the Afton Canyon, Amargosa River, and Carson Slough ACECs).

- Congress should fund BLM to fully implement the wildlife protections authorized for ACECs throughout the Mojave region. Activity Plans for the ACECs should be updated and implemented. Goals for enforcement should be established and implemented in these special habitat areas to prevent habitat degradation by unauthorized activities.

b. Stabilize groundwater levels and recharge depleted sub-basins of the Mojave River Basin, restoring groundwater to levels that support riparian habitat.

- The court-adjudicated groundwater management agreement of the Mojave River Basin should continue to ramp down the free production rights for groundwater and use all means possible to increase importation of water to alleviate the current groundwater overdraft and to meet growth demands.

- The state should consider providing matching funds to be used in conjunction with funds of the Biological Resources Trust Fund for the benefit of restoring riparian habitat along the Mojave River corridor.

- The Wildlife Conservation Board, federal resource agencies, and nongovernmental conservation organizations should secure additional water rights throughout the basin for wildlife resources. Additional agricultural lands with water rights should be purchased to set aside water for wildlife resources.

c. Stabilize groundwater levels and secure wet habitats in the Amargosa River Basin. This action will help protect the endangered Amargosa vole and the Amargosa pupfish, among other species.

- California and Nevada should establish a groundwater overdraft prevention policy for the Amargosa Basin and seek agreement on an MOU to implement the policy. Federal legislation should protect the groundwater and wet habitats of the Amargosa River Basin if the states cannot resolve the issues.

- The State Water Resources Control Board should work with federal agencies and nongovernmental organizations to secure water rights for wildlife and riparian habitat in the basin.

- BLM should fully document water resources, wildlife, and biological attributes in the Amargosa River ACEC and assess instream flow requirements to maintain aquatic ecosystems and wildlife resources within the ACEC and the Kingston Range Wilderness Area.

d. Provide maximum federal and state protection for remaining riparian, spring, seep, and wetland habitats, and restore degraded riparian, spring, seep, and wetland areas.

See Statewide Action g, Chapter 4.

Conserving these wet habitats is key for maintaining wildlife diversity in the desert.

- State and federal wildlife and land management agencies should create a Mojave Riparian and Spring Habitat Taskforce to provide oversight and focus to restore and protect these habitats.

- The state should establish a riparian, spring, and wetland habitat degradation-prevention policy for the desert. Flood control and other activities should be excluded from riparian, spring, and wetland areas unless they are proven not to have a negative effect on ecosystem function and wildlife diversity.

- State and federal agencies should expand efforts to work with ranchers to conserve and restore riparian habitats on private lands. Such efforts may involve developing water sources outside of riparian areas and then excluding livestock from these habitats.

- State and federal land management agencies should work with the off-road vehicle community to reduce impacts of off-road vehicles on sensitive riparian, spring, and wetland habitats and establish half-mile buffers around identified sensitive sites.

- Federal land managers should continue to reduce burro and horse numbers where they have a detrimental effect on riparian and other sensitive habitats for wildlife by assessing the number of burros and horses on the specific sensitive sites, and calculating and implementing new appropriate management levels of burros and horses that will protect these sites.

- BLM managers should seek funding to fully implement the provisions of the California Desert Conservation Act Plan for protection and restoration of unusual plant assemblages classified as wetland riparian.

e. The Bureau of Land Management should improve, and, upon approval, implement the West Mojave Plan with conservation measures to address all special status species and to maintain wildlife diversity.

- The proposed West Mojave Plan must provide scientifically sound measures to ensure recovery of the Mohave ground squirrel and the desert tortoise and the protection of other species covered in the plan in a manner that precludes the need to consider listing them in the future. The proposed plan identifies 49 species that it would cover and make eligible for take permits pursuant to state and federal endangered species law (Morey 2005).

- The plan should assist in funding protective measures called for in previously approved conservation and recovery plans and ACEC management plans.

- The plan should provide for independent monitoring of species and ecosystems and have a mechanism to adapt conservation measures to new information and changes in the status of species.

- The plan should include a reliable funding plan, supported by the Department of Interior, for additional BLM positions, conservation activities, and adaptive management that would be described in the implementation agreement and is above and beyond existing management obligations.

f. Reduce off-road vehicle damage to wildlife habitats.

- State and federal wildlife agencies should work with State Parks and federal land managers to identify and permit additional sites for quality off-road vehicle recreation where there would be minimal conflict with wildlife restoration and conservation goals.

- State and federal land management agencies should identify all off-highway vehicle open-area boundaries and provide adequate driver/rider education and increased enforcement.

- Enlarge exclusion buffer areas between off-highway vehicle parks and sensitive closed areas. Avoid designating parks and open areas for these vehicles near closed areas for sensitive habitat.

- Increase fines and penalties for illegal off-highway vehicle use at designated riparian and sensitive-habitat closed areas.

- Provide land managers with adequate staff and resources to manage and enforce off-highway vehicle activities.

g. Federal, state, and local agencies should provide greater resources and coordinate efforts to eradicate or control existing occurrences of invasive species and to prevent new introductions.

See Statewide Action g, Chapter 4.

- Increase funding for coordinated regional efforts to remove tamarisk and restore riparian ecosystems.

- Increase funds for research on biological control of Sahara mustard and other prolific invasive species.

h. Fully implement the recovery plans for the Mojave tui chub, Amargosa vole, and Inyo California towhee.

- Update regional conservation plans to meet the requirements for recovery of species as identified in the recovery plans.

- Devote adequate resources to update and implement the recovery plans.

i. Fish and Game, BLM, and the three military bases that support the Mohave ground squirrel should develop a collaborative conservation and recovery strategy for the Mohave ground squirrel so that federal listing is not necessary.

The conservation strategy should include field studies and genetic analyses to clarify the status of squirrel populations and a plan to acquire squirrel habitat core areas and connecting corridors.

Colorado Desert Region

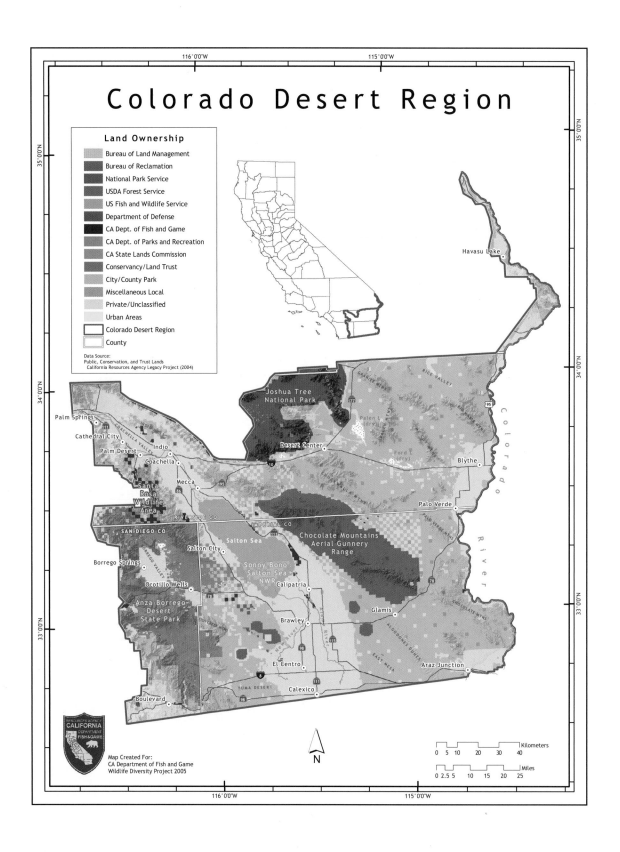

Land Ownership

- Bureau of Land Management
- Bureau of Reclamation
- National Park Service
- USDA Forest Service
- US Fish and Wildlife Service
- Department of Defense
- CA Dept. of Fish and Game
- CA Dept. of Parks and Recreation
- CA State Lands Commission
- Conservancy/Land Trust
- City/County Park
- Miscellaneous Local
- Private/Unclassified
- Urban Areas
- Colorado Desert Region
- County

Data Source:
Public, Conservation, and Trust Lands
California Resources Agency Legacy Project (2004)

CALIFORNIA
DEPARTMENT
FISH&GAME

Map Created For:
CA Department of Fish and Game
Wildlife Diversity Project 2005

N

Kilometers
0 5 10   20   30   40

Miles
0 2.5 5   10   15   20   25

8 *Colorado Desert Region*

Tim Palmer

Clifornia's Colorado Desert is part of the larger Sonoran Desert, which extends across southwest North America. The Colorado Desert region encompasses approximately 7 million acres, reaching from the Mexican border in the south to the higher-elevation Mojave Desert in the north and from the Colorado River in the east to the Peninsular mountain range in the west.

Most of the Colorado Desert lies at a relatively low elevation, below 1,000 feet, with the lowest point of the desert floor at 275 feet below sea level in the Salton Trough. Although the highest peaks of the Peninsular Range reach elevations of nearly 10,000 feet, most of the region's mountains do not exceed 3,000 feet. These ranges block moist coastal air and rains, producing the region's arid climate.

The Colorado Desert's climate distinguishes it from other deserts. The region experiences greater summer daytime temperatures than higher-elevation deserts and almost never receives frost. In addition, the Colorado Desert, especially toward the southern portion of the region, has two rainy seasons per year, in the winter and late summer, while the more northerly Mojave Desert receives only winter rains.

The region's terrestrial habitats include creosote bush scrub; mixed scrub, including yucca and cholla cactus; desert saltbush; sandy soil grasslands; and desert dunes. Higher elevations are dominated by pinyon pine and California juniper, with areas of manzanita and Coulter pine. In addition to hardy perennials, more than half of the desert's plant species are herbaceous annuals, and appropriately timed winter rains produce abundant early spring wildflowers. In the southern portion of the region, the additional moisture supplied by summer rainfall fosters the germination of summer annual plants and supports smoketree, ironwood, and palo verde trees. Common desert wildlife include mule deer, bobcat, desert kangaroo rat, cactus mouse, black-tailed jackrabbit, Gambel's quail, and red-diamond rattlesnake. Among **sensitive species** are flat-tailed horned lizard, Coachella Valley fringe-toed lizard, desert tortoise, prairie falcon, Andrews' dune scarab beetle, Peninsular bighorn sheep, and California leaf-nosed bat.

In the Colorado Desert's arid environment, aquatic and wetland habitats are limited in extent but are critically important to wildlife. Groundwater springs and runoff from seasonal rains form canyon-mouth-associated alluvial fans, desert arroyos, desert fan palm oases, freshwater marshes, brine lakes, desert washes, ephemeral and perennial streams, and riparian vegetation communities dominated by cottonwood, willow, and non-native tamarisk. Two of the region's most significant aquatic systems are the Salton Sea and the Colorado River.

While most desert wildlife depend on aquatic habitats as water sources, a number of species, such as arroyo toad, desert pupfish, Yuma clapper rail, and southwestern willow flycatcher, are restricted to these habitats. In some places, summer rains produce short-lived seasonal pools that host uncommon species, such as Couch's spadefoot toad.

Desert fan palm oases are rare ecological communities found only in the Colorado Desert. They occur only where permanent water sources are available, such as at springs or along fault lines, where groundwater is forced to the surface by the movement of hard, impermeable rock (NPS 2002), and can be found in the San Jacinto, Santa Rosa, and Little San Bernardino mountains, Indio and Mecca-Orocopia hills, and in the canyons of Anza Borrego Desert State Park. With an **overstory** of desert fan palm trees, these communities provide unique islands of shade, moisture, and vegetation in an otherwise arid and sparse landscape. Fan palm oases host species found nowhere else in the desert, like the two-inch, blue-black, giant palm-boring beetle, which is **endemic** to this community, and the Western yellow bat, which is strongly associated with this habitat. The oases also allow a number of other species, normally found in more **mesic** coastal and forest environments, to live in the desert, including California mountain king snake, gopher snake, Western screech-owl, bobcat, and hooded oriole (Barrows 2005 pers. comm.).

Public lands in the desert are managed by several different federal and state agencies, all of which have differing sets of missions that often expand beyond wildlife conservation. The Bureau of Land Management (BLM) is the Colorado Desert region's largest land manager, with about 2.9 million acres, or 43.1 percent of the region. Department of Defense lands account for about 500,000 acres, or 7 percent, of the region. A number of other public landholdings occur around the Salton Sea, with the California Department of Parks and Recreation, the Department of Fish and Game, and the U.S. Fish and Wildlife Service managing lands along and under the sea. Joshua Tree National Park spans the transition from the Mojave to the Colorado Desert, with slightly less than half the park, about 340,000 acres, in the Colorado Desert. Anza Borrego Desert State Park encompasses over 600,000 acres, or nearly 9 percent, of the region, and the Santa Rosa Wildlife Area, which includes Fish and Game, State Lands Commission, and BLM lands, encompasses about 100,000 acres. Together, Joshua Tree National Park, Anza Borrego Desert State Park, and the Santa Rosa Wildlife Area, along with other protected lands in the Mojave Desert, are part of the Mojave and Colorado Deserts Biosphere Reserve, designated by the United Nations as an important global site for preservation of the biological and cultural resources of these two desert regions.

Although the Colorado Desert remains one of the least-populous regions in California, human activities have had substantial impacts on the region's habitats and wildlife. Many unique communities, particularly aquatic and dune systems, are limited in distribution and separated by vast expanses of inhospitable, arid desert terrain. Even limited human disturbances can have markedly deleterious effects on the endemic and sensitive species supported by these unique regional systems.

Some of the greatest human-caused effects on the region have resulted from the water diversions and flood control measures along the Colorado River. These measures have dramatically altered the region's hydrology by redistributing the region's water supply to large expanses of irrigated agriculture and metropolitan coastal areas. The once-dynamic Salton Sea and Colorado River ecosystems are now controlled by human water management. Because of the scarcity of water resources in the desert environment, these alterations have had substantial impacts on regional wildlife and habitats. In addition, portions of the region are experiencing substantial growth and development pressures, most notably the Coachella Valley.

Species at Risk

The Plan development team updated vertebrate and invertebrate species information in the California Natural Diversity Database (CNDDB) during 2004–2005. The following regional summary of numbers of wildlife species, endemic species, and **species at risk** is derived from the updated CNDDB.

The diverse wildlife inhabiting the Colorado Desert include many species specially adapted to the unique desert habitats. There are 481 vertebrate species that inhabit the Colorado Desert region at some point in their life cycle, including 282 birds, 82 mammals, 66 reptiles, 16 amphibians, and 35 fish. Of the total vertebrate species that inhabit this region, 84 bird **taxa**, 34 mammalian taxa, 21 reptilian taxa, five amphibian taxa, and four fish taxa are included on the **Special Animals List**. Of these, four are endemic to the Colorado Desert region, and four other species found here are endemic to California but not restricted to this region (Table 8.1).

Table 8.1: State-Endemic Special Status Vertebrates of the Colorado Desert Region

	Anniella pulchra pulchra	Silvery legless lizard
*	*Batrachoseps major aridus*	Desert slender salamander
	Gopherus agassizii	Desert tortoise
	Lampropeltis zonata	California mountain kingsnake (San Diego population)
	Ovis canadensis nelsoni dps	Peninsular bighorn sheep
*	*Perognathus longimembris bangsi*	Palm Springs pocket mouse
	Spermophilus tereticaudus chlorus	Palm Springs round-tailed ground squirrel
*	*Uma inornata*	Coachella Valley fringe-toed lizard
*	*Xantusia gracilis*	Sandstone night lizard

* denotes taxon is endemic to region

The number of arthropod species is so great, and they are so poorly known taxonomically, that it is presently impossible to accurately estimate the total number of invertebrate species occurring in the state. In the Colorado Desert region, however, 15 invertebrate taxa are included on the Special Animals List, including 12 arthropod taxa and three mollusk taxa. Of these, eight are endemic to the Colorado Desert region, and five other taxa found here are endemic to California but not restricted to this region (Table 8.2).

Table 8.2: State-Endemic Special Status Invertebrates of the Colorado Desert Region

*	*Anomala carlsoni*	Carlson's dune beetle
*	*Anomala hardyorum*	Hardys' dune beetle
	Calileptoneta oasa	A leptonetid spider; no common name
*	*Ceratochrysis bradleyi*	Bradley's chrysidid wasp
*	*Dinacoma caseyi*	Casey's June beetle
*	*Eremarionta immaculata*	White desertsnail
	Eremarionta morongoana	Morongo (=Colorado) desertsnail
*	*Eremarionta rowelli mccoiana*	California McCoy snail
*	*Hedychridium argenteum*	A chrysidid wasp; no common name
	Macrobaenetes valgum	Coachella giant sand treader cricket
	Parnopes borregoensis	A chrysidid wasp; no common name
*	*Pseudocotalpa andrewsi*	Andrews' dune scarab beetle
	Stenopelmatus cahuilaensis	Coachella Valley Jerusalem cricket

* denotes taxon is endemic to region

The Wildlife Species Matrix, including data on listing status, habitat association, and population trend for each vertebrate and invertebrate species included on the Special Animals List, is available on the Web at http://www.dfg.ca.gov/habitats/wdp/matrix_search.asp. For vertebrates, the matrix also includes links to species-level range maps. Additionally, a link to the California Department of Fish and Game's online Field Survey Form is available to assist in reporting positive sightings of species on the Special Animals List to the California Natural Diversity Database (CNDDB).

Two Species at Risk

Note: *The following discussion of two species at risk illustrates how stressors or threats affect species and highlights conservation challenges and opportunities. These species discussions are not intended to imply that conservation should have a single-species approach.*

Of the region's species at risk, many are dependent on habitats that have limited distribution. Threats from population growth and development are particularly acute for species that depend on restricted habitats, such as Peninsular bighorn sheep. The populations of many species associated with regional aquatic and wetland habitats have declined due to loss and alteration of these habitats. A number of species have also become dependent on habitats created by use and transport of water for irrigated agriculture. Desert pupfish, once widely distributed in the Colorado Basin but now restricted to a handful of locations associated with the Salton Sea, exemplify this pattern.

Peninsular Bighorn Sheep

Jeff Dye

Restricted to the Peninsular mountain ranges, Peninsular bighorn sheep are a distinct segment of the larger bighorn sheep population. They inhabit dry, rocky, low-elevation desert slopes, canyons, and alluvial fans from the San Jacinto and Santa Rosa Mountains near Palm Springs south into Baja California (CDFG 2005b).

Surveys in the early 1970s showed a population already limited by disease transmitted from domestic sheep. The highest recorded population estimate was 1,171 sheep in 1974 (CVAG 2004). Peninsular bighorn sheep were listed as threatened by the state in 1971 and as an endangered population segment under the federal Endangered Species Act in 1998. Between the 1970s and 2000, numbers steadily declined as a result of habitat loss and degradation, disease, and predation.

Connectivity between habitat areas is crucial for the long-term survival of Peninsular bighorn sheep. Bighorn sheep must be able to move on a daily and seasonal basis to make use of the limited water and sparse plant forage found in this dry desert environment. Additionally, they need to be able to move between subpopulations (or ewe groups) to allow genetic exchange and maintain a healthy population structure. Habitat fragmentation can result in genetic isolation and restrict the species' ability to recolonize if population numbers decline (Boyce 2005 pers. comm., USFWS 2000c).

Urban encroachment on Peninsular bighorn sheep habitat is particularly severe in the northern portion of their range. Residential and resort developments are expanding westward from the urban centers around Palm Springs into canyon mouths and up the lower mountain slopes of the San Jacinto and Santa Rosa mountains. Besides habitat loss and fragmentation, bighorn sheep face numerous hazards at the urban-wildland interface. They have been poisoned by toxic ornamental plants, exposed to toxic pesticides and herbicides, drowned in swimming pools and concrete-lined agricultural canals, entangled in fences, harassed by domestic dogs, and killed on roads. A six-year study of sheep in the Coachella Valley area showed that urbanization accounted for 34 percent of adult bighorn mortalities (CDFG 2005b).

Degradation of habitat quality is also an issue for Peninsular bighorn sheep. Critical watering sources are threatened by human recreation, water development, and the spread of invasive plants. Human recreational use can discourage sheep from accessing watering areas around seeps and springs. Tamarisk, a non-native shrub, invades springs and consumes groundwater before it reaches the surface. Groundwater pumping for orchards, particularly near the northwestern corner of Anza Borrego State Park, also threatens the availability of spring water (Boyce 2005 pers. comm.).

 In the 1990s, predation by mountain lions was found to be a major factor contributing to Peninsular bighorn sheep mortality. Although a healthy bighorn population can withstand predation, a population already reduced to low numbers can be substantially diminished (CDFG 2005b). Land management practices and resulting habitat alterations may be contributing to unusually high rates of mountain lion predation. Fire suppression results in thicker, brushier vegetation, which may make it more difficult for bighorn sheep to detect and avoid lions and may affect the distribution of lion's preferred prey, mule deer (Boyce 2005 pers. comm.).

In 2000, a federal recovery plan for Peninsular bighorn sheep was completed. The plan's primary provisions include protection of an adequate habitat base, effective management of conserved lands, establishment of adequate buffering zones along the urban interface, and prudent management of human activity within bighorn range. The Peninsular Bighorn Sheep Recovery Team—including representatives from the University of California, Fish and Game, and the Bureau of Land Management—advises the U.S. Fish and Wildlife Service on plan implementation. Efforts to protect bighorn sheep habitat and prevent conflicts between bighorns and humans have been instituted. For example, land acquisitions at the wildland-urban interface have allowed for the construction of barrier fencing along roadways to prevent road kill and limit bighorn sheep exposure to urban hazards (CDFG 2005b).

Monitoring indicates that these conservation efforts may be benefiting the sheep population. In 1994, the number of bighorn sheep in the Peninsular Ranges was estimated at 360 adults. Subsequent surveys have suggested an upward population trend. In 2002, the total number of sheep occupying the Peninsular Ranges was estimated to be 670. In 2003, the status of Peninsular bighorn sheep was characterized as increasing (CDFG 2005b).

Nonetheless, threats from disease outbreaks, predation, habitat loss, and recreational disturbance remain substantial. Ongoing habitat protection and management, as well as long-term monitoring to provide information on sheep ecology—including the relationship between fire, vegetation communities, and predator-prey interactions; disease exposure; survival rates and causes of death; and the levels and effects of human recreation in sheep habitat—are needed to achieve conservation goals.

Desert Pupfish

Sean Lema

Historically, desert pupfish occurred in the main channel of the lower Colorado River and in the backwaters and sloughs along the river from Needles downstream through the river delta habitats. Pupfish were also distributed through springs, seeps, and slow-moving streams of the Salton Basin (USFWS 1993a).

Pupfish require shallow, slow-moving, clear water with a moderate amount of aquatic vegetation and soft substrate. They are, however, well adapted to systems with cyclical flooding and drying, such as those that historically occurred in the Colorado River system, and can tolerate temperature extremes, high salinity, low oxygen levels, and desiccation of their eggs. In spite of this hardiness, desert pupfish have disappeared from much of their former range. In the Colorado Desert, pupfish occur only in two desert creeks that drain into the Salton Sea (Salt Creek and San Felipe Creek, with its associated San Sebastian marshlands), in shoreline pool habitats and irrigation canals along the Salton Sea, and in artificial **refugia**. Along the Colorado River, dams, water diversions, and channelization have sufficiently altered flow, temperature, and water quality to eliminate pupfish habitat. Many of the backwater channels they inhabited have been destroyed or are now inhabited by introduced predatory fish species (CDFG 2005b, USFWS 1993a).

Pupfish move along the edges of the Salton Sea between shoreline pools, agricultural drains, and creek habitats associated with the sea. This connectivity between populations maintains genetic diversity and allows for repopulation of areas where pupfish may be temporarily eliminated by changing environmental conditions. Biologists currently working on a regional habitat conservation plan note that it will be important to find ways to maintain this connectivity if changing water levels or salt concentrations restrict pupfish use of the Salton Sea (Crayon 2005 pers. comm.). Desert pupfish were listed as endangered by the state of California in 1980, and they were federally listed as endangered in 1987. The U.S. Fish and Wildlife Service issued a recovery plan in 1993. Its primary recovery measures include protection of existing populations; establishment of new populations through introductions into the best available unoccupied natural habitats; and establishment of refugia populations in artificial or semi-natural pools and ponds.

Stressors Affecting Wildlife and Habitats

- Water management conflicts and water transfer effects
- Inappropriate off-road vehicle use
- Loss and degradation of dune habitats
- Growth and development
- Invasive species

Water Management Conflicts and Water Transfer Impacts

The primary threats to aquatic habitats are the diversion of Colorado River water and the modification of its habitats, the decline of the Salton Sea, and the conversion or alteration of agricultural lands and canals.

Alteration of Colorado River Habitats

Water is a limited and precious resource in the arid Colorado Desert. The Colorado River is the region's largest perennial waterway, with aquatic species inhabiting the river's main stem and backwaters. Numerous bird species and other wildlife are dependent on the Colorado River riparian areas and the river delta at the Sea of Cortez.

The diversion of the Colorado River for agricultural and urban water uses substantially affects the region's wildlife and ecosystems. Urban demands for water are increasing. Locally, rapid urbanization in the Coachella Valley is increasing water-supply needs. Meanwhile, water districts of Southern California are ready to buy any available surplus irrigation water from the region.

More than a dozen large dams control, store, divert, and allow for the consumptive use of nearly all the water in the Colorado River (Pitt 2001). These dams, as well as channelization, flood control structures, and flow regulation practices have drastically altered the river's flows and sediment transport processes (Briggs and Cornelius 1998). Flows are much reduced and have less variation (Busch and Smith 1995, Cohen and Henges-Jeck 2001). The delta wetlands at the Sea of Cortez have been reduced to about one-tenth of their original 2 million acres (Pitt 2001). Additionally, water is not available to recharge the groundwater table. In many locations, groundwater levels in riparian areas along the Colorado River have receded from historical levels of less than 3 feet to more than 10 feet below the surface (Hayes 2004 pers. comm.).

Historically, sediment was deposited at the river delta or along the river's banks by flood events, creating deep floodplain soils (Busch and Smith 1995, Poff et al. 1997). Over-bank flooding also flushed the soils of built-up salts, creating more favorable conditions for vegetation. Today, however, sediment transport is blocked by dams, and natural flooding is prevented along most of the river's length.

This groundwater decline and decreased flooding have stressed native riparian cottonwood and willow habitat, favoring the establishment of invasive tamarisk, which can withstand drier conditions and saltier soils (Briggs and Cornelius 1998, Poff et al. 1997). Tamarisk provides inferior wildlife habitat compared to native vegetation and now dominates the Colorado River's riparian areas.

Decline of the Salton Sea

The Salton Sea is the most recent in a series of inland lakes that have historically occupied the Salton Basin. Sustained today by agricultural drainage water, the Salton Sea can be considered neither a natural nor an entirely artificial ecosystem. (See Conditions in the Salton Sea at the end of this chapter.) It is clear, however, that the sea provides critical resources for the region's wildlife, particularly for a great diversity of birdlife. More than 400 bird species have been recorded in the Salton Sea area, including approximately 100 locally breeding species.

The sea's importance stems from its status as the major remaining aquatic habitat of inland Southern California, from its location on the Pacific Flyway, and from the diverse array of habitat types it provides. The sea provides adjacent freshwater marshes and mud flats and offers deep waters that sustain fish populations and support fish-eating birds. The sea's proximity to the Imperial Valley's canals and fields creates a landscape mosaic uniquely able to fulfill multiple habitat requirements for nesting, foraging, and breeding.

The Salton Sea is vital to migratory, wintering, and breeding waterbirds (Shuford et al. 2002). Birds may number in the millions during the winter. In some years, eared grebe numbers alone have been as high as 3.5 million. Nineteen waterbirds of high conservation concern inhabit the sea, including brown pelican, American bittern, white-faced ibis, and ruddy duck. A significant portion of the North American populations of several sensitive species, including the eared grebe, American white pelican, and Yuma clapper rail, are supported by the sea. Threatened by a number of environmental problems, ranging from reduced freshwater inflows and increasing salinity to eutrophication, avian disease outbreaks, and the presence of toxic contaminants, the sea's health is declining, and birds that rely on the sea are at risk.

The sea's decline prompted local agencies in 1993 to establish the Salton Sea Authority (composed of Imperial Irrigation District, Coachella Valley Water District, Imperial County, Riverside County, and the Torres Martinez Tribe) to address both biological and economic recovery. Most recently, the state of California established a Salton Sea Restoration Fund and took on responsibility for selecting a method for its restoration.* At the federal level, the need to restore the sea was recognized with the enactment of the 1998 Salton Sea Reclamation Act, which charged the Department of the Interior and Bureau of Reclamation with responsibility for restoring the sea. Although both state and federal agencies recognize the importance of restoring the sea, they have not yet agreed on a plan for restoration that both agencies will support.

Aquatic and Terrestrial Habitats of Agricultural Lands

With the natural aquatic and wetland systems of the Colorado River dramatically altered and diminished, wildlife species in the region depend on the features of irrigated agricultural lands. The once-arid landscape is now transected by a network of water delivery and drainage canals. Imperial Valley's 475,000 irrigated acres and Coachella Valley's 75,000 acres receive 3.2 million acre feet of Colorado River water annually (Cohn 2000, Cohen et al. 1999). Orchards and date palm plantations in the Coachella Valley and fields of cotton, alfalfa, Sudan grass, lettuce, sugar beets, onions, and melons in the Imperial Valley have replaced native desert communities. The New and Alamo rivers, created when the Colorado River formed the Salton Sea, are now fed principally by agricultural drainage water and provide isolated pools, marshlands, and mudflats used by shorebirds. The drains and canals used to transport water now support wetland vegetation communities and a number of sensitive species, including California black rail, Western burrowing owl, and desert pupfish. Agricultural fields also provide wintering habitat for mountain plover, long-billed curlew, and sandhill crane (Wunder and Knopf 2003).

Water Transfer Effects

In recent years, a number of regional agreements have been negotiated to transfer water from agricultural use to meet growing urban needs in other parts of the state. These water

* The state took on responsibility for the restoration of the Salton Sea through the passage in 2003 of SB 654. Along with SB 277 and 317, it requires the state to provide to the legislature by December 31, 2006, a preferred alternative for restoration of the Salton Sea and establishment of a Salton Sea Restoration Fund.

transfers will help the state to reduce its use of Colorado River water to its federal apportionment of 4.4 million acre-feet/year.

In 2003, the Quantification Settlement Agreement (QSA) and related agreements allowed the transfer of 300,000 acre-feet/year of Colorado River water from the Imperial Irrigation District to urban areas, primarily in coastal Southern California. The parties to these agreements included the Imperial Irrigation District, San Diego County Water Authority, the Metropolitan Water District of Southern California, U.S. Bureau of Reclamation, and the state of California. Ultimately, water conservation through irrigation efficiency measures and lining canals with concrete (to prevent water loss through seepage) will supply the water for the transfer. Initially, however, large-scale fallowing of agricultural fields will provide surplus water for transfer.

In addition to the water transfers covered by the QSA agreements, other changes in the management of Colorado River water are planned in California and in the lower Colorado River basin states. These changes include additional agriculture-to-urban water transfers, increased water-transport efficiency, and changes in diversion points and dam release schedules to meet water supply and power generation needs. The environmental effects of these changes will be addressed by the 2005 Lower Colorado River Multi-Species Conservation Program (Lower Colorado River Program). (The federal Lower Colorado Program allows changes in diversion points and dam release schedules on the Colorado River by water and power agencies in California, Arizona, and Nevada, as well as by the U.S. Bureau of Reclamation and sovereign Native American tribes. The program allows total water transfers of up to 1.574 million acre-feet of Colorado River water per year.) In California, the program will allow up to 800,000 acre-feet of Colorado River water to be transferred annually. These include transfers to urban areas, including some areas in Coachella Valley, from the Imperial Irrigation District, the Palo Verde Irrigation District, and the Bard Water District.*

If unmitigated, these water transfers would have substantial effects on the region's aquatic habitats and the wildlife species that depend on them. With less water applied to agricultural fields, less **tailwater** will flow through drains and be available to sustain the Salton Sea. Canal, drain, and irrigation-fed river habitats will be reduced. Lining canals with concrete

* California's permittees under the Lower Colorado Program are the Bard Water District, City of Needles, Coachella Water District, Colorado River Board of California, Imperial Irrigation District, Palo Verde Irrigation District, San Diego County Water Authority, Southern California Public Power Authority, the Metropolitan Water District of Southern California, Southern California Edison Company, and the City of Los Angeles Department of Water and Power.

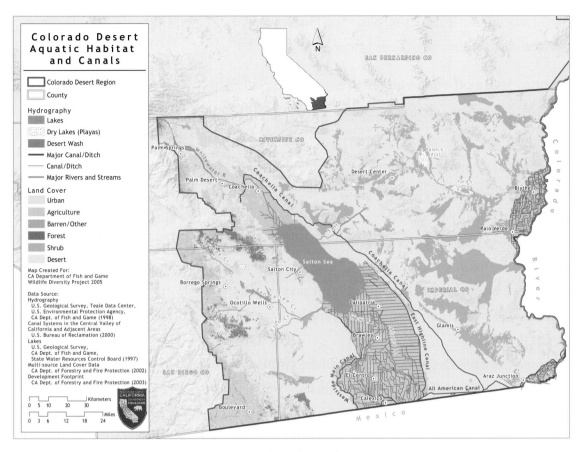

Fig. 8.1: Colorado Desert Aquatic Habitat and Canals

Water management activities have dramatically altered the region's aquatic and wetland habitats. Colorado River water is diverted to an extensive irrigation canal system, transforming large portions of the desert from arid landscapes to agricultural fields and orchards. Agricultural runoff water sustains the Salton Sea and the New and Alamo rivers.

will prevent groundwater recharge, reducing the amount of water that feeds seeps and springs as well as the Salton Sea. At the sea, lower water levels will affect shoreline habitat, and salinity will increase more rapidly with less incoming fresh water. Additionally, changes in water diversion points and in the timing of dam releases in the upper Colorado River basin will affect flows, habitats, and species in the lower Colorado River.

To address these effects, parties to the QSA and the Lower Colorado River Program committed to a number of conservation measures to mitigate for the water transfers. Permits issued in conjunction with these agreements will allow for the **take** of protected species under the California and federal Endangered Species Acts that results from the water management activities covered by these agreements. The QSA also includes commitments to work toward restoration of the Salton Sea. (See the QSA and Lower Colorado River Program Commitments at the end of this chapter.)

Inappropriate off-road vehicle use

Off-road vehicles have the potential to harm both plants and animals directly, as well as to modify desert ecosystems, making them less habitable (Hall 1980). These vehicles may crush plants, cover them with soil, and expose their roots. They can also run over wildlife, collapse burrows, and damage seasonal pools. Soil compaction reduces water availability and affects plants' ability to root and germinate and animals' ability to burrow. Off-road vehicles may also carry in seeds of invasive plant species. Any of these alterations can have cascading effects on the larger community. Changes in vegetation composition also affect available habitats for invertebrates, thus changing the prey base for other desert wildlife. (The effects of off-road vehicle use on desert habitats are discussed in greater detail in Chapter 7, Mojave Desert Region.)

In the Colorado Desert region, some of the greatest levels of off-road vehicle use occur in sand dune habitats. As discussed below, these communities are particularly susceptible to degradation by heavy recreational use. Off-road vehicle use and trespass also has substantial effects on areas along the U.S.–Mexico border in Anza Borrego Desert State Park, and in stream beds and washes surrounding the Salton Sea.

Loss and Degradation of Dune Habitats

Desert sand dune ecosystems support some of the most diverse communities of plants and animals in the deserts of the southwestern United States. Although dune habitats account for only about 7 percent of California's desert landscape, many rare and sensitive species depend on these unique ecosystems.

Dunes are dynamic systems, dependent on movement of sand by wind and water. Active dune systems require sources of sand, as well as landscape features and corridors that allow sand transport and dune migration. Harsh, extreme conditions characterize dune environments, including frequent disturbance of the shifting sandy soils, low nutrients, hot and dry climates, limited water availability, and sparse vegetation for forage or cover.

The flora and fauna that live on dunes frequently have adaptations that enable them to survive in these unusual and challenging conditions. For example, many dune plants are covered with fine white hairs to protect against strong sun, and others have very small leaves to reduce the amount of water that evaporates through the leaves' pores. Fringe-toed lizard species have elongated scales ("fringes") on their hind feet that provide traction, a shovel-shaped head that facilitates burrowing, ear-covering scales to keep out sand, and an internal nostril structure to allow breathing below sand.

Functioning as isolated "sand-islands," dune habitats foster the evolution of unique species. In California, there are three species of fringe-toed lizards (genus *Uma*), each restricted to a separate dune system: in the Algodones dunes, *Uma notata* (listed as a Fish and Game species of concern); in the Coachella Valley, *Uma inornata* (state listed as threatened, federally listed as endangered); and in the Mojave dunes, *Uma scoparia* (listed as a Fish and Game species of concern).

The three primary threats to desert dune systems are the disruption of sand source and sand transport processes, invasive plant species, and off-road vehicle use.

To ensure their continued existence, sand dunes need replenishing. Roads and buildings can cut dunes off from sand sources, blocking and fragmenting corridors for sand movement. Dunes also migrate, and construction and development can destroy their destinations along with their sources of sand. Residential development adjacent to dune areas is often followed by public demand to control naturally blowing sand, resulting in the construction of sand fences that prevent sand from moving through these areas.

Colonization by invasive plant species that either stabilize dunes with extensive root systems or block sand movement prevents natural migration and shifting. These invasives often spread from adjacent development or along road corridors. Principle species of concern include Russian thistle, Saharan mustard, annual grasses of the genus *Schismus*, and planted tamarisk.

Off-road vehicles are particularly problematic in dune environments because compaction can inhibit the sand movement that is vital to dune replenishment and migration. Sand compaction may also negatively affect fringe-toed lizards, which can only burrow in fine, loose sand.

In the Colorado Desert, the most significant dune systems are the Algodones Dunes, also known as Imperial Dunes (approximately 160,000 acres), the Superstition Hills, also known as West Mesa (approximately 100,000 acres), and the Coachella Valley dunes (once approximately 64,000 acres, with fewer than 8,000 acres remaining).

These dune systems face differing threats, depending on land ownership, intended land use, and surrounding land uses. The Algodones Dunes and Superstition Hills are in remote areas without significant population or development pressures. Both areas are largely in federal ownership. BLM manages portions of both of these systems as off-road vehicle recreation areas. The use of these vehicles in the Superstition Hills, where less than 15 percent of the dunes is open to vehicles, is far less contentious than in the Algodones Dunes, where up to 85 percent of the dunes has historically been open to varying levels of vehicle use. The remaining Coachella Valley dunes are threatened by development that impedes natural sand movement and dune replenishment and by off-road-vehicle trespass on preserve lands.

It is critical for public land managers to find ways to provide opportunities for recreational access and off-road-vehicle use while adequately protecting biologically sensitive areas and important wildlife habitats.

Algodones Dunes

Stretching 40-plus miles northward from the U.S.–Mexico border, and ranging from 6 to 10 miles across, the Algodones Dunes are the United States' largest dune system. One hundred sixty plant and animal species inhabit the Algodones Dunes, many of which are rare or endemic. Sensitive wildlife include the flat-tailed horned lizard, Colorado Desert fringe-toed lizard, and Couch's spadefoot toad (all three of which are Fish and Game species of concern), and at least four endemic beetle species, including the Andrews' dune scarab beetle. Plants that are found only in active dune habitats include Algodones dunes sunflower, Wiggins' croton, giant Spanish needle, sand food, desert eriogonum, and Peirson's milkvetch, which is federally listed as threatened and occurs only in a band of habitat across the central portion of the Algodones dunes.

The North Algodones Dune Wilderness Area (approximately 30,000 acres) is off-limits to off-road vehicles. Additional protected acreage may be necessary to ensure the survival of the dunes' rare and endemic species. Some of the best habitat for these species is located in areas designated as open to vehicle use, and in recent years user numbers have reached more than 200,000 on peak weekends.

In 1998, BLM initiated a monitoring program to evaluate the effects of off-road vehicle use on six special-status plant species, including Peirson's milkvetch. The results showed that significant impacts occur around the vehicles' staging areas, with areas immediately surrounding staging areas almost entirely devoid of plant life. However, impacts decrease with distance away from these access points. At distances of 1 to 2 miles away from staging areas, trails are very limited, and populations of all the plant species persist (Knauf 2004 pers. comm.).

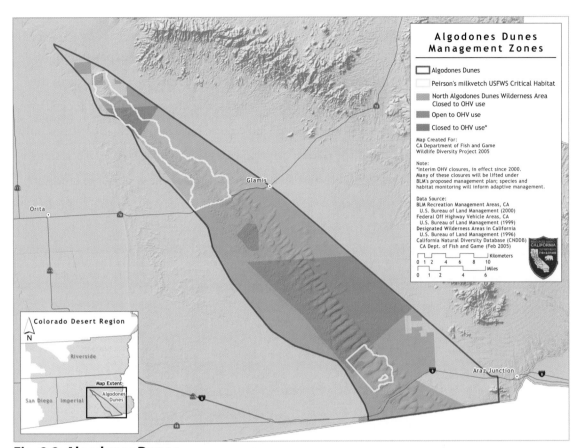

Fig. 8.2: Algodones Dunes

The Algodones Dunes harbor a number of endemic and sensitive species. The North Algodones Dunes Wilderness Area is permanently closed to off-highway-vehicle use. A new BLM management plan for the dunes may repeal the additional closures instated in 2000 while concurrently instituting adaptive management measures to track off-highway-vehicle effects on sensitive dune species.

In 2000, a court settlement between nongovernmental conservation organizations and off-road vehicle advocacy groups resulted in interim closures of 19,000 additional acres (for a total of approximately 49,000 protected acres), leaving roughly half the dunes open to vehicle use. In 2003, BLM released a new management plan proposing to reopen many of the closed areas. BLM maintains that the plan will safeguard sensitive species populations through adaptive management, such as stipulations to limit vehicle use if visitation exceeds certain levels or if populations of Peirson's milkvetch drop below certain levels. The plan also includes monitoring of the fringe-toed lizard, flat-tailed horned lizard, bird species, and microphyll woodlands. In January 2005, the U.S. Fish and Wildlife Service issued a Biological Opinion approving the management plan, which will allow BLM to put the plan into effect and to lift the interim off-road-vehicle closures.

Coachella Valley Dunes

The primary threat to sand dune habitats in the Coachella Valley is the expansion of residential and resort development surrounding Palm Springs in the northwestern areas of the valley. The vital sand movement processes that keep dunes alive are increasingly blocked and fragmented. Currently, the majority of remaining viable dune habitat (which constitutes only between 5 percent and 10 percent of the dunes' original extent) is encompassed in a system of preserves owned by state and federal resources agencies. Some of these preserve lands are threatened by illegal off-road vehicle use.

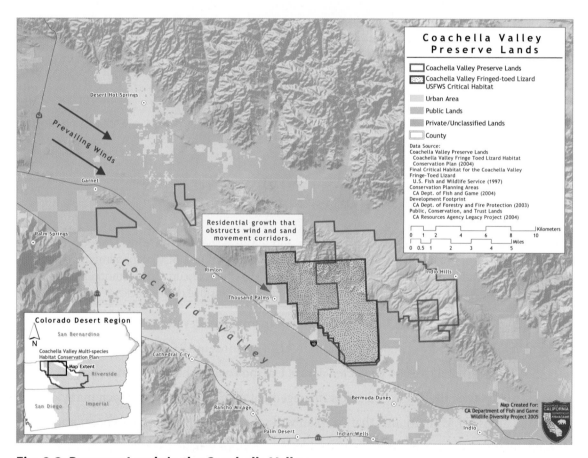

Fig. 8.3: Preserve Lands in the Coachella Valley
The Coachella Valley Dunes, which have been reduced to less than 10 percent of their original extent, harbor endemic and sensitive species such as the Coachella Valley fringe-toed lizard. Although the majority of remaining dunes are protected, portions of the wind- and sand-movement corridors needed to sustain the dunes are still in need of protection.

One hundred eighty plant and animal species inhabit the Coachella Valley preserve. Sensitive wildlife that are endemic to the dunes include the Palm Springs pocket mouse and Coachella round-tailed ground squirrel (both of which are Fish and Game species of concern), Coachella giant sand treader cricket, Coachella Valley Jerusalem cricket, Barrows' dune beetle, giant red velvet mite, and the Coachella Valley fringe-toed lizard (federally listed as threatened, state listed as endangered). Plants that characterize Coachella Valley's dune habitats include sand verbena, dune evening primrose, spectacle pod, bugseed, and the endemic Coachella Valley milkvetch (federally listed as endangered).

The Coachella Valley preserve system was first established in 1986 to protect the threatened Coachella Valley fringe-toed lizard. While the goal of the preserve was to protect dune habitats, an ecological model showed that wind and sand movement corridors, as well as sand source locations, also need to be protected to preserve the dunes. The preserve system's design includes three separate units, each with separate sand sources, to ensure that dune habitats will be protected even if major unforeseen impacts occur at any one site. Reevaluation of the ecological model in 1993 indicated that the primary sand source for one of the units was not adequately protected. Fortunately, the sand source and the path to the preserve had not been severely affected by development, so options for correcting the preserve design were still available. Since then, about half of the desired lands have been acquired.

With continuing population growth in the Coachella Valley, off-road vehicle trespass is becoming an increasingly serious problem on Coachella Valley preserve lands. Particularly on recently acquired lands that were previously private and open to their use, there is some difficulty in enforcing and educating the vehicles' users about new preserve boundaries.

Growth and Development

As a whole, the Colorado Desert region does not face the level of population and development pressure experienced across most of California, and it remains the state's second-least populous region (CERES 2004). However, some areas of the Colorado Desert have seen significant growth in recent decades and are facing the resulting challenges to regional wildlife. The two most notable examples are the Coachella Valley and southern Imperial County near the U.S.–Mexico border cities of Calexico and Mexicali.

Coachella Valley is home to a series of fast-growing communities stretching from Palm Springs eastward to Indio and including outlying communities of Mecca, Coachella, Thermal, and North Shore in the southeast (BLM 2002a). For example, Cathedral City grew by 42 percent between 1990 and 2000; Palm Desert grew by 77 percent (CDOF 2004). New residential development, resort complexes, and golf courses have expanded steadily over recent decades, moving further up the canyons onto the lower slopes of the Peninsular Mountain Range and spreading across the natural communities and agricultural areas of the valley floor. Population in the valley's nine cities and surrounding unincorporated areas is projected to increase from approximately 330,000 in 2000 to between 475,000 and 518,000 residents in 2020 (CVAG 2004).

The Coachella Valley's unique and diverse habitats host a number of sensitive, rare, and endemic species. Conflicts between these species and the rapid pace of development are at the forefront of wildlife agencies' concerns. Since the passage of the California Desert Conservation Act in 1980, 10 Coachella Valley species have been listed as federally protected. Federal, state, and local agencies, along with conservation organizations, are attempting to address these issues through the development of a regional habitat conservation plan, the Coachella Valley Multi-Species Habitat Conservation Plan.

Growth is also noteworthy in southern Imperial County, near the border cities of El Centro and Calexico on the U.S. side and Mexicali on the Mexico side. Some residents, drawn from coastal areas by affordable housing, commute up to two hours to the San Diego area. El Centro grew by 21 percent to 37,835 residents between 1990 and 2000; Calexico grew by 46 percent to a population of 27,000 (CDOF 2004). Conversion of agricultural fields to residential development presents a major threat to wildlife. As previously described, irrigated agricultural fields are a critical component of the habitat mosaic that sustains the great diversity and number of birds in this region. Among the species most reliant upon the Imperial Valley's agricultural fields are mountain plover and western burrowing owl (each a Fish and Game species of concern and a federal species of special concern), California black rail (state listed as threatened and a federal species of concern), and sandhill crane (state listed as threatened).

Expanding communities also increase the need for infrastructure, including roads, powerlines, and water supply. As in other areas of the state, threats to wildlife include direct destruction of habitat, pollution, fragmentation of habitats, blockage of migratory corridors, and introduction of non-native and potentially invasive species. Population growth in neighboring regions, especially along the South Coast and across the larger Sonoran Desert, also puts demands on the resources of the Colorado Desert. Utility corridors that traverse the desert—including electric lines, gas and oil pipelines, aqueducts, and supporting service

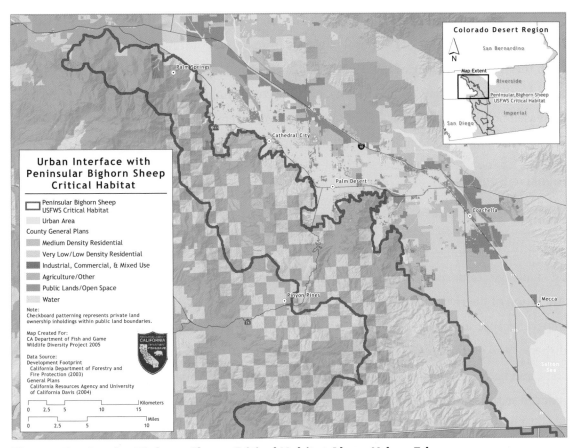

Fig. 8.4: Peninsular Bighorn Sheep Critical Habitat Along Urban Edge
In the northwestern portion of the Coachella Valley, urban development is expanding immediately adjacent to portions of the Peninsular Range that have been designated by the U.S. Fish and Wildlife Service as critical habitat for Peninsular bighorn sheep.

roads—are continually expanded; increasing amounts of Colorado River water are directed to growing urban areas; and visitors seek recreation opportunities in the desert's open landscapes.

Wind power development and renewed gold mining are also growing concerns. BLM and county planners are receiving large numbers of applications for windmill development, many of which are located in remote parts of the region, raising concerns over the possible negative environmental effects associated with construction, maintenance, and access. Wind power expansion is a particular concern for birds and bats, because poorly designed or sited windmills and transmission lines can interfere with flight corridors and cause local mortality (Jones 2005 pers. comm.). Expanding gold mining operations also disturb desert habitats. Toxic contaminants from these operations present hazards to wildlife, and important roosting and foraging sites for bats have been lost and degraded (Bolster 2005 pers. comm.).

Waste management is also an issue in the region. There are currently plans to build two large landfill facilities for the disposal of wastes from desert communities and imported from the South Coast; one of these is to be built adjacent to Joshua Tree National Park. The introduction of nutrients and pollutants, possible contamination of air and water quality, and increased numbers of nuisance species like common ravens could harm desert wildlife if such facilities are not operated in an environmentally responsible manner.

Invasive Species

Plants

In the Colorado Desert region, non-native saltcedar, or tamarisk, presents the greatest challenge. Tamarisk is virtually ubiquitous in riparian areas along the Colorado River. Alteration of the river's natural flow regime favors invasive tamarisk over native vegetation, in part because some native species are adapted to the historical seasonal flooding regime for dispersal and germination. Decreased flooding frequency results in salt buildup in riparian soils, and native species are less salt-tolerant than tamarisk. Tamarisk can also withstand reduced sediment deposition and lowered groundwater levels. In many places, tamarisk has completely replaced native cottonwood, willow, and mesquite and grows in dense mono-species stands. Even where native riparian trees remain, tamarisk usually grows among them (Glenn et al. 2001). It can also be found along most of the region's other waterways and aquatic habitats, including irrigation canals and drains and some springs. Tamarisk provides lower-quality habitat than native trees for nesting birds and other wildlife (including the southwestern willow flycatcher) and uses larger quantities of water than native vegetation, lowering groundwater levels and drying up desert springs while raising soil salinity.

In dune habitats, non-native species block sand movement or stabilize dunes with their roots. As noted in the section on dune habitats, these species include tamarisk (which blocks sand), Russian thistle, Saharan mustard, and introduced annual grasses. These species tend to spread from adjacent developments or can be distributed by off-road vehicles.

Animals

Non-native burros were introduced to the Colorado Desert more than a century ago and now range throughout the region. They can be particularly damaging to riparian areas and at springs. Along the Colorado River and around springs in the Chocolate Mountains where they congregate, burros consume available forage, increase sediment runoff, and compete with bighorn sheep and other native wildlife for access to drinking water. Under the BLM North Eastern Colorado Desert Plan, target limits were set for burro herd size. Because of the requirement under the Wild Horse and Burro Act that burros be managed through capture and relocation, herd control is time-consuming, labor-intensive, and costly. Burros have high reproduction rates. Thus, even where target herd-size limits have been set, herd sizes exceed target numbers.

Brown-headed cowbirds thrive in many human-altered habitats, including fragmented landscapes like suburban developments and golf courses, as well as in agricultural and grazing lands, where they are attracted to livestock droppings and feed. With the expansion of these land uses over the last century, cowbird populations have increased substantially in the Colorado Desert region, particularly in the Imperial and Coachella valleys. Brown-headed cowbirds lay eggs in flycatcher nests, and the flycatcher parent birds may desert the nest or raise the cowbird young at the expense of their own. In California, brown-headed cowbirds have been reported using from 50 percent to 80 percent of flycatcher nests (CVAG 2004). Parasitism of southwestern willow flycatcher nests by brown-headed cowbirds has been identified as a major cause of the flycatcher's decline (USFWS 2002d).

Another regionally sensitive species threatened by exotic species is the desert pupfish, state and federally listed as endangered. Competition, disturbance, and predation by introduced fish species, particularly sailfin molly, mosquito fish, and tilapia and crayfish species, threaten desert pupfish populations (CDFG 2005b).

Conservation Actions to Restore and Conserve Wildlife

In addition to the recommended regional actions described below, see the recommended statewide conservation actions as given in Chapter 4 and recommendation "a" in the Mojave Desert chapter related to the Desert Tortoise Recovery Plan.

a. **Federal, state, and local agencies, along with nongovernmental conservation organizations, should work together to reach agreement upon and fund a restoration plan for the Salton Sea.**

- **The Salton Sea ecosystem should be maintained and restored in a form that provides vitally important aquatic habitats.**

   The restoration plan should ensure that the sea's current habitat values will be provided by the new restored form of the sea or adequately met elsewhere in the region. Important habitats include deep water to support fish production, freshwater marshes, shoreline, shallow water, and mudflats (Levin and Cooper 2003). Restoration solutions should be designed to avoid degrading existing habitats.

- **Ecosystem restoration goals for bird species should be set by reviewing habitat needs on a species-by-species basis.**

  Consideration should be given to which species are represented only at the sea, which ones have the capability to fly longer distances to other sites, and which species use each habitat type. This information can determine the required size and character of habitats needed to maintain wildlife diversity. Appropriate nongovernmental organizations and research institutions should assist government agencies with conducting research and reviewing the avian life-history information needed to set these goals.

- **The water quality of inflows to the sea should be improved by addressing both the quality of the agricultural drainage water and water quality in the Alamo and New rivers, the sea's main tributaries.**

  Agricultural practices that protect environmental quality, such as reducing the use of fertilizers and pesticides and constructing tailwater wetland systems, should be implemented. Government agencies and nongovernmental organizations should continue to research the feasibility and effectiveness of using created wetland projects to filter aquatic contaminants and improve water quality. Wetlands projects created by Wildlife Unlimited on the New and Alamo rivers have been cost efficient and have shown promising results in improving water quality; they are available on the Web at http://www.newriverwetlands.com. Additional research is needed to determine the ultimate fate of selenium sequestered in remediation wetlands.

The Regional Water Quality Control Board should work to finalize **Total Maximum Daily Load** (TMDL) standards for tributaries to the sea. The federal Clean Water Act requires TMDL standards to set limits on pollutant levels allowed to enter currently impaired waterways and then to allocate the emissions amount that is allowable for each of the sources of the pollutant. Adequate TMDL standards should be established for all pollutants entering the sea, with particular focus on nutrients like phosphorous. Recent modeling efforts for the Salton Sea have shown that reducing phosphorus inputs could substantially decrease the occurrence of algae blooms and large fish kill events (Anderson and Amrhein 2002).

b. **Federal and state wildlife agencies should work to ensure that environmental impacts resulting from water transfers (both those permitted under the Quantification Settlement Agreement [QSA] and any future transfers) are mitigated and that the related habitat conservation plans are fully implemented.**

All commitments in the Salton Sea and Imperial Valley Habitat Conservation Plan and the related Biological Opinion should be carried out. (See the QSA and Lower Colorado River Plan Commitments at the end of this chapter.)

It is unlikely that the $133 million funding cap on implementation costs agreed to by the water agencies will be able to cover the full costs of carrying out the Salton Sea and Imperial Valley Habitat Conservation Plan and the related Biological Opinion. Therefore, it will also be important for the state to help secure funding to complete all components of the plan.

All commitments in the Lower Colorado River Multi-Species Conservation Plan should be carried out. (See the QSA and Lower Colorado River Program Commitments.)

As the Multi-Species Conservation Plan is implemented and developed into site-specific plans, adequate staff and funding resources for active management should be ensured, both until the created and restored wetland and riparian habitats are established and for long-term management needs, such as invasive species control. Efforts should also be made to protect and augment existing patches and areas of native vegetation along the Colorado River and delta. Where native fish-stocking programs are employed, resources should be invested in programs to restore and improve instream and backwater habitats and to control invasive aquatic wildlife species.

c. Federal and state wildlife agencies, water management agencies, and nongovernmental conservation organizations should develop and invest in restoration and protection efforts for the Salton Sea, the Colorado River delta, and other regional wildlife habitats.

In managing the Salton Sea, Colorado River, and regional agricultural habitats, these systems must be considered as part of the larger combined Colorado Basin ecosystem. Restoration and preservation actions at any of these habitats can benefit many of the same species. State legislation passed as a part of the QSA process says the QSA mitigation funds may be applied to Colorado River delta restoration. Restoring a portion of the Colorado River delta would enhance the region's ability to sustain wildlife.

The Audubon Society and other nongovernmental conservation groups should continue to work with private landowners and land managers in Imperial County to institute wildlife-friendly management practices on agricultural lands, to establish conservation easements on agricultural lands that can be managed to provide important wildlife habitat, and to work with willing sellers to bring some habitat areas into conservation ownership.

Increased Colorado River flows and occasional flood flows are needed to restore the delta. The Colorado River Board of California, working with California's Colorado River users, California Department of Water Resources, Fish and Game, U.S. Bureau of Reclamation, U.S. Fish and Wildlife Service, and U.S. International Boundary and Water Commission should work together and with their Mexican counterparts to develop and implement a plan to acquire water for dedicated instream flows for the Colorado River and delta.

d. Wildlife-agency staff developing the Imperial Valley Habitat Conservation Plan, working with Imperial County planners and nongovernmental conservation organizations, should identify and protect critical avian habitats in southern Imperial County.

Vital habitats for birds need to be identified and adequately protected in areas where development and urbanization are transforming the agricultural fields of southern Imperial County. New development should set aside protected areas for bird habitat. Initial surveys of avian habitats in and around Imperial Valley agricultural fields were undertaken in 1999 and can provide guidance for further research (Shuford et al. 2002). Additional studies to determine the most important crops and agricultural management practices for wildlife should be a research priority. As rapid development continues near border cities, local, county, and General Plans should take these vital habitats into account.

Before fallowing large acreages of crops for water conservation efforts, consideration should be given to the agricultural habitats that would be lost. Even in cases where agricultural water leases could be purchased for ecosystem restoration uses, such as increased Colorado River flows, the habitat values that would gained by returning water to the river must be balanced against the agricultural habitats that would be lost if large acreages of crops are taken out of production.

e. The Bureau of Land Management, working with state and federal wildlife agencies and nongovernmental conservation organizations, should protect and restore biologically significant habitats in the Algodones Dunes.

- **Ongoing monitoring of Algodones Dunes' habitats and endemic and sensitive species is needed to determine appropriate off-road vehicle restrictions.**

  The U.S. Fish and Wildlife Service and BLM, with the input of regional biologists (including representatives of the California Native Plant Society), should continue to cooperate to develop and implement monitoring programs to assess the effects of off-road-vehicle use on dune species and habitats. As monitoring protocols are revised and developed, they should receive peer review to ensure they are scientifically rigorous and designed appropriately to identify changes caused by vehicle activity. Future monitoring protocols should be designed to assess community-level ecological effects (rather than focusing exclusively on listed species) by evaluating indicators of community health, such as arthropod diversity and numbers, soil compaction, and reproductive success of both plant and animal species (Barrows et al. 2005). In order for BLM to implement the community-level components of their 2003 management plan, such as monitoring of plant communities and bird species, additional staff and funding will be needed.

- **If the interim closures in the southern sections of the dunes (instituted in 2000) are lifted, careful monitoring should be used to track effects on the dunes' sensitive biological resources.**

  If negative effects are documented, BLM should consider reinstating the interim closures and making them permanent through a wilderness designation.

- **Dune protection requires greater management and enforcement resources.**

  Law enforcement in the Algodones Dunes recreation areas is provided primarily by nine BLM patrol rangers, giving each officer responsibility for approximately 20,000 acres. On peak visitation weekends, up to 50 additional staff from local sheriff's offices and border patrol offices are employed to maintain public safety. It is important that large staff deployments on peak weekends not only address crowd control but also enforce vehicle-use restrictions designed to protect the dune's resources. Fish and Game enforcement officers should be used to bolster patrol efforts on peak visitation days. Additionally, as called for in the Draft Imperial Sand Dunes Recreation and Management Plan, increased law enforcement is also needed on a regular basis to perform normal patrols for dumping, vegetation destruction, and trespass violations (BLM 2003b).

f. **State and federal agencies and nongovernmental partners should collaborate to develop a comprehensive Southern California Outdoor Recreation Program (for the South Coast and Colorado Desert regions) to provide recreational opportunities and access that do not conflict with wildlife habitat needs. Areas for intensive recreational access and off-road vehicle use should be developed on the least-sensitive public lands in order to direct pressures away from sensitive habitats.**

See off-highway vehicle workshop discussion results, http://www.dfg.ca.gov/habitats/wdp/ohv.pdf.

g. **Federal, state, and local agencies and nongovernmental conservation organizations should work to protect and restore biologically significant habitats in the Coachella Valley.**

Wildlife agencies and local governments should finalize the Coachella Valley Multiple Species Habitat Conservation Plan (Coachella Plan) in order to secure funding for continuing acquisition of lands in the proposed reserve system. Once the Coachella Plan is completed, all parties should work to implement their commitments under the plan.

In addition to the provisions in the Coachella Plan, long-term protection of the preserve system requires restriction on off-road vehicle use. As the valley's population continues to grow, demands for vehicle recreation areas will increase. Currently, the closest large, open off-road vehicle area is in Mecca Hills, approximately 45 minutes away from the valley's population centers. Establishing a closer open area could reduce pressures on protected dune areas.

h. Nongovernmental conservation organizations should continue to work to protect important wildlife habitat areas.

Regionally active citizen-supported groups, such as the Friends of the Desert Mountains, the Wildlands Conservancy, the Mojave Desert Land Trust, the Anza Borrego Foundation, and others, should continue to identify opportunities for habitat conservation, including the use of land acquisitions from willing sellers and conservation easements to protect biologically significant areas and private inholdings within public lands.

Priority areas for protection include inholdings in Anza Borrego Desert State Park, the margins of Joshua Tree National Park, especially where there are strong growth and development pressures, the sand-movement corridors and sand sources needed to sustain the Coachella Valley Dunes Preserve System, important avian habitats in Imperial County, remaining native riparian communities along the lower Colorado River, and others.

i. Permitting agencies, county and local planners, and land management agencies should work to ensure that infrastructure development projects are designed and sited to avoid harmful effects on sensitive species and habitats.

As demands for roads, power, water, and waste disposal sites grow, efforts should be made to update and upgrade existing infrastructure to meet those needs. For example, rather than developing additional wind farms, existing wind farms can be updated to produce more electricity per windmill, and transmission lines can be upgraded to higher voltage lines to avoid the need for new utility corridors across undeveloped lands.

Wherever possible, infrastructure development projects should be sited near existing urban areas and development corridors and away from areas that are relatively undeveloped or with significant biological resources.

If new landfill facilities are built in the region, permitting agencies should work with project developers to ensure that all possible measures are taken to prevent environmental impacts, such as using closed-top landfill pits and reliably sealed liners to prevent water and soil contamination.

j. Federal, state, and local agencies should work with nongovernmental organizations to provide greater resources to eradicate or control and limit introductions of invasive species in the region.

Agencies should increase research and monitoring of exotic species that compete with, predate, or parasitize sensitive native species or degrade important habitats. Watchlists of highly invasive species and maps of major invasive species' occurrences should be continually updated and publicized.

Working in cooperation with pest control councils, coordinated weed management areas, and conservation organizations, agencies should develop and implement eradication and control programs for invasive species. These programs must include adaptive management approaches, integrated pest management, participation by many different organizations, and planning at a landscape scale. Public education about the threats presented by invasive species and support for and publicity about the efforts of citizen task-force groups working to control invasive species should be included as part of these programs.

Agencies should increase efforts to remove invasive tamarisk and restore native vegetation in riparian areas and springs and should support task-force groups focused on tamarisk control. Where possible, consider restoration of natural flow and flood regimes that favor native riparian species. Headwaters, areas that support sensitive species, and areas with light infestations are priority candidates for tamarisk control.

Working in cooperation with local planners and nongovernmental conservation groups, agencies should encourage planting of native plant species (and control of invasives) in urban edge and wilderness interface zones, particularly along the Peninsular Range, Coachella Valley Dunes, Anza Borrego Desert State Park, and Joshua Tree National Park. Known invasive species should not be used for landscaping new developments in the area. Native species should be used in all restoration and habitat enhancement work and in critical habitat zones. This is particularly important for Colorado River riparian restoration projects, in Salton Sea–associated wetlands that are managed as wildlife refuges, and in the large-scale managed marsh that will be created in Imperial County as a Quantification Settlement Agreement mitigation measure.

Conditions in the Salton Sea

The Salton Sea is 35 miles long, about 12 miles wide, approximately 36 feet deep, and spans the border between Imperial and Riverside counties. The current sea formed in 1905 when Colorado River floodwaters broke through irrigation barriers. For almost two years, until engineers could reroute the flow, nearly all of the river's water flowed into the Salton basin (Cohn 2000, Cooper 2003). Although the sea resulted from this irrigation accident, a number of naturally formed water bodies have occupied the low-lying Salton basin in the past. Thousands of years ago, an arm of the Sea of Cortez extended into the basin, providing a delta fishery for Native Americans (Cooper 2003). Before the Colorado River was controlled by impoundments and channelization, the river's natural meanderings and winter floods sporadically flowed into the Salton basin, and, until 300 years ago, a water body larger than the Salton Sea (known as Lake Cahuilla) intermittently covered the area. Between 1824 and 1904, Colorado River flows spilled into the basin eight times, creating freshwater lakes that gradually evaporated (USBOR 2003).

The current Salton Sea has not evaporated because it is sustained by agricultural drainage water that feeds the sea's major tributaries, the New and Alamo rivers. Approximately 1.35 million acre feet of water enter the sea annually, more than 75 percent of which is U.S. agricultural drainage water. Ten percent of inflows to the sea originates in Mexico; 75 percent of this also is agricultural drainage, and 25 percent is municipal and industrial effluents (Cohen et al. 1999). Today, the amount of agricultural water feeding the sea is decreasing because water conservation measures and water-transfers to urban areas are reducing agricultural water use.

The sea's water quality is determined by the quality of these inflows. Water quality problems include high salinity, nutrient loading, and toxic contamination. The problems presented by these inputs are magnified because the sea is a closed basin with no natural outflows. Water exits the sea only by evaporation, thus concentrating the salts, nutrients, and contaminants. The sea is now 30 percent saltier than ocean water. Salinity increases at approximately 1 percent per year (RWQCB 2003), threatening invertebrate and fish populations and the food chain that supports the sea's fish-eating birds (Shuford et al. 2002).

Besides salts, agricultural drainage water contains fertilizers, pesticide residues, and naturally occurring elements, such as selenium, that can be toxic at high concentrations (Cohn 2000, Kaiser 1999). Nitrogen and phosphorous also enter in sewage wastewater, primarily via the New River (Kaiser 1999). High nutrient levels create a eutrophic system, characterized by algal blooms and subsequent die-offs, which result in low dissolved oxygen, high ammonia and hydrogen sulfate levels, and fish kills (RWQCB 2003). Eutrophic conditions may also foster the spread of avian disease (Cohen et al. 1999). The toxic contaminants of greatest concern are selenium and DDT and its derivatives. Although current contaminant levels are too low to cause direct toxicity, concerns remain about the potential for **bioaccumulation**, about recent detections of DDT (in spite of long-time bans), and about the exposure of contaminated sediments as sea levels decline, which could present an air quality hazard if those sediments become airborne dust. The sea's water quality problems could be exacerbated by planned water conservation measures for regional irrigated agriculture. Decreasing the volume of drainage water entering the sea will lessen the dilution rate of salts and contaminants in the sea (Cohen et al. 1999).

Restoration of the sea is a complex issue. Currently, biologists are attempting to identify which of the sea's habitats and resources are vital to wildlife and bird populations. Figuring out how to preserve these aspects while establishing a healthy ecosystem will be the key to restoration efforts.

The Colorado River Quantification Settlement Agreement (QSA) and Lower Colorado Program Commitments

Under the QSA and associated state and federal Endangered Species Act permits, commitments to mitigate for water transfer impacts to the Salton Sea and Imperial Valley agricultural lands and drains include:

1) The San Diego County Water Authority, Coachella Valley Water District, and Imperial Irrigation District agreed to complete an Imperial Irrigation District Habitat Conservation Plan/Natural Community Conservation Plan by 2006 to mitigate for activities in the Imperial Valley that will result from the water transfer. These water agencies are responsible for plan implementation costs of up to $133 million. Through cost-sharing agreements, the Southern California Metropolitan Water District and the U.S. Bureau of Reclamation are also responsible for funding portions of various mitigation measures. The state of California has assumed financial responsibility for any costs that exceed the capped amounts agreed to by parties to the QSA (QSA JPA 2003a, SB 654 2003).

The Imperial Irrigation District Habitat Conservation Plan (QSA JPA 2003b) is anticipated to:

a. Include up to 96 species and provide conservation strategies for the five primary habitat types used by those species: drains, tamarisk scrub,* agricultural fields, desert, and the Salton Sea. Species-specific conservation measures will be included for the burrowing owl, desert pupfish, and razorback sucker.

b. Require the Imperial Irrigation District to discharge enough mitigation water (conserved through fallowing) to the Salton Sea to ensure that inflows will not decrease over the next 15 years. (A State Water Resources Control Board Order also mandates this inflow requirement, along with salinity and elevation monitoring.)

c. Create a managed marsh as habitat for Yuma clapper rails, California black rails, and other wetland-associated species to mitigate operation and maintenance activities and selenium impacts in Imperial Valley drains and canals.

d. Maintain drain habitat suitable for the desert pupfish. If Salton Sea salinity increases to the point where desert pupfish can no longer travel between drains by traversing the sea, the agricultural drains will be extended and linked, so that pupfish populations will remain connected for genetic exchange. Additionally, the results of ongoing research on selenium concentrations in drainwater and effects on pupfish will be incorporated through adaptive management.

e. Require Imperial Irrigation District to hire a full-time biologist/project manager to oversee implementation of the plan.

2) The Imperial Irrigation District, San Diego County Water Authority, and Coachella Valley Water District are responsible for installing oceanic roosts on the Southern California coast to serve brown pelicans that now depend on deepwater fishery habitats at the Salton Sea. Two roosts with the capacity to support at least 1,200 pelicans will be constructed by 2018 (State of California 2004).

* Where tamarisk has replaced native riparian vegetation, it is utilized by wildlife. Loss of riparian tamarisk habitat must be mitigated by the creation of native riparian habitats suitable for use by willow flycatchers or other target species.

The Lower Colorado River Program

Under the federal Lower Colorado River Multi-Species Conservation Program and associated California Endangered Species Act permits, commitments to mitigate for water transfer impacts to the lower Colorado River include:

California's permittees* under the Lower Colorado River Program are responsible for funding implementation costs for the plan, up to $156.5 million. The U.S. Bureau of Reclamation has assumed responsibility for any costs that exceed the capped amounts agreed to by other program permittees. In addition to the federal requirements, California's permittees are also responsible for funding the management of some of the mitigation lands in perpetuity in order to meet standards for permits under the California Endangered Species Act (State of California 2005, US DOI 2005, USFWS 2005).

The Lower Colorado Program will:

a. Cover 26 species. Species that figured most prominently in the planning process were the Yuma clapper rail, California black rail, yellow-billed cuckoo, southwestern willow flycatcher, razorback sucker, and bonytail.

b. Create and manage more than 8,000 acres of native wetlands and riparian habitat along the Colorado River (of which at least 3,000 acres will be in California), including a total of more than 5,000 acres of cottonwood-willow riparian habitat to benefit the southwestern willow flycatcher, more than 1,000 acres of marsh, and more than 1,000 acres of open backwaters. Restoration projects will include restoration of agricultural lands to native cottonwood, willow, and mesquite habitat and improvement of existing protected lands by removing tamarisk and planting native trees.

c. Augment populations of razorback suckers, bonytail, and flannelmouth suckers in the Colorado River.

* California's permittees under the Lower Colorado Program are the Bard Water District, City of Needles, Coachella Water District, Colorado River Board of California, Imperial Irrigation District, Palo Verde Irrigation District, San Diego County Water Authority, Southern California Public Power Authority, the Metropolitan Water District of Southern California, Southern California Edison Company, and the City of Los Angeles Department of Water and Power.

The Draft Coachella Valley Multiple Species Habitat Conservation Plan

Some of the Colorado Desert region's most important wildlife habitats are found in the Coachella Valley. A variety of land forms and accompanying differences in temperature, water availability, and other environmental conditions contribute to the area's high biological diversity. Elevations range from 150 feet below sea level at the desert floor to 10,000 feet in the surrounding mountains. The area's unique communities include ephemeral streams, riparian areas, alluvial fans, palm oases, and a sand dune system created by strong winds that funnel through the San Gorgonio Pass.

The intersection of sensitive species' habitat and suburban development is at the crux of conservation planning in the Coachella Valley. For example, expanding developments overlap with Peninsular bighorn sheep habitat where the valley floor meets the low elevation slopes and canyon mouths of the Peninsular Range. Along this interface, there are currently five golf courses and residential developments under construction or approved to be built. (See Fig. 8.4.)

The major challenges resulting from development pressures identified by the Draft Coachella Valley Multiple Species Habitat Conservation Plan (the Coachella Plan) are habitat loss; impacts of exotic species; unauthorized off-road vehicle use; disturbance from dumping; compromised sand process dynamics; blocked wildlife movement corridors; groundwater overdraft; and changes in water availability (CVAG 2004).

Through the establishment of a roughly 730,000-acre preserve system and implementation of improved land management practices, the Coachella Plan aims to maintain or restore populations of all species included in the plan (five plants, two insects, one fish, one amphibian, three reptiles, 11 birds, and four mammals), and to preserve examples of the valley's 27 natural communities. The Coachella Plan also emphasizes the importance of sustaining ecological and evolutionary processes and adapting preserve management to changing conditions.

Among the natural-community types identified in the Coachella Plan, sand-dependent communities and alluvial fan habitats face the greatest threats. These habitats once covered most of the valley floor but are now restricted to a small fraction of their former range. Alluvial fan communities are vulnerable because they form along the base of the mountain range, a desirable location for housing and recreational facilities. Alluvial fans are important aquatic features after rains, especially for amphibians like Woodhouse's toad. The plan targets these communities for protection and builds upon the existing Coachella Valley Preserve system by identifying linkages and sand transport corridors that are not yet protected.

Another important management issue addressed in the Coachella Plan is regulation of recreational trails in Peninsular bighorn sheep habitat. The draft Coachella Plan recognizes the potential adverse impacts of trail use on bighorn sheep access to foraging areas and water sources (particularly during critical periods such as lambing season) and includes an adaptive management and monitoring program to address these issues. Construction of new, lower-elevation trails around the base of the mountain range will also reduce the volume of use of higher elevation trails and serve as a buffer zone and barrier between sheep habitat and the urban edge.

The projected timeline for the Coachella Plan calls for preserve system acquisitions to be complete in 30 years and for management and monitoring programs to be funded in perpetuity.

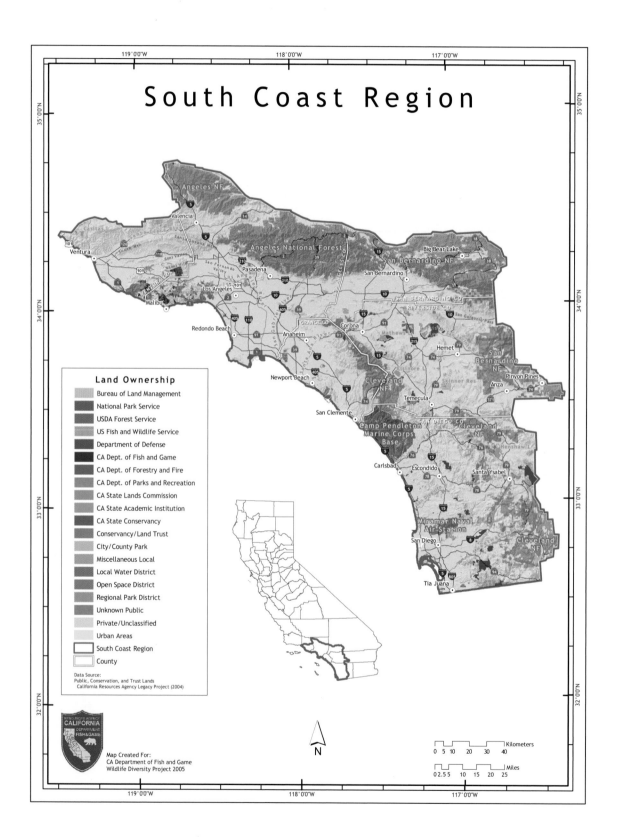

South Coast Region

Land Ownership

- Bureau of Land Management
- National Park Service
- USDA Forest Service
- US Fish and Wildlife Service
- Department of Defense
- CA Dept. of Fish and Game
- CA Dept. of Forestry and Fire
- CA Dept. of Parks and Recreation
- CA State Lands Commission
- CA State Academic Institution
- CA State Conservancy
- Conservancy/Land Trust
- City/County Park
- Miscellaneous Local
- Local Water District
- Open Space District
- Regional Park District
- Unknown Public
- Private/Unclassified
- Urban Areas
- South Coast Region
- County

Data Source:
Public, Conservation, and Trust Lands
California Resources Agency Legacy Project (2004)

Map Created For:
CA Department of Fish and Game
Wildlife Diversity Project 2005

Kilometers
0 5 10   20   30   40

Miles
0 2.5 5   10   15   20   25

N

9   *South Coast Region*

Californiaʼs South Coast Region encompasses more than 8 million acres, extending along the coast from the middle of Ventura County in the north to the Mexican border in the south. Inland, the region is bounded by the Peninsular mountain ranges and the transition to the Mojave and Colorado deserts on the east and by the Transverse mountain ranges on the north. It is an area of strikingly varied landscapes, ranging from wetlands and beaches to hillsides, rugged mountains, arid deserts, and densely populated metropolitan areas.

The region's coastal habitats include coastal strand, lagoons, and river-mouth **estuaries** that transition from **riparian** wetlands to fresh and saltwater marshes. California least tern, Western snowy plover, light-footed clapper rail, California brown pelican, and other waterfowl and shorebirds depend on these habitats. Moving inland, the predominant hillside and bluff communities are coastal sage scrub and chaparral. Southern California's coastal sage scrub is composed of a mix of drought-resistant shrubs and **forbs** found no place else in the country, commonly including California sagebrush, bush monkeyflower, buckwheat species, and black, purple, or white sage. Chaparral plant communities, also drought tolerant, are characterized by a greater component of woody species, including chamise, manzanita,

California lilac, and scrub oak. Inhabitants of sage scrub and chaparral communities include the coast horned lizard, rosy boa, California gnatcatcher, San Diego cactus wren, and Quino checkerspot butterfly. Isolated grasslands and **vernal pool** habitats are interspersed in the coastal landscape and support unique and endemic species such as Stephens' kangaroo rat and fairy shrimp species. Low- to mid-elevation uplands often feature oak woodlands, including Engelmann oak. Higher-elevation mountainous areas are dominated by coniferous forests, including Jeffrey pine, ponderosa pine, big-cone Douglas fir, and white fir, and support sensitive species such as the San Bernardino flying squirrel and long-eared and long-legged myotis bats. Along the Peninsular mountain range, coniferous forests transition to the western edge of the Colorado and Mojave desert ecosystems.

The region's largest river drainages include the Tijuana, San Diego, San Luis Rey, Santa Margarita, Santa Ana, San Gabriel, Los Angeles, Santa Clara, and Ventura rivers. Pine forests occur along high-elevation stream reaches, and mountain drainages host mountain yellow-legged frog, California red-legged frog, Santa Ana sucker, and Santa Ana speckled dace. Lower-elevation river reaches support riparian vegetation species, including cottonwood, willow, sycamore, and coast live oak, which provide habitat for such riparian bird species as the least Bell's vireo, southwestern willow flycatcher, Swainson's thrush, and yellow warbler, as well as the arroyo toad. In urbanized coastal areas, many sections of the region's river corridors are channelized with concrete.

The region is recognized as one of the world's hotspots of biological diversity and is home to a total of 476 vertebrate animal species, approximately 38 percent of all the vertebrate species found in California. It is also distinguished by the tremendous population growth and urbanization that have transformed the landscape since the 1940s. This intersection of biological resources and urbanization has made the South Coast the most-threatened biologically diverse area in the continental U.S. (USGS 2003). More than 150 species of vertebrate animals and 200 species of plants are either listed as protected or considered **sensitive** by wildlife agencies and conservation groups (Hunter 1999).

Despite the region's rapid growth and subsequent loss of habitat, Southern California retains some large and valuable natural lands, including the national forests, which form an interconnected system of wildlands flanking the coast's metropolitan areas. Wide-ranging species, including the mountain lion, coyote, and golden eagle, can still be found in these large habitats.

On the outskirts of Los Angeles, hiking trails traversing canyons in the Santa Monica Mountains pass through the range of the mountain lion and golden eagle. Only from the mountaintops, where the view reveals the Los Angeles metropolis spreading to the ocean, is it clear that these natural lands exist within one of the world's most urbanized regions. This juxtaposition of urban landscapes with remaining significant natural areas is one of the defining characteristics of the South Coast. The ongoing pressures of growth and urbanization require substantial and timely efforts to preserve the region's remaining wildlife diversity.

Species at Risk

The Plan development team updated vertebrate and invertebrate species information in the California Natural Diversity Database (CNDDB) during 2004–2005. The following regional summary of numbers of wildlife species, **endemic** species, and **species at risk** is derived from the updated CNDDB.

The South Coast's widely variable geography and diverse climate have given rise to remarkable biological diversity. There are 476 vertebrate species that inhabit the South Coast Region at some point in their life cycle, including 287 birds, 87 mammals, 52 reptiles, 16 amphibians, and 34 fish. Of the total vertebrate species that inhabit this region, 82 bird **taxa**, 40 mammalian taxa, 19 reptilian taxa, eight amphibian taxa, and nine fish taxa are included on the Special Animals List. Of these, 14 are endemic to the South Coast Region, and 14 other species found here are endemic to California but not restricted to this region (Table 9.1).

Table 9.1: State-Endemic Special Status Vertebrates of the South Coast Region

	Ambystoma californiense	California tiger salamander
	Anniella pulchra pulchra	Silvery legless lizard
*	*Batrachoseps gabrieli*	San Gabriel slender salamander
	Catostomus santaanae	Santa Ana sucker
	Charina umbratica	Southern rubber boa
	Diadophis punctatus modestus	San Bernardino ringneck snake
*	*Dipodomys merriami parvus*	San Bernardino kangaroo rat
*	*Dipodomys stephensi*	Stephens' kangaroo rat
	Eucyclogobius newberryi	Tidewater goby
*	*Gasterosteus aculeatus santannae (=ssp. 1)*	Santa Ana (=Shay Creek) threespine stickleback
	Gasterosteus aculeatus williamsoni	Unarmored threespine stickleback

	Gila orcutti	Arroyo chub
*	*Glaucomys sabrinus californicus*	San Bernardino flying squirrel
*	*Lampropeltis zonata*	California mountain kingsnake (San Bernardino population)
	Lampropeltis zonata	California mountain kingsnake (San Diego population)
*	*Microtus californicus stephensi*	South Coast marsh vole
*	*Myotis lucifugus*	Little brown bat (San Bernardino Mountains population)
	*Ovis canadensis nelsoni dps***	Peninsular bighorn sheep
*	*Perognathus alticolus alticolus*	White-eared pocket mouse
	Perognathus alticolus inexpectatus	Tehachapi pocket mouse
*	*Perognathus longimembris brevinasus*	Los Angeles pocket mouse
*	*Rhinichthys osculus ssp. 3*	Santa Ana speckled dace
*	*Sorex ornatus salicornicus*	Southern California saltmarsh shrew
*	*Spermophilus laterlis bernardinus*	San Bernardino ground squirrel
	Spermophilus tereticaudus chlorus	Palm Springs round-tailed ground squirrel
	Tamias speciosus speciosus	Lodgepole chipmunk
	Taricha torosa torosa	Coast Range newt
*	*Thamnophis sirtalis ssp.*	South Coast garter snake

* denotes taxon is endemic to region
** dps=distinct population segment

The number of arthropod species is so great, and they are so poorly known taxonomically, that it is presently impossible to accurately estimate the total number of invertebrate species occurring in the state. In the South Coast Region, however, 43 invertebrate taxa are included on the Special Animals List, including 38 arthropod taxa and five mollusk taxa. Of these, 29 are endemic to the South Coast Region, and nine other taxa found here are endemic to California but not restricted to this region (Table 9.2).

Table 9.2: State-Endemic Special Status Invertebrates of the South Coast Region

*	*Branchinecta sandiegonensis*	San Diego fairy shrimp
*	*Brennania belkini*	Belkin's dune tabanid fly
	Calileptoneta oasa	A leptonetid spider; no common name
*	*Carolella busckana*	Busck's gallmoth
	Ceratochrysis longimala	A chrysidid wasp; no common name
*	*Cicindela gabbii*	Gabb's tiger beetle
	Cicindela hirticollis gravida	Sandy beach tiger beetle

*	*Cicindela latesignata latesignata*	A tiger beetle; no common name
*	*Cicindela senilis frosti*	A tiger beetle; no common name
*	*Cicindela tranquebarica viridissima*	Greenest tiger beetle
	Coelus globosus	Globose dune beetle
*	*Euchloe hyantis andrewsi*	Andrew's marble butterfly
*	*Eucosma hennei*	Henne's eucosman moth
*	*Euphilotes battoides allyni*	El Segundo blue butterfly
*	*Glaucopsyche lygdamus palosverdesensis*	Palos Verdes blue butterfly
*	*Halictus harmonius*	Harmonius halictid bee
*	*Helminthoglypta milleri*	Miller's shoulderband
	Helminthoglypta taylori	Westfork shoulderband
*	*Helminthoglypta traski coelata*	Peninsular range shoulderband
*	*Hydroporus simplex*	Simple hydroporus diving beetle
*	*Incisalia mossii hidakupa*	San Gabriel Mountains elfin butterfly
*	*Linderiella santarosae*	Santa Rosa Plateau fairy shrimp
	Macrobaenetes valgum	Coachella giant sand treader cricket
*	*Mitoura thornei*	Thorne's hairstreak
*	*Neduba longipennis*	Santa Monica shieldback katydid
*	*Onychobaris langei*	Lange's El Segundo dune weevil
*	*Panoquina errans*	Wandering (=saltmarsh) skipper
*	*Plebejus saepiolus aureolus*	San Gabriel Mountains blue butterfly
	Psychomastax deserticola	Desert monkey grasshopper
*	*Pyrgus ruralis lagunae*	Laguna Mountains skipper
*	*Rhaphiomidas terminatus abdominalis*	Delhi sands flower-loving fly
*	*Rothelix warnerfontis*	Warner Springs shoulderband
*	*Socalchemmis gertschi*	Gertsch's socalchemmis spider
*	*Socalchemmis icenoglei*	Icenogle's socalchemmis spider
	Stenopelmatus cahuilaensis	Coachella Valley Jerusalem cricket
*	*Trigonoscuta dorothea dorothea*	Dorothy's El Segundo dune weevil
*	*Trimerotropis occidentaloides*	Santa Monica grasshopper
	Tryonia imitator	Mimic tryonia (=California brackishwater snail)

* denotes taxon is endemic to region

The Wildlife Species Matrix, including data on listing status, habitat association, and population trend for each vertebrate and invertebrate species included on the Special Animals List, is available on the Web at http://www.dfg.ca.gov/habitats/wdp/matrix_search.asp. For vertebrates, the matrix also includes links to species-level range maps. Additionally, a link to the California Department of Fish and Game's online Field Survey Form is available to assist in reporting positive sightings of species on the Special Animals List to the California Natural Diversity Database (CNDDB).

Two Species at Risk

Note: *The following discussion of two species at risk illustrates how stressors or threats affect species and highlights conservation challenges and opportunities. These species discussions are not intended to imply that conservation should have a single-species approach.*

The threats facing the Quino checkerspot butterfly and the light-footed clapper rail illustrate some of the region's most important conservation issues. Urbanization has transformed a large portion of the South Coast's landscape, and species that were once common and widespread now remain only on remnants of their former range. The Quino checkerspot butterfly illustrates this trend and demonstrates the importance of habitat connectivity in maintaining resilient wildlife populations. Regional growth also affects species that depend on unique, narrowly distributed habitat types. Urbanization can severely reduce already-limited habitat areas. The light-footed clapper rail, for example, relies on coastal salt marsh habitats and has been notably affected by coastal development.

Quino Checkerspot Butterfly

Debbie Leonard

Until the 1950s, the Quino checkerspot butterfly was abundant in southern California (USFWS 2003b). Its historic range included coastal areas from Los Angeles County south into northwestern Baja California and the inland valleys south of the Tehachapi Mountains. The butterfly inhabits coastal sage scrub, open chaparral, juniper woodlands, and native grasslands and ranges from approximately 500 feet to 5,000 feet above sea level (USFWS 2003b). Suitable habitat areas offer larval host plants, adult nectar resources, and diverse topography that includes ridges and hilltops.

The butterfly has been eliminated from more than 75 percent of its former range, including 90 percent of its coastal mesa and bluff distribution (USFWS 2003b). It is now rare even within remaining habitats, occurring at such low densities that it was once thought to be extinct. After nearly 10 years with no sightings, in the early 1990s the Quino checkerspot butterfly was rediscovered in Riverside and San Diego counties. It is presently found only in those two counties and northwestern Baja California. The butterfly was federally listed as endangered in 1997.

In this highly urbanized region, habitat loss and fragmentation are the most significant threats to the Quino checkerspot. Remaining habitats are often degraded by recreational vehicle use, unauthorized dumping, and grazing (USFWS 2003b). These fragmented areas are also vulnerable to incursion by **invasive** species, including predatory Argentine ants, Brazilian fire ants, and Mediterranean annual grasses. A major threat to the butterfly's remaining habitat is conversion of native vegetation communities to non-native annual grasslands, a process facilitated by increased fire frequency resulting primarily from human activity (Keeley 2004).

The U.S. Fish and Wildlife Service recovery plan for the Quino checkerspot recommends immediate protection (via acquisition and easement) of remaining habitats and active management and restoration of native vegetation communities in habitats that presently support the butterfly. Landscape connectivity is very important for the stability and resilience of this species. Quino checkerspot butterfly populations naturally fluctuate sharply in response to environmental changes. In some cases, butterfly subpopulations have disappeared from protected areas when development isolated those areas from other habitat patches (USFWS 2003b). Therefore, it is critical to protect large habitat areas that are buffered from surrounding development. These areas can also support larger butterfly populations that are less likely to be quickly **extirpated** by changing environmental conditions. Protection of dispersal corridors between occupied habitat areas is also crucial for recolonization and genetic exchange (USFWS 2003b). Research needs include investigating the species' life history requirements and understanding the effects of fires on butterfly populations and host plants.

Light-footed Clapper Rail

A subspecies of clapper rail, the light-footed clapper rail inhabits coastal cordgrass-pickleweed salt marshes from Santa Barbara County to northern Baja California. Over the last two decades, survey counts of the California population have ranged from 142 breeding pairs (in 1985) to 350 (in 2004), representing one of the smallest known populations of any bird on the North American Pacific coast (CDFG 2005b). Light-footed clapper rails

are protected as a federally listed endangered species and by the state's designation as an endangered and fully protected species.

Over the past century, the greatest threats to the light-footed clapper rail have been degradation and destruction of habitat. The majority of Southern California's coastal wetlands have been drained or filled and converted to agricultural and urban uses. No more than one-third of the habitat's historical extent remains (CDFG 2004, 2005b).

The South Coast's salt marshes are naturally relatively limited in extent and scattered along the coast, mostly at river mouths. Thus, even historically, the rails' distribution was discontinuous and restricted to limited areas. With many of these historical habitat areas eliminated or degraded, the distribution of light-footed clapper rails has become even more limited and disconnected.

Most salt marshes along the California coastline once supported clapper rails (USFWS 1985). Currently, most of the light-footed clapper rails in California occur at three sites: Upper Newport Bay Ecological Reserve in Orange County; Tijuana River Marsh National Estuarine Research Reserve in San Diego County; and Anaheim Bay in Orange County (CDFG 2005b). Sixteen other sites host the birds but have very few breeding pairs (CDFG 2004, 2005b). Remaining rail populations are isolated from each other and tend to have low dispersal rates and low genetic variability (CDFG 2004, 2005b).

Introduced predators, including feral cats, red foxes, and black rats, have also proven a substantial threat to light-footed clapper rails (USFWS 1985, CDFG 2005b). Where development encroaches on wetland habitats, predators have greater access to rail habitats, and their population numbers are higher.

The U.S. Fish and Wildlife Service 1985 recovery plan recommended enhancing and restoring marsh habitat and preserving tidal action by keeping marshes open to the sea. Minimizing human disturbance and losses to predators were also important priorities. More recently, programs to aid genetic mixing and to augment existing populations have been initiated. These include efforts to move eggs and young rails to restored marshes and a captive breeding program (CDFG 2005b).

Over the last two decades, a number of important coastal wetland sites (including Upper Newport Bay in Orange County, Goleta Slough in Santa Barbara County, and Tijuana Marsh in San Diego County) have been protected. In recent years, clapper rail numbers have shown an upward trend. In 2004, a total of 350 breeding pairs were recorded, up from 286 in 2003 (CDFG 2005b). However, birds reared in captivity have been released in California and may have contributed to this increase. Overall, the species is believed to be responding to major habitat protection and restoration programs combined with increased predator control at key locations. Nonetheless, year-to-year fluctuations in the population and in the number of occupied marshes, along with the small total population size, demonstrate that the species remains critically endangered (CDFG 2005b). Continuing predator control, restoration, and protection of remaining coastal salt marsh habitats are needed for the survival of the light-footed clapper rail (CDFG 2005b).

Stressors Affecting Wildlife and Habitats

- Growth and development
- Water management conflicts and degradation of aquatic ecosystems
- Invasive species
- Altered fire regimes
- Recreational pressures

Growth and Development

Intensive population and development pressures have resulted in a greater number of threatened and endangered species in the South Coast region than any other location in the continental U.S. (USGS 2003). By far, the most significant stressor on the South Coast's wildlife is urban, suburban, and rural development and resulting habitat loss and fragmentation. With approximately 18.5 million residents, the area is the state's most populous region (CDOF 2004). Nearly half of California's residents live in a region that encompasses less than one-tenth of the state's land area (FRAP 1997).

Following World War II, Southern California experienced an economic and population boom spurred by military and industrial growth. The region's development patterns followed agricultural land uses and the availability of easily developed land. Across inland valleys that had supported citrus orchards and grazing, small agricultural towns grew to meet the needs of growing industry. Along the coast, development spread across the relatively flat coastal plains and mesas. Between 1940 and 2000, Los Angeles County grew from 2.79 million residents to 9.52 million, San Diego County from 289,000 to 2.81 million, and Orange County from 131,000 to 2.85 million (CDOF 2004, SCAG 2004).

Large portions of the region's natural areas have been converted to other uses; currently, nearly 40 percent the South Coast's land area is in urban and suburban use (California Legacy Project/UC Davis Information Center for the Environment 2004, CDF 2002). Beyond the immediate footprint of development, urban, suburban, and rural growth patterns have fractured the landscape. Land-use planning and zoning laws have allowed sprawling development, including residential projects that are located far from existing urban centers, requiring new roads and infrastructure, along with communities designed with large lot sizes and little or no preserved open space. Presently, the region's remaining rural areas and natural lands are highly threatened by zoning for 4- to 8-acre lots for rural ranchette-style development.

As in other regions, these development patterns not only reduce the amount of habitat available but also degrade the quality of adjacent habitat. With the expansion of the urban-wildland interface, remaining natural lands become more vulnerable to the incursion of invasive plants and animals, air and water pollution, and altered **fire regimes**. Developed areas, roads, and utility corridors fragment landscapes and sever connections between habitat areas.

Water Management Conflicts and Degradation of Aquatic Ecosystems

The region's aquatic habitats—perennial and ephemeral rivers and streams, riparian areas, vernal pools, and coastal wetlands—support a diverse array of flora and fauna, including 150 animal and 52 plant species that are designated state or federal special status species (CCC 2001). Many of the South Coast's streams and rivers flow to the coast over steeply sloping terrain. These high-gradient waterways naturally carry high sediment loads and experience highly variable flows in response to rainfall. Riparian forests occur primarily along the region's waterways that travel over more gradually sloping topography. Historically, all of Southern California's rivers that flowed to the ocean supported river-mouth estuaries that transitioned from riparian areas to freshwater, brackish, and salt marshes. However, owing to the region's rugged coastal topography and narrow coastal shelf, coastal wetland systems were never as extensive as on the Atlantic or Gulf coasts.

Coastal and inland wetlands provide important wildlife habitat and serve important ecological functions, including filtering and transforming pollutants in runoff water, controlling floods, moderating sediment delivery, promoting groundwater recharge, and protecting shorelines from erosion.

Population growth and development have severely altered the region's waterways and wetlands. Flood control measures, utilization of rivers for water supply and limited hydropower development, generation of pollutants, and draining of wetlands have accompanied urbanization. Loss of historical acreage is estimated at 90 percent across all of the region's wetland types.

Vernal Pools

Vernal pools occur in small depressions underlain by impenetrable clay soils that allow water to accumulate in winter and spring wet seasons. The pools host a unique community of invertebrates and annual plants that, in turn, constitute an important part of the food web supporting amphibians and migratory waterfowl. Many sensitive plant and animal species rely on regional vernal pools, including San Diego button celery, San Diego thornmint, San Diego fairy shrimp, and Riverside fairy shrimp, each federally listed as endangered. Now reduced to less than five percent of their historical extent (USFWS 1998a), remaining vernal pool habitats in Southern California are threatened by continued conversion to urban uses, altered hydrology (due to increased runoff caused by urbanization), and off-highway vehicle activity. Much of the region's historical vernal pool habitat occurred on coastal mesas that have been largely converted to residential developments.

River Systems and Riparian Wetlands

Many of Southern California's river systems are partially or completely channelized for flood control or diverted and dammed to supply water. The South Coast has more flood-control dams (exceeding 200), more debris basins (nearly 200), and more miles of cemented stream channel than any other region in the country (CCC 2001). The Los Angeles River, for example, is lined with concrete along 47.9 miles of its 51-mile length (LACDPW 2005). Losses of riparian wetlands are estimated to be as much as 95 percent for the region (CCC 2001). Dams for flood-control and groundwater recharge, like those on the Santa Ana and San Gabriel rivers, often release water on irregular schedules, hindering the development of downstream riparian and fish communities (Swift 2005 pers. comm.). Dam releases can also contribute to **turbidity**. The operations of wastewater treatment facilities affect instream flows, and interruptions in water releases can substantially reduce flows for limited periods of time (Swift 2005 pers. comm.). Groundwater pumping, water imports from other regions, and increased runoff from impervious land cover and residential and agricultural irrigation also affect river systems. Invasive plant species—particularly arundo and tamarisk—can also alter river flows substantially. (See additional discussion in Invasive Species section.)

Sediment transport and deposition by waterways is a natural process and can create important habitat features for some species. For example, arroyo toad breeding sites are created when floods deposit sediments as sandbars. However, where human activities have fragmented **watershed** and changed natural sediment dynamics and flow regimes, sedimen-

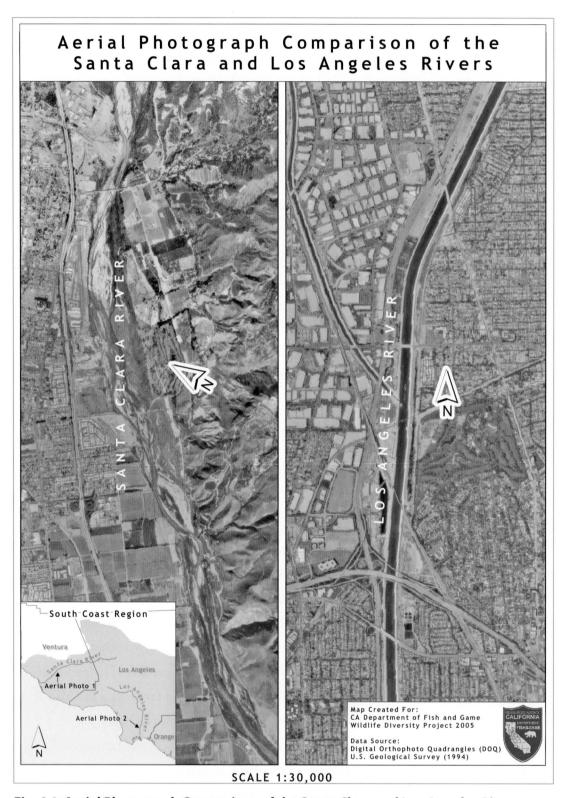

Fig. 9.1: Aerial Photograph Comparison of the Santa Clara and Los Angeles Rivers
The Los Angeles River has been channelized along most of its length, while the Santa Clara River remains free-flowing and retains its natural channel structure. Channelized rivers lose important habitat features such as braided-channel structure, backwater areas, and variable depth and flow.

tation events can be devastating for aquatic habitats and species. Intensive recreational uses, ground disturbance due to development, and wildfires can increase erosion and sediment deposition. Dams can also accumulate and release flushes of sediment. Fine sediments and silt cover natural creekbed substrates and fill in deep pools, degrading important habitats for native fish and invertebrates. Historically, greater connectivity between watersheds allowed species to recolonize after sedimentation events. Today, however, roads and water diversions have fragmented and isolated stream systems, making it difficult for species to recolonize areas where they have been locally extirpated.

Hydrologically, many of the region's rivers scarcely resemble their natural state, due to alterations of the quantity and timing of surface water flows, sediment transport functions, and flood regimes (CCC 2001). Water pollution is also a serious issue for the region's rivers, with water quality degraded by urban runoff, wastewater treatment plants, and industrial effluents.

Southern California's river and riparian habitats are important to a number of sensitive species, including least Bell's vireo (both federally and state listed as endangered), California red-legged frog (federally listed as threatened and a state species of special concern), Southern California mountain yellow-legged frog and arroyo toad (each federally listed as endangered and a state species of special concern), and southern steelhead (federally listed as threatened and a state species of concern). Steelhead illustrate the severity of the situation, having declined from historical populations in the tens of thousands to current numbers of between 200 and 300 fish (CCC 2001, Larson 2005 pers. comm.).

Coastal Wetlands

Southern California's coastal wetlands are among the most productive habitats on the Pacific Coast, providing feeding and nesting habitat for birds on the Pacific flyway and important nursery habitats for oceanic and estuarine fish. More than 60 species of fish and at least 195 species of birds have been recorded in Southern California wetlands (CCC 2001). Habitats range from salt marshes with associated tidal channels and mudflats to river mouth estuaries, canyon mouth estuaries, bays, and lagoons. The U.S. Fish and Wildlife Service nominated the coastal wetlands between Point Mugu in Ventura County to the Tijuana estuary as wetlands of international significance under the **Ramsar Convention** because of their importance for migratory birds, fisheries, and endangered species.

Estimates of total historical coastal wetland acreage range from 44,000 acres up to 55,000 acres. Today, only about 13,000 acres remain (CCC 2001). During the second half of the 19th

Fig. 9.2: Urban and Protected Lands Along Coast
The majority of the South Coast's coastal wetlands have been drained and filled for urban land uses. A comparison of the historic and current extent of wetlands at Huntington Beach and Upper Newport Bay illustrates this pattern.

century, federal, state, and local policies encouraged conversion of wetlands to agricultural and urban uses by draining and filling them. Urban development has replaced or degraded many coastal habitats, with urban and suburban land uses currently occurring along more than 70 percent of the coastline (CDF 2002, California Legacy Project 2004). Most remaining regional wetlands have been severely degraded by activities such as dumping, oil extraction, and creation of ponds for salt extraction and sewage treatment. Agricultural and urban runoff, wastewater treatment plants, and industrial effluents are significant pollution sources. Activities affecting the streams and rivers that feed coastal wetlands, including water diversion, flood control, and development, also degrade the wetlands. As described above, natural sediment transport processes have been altered, resulting in both sediment depletion and excessive sedimentation in coastal habitats. Dams can block sediment transport and result in depletion of coastal beach and dune areas. Construction activities that result in erosion upstream can cause excess sediment to fill in wetlands and cut off tidal flows. In the Tijuana estuary, for example, altered sedimentation regimes are believed to facilitate the establishment of non-native tamarisk, with negative effects on habitat quality for endangered bird species (Morrison 2005 pers. comm.).

The loss and degradation of Southern California's coastal wetland habitat have left many species struggling to survive, including the tidewater goby (federally listed as endangered), Belding's Savannah sparrow (state listed as endangered), light-footed clapper rail (federally and state listed as endangered), California brown pelican (federally and state listed as endangered), and California least tern (federally and state listed as endangered).

Invasive Species

As in other regions across the state, invasive species problems on the South Coast are tied to regional land use and management issues.

In terrestrial ecosystems, a number of highly aggressive non-native plant species invade grasslands and scrub, including yellow starthistle, artichoke thistle, medusahead, Pampas grass, fennel, pepper weed, black mustard, and castor bean. These species lower habitat quality for sensitive wildlife species such as the Quino checkerspot butterfly and the California gnatcatcher. Some of these species dry out earlier in the summer than native species and contribute to increased wildfire frequencies. Access roads and rights-of-way for infrastructure and powerline maintenance, as well as recreational use of natural areas, can facilitate the spread of these species.

Among terrestrial animals, Argentine ants pose a significant regional threat. Favoring irrigated areas and edge habitats, such as irrigated golf courses and residential neighborhoods, Argentine ants tend to outcompete and displace native ants in the region's fragmented landscapes, disrupting larger community food-web relationships. For example, the coast horned lizard (a state species of concern), whose major prey is native harvester ants, cannot sustain itself on a diet of Argentine ants and so can be driven locally extinct in fragmented habitat patches.

Nest parasitism by brown-headed cowbirds also threatens many of the region's sensitive bird species, including least Bell's vireo, southwestern willow flycatcher, and California gnatcatcher. Cowbirds thrive in many human-altered habitats, including suburban areas and agricultural and grazing lands, where they are attracted to livestock droppings and feed. With the expansion of these land uses over the last century, cowbirds have thrived, greatly expanding both their range and population across California. Other problems are caused by introduced red fox, feral animals, and pets, which prey upon native wildlife, particularly ground-nesting birds.

The European starling, introduced from Europe and now widespread in the region and in most human-modified habitats across much the state, aggressively competes with native woodpeckers, bluebirds, and other native song birds for cavity nest sites.

In aquatic systems, the most problematic exotic plant species is arundo, or giant reed. Arundo is widespread along major coastal river basins, particularly the Ventura, Santa Clara, Santa Ana, Santa Margarita, San Luis Rey and San Diego rivers. Tamarisk is less widespread but also invades regional riparian habitats. Tamarisk is distributed in coastal and desert drainages (Stephenson and Calcarone 1999). Both species choke waterways, increase flash flood risks, crowd out native plants, and provide inferior habitat for riparian species. Tamarisk also consumes prodigious amounts of water, reducing available surface water, and arundo provides limited shade, resulting in higher water temperatures and lower dissolved oxygen levels.

Among exotic wildlife species, bullfrogs, African clawed frogs, non-native crayfish, mosquito fish (which are sometimes introduced for mosquito control), and introduced sport and bait fish (including sunfish, bass, and bluegill) all pose predatory or competitive threats to native fish and amphibians. Many of these species are well adapted to the deep water conditions in ponded areas above dams, and dam releases can introduce them to downstream habitats. Most voracious and widespread are bullfrogs, which are documented predators of California red-legged frogs, arroyo toads, Western pond turtles, and two-striped garter snakes (Stephenson and Calcarone 1999). A broad diet and an extended breeding season give bullfrogs a competitive advantage over native amphibians. Bullfrogs are also favored by human-modified habitats. They can tolerate elevated water temperatures and, unlike native amphibians, make use of standing pools resulting from urban runoff to complete their two-year life cycle.

Altered Fire Regimes

Wildfire is a natural and important ecological process in the South Coast. Widespread forest management practices, as well as increases in human-caused wildfires, have altered fire regimes, in some cases causing dramatic changes in regional habitats. Efforts to establish fire regimes that approximate historical fire patterns and frequencies while also minimizing loss of property and life are important to maintain and restore wildlife habitat.

Dry conditions and annual hot, dry Santa Ana winds make all of the region's ecosystems fire-prone. Between 1999 and 2003, the South Coast experienced a four-year drought that left these ecosystems especially dry and vulnerable to fire. Furthermore, the expansion of residential development into rural and natural areas has increased the incidence of human-caused fire. In the 1990s and early 2000s, extensive wildfires affected the entire region, and costs from property loss and fire suppression have risen into billions of dollars annually. In 2003, almost 400,000 acres burned, costing more than $1.2 billion for fire suppression efforts and to repair damages resulting from the fires (CDF 2004).

The causes and ecological consequences of wildfires differ among the region's ecological communities. In sage scrub, chaparral, and grassland systems, lightning-induced fires are fairly infrequent. Human-caused fires, however, have resulted in unnaturally high fire frequencies, especially along roads and near the urban-wildland interface, with some locations experiencing three fires within a period of 15 to 20 years (Spencer 2004 pers. comm.). Increased fire frequencies favor the Mediterranean grasses that were introduced to the region with the arrival of European settlers and livestock. Once established, the non-native grasses grow in a dense-thatch pattern that chokes out native vegetation and lowers habitat quality for wildlife. The dense grass also provides ample fuel for the cycle of frequent burning (Keeley 2004).

Attempts at fire prevention have not stopped the region's scrub and chaparral lands from burning, and it is the rate of human-caused fire and the Santa Ana wind conditions, rather than fuel build-up, that determines the extent and frequency of wildfire in these systems (Halsey 2004, Keeley 2001). Although frequent fires can promote the spread of non-native grasses, fire's effects on grassland and shrubland ecosystems depend on the time of year the fire occurs. Prescribed burning can be an effective management tool, with spring fires helping to control invasive exotics if they occur before exotic plants set seed.

Fire management issues in forest communities are different than those in scrub, chaparral, and grasslands. Lightning-induced wildfires are a more regular part of the ecology of the South Coast's coniferous forests and oak woodlands and do not result in the same threat of conversion to non-native grasslands. In some forest communities, fire suppression and other forest management practices—including livestock grazing and historical logging practices—have led to dense, even-aged forest stands, fuels buildup, and other changes to forest structure and composition (Baker and Shinneman 2004, Kaufmann 2004). In some forests, the density of white fir and incense cedar has increased at the expense of live and black oaks, which are very important to many wildlife species, including acorn woodpecker, band-tailed pigeon, black bear, and dusky-footed woodrat (Loe 2004 pers. comm.). Western pine bark beetle infestations have killed 50 percent of the coniferous trees in the region's drought-stressed forests, making forests more fire-prone (Loe 2004 pers. comm.). The relative importance of these various factors in shaping fire patterns in the region's forests is uncertain.

Climate is also a primary determinant of fire patterns (Halsey 2004). In light of this, climate change will add a significant variable to efforts to understand historical fire regimes and to find management measures that can maintain the region's mosaic of habitats (Grissino-Mayer and Swetnam 2000). Additionally, the expansion of residential communities into fire-dependent forest ecosystems creates a conflict between maintaining forests' ecological integrity and protecting property.

Recreational Pressures

With nearly 20 million people living within driving distance of the region's national forests and other public lands, recreational access and its subsequent effects are a major concern. Recreational off-road vehicle use can have adverse effects on natural communities and sensitive species. On public lands, off-road vehicle trails open relatively undisturbed areas to increased use. The vehicles can disturb or run over wildlife, crush and uproot plants, spread seeds of invasive plants, and disturb soils, contributing to erosion and sedimentation of aquatic habitats (Hall 1980). Off-road vehicle use also increases the risk of human-caused fires.

Concentrated recreational use of streams and riparian areas is particularly troublesome. Not only off-road vehicles but hikers, picnickers, and equestrians in large numbers can damage these systems, reducing vegetative cover and disturbing sensitive species. Some recreational users build rock dams on streams to create ponds for swimming. The San Gabriel River, for example, has been altered by extensive ponded areas, as well as other effects of heavy recreational use, such as the deposition of trash and human waste (Ally 2001, Miller 2005 pers. comm.). Particularly vulnerable riparian species include the two-striped garter snake, mountain yellow-legged frog, and arroyo toad (Stephenson and Calcarone 1999). The mountain yellow-legged frog, which once lived in more than 50 of the national forests' creeks, is now limited to a handful of those creeks, and biologists have documented trampling of their egg masses by hikers (Stephenson and Calcarone 1999).

Conservation Actions to Restore and Conserve Wildlife

In addition to the recommended regional actions described below, see the recommended statewide conservation actions as given in Chapter 4.

a. Wildlife agencies and local governments should work to improve the development and implementation of regional Natural Community Conservation Plans (NCCPs), which is the primary process to conserve habitat and species in the region's rapidly urbanizing areas.

See discussion of Southern California NCCP at the end of this chapter and the conservation planning section in Chapter 6.

The U.S. Fish and Wildlife Service and Fish and Game need additional conservation planning staff and additional funds to ensure the intended implementation of NCCPs and to meet their obligations under the plans. Wildlife agencies must help carry out the management and monitoring of preserve system lands and ensure that local partners are carrying out their responsibilities.

For local governments currently working on NCCPs, or in areas where new NCCPs are being developed, the state could facilitate local governments' participation in the planning process by providing educational materials, leadership training, and collaborative group forums to educate local leaders about conservation planning.

Plans that are still under development should include guidelines directing federal, state, and local agencies to coordinate management and monitoring on public reserve lands, regardless of the lands' ownership. Within plan areas, multiagency management and monitoring teams should be used where possible to increase efficiency and improve effectiveness.

Fish and Game is working to standardize monitoring across preserve lands and to develop a centrally accessible repository for biological data (known as BIOS), including NCCP monitoring data. Additional funding is needed to continue the development of BIOS. (For more information on BIOS, see Appendix D.)

Monitoring data from local reserve lands should be used to inform collaborative adaptive management for all reserve lands in the region.

The state should evaluate the potential benefits and applicability of developing NCCPs for Santa Barbara, Ventura, and San Bernardino counties.

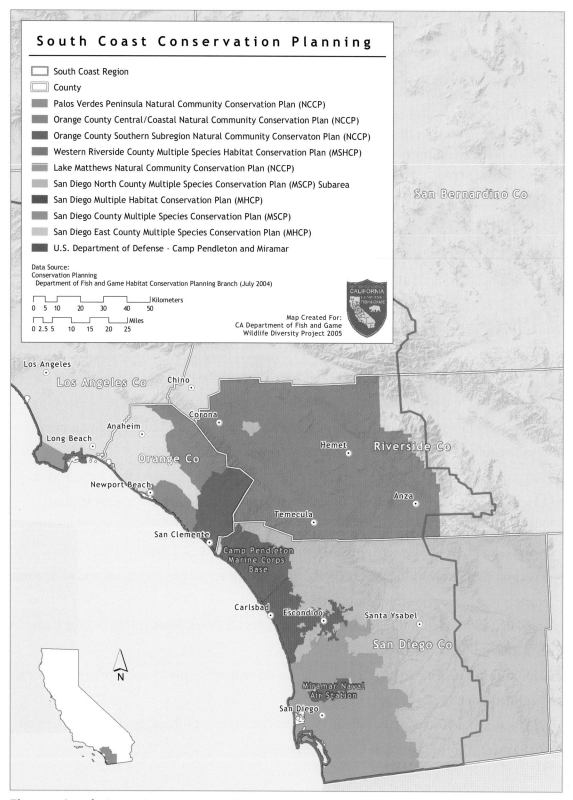

Fig. 9.3: South Coast Conservation Planning
Natural Community Conservation Planning efforts by local jurisdictions cover more than 3.7 million acres in Southern California.

The Orange County Southern Subregion NCCP

There are a number of NCCPs under development in the South Coast, all of which will require continued staffing and funding to complete. Completion of the Orange County Southern Subregion NCCP is of particular concern because of imminent development threats in the plan area. Continuing attention and negotiation will be required if the plan is to achieve its conservation purpose.

Wildlife agencies, land owners, and local governments should complete Natural Community Conservation Planning for the Orange County Southern Subregion. The plan should address the entire Rancho Mission Viejo Company's property and the Foothill-Trabuco area, which provides important biological connectivity to habitat areas in the Orange County Central Coastal Subregion and the Western Riverside Multi-Species Habitat Conservation Plan.

The Rancho Mission Viejo property is ecologically important because it constitutes a core block of habitat continuous with Camp Pendleton's open space and creates continuity with portions of Cleveland National Forest and other smaller conservation lands belonging to the Audubon Society and Caspers Regional Park. The San Mateo Creek watershed, of which the ranch is a part, supports high-quality coastal sage scrub habitat and is one of few South Coast drainages with a returning steelhead trout population.

Plans for residential and commercial subdivisions on the Rancho Mission Viejo Company's property have been approved by Orange County in advance of the anticipated NCCP plan. Continued conservation planning for the area through the Orange County Southern Subregion NCCP process is important. A comprehensive conservation strategy will most effectively address the effects of development and the mitigation requirements for the **take** of protected species.

b. Wildlife agencies should establish regional goals for species and habitat protection and work with city, county, and state agency land-use planning processes to accomplish those goals.

See Statewide Action a in Chapter 4.

Priorities specific to this region include:

As a complement to NCCP planning, wildlife agencies should work with local governments to develop General Plans and zoning regulations that are compatible with conservation goals. In particular, local land-use plans should direct growth within established communities and along existing infrastructure and transportation corridors, restrict rural residential subdivision, and support those ranching and agricultural land uses that maintain habitat values and benefit environmental quality.

Land-use planning should be improved to limit the expansion of residential development into wildland and open space areas. Among the benefits of limiting the urban-wildland interface would be a decrease in the incidence of human-caused fires, which would, in turn, reduce the need for fire management practices that disturb ecologically intact habitat lands, prevent unnaturally frequent fire frequencies that promote the expansion of non-native grasses into native vegetation communities, and decrease fire risks to human life and property.

For further discussion of goals and means for improved integration of conservation planning with land-use planning, see the conservation planning section in Chapter 6.

c. Safeguard and build upon Camp Pendleton's contribution to the regional network of conservation lands. Similarly, protect habitats on lands adjacent to the Marine Corps Air Station Miramar.

Management of the base property and any future plans for the base should ensure protection of sensitive species and important habitats on this critical property.

Currently, Camp Pendleton's management of natural resources is guided by an Integrated Natural Resources Management Plan (http://www.cpp.usmc.mil/base/environmental/inrmp. htm) as well as a Programmatic Assessment for riparian, estuarine, and beach ecosystems. (See description of Camp Pendleton at the end of this chapter.) State and federal wildlife agencies should continue to work with the base to review management success and to renew and update plans as needed. Completion of the Programmatic Assessment for uplands that is under development is also important. Because uplands constitute the majority of base property, this planning effort affects a larger portion of the base than previous single-species or aquatic habitat plans.

Regional conservation organizations and wildlife agencies should work with Camp Pendleton to protect important habitats, wildlife corridors, and open space areas adjacent to the base property. This should be done in a manner that protects the mission of the base, reduces conflicts between the base's mission and sensitive species, and enhances the base's contribution to the regional network of conservation lands.

Camp Pendleton has access to Department of Defense funds to invest in conservation activities in areas surrounding the base. In order to apply these funds to land acquisition, the base needs suitable partners to serve as landholders; such partners could include nongovernmental conservation organizations or public agencies, such as counties establishing their NCCP reserve networks.

Although Camp Pendleton's primary mission is military training, natural resources management is also an important goal. Currently, Camp Pendleton's management of natural resources is guided by an Integrated Natural Resources Management Plan (US DOD 2001) as well as a Programmatic Assessment for riparian, estuarine, and beach ecosystems. The first is the Santa Margarita River corridor, which connects Camp Pendleton to protected lands abutting Cleveland National Forest and a series of inland mountain ranges. Camp Pendleton is collaborating with the South Coast Missing Linkages Project and the South Coast Conservation Forum (a consortium of regional conservation interests that includes San Diego State University Field Stations Programs, The Nature Conservancy, Trust for Public Land, and Riverside and San Diego counties) to identify opportunities to protect this area. See further discussion of the Santa Ana-Palomar linkage in action item d, below.

Also important are Rancho Mission Viejo Company's currently undeveloped ranch lands adjacent to the base's northern boundary. Opportunities to protect this area include continued conservation planning for the area through the Orange County Southern Subregion NCCP process, purchase of lands by conservation buyers, and collaboration with the U.S. Army Corps of Engineers Special Area Management Plan to protect and restore the San Juan Creek and San Mateo Creek watersheds. Marine Corps Air Station Miramar and adjacent lands provide habitat for wildlife species at risk, have sensitive plant species and vernal pools, and serve as wildlife corridors for the region. Conserving adjacent lands to the base will benefit biodiversity in the region. (Additional information can be found at http:// www.miramar.usmc.mil/WebPages/Environmental/IntegratedNaturalResources.htm.)

d. To address regional habitat fragmentation, federal, state, and local agencies, along with nongovernmental conservation organizations, should support the protection of the priority wildlands linkages identified by the South Coast Missing Linkages project.

See Statewide Action d in Chapter 4.

Priorities specific to this region include:

The South Coast Missing Linkages project aims to protect the remaining corridors between regional wildlands and natural areas that allow them to function as one interconnected ecological system. Based on the size of the connected habitat areas, degree of threat, and irreplaceablity, 15 linkage areas have been designated as high-priority conserva-

Tim Palmer

tion issues for the region. Given the patterns of urbanization and protected lands in the region, these are primarily linkages between mountain ranges having significant public ownership (e.g., National Forest lands).

Creating and maintaining these linkages will require a combination of land protection through acquisitions and easements, focused habitat management, and construction of underpasses and overpasses to enable wildlife to get across major roadways. Public agencies and nongovernmental conservation organizations should work to support and build upon existing protection activities in these linkages.

The Santa Ana–Palomar linkage and the Tehachapi linkage are two priority linkages where protection activities are under way. The Santa Ana–Palomar linkage extends from the Camp Pendleton Marine Corps Base and Fallbrook Naval Weapons Station in the west to the Cleveland National Forest Palomar Range District in the east. This linkage is made up of the last remaining natural habitats that connect the Santa Ana Mountains and the coastal lowland areas of Camp Pendleton to an inland chain of largely protected mountain ranges (the Palomar, San Diego, San Jacinto, and San Bernardino mountains).

The Tehachapi linkage serves to connect the natural lands of the South Coast with habitats in other regions. It is the sole remaining wildland connection between two major mountain systems, the Sierra Nevada and the Sierra Madre, and links the Sequoia and Los Padres national forests. The linkage area lies at the confluence of four regions, the South Coast, Sierra Nevada, Central Valley, and Mojave Desert, each with its own distinct terrain, flora, and climate patterns. The convergence of these biogeographic elements in one contiguous area underlies the Tehachapi linkage's remarkable biodiversity (CBI 2004b, Penrod et al. 2003). The area supports 23 different vegetation communities, including low-elevation grasslands and oak woodlands that are underprotected in the region. The area also provides designated critical habitat for the endangered California condor and potential habitat for as many as 20 state and federally listed species and more than 60 other rare and endemic species (CBI 2004b).

e. Federal, state, and local agencies, along with nongovernmental conservation organizations, should protect and restore the best remaining examples of coastal wetlands that provide important wildlife habitat.

Wildlife agencies and conservation organizations should continue to utilize and build on the work of the Southern California Wetlands Recovery Program to develop a regional prioritization plan for the protection and restoration of Southern California's wetlands. The Wetlands Recovery Program is a collaborative effort of public agencies, including the California Coastal Conservancy, county task forces, Fish and Game, the National Marine Fisheries Service, the U.S. Fish and Wildlife Service, and others. The program has worked to identify priority sites for acquisition and restoration efforts, to develop plans for priority sites, and to identify opportunities to develop partnerships and to pool funds to undertake these projects. (More information can be found at http://www.scwrp.org.)

Important conservation actions identified in the Southern California Wetlands Recovery Program Regional Strategy include:

- Acquiring or negotiating conservation easements on remaining coastal wetlands that are partially or entirely in private ownership. These include Ormond Beach/Oxnard Plain in Ventura County, Los Cerritos Wetlands in Orange and Los Angeles counties, and Huntington Beach/Santa Ana River mouth in Orange County.
- Completing coastal wetland restoration projects that are currently under way to protect remaining coastal wetland species. Needed restoration activities include removing excess sediment resulting from development and construction; rerouting of excess freshwater runoff inputs; excavating channels to restore tidal exchange; controlling invasive species; improving habitats affected by highway and railway crossings; and removing derelict oil wells and infrastructure. Restoration along inflowing waterways is also needed to address sediment,

nutrient, and contaminant inputs. The most significant coastal wetland restoration projects being planned or implemented include the south arm of the Tijuana Estuary in San Diego County; coastal lagoons in northern San Diego County; Upper Newport Bay in Orange County; Huntington Beach Wetlands in Orange County; Bolsa Chica Wetlands in Orange County; Ballona Wetlands in Los Angeles County; Ormond Beach/Oxnard Plain in Ventura County; and Goleta Slough in Santa Barbara County.

f. Public agencies and nongovernmental conservation organizations should invest in efforts to protect and restore the best remaining regional examples of ecologically intact river systems.

Benefits to water quality and sensitive aquatic species can be achieved by preserving natural functioning in aquatic systems. Riparian vegetation, wetlands, and large natural land areas within a watershed filter inflow and reduce nutrient, bacteria, sediment, and other pollutant levels. Native species are often adapted to natural seasonal flow regimes. The remaining riparian habitat of the South Coast Region also serves as important stopover habitat for migratory birds, as well as essential breeding habitat for listed species such as the southwestern willow flycatcher and the least Bell's vireo.

Efforts to maintain relatively intact systems are more cost effective than subsequent measures to mitigate environmental damage, treat degraded water quality, or restore dramatically altered systems.

Restoration and protection efforts should be focused on the region's most ecologically intact drainages, which include those that provide existing or potential habitat for southern steelhead trout; those that remain largely unchannelized; those that support riparian vegetation communities; and those with functioning floodplains (or where construction and development in riparian areas is limited enough to reestablish functioning floodplains).

Because of the high level of urbanization in the South Coast Region, even the most intact systems will typically need some restoration work. Important restoration actions include enhancing riparian habitat and vegetation; relocating or removing confining levees to allow river-channel meandering and reconnection of rivers with their floodplains; removing dams, diversions, or other obstacles to sediment transport and fish passage; and providing more water for instream flows.

To protect water quality and aquatic habitats, wildlife agencies, local governments, and conservation organizations should work to protect land and limit development within targeted priority watersheds through acquisitions, easements, or zoning regulations. Recognizing these benefits and applying water quality protection and flood-control funds to land protection mark an innovative use of state conservation bond funds.

Regionally, important opportunities to protect and restore largely intact drainages include the Santa Clara, Ventura, Santa Margarita, San Jacinto, and San Luis Rey rivers and San Mateo Creek (California Legacy Project 2003, CCC 2001, Morrison 2004 pers. comm.).

g. Federal, state, and local agencies should provide greater resources and coordinate efforts to eradicate or control existing occurrences of invasive species and to prevent new introductions.

See Statewide Action f in Chapter 4.

Priorities specific to this region include:

Agencies should increase efforts to control invasive aquatic animals, particularly bullfrog, African clawed frog, and introduced crayfish species, through a combination of eradication and trapping efforts and improved water-management practices. Drainage systems for urban runoff water should be altered where necessary to avoid conditions that favor bullfrogs.

Agencies should design and implement measures to prevent infrastructure development and utility maintenance projects from introducing non-native species. Ensure that public works projects, such as post-fire reseeding projects to prevent erosion, are carried out with native species.

Agencies and conservation organizations should increase public education about invasive species, including the potential threats presented by the release of aquarium fish or plant species.

h. Federal, state, and local public agencies should sufficiently protect sensitive species and important wildlife habitats on their lands and should be adequately funded and staffed to do so.

Across the South Coast, public lands total nearly 2.4 million acres, or nearly 34 percent of the region. The U.S. Forest Service is the region's largest public land manager; together, the Cleveland, San Bernardino, and Angeles national forests encompass 1.7 million acres. Other public land agencies with substantial land management responsibilities include BLM, with more than 150,000 acres; Camp Pendleton Marine Base and Air Station, with 125,000 acres; Marine Corps Air Station Miramar, with 23,000 acres; California Department of Parks and Recreation, with 114,000 acres; Fish and Game, with more than 60,000 acres; the National Park Service, with more than 22,000 acres; the U.S. Fish and Wildlife Service, with 11,000 acres; and city and county parks that total 44,000 acres, including many coastal wetland reserves.

Because of the high level of urbanization in the region, many of the region's public lands are vulnerable to the negative ecological effects of nearby development, including the spread of invasive species, air and water pollution, and altered fire regimes. Dumping, trespass, and illegal off-highway vehicle use can also present major challenges. As a result of these pressures, public agencies need adequate staff and funding resources for management.

Public agencies should adopt management policies that safeguard natural resources and wildlife habitat, even as they manage for multiple uses or for mandates that emphasize other objectives.

- Public agencies should monitor all public and recreational uses, and, through adaptive management, determine the appropriate uses for a specific area. Where agencies determine that use restrictions are needed to protect sensitive species and habitats, those restrictions should be adequately enforced.

- Streams and watersheds on public lands should be protected and restored. In light of the stresses posed by drought and human water use, public agencies should work to provide adequate instream flows for aquatic species by reducing or eliminating water diversions on public lands.

- Infrastructure and resource-extraction projects should be designed and sited to avoid harmful effects on sensitive species and habitats and to preserve connectivity between existing natural lands and habitat areas.

- Based on the best available science and site-specific conditions, fire management policies and practices should be designed to restore the ecological integrity of the region's natural communities.

- Public agencies, along with nongovernmental conservation organizations, should work to protect lands that enhance the ecological and habitat values of existing public lands. Means for protection may include employing conservation easements and management agreements with landowners and acquiring public land from willing sellers. Priority areas for protection include private inholdings within the national forests, adjacent natural areas that buffer against the adverse effects of urbanization, and areas where development pressures threaten connectivity between public lands.

i. **Federal and state agencies and nongovernmental partners should collaborate to institute appropriate fire management policies and practices to restore the ecological integrity of the region's ecosystems while minimizing loss of property and life.**

- Continued research is needed to better understand the fire regimes required to maintain the health of different vegetation communities (shrub, chaparral, grasslands, and forests) and to understand the most ecologically appropriate management for lands that have experienced large-scale wildfires.

- State and federal land managers and wildlife biologists should work cooperatively to design prescribed-fire treatments and other management practices that will mimic the ecological role of wildfire in creating habitat mosaics.
- Fuel control treatments and fire suppression efforts should be focused on the interface between residential areas and wildlands.

j. The state should coordinate the development of a model ordinance and building codes for new or expanding communities in fire-adapted landscapes to make those communities more fire compatible and reduce the state's liability for fire suppression.

Counties need to consider adopting development restrictions requiring planning and accommodation for wildfire consistent with the local historical fire regime, and such measures should be incorporated into the public-safety elements of the county General Plans. In addition, specific ordinances should be adopted:

- The model ordinances should address the design of new development to ensure new communities are safer and compatible with natural forest fires.
- The model ordinances should address maintenance of existing residential and commercial areas to ensure firebreaks are maintained to improve compatibility with forest fires.
- Model building codes should specify that all new construction employ materials and design features to make them more fire resistant.
- The state should encourage adoption of the model fire ordinances and building codes by cities and counties in forested areas.

k. State and federal wildlife agencies, the U.S. Forest Service, state and county parks, BLM, and nongovernmental partners should collaborate to develop a comprehensive Southern California Outdoor Recreation Program to provide recreational opportunities and access that do not conflict with wildlife habitat needs.

With more than 18 million people living within driving distance of many of the region's public lands, the demand for outdoor recreation opportunities and the resulting pressures on natural resources continue to increase.

A comprehensive, regionwide program is needed to evaluate which public land areas are most appropriate for different forms of recreation, to develop recreational opportunities in these areas, and to direct inappropriate recreational uses away from biologically sensitive areas and important wildlife habitats. The program should determine where funding for recreational facilities and access should be directed, where user fees should be instituted, and where public safety and law enforcement staff are most needed. Additionally, education programs should be expanded to provide information about which public land areas are open to which uses, about how to minimize the impacts of recreation, and about the unique natural resources of the South Coast.

Southern California Natural Community Conservation Planning

The California Natural Community Conservation Planning (NCCP) program, initiated in 1991, has been a primary tool to address habitat loss and limit fragmentation in the region. (See additional discussion of NCCPs in Chapter 6.) The program brings together state and federal wildlife agencies, local governments, developers, landowners, and other stakeholders to collaborate on regional conservation plans. The plans designate where and how much development can occur and identify areas that are important to preserve as habitat for protected or sensitive species. The program's goal is to create regional reserve networks of relatively large, connected habitat blocks rather than protecting species on a species-by-species, project-by-project basis. Once a regional plan is approved by the U.S. Fish and Wildlife Service and the California Department of Fish and Game—including guidelines for permissible development and for the establishment of a permanent reserve system—local jurisdictions receive federal and state permits for the take of species covered in the plan.

The initial focus of the NCCP effort was the coastal sage scrub ecosystem. The decline of coastal sage scrub and the California gnatcatcher illustrates the toll that Southern California's population growth has taken on regional wildlife. As of the early 1990s, about 400,000 acres of sage scrub remained, representing no more than 18 percent of its historic extent (Jasny et al. 1997, Pollak 2001a). Scattered in patches across five counties, the remaining sage scrub resembled islands in a sea of development and was often degraded by grazing, weed invasion, fires, recreation, and other human impacts (Pollak 2001a).

The gnatcatcher exemplified the issues that brought a sense of crisis to conservation issues in Southern California. Once considered common, the sage-scrub-dependent California gnatcatcher was steadily declining. The U.S. Fish and Wildlife Service estimated in 1993 that fewer than 2,500 gnatcatcher pairs remained (Jasny et al. 1997), and the species was proposed for listing under the Endangered Species Act. Local development interests believed that federal protection of the bird could have halted development on large areas of highly valued coastal land. The proposed federal and California Endangered Species Act listings of the gnatcatcher seemed to place economic interests and wildlife conservation on a collision course.

Under the leadership of the state, and with the support of the Department of the Interior, California's NCCP program was developed to help avert conflict. In 1993, the gnatcatcher was federally listed as threatened. Accompanying the listing were interim rules that tied into the NCCP process, allowing the limited take of gnatcatchers until an NCCP plan is approved and permitted. These rules authorized the loss of up to 5 percent of the remaining coastal scrub habitat, so long as it resulted from activities conducted in accordance with the NCCP guidelines and wouldn't preclude design and creation of an adequate reserve system. The loss of coastal sage scrub habitat also required appropriate mitigation (USFWS 1993b).

Once adopted, final NCCPs will supersede the interim take rules, and federal and state permits for the take of species covered in the plan will be granted along with the plan's final approval.

The Southern California NCCP planning area includes portions of Los Angeles, Riverside, San Diego, Orange and San Bernardino counties. There are now nine NCCPs completed (including sub-area plans), covering an area of over 2 million acres, with 14 additional plans under way in Southern California, covering an additional 1.7 million acres. Reserve systems include existing public lands as well as private lands either purchased or dedicated through a land-use process.

The current status of the major regional plans is summarized in the table on the following page.

Table 9.3: Regional Planning Status

Local Jurisdiction Planning Effort	Approval Status	Coverage
Orange County Central-Coastal NCCP	Approved 1996	Planning area of 131,000 acres in Orange County; 37,000-acre reserve system
Orange County Southern Subregion NCCP	Planning	Planning area of 91,000 acres (33,000 of which are currently developed); reserve system size yet to be determined
Palos Verdes Peninsula NCCP (in Los Angeles County)	Near completion	Planning area of 8,559 acres on Palos Verdes Peninsula; proposed reserve system size of 1,500 acres
San Diego County MSCP (includes sub-area plans for incorporated cities, some of which are complete; others are pending and close to approval)	Approved 1997	Planning area of 582,000 acres of southwest San Diego County; includes unincorporated areas of the county and the incorporated areas of San Diego, Poway, Santee, La Mesa, Chula Vista, and El Cajon; 170,000-acre reserve system
San Diego County MHCP (includes sub-area plans for incorporated cities, one of which has been approved)	Approved 2003	Planning area of 118,000 acres in northern coastal San Diego County; includes the incorporated areas of Carlsbad, Encinitas, Escondido, Oceanside, San Marcos, Solana Beach, and Vista; 20,000-acre reserve system
San Diego North County MSCP Sub-area	Planning	Planning area of 315,000 acres in northwestern San Diego County to the east of MHCP area
San Diego East County MSCP	Planning in initial stages	Planning area of over 1 million acres in far eastern San Diego County (an area with lower development pressure)
Western San Bernardino County NCCP	Stalled; inactive	Planning area of 320,000 acres in western San Bernardino County
Western Riverside County MSHCP	Approved 2004	Planning area of 1.2 million acres; 500,000 acre reserve system

Camp Pendleton

The Camp Pendleton Marine Corps Base and Marine Corps Air Station (collectively known as Camp Pendleton) is located between two major metropolitan areas, with Los Angeles and Orange County to the north and San Diego to the south. The largely undeveloped 125,000-acre installation stands out from surrounding areas of coastal development. As on other military installations across the country, large open space areas have been preserved for training exercises. Because rapid urbanization has spared few natural areas on the South Coast, Camp Pendleton has inadvertently become a critical refuge for a number of sensitive and protected species.

Camp Pendleton is one of only two places on the South Coast where coast-to-mountains habitat continuity remains. The base hosts a variety of community types, including oak woodlands, chaparral, grasslands, coastal dunes, riparian communities, and coastal lagoons. Particularly significant habitats are vernal pools, the large extent of undeveloped shoreline (17 miles), and one of the largest remaining contiguous areas of coastal sage scrub. This habitat diversity results in a rich flora and fauna. More than 800 plant species, hundreds of invertebrate, 300 bird, 50 mammalian, 30 reptilian, 10 amphibian, and 60 fish species have been identified on Camp Pendleton. Eighteen federally protected species make use of habitats on the base, including California least tern, coastal California gnatcatcher, southwestern willow flycatcher, least Bell's vireo, light-footed clapper rail, Western snowy plover, Pacific pocket mouse, Stephens' kangaroo rat, southern steelhead trout, tidewater goby, arroyo toad, Riverside fairy shrimp, and San Diego fairy shrimp.

Camp Pendleton's management of natural resources is guided by an Integrated Natural Resources Management Plan and a Programmatic Assessment for riparian, estuarine, and beach ecosystems (a Programmatic Assessment for upland areas, including vernal pools, is forthcoming), which were developed in cooperation with the U.S. Fish and Wildlife Service and Fish and Game (MCB/MCAS Camp Pendleton, 2001). The plans outline management activities to protect important species and habitats on the base. Compliance with the plans allows the base to receive limited take permits for covered species. Measures in the Integrated Natural Resources Management Plan include introduced predator and exotic species control, notably removal of arundo in the Santa Margarita River riparian area; yearly surveys for California gnatcatcher and least Bell's vireo; control of brown-headed cowbirds; and restrictions on beach use during Western snowy plover and least tern nesting season. The Programmatic Assessments focus on protection of ecosystems, rather than on management for individual species; for instance, the assessments identify areas where training operations could harm important natural communities and make recommendations for appropriate training locations.

Camp Pendleton officials and planners are also concerned about patterns of residential and commercial growth surrounding the base. Urban encroachment surrounding the base could adversely affect the military mission (because of noise ordinances and other restrictions near residential areas adjacent to the base and increased flooding risks associated with runoff from urbanizing watersheds [Steinitz 1996]). Additionally, as important habitat areas are lost regionally, greater numbers of species depend largely on Camp Pendleton for habitat, placing ever-greater management responsibilities and restrictions on the base. Camp Pendleton officials and planners therefore have an interest in protecting regional habitats and are involved with conservation planning efforts for nonmilitary lands surrounding the base.

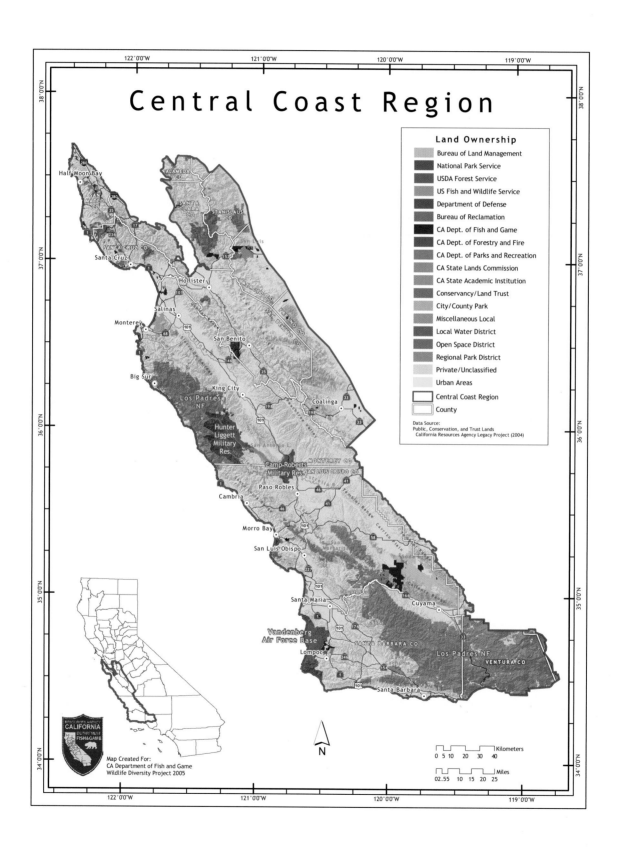

Central Coast Region

Land Ownership

- Bureau of Land Management
- National Park Service
- USDA Forest Service
- US Fish and Wildlife Service
- Department of Defense
- Bureau of Reclamation
- CA Dept. of Fish and Game
- CA Dept. of Forestry and Fire
- CA Dept. of Parks and Recreation
- CA State Lands Commission
- CA State Academic Institution
- Conservancy/Land Trust
- City/County Park
- Miscellaneous Local
- Local Water District
- Open Space District
- Regional Park District
- Private/Unclassified
- Urban Areas

☐ Central Coast Region
☐ County

Data Source:
Public, Conservation, and Trust Lands
California Resources Agency Legacy Project (2004)

Half Moon Bay
SAN MATEO CO.
SANTA CLARA CO.
ALAMEDA CO.
STANISLAUS CO.
SANTA CRUZ CO.
Santa Cruz
Hollister
MERCED CO.
SAN BENITO CO.
Salinas
Monterey
San Benito
Big Sur
King City
Los Padres NF
Coalinga
Hunter Liggett Military Res.
San Antonio L.
MONTEREY CO.
Camp Roberts Military Res.
SAN LUIS OBISPO CO.
Cambria
Paso Robles
Morro Bay
San Luis Obispo
Santa Maria
Cuyama
Vandenberg Air Force Base
SANTA BARBARA CO.
Los Padres NF
VENTURA CO.
Lompoc
Santa Barbara

Map Created For:
CA Department of Fish and Game
Wildlife Diversity Project 2005

CALIFORNIA
DEPARTMENT
FISH & GAME

N

Kilometers
0 5 10 20 30 40

Miles
02.55 10 15 20 25

10   Central Coast Region

California's Central Coast Region encompasses approximately 8 million acres and extends from the southern boundary of the Los Padres National Forest north to the San Francisco Bay lowlands. Inland, the region is bounded east of the Diablo and Temblor mountain ranges. The Central Coast landscape is characterized by a rugged coastline, small mountain ranges that roughly parallel the coast, river valleys with rich alluvial soils, and arid interior valleys and hills. Across the region, differences in climate, geography, and soils result in widely varying ecological conditions, supporting diverse coastal, montane, and desertlike natural communities.

Sand dunes and wetlands occur along the coast. River-mouth estuaries, lagoons, sloughs, tidal mudflats, and marshes make up coastal wetland communities, a unique environment where marine, freshwater, and terrestrial systems meet. Coastal habitats support numerous shorebirds, including the Western snowy plover, willet, whimbrel, long-billed curlew, marbled godwit, and American avocet. Coastal estuaries provide important nursery habitats for **anadromous** and oceanic fish, especially in watersheds where small or seasonally dry upper tributaries provide limited rearing capacity (CDFG 1996). Elkhorn Slough and Morro Bay are the region's two largest estuaries, with other significant wetlands found at the Pajaro, Salinas, and Santa Maria river mouths, Devereux Slough, and Goleta Slough (Page and Shuford 2000).

Other coastal habitats include coastal scrub and maritime chaparral. Coastal scrub and grasslands also extend inland along river valleys, like the lower Salinas Valley, where the moist maritime climate reaches through gaps in the coastal ranges. Maritime chaparral, characterized by manzanita and California lilac species adapted to the foggy coastal climate, once dominated sandy hills along Monterey Bay, Nipomo Mesa, Burton Mesa, and Morro Bay. Maritime chaparral is now one of the region's most threatened community types, with its extent severely reduced by development. These scrub and chaparral communities provide important habitat for Morro Bay-, Santa Cruz-, and Pacific kangaroo rat species and the San Diego desert woodrat, as well as shrubland bird species, including California quail, sage sparrow, rufous-crowned sparrow, and the sensitive California thrasher and Costa's hummingbird.

The outer coast ranges, including the Santa Cruz and Santa Lucia mountains, run parallel to the coastline. Well-watered by the moist ocean air, these slopes are drained by streams that run all year. The Santa Lucia Mountains provide most of the water supply to the Salinas River. These ranges support mixed coniferous forests and oak woodlands. The dominant coniferous species include ponderosa pine, Douglas fir, red alder, and, in the north, redwoods. The oak woodlands are dominated by coast live oak and valley oak. Rarer, **endemic** tree species include Monterey pine and Santa Lucia fir. Wildlife inhabitants of the outer coast mountains include wide-ranging species such as mountain lion and bobcat and **sensitive species** that include the California spotted owl, American badger, peregrine falcon, and golden eagle.

Moving inland across the Gabilan, Diablo, Temblor, and Sierra Madre mountain ranges, the climate becomes progressively drier, and the vegetation shifts to oak woodlands, grasslands, interior chaparral, and desert-like interior scrub. Interior streams are mostly intermittent, drying in the summer and fall, except at the higher elevations of the Sierra Madre ranges, where streams run year round. Biologically diverse oak woodland communities support more than 200 species of plants, 300 vertebrates, and 5,000 invertebrates (Thorne et al. 2002, TNC 1997). Inhabitants of oak woodlands include Western gray squirrel, dusky-footed woodrat, Monterey dusky-footed woodrat, pallid bat, and Townsend's big-eared bat (the latter three being Fish and Game species of concern). Large expanses of annual grasslands, now dominated by non-native grasses, are inhabited by California ground squirrel and black-tailed jackrabbit, along with sensitive species that include the giant kangaroo rat, burrowing owl, San Joaquin kit fox, American badger, and, in the southern portion of the region, reintroduced tule elk and pronghorn. Interior chaparral habitats support drought-resistant woody shrubs, including manzanita, California lilac, and chamise.

The Central Coast's largest drainages include the Salinas, Santa Maria, Pajaro, and Santa Ynez watersheds. Riverine and riparian habitats are important to amphibian and reptile species, including the California red-legged frog, foothill yellow-legged frog, and Western pond turtle, and birds such as the bank swallow, Lawrence's goldfinch (on Fish and Game's Special Animals List), and least Bell's vireo (federally listed as endangered). Steelhead and coho salmon (both federally listed as threatened) are still present, in small numbers, in most of the streams where they historically occurred. Mammals that use riparian habitats include gray fox, striped skunk, mole and shrew species, and ringtail.

Higher-elevation riparian vegetation in moist coastal climates includes willow, alder, bay, maple, Douglas fir, and sometimes redwood, while valley-bottom riparian communities are dominated by sycamore, willow, alder, and cottonwood. Steep coastal streams in the forested Santa Cruz and northern Santa Lucia mountains are some of the region's most intact systems and host relatively healthy anadromous fish populations (CDFG 1996). In contrast, the majority of the region's large river-valley floodplain and riparian forests have been replaced by agriculture, and lowland fish assemblages have been severely compromised.

Seasonal vernal-pool wetland complexes are found in many parts of the region, including the Salinas River drainage and coastal dune terraces and mesas of Santa Barbara County, and seasonal sag ponds are found along the San Andreas fault zone, particularly in the eastern portion of San Luis Obispo County. California tiger salamanders, Western spadefoot toads, fairy shrimp species, and many endemic plant species depend on these unique seasonal pool habitats.

The San Andreas Fault runs the length of the region and shapes much of the region's geography. Most of the north-south running mountain ranges and valley depressions have been formed as a result of pressure between the two continental plates meeting at this fault zone. Compression, chemical interaction, and surfacing of ancient seabed sediments have produced serpentine soils that are rich in such metals as chromium, nickel, and cobalt, but poor in nutrients. A number of plants have adapted to these harsh, near-toxic conditions, resulting in unique, island-like ecological communities largely restricted to serpentine areas.

Several sensitive invertebrates, such as Opler's longhorn moth, also are dependent on or strongly associated with serpentine plant species (USFWS 1998e, TNC 1997).

Historically, urban centers have been located along the region's coastal lowlands, with crop production concentrated in valley-floor areas and grazing and natural lands occupying the surrounding foothills and mountainous areas. In recent years, however, population pressures have increased, and growth and development have expanded from urban centers to adjacent farmlands and rural areas both on the coast and in the interior portions of the region. Along with population growth, the greatest threats to regional wildlife diversity are expansion of intensive types of agriculture, invasions by exotic species, and overuse of regional water resources. In spite of these significant regional stressors, large blocks of undeveloped natural lands remain, and the region presents many opportunities to accomplish conservation on a landscape-scale.

Species at Risk

The Plan development team updated vertebrate and invertebrate species information of the California Natural Diversity Data Base (CNDDB) in 2004–2005. The following regional summary of numbers of wildlife species, endemic species, and **species at risk** is derived from the updated CNDDB.

The Central Coast's wide range of habitats has given rise to remarkable biological diversity. There are 482 vertebrate species that inhabit the Central Coast region at some point in their life cycle, including 283 birds, 87 mammals, 42 reptiles, 25 amphibians, and 45 fish. Of the total vertebrate species that inhabit this region, 80 bird **taxa**, 36 mammalian taxa, 14 reptilian taxa, eight amphibian taxa, and 15 fish taxa are included on the **Special Animals List.** Of these, 13 are endemic to the Central Coast region, one is endemic to California but introduced to this region, and 24 other species found here are endemic to California but not restricted to this region (Table 10.1).

Table 10.1: State-Endemic Special Status Vertebrates of the Central Coast Region

	Ambystoma californiense	California tiger salamander
*	*Ambystoma macrodactylum croceum*	Santa Cruz long-toed salamander
	Ammospermophilus nelsoni	Nelson's antelope squirrel
*	*Anniella pulchra nigra*	Black legless lizard
	Anniella pulchra pulchra	Silvery legless lizard

	Archoplites interruptus	Sacramento perch
	Catostomus santaanae	Santa Ana sucker
	Charina umbratica	Southern rubber boa
	Dipodomys heermanni berkeleyensis	Berkeley kangaroo rat
*	*Dipodomys heermanni morroensis*	Morro Bay kangaroo rat
	Dipodomys ingens	Giant kangaroo rat
	Dipodomys nitratoides brevinasus	Short-nosed kangaroo rat
*	*Dipodomys venustus elephantinus*	Big-eared kangaroo rat
	Dipodomys venustus venustus	Santa Cruz kangaroo rat
	Eucyclogobius newberryi	Tidewater goby
	Gambelia sila	Blunt-nosed leopard lizard
	Gasterosteus aculeatus williamsoni	Unarmored threespine stickleback
	Geothlypis trichas sinuosa	Saltmarsh common yellowthroat
+	*Gila orcutti*	Arroyo chub
*	*Lavinia exilicauda harengus*	Pajaro/Salinas hitch
	Lavinia symmetricus ssp. 1	San Joaquin roach
*	*Lavinia symmetricus subditus*	Monterey roach
	Masticophis flagellum ruddocki	San Joaquin whipsnake
	Masticophis lateralis euryxanthus	Alameda whipsnake
*	*Microtus californicus halophilus*	Monterey vole
*	*Neotoma fuscipes annectens*	San Francisco dusky-footed woodrat
*	*Neotoma macrotis luciana*	Monterey dusky-footed woodrat
	Onychomys torridus tularensis	Tulare grasshopper mouse
	Perognathus alticolus inexpectatus	Tehachapi pocket mouse
	Perognathus inornatus inornatus	San Joaquin pocket mouse
	Perognathus inornatus neglectus	McKittrick pocket mouse
*	*Perognathus inornatus psammophilus*	Salinas pocket mouse
	Rallus longirostris obsoletus	California clapper rail
*	*Reithrodontomys megalotis distichlis*	Salinas harvest mouse
*	*Sorex ornatus salarius*	Monterey shrew
*	*Sorex vagrans paludivagus*	Monterey vagrant shrew
	Tamias speciosus callipeplus	Mount Pinos chipmunk
	Taricha torosa torosa	Coast Range newt
	Thamnophis sirtalis tetrataenia	San Francisco garter snake
	Vulpes macrotis mutica	San Joaquin kit fox

* denotes taxon is endemic to region
+ denotes taxon is endemic to California but introduced in this region

The number of arthropod species is so great, and they are so poorly known taxonomically, that it is presently impossible to accurately estimate the total number of invertebrate species occurring in the state. In the Central Coast region, however, 60 invertebrate taxa are included on the Special Animals List, including 57 arthropod taxa and three mollusk taxa. Of these, 32 are endemic to the Central Coast region, and 25 other taxa found here are endemic to California but not restricted to this region (Table 10.2).

Table 10.2: State-Endemic Special Status Invertebrates of the Central Coast Region

*	*Ablautus schlingeri*	Oso Flaco robber fly
	Adela oplerella	Opler's longhorn moth
	Aegialia concinna	Ciervo aegilian scarab beetle
*	*Ammopelmatus muwu*	Point Conception Jerusalem cricket
*	*Areniscythris brachypteris*	Oso Flaco flightless moth
	Branchinecta longiantenna	Longhorn fairy shrimp
	Caecidotea tomalensis	Tomales isopod
*	*Calicina minor*	Edgewood blind harvestman
*	*Calicina arida*	A harvestman; no common name
*	*Calileptoneta ubicki*	Ubick's calileptoneta spider
	Ceratochrysis longimala	A chrysidid wasp; no common name
	Certaochrysis menkei	Menke's chrysidid wasp
	Chrysis tularensis	Tulare chrysidid wasp
	Cicindela hirticollis gravida	Sandy beach tiger beetle
*	*Cicindela ohlone*	Ohlone tiger beetle
	Coelus globosus	Globose dune beetle
	Coelus gracilis	San Joaquin dune beetle
	Desmocerus californicus dimorphus	Valley elderberry longhorn beetle
*	*Euphilotes enoptes smithi*	Smith's blue butterfly
	Euphydryas editha bayensis	Bay checkerspot butterfly
*	*Fissilicreagris imperialis*	Empire Cave pseudoscorpion
*	*Helminthoglypta sequoicola consors*	Redwood shoulderband (snail)
*	*Helminthoglypta walkeriana*	Morro shoulderband (=banded dune) snail
*	*Hubbardia secoensis*	A schizomid arachnid; no common name
	Hydrochara rickseckeri	Ricksecker's water scavenger beetle
	Hydroporus leechi	Leech's skyline diving beetle
	Icaricia icarioides missionensis	Mission blue butterfly
*	*Icaricia icarioides moroensis*	Morro Bay blue butterfly
*	*Idiostatus kathleenae*	Pinnacles shieldback katydid

	Incisalia mossii bayensis	San Bruno elfin butterfly
*	*Lichnanthe albipilosa*	White sand bear scarab beetle
	Lichnanthe ursina	Bumblebee scarab beetle
	Linderiella occidentalis	California linderiella
	Lytta hoppingi	Hopping's blister beetle
	Lytta morrisoni	Morrison's blister beetle
*	*Meta dolloff*	Dolloff Cave spider
*	*Microcina edgewoodensis*	Edgewood Park micro-blind harvestman
	Microcina homi	Hom's micro-blind harvestman
*	*Minymischa ventura*	Ventura chrysidid wasp
*	*Necydalis rudei*	Rude's longhorn beetle
*	*Neochthonius imperialis*	Empire Cave pseudoscorpion
	Nothochrysa californica	San Francisco lacewing
*	*Optioservus canus*	Pinnacles optioservus riffle beetle
*	*Philanthus nasalis*	Antioch sphecid wasp
*	*Polyphylla barbata*	Mount Hermon (=barbate) June beetle
*	*Polyphylla nubila*	Atascadero June beetle
*	*Protodufourea wasbaueri*	Wasbauer's protodufourea bee
*	*Protodufourea zavortinki*	Zavortink's protodufourea bee
*	*Socalchemmis monterey*	Monterey socalchemmis spider
*	*Speyeria adiaste adiaste*	Unsilvered fritillary
	Speyeria zerene myrtleae	Myrtle's silverspot
*	*Stygobromus mackenziei*	Mackenzie's cave amphipod
*	*Thessalia leanira elegans*	Oso Flaco patch butterfly
	Trachusa gummifera	A megachilid bee; no common name
*	*Trimerotropis infantilis*	Zayante band-winged grasshopper
*	*Trimerotropis occulens*	Lompoc grasshopper
	Tryonia imitator	Mimic tryonia (=California brackishwater snail)

* denotes taxon is endemic to region

The Wildlife Species Matrix, including data on listing status, habitat association, and population trend for each vertebrate and invertebrate species included on the Special Animals List, is available on the Web at http://www.dfg.ca.gov/habitats/wdp/matrix_search.asp. For vertebrates, the matrix also includes links to species-level range maps. Additionally, a link to the California Department of Fish and Game's online Field Survey Form is available to assist in reporting positive sightings of species on the Special Animals List to the California Natural Diversity Database (CNDDB).

Two Species at Risk

Note: *The following discussion of two species at risk illustrates how stressors or threats affect species and highlights conservation challenges and opportunities. These species discussions are not intended to imply that conservation should have a single-species approach.*

The threats facing the California red-legged frog and the San Joaquin kit fox illustrate some of the most important conservation issues in the region. The expanding vineyards and rural residential developments impinging on San Joaquin kit fox movement corridors reflect the land-use changes threatening habitat connectivity throughout the region. Habitat protection for the San Joaquin kit fox also will require ecologically sound grazing lands management. The California red-legged frog depends on the region's aquatic habitats. In many areas of the Central Coast, aquatic systems have been severely altered, both by watershed-wide land uses and increasing demands for water for human use.

California Red-Legged Frog

Karen McClymonds

California red-legged frogs live in aquatic, riparian and, less frequently, upland habitats. Frogs depend on streams, ponds (both natural and artificial stock ponds), and wetlands with relatively deep and slow-moving water, but they also spend considerable time in riparian areas with relatively dense shrubby or emergent vegetation and travel through upland areas when dispersing.

Throughout its range, the frog is threatened by habitat loss and fragmentation caused by urban and residential development, draining of wetlands, reservoir construction, water diversion, and predatory non-native species. Development or flood-control activities that disconnect creeks and rivers from their floodplains isolate frogs in limited habitat areas and restrict their access to different habitat types. Habitat and water quality are degraded by sediment and chemical runoff from inappropriate agricultural, rangeland, and forestry practices and from urban areas. Non-native plant species reduce the suitability of riparian habitats, while introduced fish, crayfish, and bullfrogs prey on California red-legged frogs. Bullfrogs are favored by such factors as elevated water temperatures and permanent water sources, conditions that occur in human-disturbed areas.

The California red-legged frog has been eliminated from more than 70 percent of its historic range and now occurs in only 238 drainages, representing about 10 percent of those it historically occupied. Of these remaining populations, only four support more than 350 adult frogs (USFWS 2001). The species was federally listed as threatened in 1996 and is a Fish and Game species of concern. The largest remaining populations of California red-legged frog occur in the coastal watersheds of Monterey, San Luis Obispo, and Santa Barbara counties in both streams and rangeland stock ponds (USFWS 2002e). Protection of the frog in the Central Coast region is therefore a high priority. Within this region, where frog populations have declined, the greatest threats are increasing numbers of exotic aquatic predators, livestock grazing in riparian areas, and decreased freshwater flows due to water use by increases in human population numbers (USFWS 2006).

Important conservation measures highlighted by the U.S. Fish and Wildlife Service's *Recovery Plan for California Red-legged Frog* include improved habitat management on agricultural land and rangelands, including establishing rangeland water quality plans, maintaining livestock ponds that provide habitat for the frog and controlling invasive species in these ponds; protecting minimum instream flows and natural hydrologic regimes; and developing exotic-species control measures for non-native vegetation and predatory introduced-wildlife species (USFWS 2002e). The recovery plan recommends that conservation efforts be focused on watersheds that currently support healthy red-legged frog populations, on corridors that provide dispersal opportunities, and on areas where good environmental and habitat conditions favor the persistence or reestablishment of red-legged frogs. For these areas, the U.S. Fish and Wildlife Service suggests developing watershed management plans that include land-use guidelines and priority locations for conservation, protection, and restoration efforts.

San Joaquin Kit Fox

Historically, the San Joaquin kit fox was widely distributed across the San Joaquin Valley floor, with smaller populations extending into both the foothills of the Sierra Nevada and the slopes and basins of the Coastal Ranges. Although the San Joaquin kit fox has been federally listed as endangered since

Jeremy Rowell

1967 and state listed as threatened since 1971, its status throughout most of its range is poorly known. As of 1975, California's kit fox population was estimated at about 7,000, representing a decline of between 20 percent and 43 percent from estimates made before 1930, and population numbers have likely declined since the 1970s (USFWS 1998h).

In the Central Coast region, the kit fox is presently found in the interior ranges of Monterey and San Benito counties, the upper portions of the Pajaro and Salinas watersheds, the Cuyama watershed, and the Carrizo Plain. With only about 5 percent of the San Joaquin Valley's original natural areas remaining untilled and undeveloped, these Central Coast habitats, particularly the Carrizo Plain, are important for the species' survival (Stafford 2004 pers. comm., USFWS 2004).

Kit foxes inhabit grasslands and scrublands. Primarily active at night, foxes hunt and forage over substantial distances, preying upon both rodents and insects. Researchers estimate the average home range size to be 1.7 square miles (Cypher et al. 2001). Some foxes have been recorded traveling over distances of between 25 and 50 miles (USFWS 1998h).

The principle threats to the species are habitat loss and fragmentation resulting from agricultural, residential, and commercial development (CDFG 2005b). Other human-induced mortality factors include shooting, poisoning, and being killed on roads. Kit foxes also face predation by and competition with other canine species, including coyote, non-native red fox, and domestic dogs. Predation, disease, and droughts that reduce prey numbers can cause large fluctuations in kit fox population numbers. Well-managed rangelands constitute important kit fox habitats, and appropriate grazing can thin out exotic grasses and improve habitat for prey species. However, kit foxes can also be harmed by overgrazing that eliminates vegetative cover and depletes rodent and insect prey species and by rodent control practices that reduce prey numbers or result in secondary poisonings (USFWS 1998h). In southern Monterey County and in San Luis Obispo County, vineyard expansion and housing developments along the Highway 101 and Highway 46 corridors pose substantial threats to kit fox habitats and movement corridors (Stafford 2004 pers. comm.).

The U.S. Fish and Wildlife Service's Recovery Plan for this species calls for the protection of a complex of fox populations (a **metapopulation**), including three core populations (the Carrizo Plain, western Kern County, and Ciervo-Panoche Natural Area) and smaller populations across the species' geographic range. The plan also recommends protecting remaining connections between populations to counteract interbreeding or declines in any one population (USFWS 1998h).

The Recovery Plan recommends efforts to improve habitat conditions on agricultural and ranch lands, so these lands can serve to maintain connectivity between population centers. Research is needed to determine the rangeland management and agricultural practices that provide usable habitat and promote prey species. Other research needs identified by the Recovery Plan include monitoring of distribution and status, studies of interactions with other canines, and studies of the effects of predator control programs.

Stressors Affecting Wildlife and Habitats

- Growth and development
- Intensive agriculture
- Excessive livestock grazing
- Water management conflicts and degradation of aquatic ecosystems
- Recreational pressures
- Invasive species

Growth and Development

Population growth in the Central Coast has mirrored the rapid pace of growth seen state-wide, with the region's population growing by approximately 13 percent to approximately 1.5 million between 1990 and 2000 (CDOF June 2004, DWR 2004). Throughout the region, urban acreage increased by 32 percent (from 182,000 acres to 241,000 acres) between 1980 and 1990 (DWR 1993) and by another 22 percent (to 293,000 acres) by 2002 (CDF 2002).

Historically, population pressures have been greatest along the coast, with inland areas primarily occupied by large ranches, agriculture, and small agricultural towns. The largest coastal population centers are Santa Cruz (with a population of 255,600 as of 2000); Monterey, Marina, and Seaside (86,500); San Luis Obispo (44,200); and Santa Barbara (92,300).

In recent years, growth pressures have shifted inland, with urban and rural residential development centered along the Highway 101 corridor. In the northern portion of the region, affordable housing draws commuters from San Jose to rapidly expanding towns like Morgan Hill (which grew by 40 percent to a population of 33,600 between 1990 and 2000), Gilroy (32 percent, to 41,500), Hollister (79 percent, to 34,400) and Watsonville (42 percent, to 44,300) (CDOF June 2004). Incorporated cities in the Salinas Valley have also seen substantial growth in recent years. In the northern portion of the valley, Salinas grew by 39 percent, to 151,100, between 1990 and 2000. In the southern Salinas Valley, Paso Robles grew by 30 percent, to 24,300, and Atascadero by 14 percent, to 26,400 (CDOF June 2004).

Coastal towns south of San Luis Obispo have also grown substantially. Arroyo Grande, Pismo Beach, and Grover Beach grew by 11 percent to a combined population of 37,500 between 1990 and 2000. Increasing growth pressures for infrastructure and services for these coastal towns extend southward and inland toward Orcutt and Buellton in the Santa Maria and Santa Ynez river valleys. In the Santa Maria River valley, Santa Maria city grew by 26 percent, to 77,400, and in the Santa Ynez River valley, Solvang, Lompoc, and Buellton grew by 10 percent to a combined total of 50,200 residents between 1990 and 2000 (CDOF June 2004).

Urbanization increases air and water pollution from industrial emissions, sewage systems, and urban runoff. Growth patterns often include residential projects located far from existing urban centers, resulting in an increased need for roads and utilities. Communities designed with large lot sizes preserve little open space. These developed areas and infrastructure corridors not only result in direct loss of habitat but also fragment the natural landscape and degrade the quality of adjacent habitat.

Even outside the portions of the region undergoing rapid growth, unused oil-lease lands and large cattle ranches that are no longer profitable are being acquired by land investors and sold as 40-acre to 160-acre residential parcels. This rural residential development also requires additional road infrastructure and fragments the natural landscape.

Fragmentation hinders ecological processes that require landscape connectivity, such as natural fire regimes, movement of wide-ranging species, and genetic exchange, and makes remaining natural lands more vulnerable to pollution and invasion by exotic plants and animals (Soule and Terbourgh 1999).

Intensive Agriculture

The Central Coast's mild, seasonally moist climate and fertile soils support a highly productive agricultural industry. Approximately 890,000 acres, or 11 percent of the region's land area, are planted in irrigated row crops, vineyards, and orchards (CDC 2002). The most extensive agricultural areas are fertile river valleys and coastal terrace lands. Major crops include lettuce, artichokes, asparagus, and strawberries, with some areas also supporting orchard-grown fruits and nuts and dry-land, unirrigated winter grains, such as barley. While these agricultural lands provide important crops for California's food supply and for export, many of the intensive agricultural practices that have enabled such large-scale production

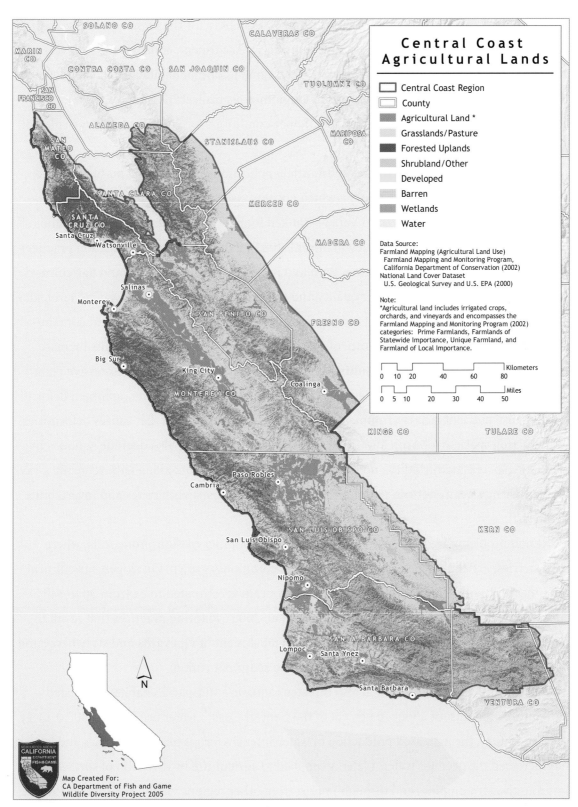

Fig. 10.1: Central Coast Agricultural Land

Many of the region's river valleys and coastal terrace lands are dominated by agricultural land uses (irrigated crops, orchards, and vineyards).

also result in ecological problems. Agricultural consequences for the region's wildlife and ecosystems include runoff of agricultural chemicals and sediment, consumption of over-subscribed water resources, and conversion and fragmentation of habitat. Private landowners and local conservation districts are working on numerous projects to mitigate these consequences, to improve water quality, and to enhance conditions for wildlife on the agricultural working landscapes of the region.

Many of the region's crops receive substantial applications of fertilizers, herbicides, and pesticides. In 2001, Monterey County—which encompasses two major agricultural regions, the Salinas Valley and lower Pajaro Valley—ranked fourth in the state for the total pounds of pesticide applied (CDPR 2001, Newman et al. 2003). Exposed soils and irrigation practices make croplands susceptible to erosion. Rain and irrigation runoff carry silt and agricultural chemicals, degrading surface water quality and sometimes reaching groundwater. Herbicides and pesticides can have toxic effects on aquatic plants and animals, and chemical contaminants can upset the ecological balance of aquatic systems. For example, nutrients increase aquatic plant and algal growth, resulting in lowered oxygen levels when the excessive plant matter decomposes. Elevated nutrient levels have also been implicated in amphibian deformities, because nutrient-rich environments favor the parasitic flatworm that causes deformities in many frog species (Johnson and Chase 2004). Silt and sediment also degrade aquatic environments, increasing turbidity and shading out aquatic vegetation, along with scouring away or smothering stream-bottom sediments that are important spawning sites and invertebrate habitats.

Runoff problems are particularly severe on steeply sloping, erosion-prone soils, where strawberries, artichokes, and vineyard grapes are commonly grown. On sloped agricultural fields near Elkhorn Slough, soil erosion after heavy rain is estimated to be from 30 to 140 times greater than from natural lands (Caffrey et al. 2002). Planting practices that result in large amounts of soil disturbance, such as the establishment of vineyards and strawberry and artichoke mounds, also contribute substantially to sediment runoff.

Agricultural water consumption also threatens aquatic and riparian habitats. Irrigated agriculture accounts for about 70 percent of the Central Coast's water use (DWR 2005a). Over the last century, the increased production of water-intensive crops like strawberries and lettuce has increased the need for water. Water is supplied to agriculture by diversion of surface water, by groundwater pumping, and through import from other regions via the State Water Project. As of 1995, groundwater provided about 84 percent of the region's water supply, and 20 percent of that was considered **overdraft**, exceeding the amount of incoming water replenishing the aquifers (DWR 1993, 2003a). As groundwater levels are depleted, flows are also reduced in streams and rivers. Diminished flows reduce aquatic systems' capacity to discharge incoming contaminants and sediment and can inhibit migration by anadromous fish.

The completion of the coastal branch of the State Water Project to San Luis Obispo and Santa Barbara counties in 1997 fostered the expansion of water-intensive agricultural practices in the southern portion of the region, including the establishment of irrigated vineyards and flood-irrigation in the Santa Maria Valley, both of which consume large amounts of water and contribute to runoff.

The growth of agriculture over the last century, particularly along valley-bottom floodplains and coastal terraces, has resulted in both the loss of important habitat areas and the fragmentation of larger natural landscapes. In recent decades, intensively cultivated crops (such as vineyards) have been expanding into areas formerly used for grazing and dry-land grain production. Intensive agricultural crops almost entirely eliminate wildlife habitat values and tax water resources.

Since 1990, the Central Coast has seen substantial growth of vineyards into both grazing lands and natural habitats, including oak woodlands and chaparral. Vineyard acreage regionwide increased by 36 percent between 1998 and 2001 (DWR 2005a). In Monterey County, vineyard acreage increased from 21,000 acres in 1991 to 38,000 acres in 2001 (Newman et al. 2003). In San Luis Obispo County, Paso Robles has been a center of vineyard expansion, and approximately 28,500 acres of new vineyards were established in the county between 1996 and 2004 (DWR 1996, SLO Co. Ag. Comm. 2004). In Santa Barbara County, approximately 10,000 new acres of vineyards were established in the Santa Maria, Los Alamos, and Santa Rita valleys in the four years between 1996 and 2000 (USFWS 2000a).

Near Paso Robles, vineyard expansion is encroaching on important San Joaquin kit fox corridors. Additionally, in preparation for vineyard cultivation, "deep-ripping" plowing practices are often used to break up dense soil layers so that water can penetrate more deeply; this disturbs natural drainage patterns and inhibits the formation of seasonal ponds (USFWS 2000a). In Santa Barbara County, the expansion of vineyards and the resulting fragmentation and destruction of California tiger salamanders' seasonal pool and upland habitats led the U.S. Fish and Wildlife Service in 2000 to make an emergency listing of the salamander's Santa Barbara population as endangered (USFWS 2000a). Establishment of vineyards can also pave the way for future residential development. If vineyards are not financially

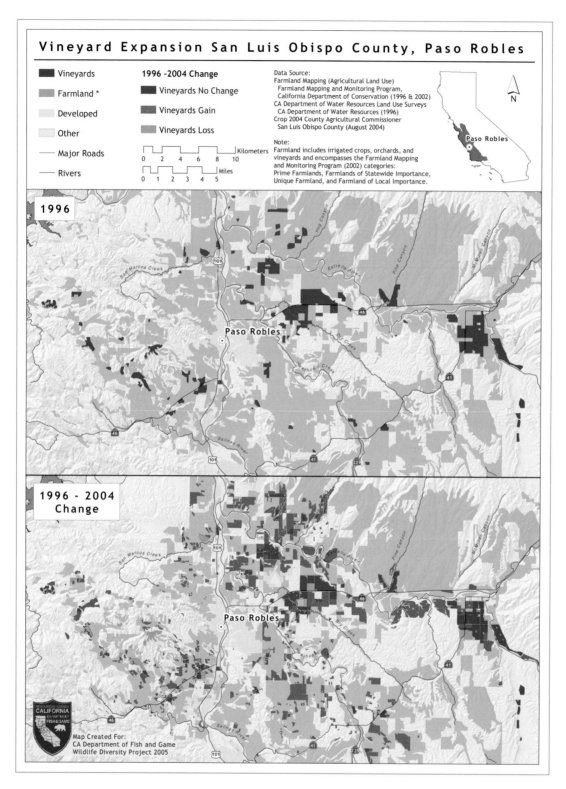

Fig. 10.2: Vineyard Expansion

In the last decade, vineyard acreage has increased dramatically in the Central Coast Region. More than 28,000 acres of new vineyards were established between 1996 and 2004 in the area surrounding Paso Robles. Other parts of the region have seen similar levels of vineyard expansion.

successful, most of the natural values that would restrict development permits are lost, and the water lines and road infrastructure needed to support residential development are already in place.

Excessive Livestock Grazing

Livestock grazing is widespread throughout the Central Coast region, especially on expansive ranch lands across the inland hills and mountain ranges (Newman et al. 2003, Thorne et al. 2002). Private grazing lands are estimated to total approximately 4.8 million acres, or 60 percent of the region's land area (FRAP 2003). Many public and conservation lands are also open to grazing, and Fish and Game, State Parks, and private land trusts make use of grazing as a habitat management tool. Grazing leases are also held on approximately 46 percent of the 1.7 million acres (Stephenson and Calcarone 1999) of the Los Padres National Forest lands within the region and on about 66 percent of the 300,000 acres of BLM land (FRAP 2003, Germano et al. 2001, Weiss 1999).

The effects of grazing on wildlife vary from beneficial to detrimental, depending upon how it is managed, including the seasonality and duration of grazing and the type and number of livestock. These effects also depend on the relative sensitivities of individual wildlife species, since not all species respond the same way to grazing.

Well-managed livestock grazing can benefit sensitive plant and animal species, particularly by controlling annual grasses and invasive plants where these have become established (Germano et al. 2001, Weiss 1999). For example, livestock grazing can benefit California tiger salamander populations by keeping annual grasses cropped relatively short, which enables the salamander to travel between breeding ponds and upland habitats, and also favors small mammal species, like the California ground squirrel, that create underground burrows inhabited by the salamander. Livestock can also prevent annual grasses' growth from choking off small seasonal pools (Marty 2005). These working lands are an essential part of the solution to conserving the state's wildlife.

While recognizing the values of appropriate grazing practices, this report is required to focus on stressors affecting wildlife species at risk. Thus, the following discussion describes those situations where excessive grazing practices stress wildlife species at risk. Excessive grazing, as used here, refers to livestock grazing at a frequency or intensity that causes degradation of native plant communities, reduces habitat values for native wildlife species, degrades aquatic or other ecosystems, or impairs ecosystem functions. Many of the region's oak woodlands are currently managed for livestock production. Livestock grazing is one factor hindering oak regeneration. Livestock consume oak seedlings and inhibit oak germination by compacting soils and disturbing leaf litter, which reduces soil moisture. Annual forage grasses also compete with oak seedlings for soil, light, and water (Barbour et al. 1993, Stephenson and Calcarone 1999). Abundant seed production by forage grasses increases rodent populations, and rodents also consume oak shoots.

Approximately 25 percent of California's rare plants and at least 10 percent of the state's endemic plant species occur in serpentine habitats (TNC 1997). Because of the limited and patchy distribution of these soils, unique serpentine ecological communities are often restricted to small, island-like areas. Excessive grazing can eliminate or substantially reduce these small populations.

While well-managed grazing may benefit native species by controlling exotic plants, excessive livestock grazing in riparian areas and vernal pools can cause problems for sensitive species associated with these environments—including California red-legged frog, spadefoot toads, Western pond turtle, and fairy shrimp species—because cattle will congregate in these habitats to use them as water sources. Livestock trampling of stream channels results in the destabilization and collapse of stream banks, elimination of deep pool areas, and widening of streams and pools, which results in increased temperatures, greater surface area, and faster evaporation (Moyle 2002, USFWS 2000a). Water runoff and soil erosion increase on cattle trails; trails produce 40 times more sediment than vegetated surfaces (CDFG 2004g). These changes alter channel shape and hydrology. Increased sediment can also shade out aquatic plants, fill important pool habitats, and scour away or smother important spawning sites and invertebrate habitats. Livestock waste also degrades water quality by contributing to elevated nutrient and microorganism levels.

Livestock also often reduce the coverage and alter the composition of riparian and wetland vegetation. This can diminishes the vegetation's capacity to filter runoff entering waterways. Loss of plant cover also reduces shade and raises water temperatures, resulting in lower dissolved oxygen content in the water (CDFG 2004g).

Besides reducing streamside vegetation and riparian habitat, livestock can have direct negative effects on native riparian species by trampling or disturbing amphibian egg masses and crushing rodent burrows that are required by amphibians for summer dormancy, affecting sensitive species such as the California red-legged frog, California tiger salamander, and Santa Cruz long-toed salamander (USFWS 2002e).

Appendix G lists good information resources regarding practices and standards for appropriate grazing management that improve conditions for wildlife and ecosystems.

Water Management Conflicts and Degradation of Aquatic Ecoystems

Throughout the Central Coast region, rivers, riparian habitats, and coastal wetlands have been degraded by the use of water resources, flood control efforts, and the effects of surrounding land uses. Resource-extraction practices, such as instream gravel mining and runoff from adjacent mining or forestry operations, also affect some regional watersheds. All of these various activities, alone or in combination, result in changes to the timing and volume of instream flows, alterations to river channel shape and instream habitat availability, and decreases in water quality, including elevated water temperature. In the region's urbanized areas, expanding coverage of the landscape by paved surfaces increases the amount of runoff and urban pollutants (CDFG 2004g).

Within the region's major watersheds, tributaries flowing through relatively undeveloped uplands are more ecologically intact, while the main-stem sections running through agricultural and urban valleys have undergone the greatest degradation. Lowland riparian areas, which once supported floodplain forests of deciduous riparian trees and shrubs, including sycamore, willow, and cottonwood, are one of the most diminished of the Central Coast's ecosystems. In many valley riparian areas, exotic species, including tamarisk and giant reed, have replaced willow and cottonwood, and low-elevation fish species, such as Coast range sculpin, tule perch, and Sacramento perch, have been **extirpated** or reduced (TPL 2001). While **salmonids** persist in nearly all of the regional waterways where they were historically present, their population numbers are substantially smaller.

Efforts to control flooding and stream-channel courses often accompany agricultural and urban land uses. Increased runoff and higher flows from agricultural and urban areas can result in flooding problems, and residential, commercial, or agricultural landowners in floodplains do not want their lands subject to floods. Flood-control efforts can include vegetation removal, dredging, channelization, **riprap** and energy dissipaters, construction of dams and levees, and, in areas where agricultural fields abut stream channels, repeated stream bank recontouring using heavy equipment.

Restricting or altering the shape of river channels disconnects a river from its natural floodplain and eliminates the benefits of natural flooding regimes, such as deposition of river silts on valley floor soils, recharge of wetlands, and flushing flows that prevent clogging of

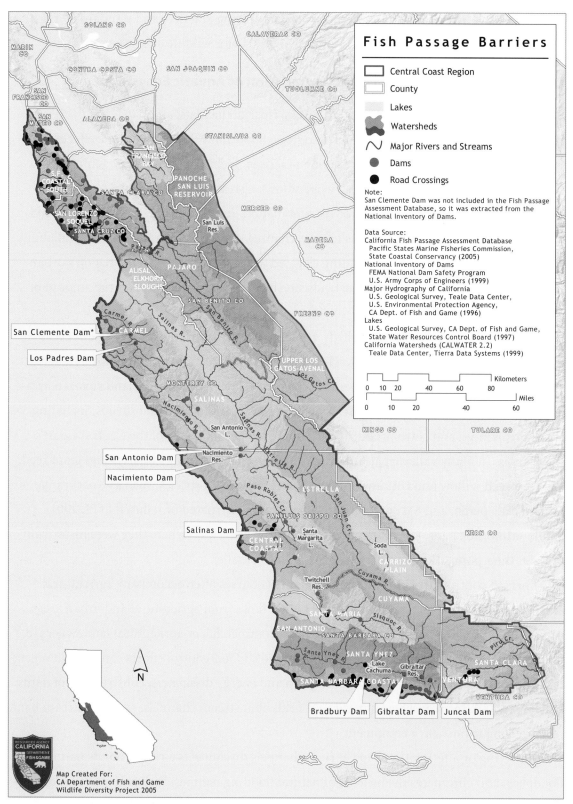

Fig. 10.3: Barriers to Fish Passage

Dams and smaller structures such as road crossings can fragment watersheds. As shown above, more than 70 dams and roads create complete barriers to fish passage.

small coastal streams. Recontouring levees and stream banks with heavy equipment results in the deposit of heavy sediment loads into the waterway.

Water diversions, dams and on-stream reservoirs, and groundwater extraction (along with imported water from the Central Valley and the Bay-Delta region) provide the region's residential and agricultural water supply. Water development activities can obstruct rivers, alter the timing and volume of river flows, and exacerbate water quality problems. Dams, diversions, and the resulting low instream flows bring about habitat conditions that preclude use by anadromous fish and block their migration to spawning grounds. Reduced flows also diminish aquatic systems' capacity to dilute contaminants and transport sediments. With limited water remaining, rivers may dry up before reaching their ocean outlets, or sediments may clog river mouths. For example, over a three-year period from 1988 to 1990, Carmel River flows were too low to breach the sand bar at the river's ocean mouth owing to the combined effects of drought, surface diversions, and groundwater pumping (CDFG 1996). Other artificial structures, such as culverts, low-water road crossings, pipeline crossings, and bridges, also block migration, stream flows, and sediment transport.

Although mining operations are not widespread in the Central Coast region, impacts at affected locations can be substantial. Instream gravel mining removes gravel from the stream channel, interrupting natural sediment transport processes, deepening and degrading the channel, and creating noise disturbance. Mining operations adjacent to rivers can result in sediment or other contaminant runoff. Both instream and adjacent mining can increase water temperature and turbidity and destroy spawning habitat (CDFG 2004g). The Pajaro River watershed has been severely degraded both by hydrologic alterations resulting from instream gravel mining and by declines in water quality due to historical mercury mine runoff. Gravel mining alongside the Arroyo Seco waterway in Monterey County has eliminated unique sycamore alluvial riparian forests (Newman et al. 2003).

Forestry land uses are fairly limited in the region, but the effects of timber harvesting are notable in coastal streams of San Mateo and Santa Cruz counties (CDFG 2004g, USFWS 2002e). Exposed soils and disturbance from logging roads increase sedimentation, while reductions in vegetative cover result in elevated stream temperatures and loss of instream debris that provides cover for fish (CDFG 2004g, USFWS 2002e). Changes in the amount and timing of incoming sediment reduce spawning habitats and success.

Urbanization and agricultural activities that degrade regional rivers also affect the coastal wetlands and estuaries fed by these waterways, resulting in sedimentation and reduced water supply. Hydrological alterations such as dikes and berm construction also harm wetland function. Moreover, excavation of naturally occurring sand bars and beaches to drain lagoons or create accessible harbors alters tidal flow and can result in both changes in salinity and scouring flows that degrade habitats and cause erosion. Unseasonal breaching of lagoons for flood control can also cause direct mortality of young anadromous fish that use them as rearing habitat (Wilcox 2005 pers. comm.) and negatively affect the breeding of tidewater goby (a Fish and Game species of concern and federally listed as endangered) (USFWS 2004b).

Recreational Pressures

Recreational pressures threaten some Central Coast habitats, particularly those that are limited in distribution and sensitive to disturbance. Beaches and dunes, serpentine habitats, and riparian areas on public lands are of particular concern.

Recreational off-road vehicle use can have pervasive effects on ecological communities. In the Central Coast, areas of greatest concern are interior forest areas in the Los Padres National Forest lands and sensitive serpentine soil areas. Off-road vehicle trails open relatively undisturbed forest areas to increased use. The vehicles can disturb or run over wildlife. They can also change plant communities by crushing or uprooting plants, causing soil compaction that prevents germination, and spreading seeds of invasive plants (Hall 1980). Changes in vegetation composition affect available habitats for invertebrates and other wildlife. Soil disturbance contributes to erosion and sedimentation of aquatic habitats. Serpentine soils are particularly susceptible to disturbance by vehicles, and the resulting erosion can contribute naturally occurring toxic metals to surrounding aquatic systems.

In beach and dune environments, growing numbers of hikers are causing increased disturbance of nesting and foraging shorebirds, including Western snowy plovers. These activities are significant on the beach and dune systems from Monterey north to the Salinas and Pajaro river mouths, which harbor a number of sensitive species, including black legless lizard, Smith's blue butterfly, and sandmat manzanita.

Invasive Species

As in other regions of California, invasive species present a noteworthy threat to the Central Coast's biological diversity and are tied to regional land uses. Besides introduced species, some native species thrive and increase in number in human-altered habitats. These species may compete with or prey upon other native species, sometimes negatively affecting their populations.

Native brown-headed cowbirds have greatly expanded their range and have undergone population increases because they thrive in suburban areas and on agricultural and grazing lands. Cowbirds can lower the reproductive success of other native birds by laying their eggs in those birds' nests, causing the targeted host birds to raise the cowbird nestlings at the expense of their own. Native raccoons, whose populations have greatly increased near housing developments and recreation facilities, threaten some native reptile species—notably Western pond turtles—due to egg predation.

Introduced feral pigs are a major problem in many habitat types across the region. Feral pigs root in the soil, creating excessive soil disturbance and decimating native plant communities. In oak woodlands, feral pigs can inhibit the germination and growth of young oaks by eating acorns and oak seedlings and removing leaf litter, causing soils to dry out (Sweet 2005 pers. comm.). In beach and dune habitats, the introduced red fox increases predation rates for sensitive coastal shorebirds such as the light-footed clapper rail (federally and state listed as endangered).

In aquatic habitats, native reptile, amphibian, fish, and invertebrate populations are threatened by predation and competition with introduced fish, crayfish, red-eared slider turtles, and bullfrogs. The most significant predatory fishes include sunfish, mosquito fish, bullhead catfish, and largemouth bass. Some of these species, including mosquito fish, bullfrog, and crayfish, require year-round water sources to complete their reproductive cycle. Many of the region's aquatic habitats, including ephemeral streams and seasonal ponds, naturally go dry in the rainless summer months. However, water management practices that create permanent water sources, including the creation of impoundments and some agricultural practices, favor these invasive species. The bullfrog, for example, a documented predator of the California red-legged frog, can tolerate elevated water temperatures and can make use of standing water habitat created by agricultural practices (USFWS 2002e). California tiger salamander populations are threatened by hybridization with non-native tiger salamander species introduced to the region as fishing bait (Bolster 2005 pers. comm.). In estuarine environments, non-native invertebrates, such as the European green crab and Japanese mud snail, are competing with native invertebrates and altering food chain dynamics (Caffrey et al. 2002).

As noted in the section on livestock grazing, a number of the region's highly invasive exotic plant species are associated with inappropriately grazed rangelands and pastures, including starthistle species, medusahead, and black mustard. Other invasive plant species in the region, including Pampas grass and cape ivy, either are or have been sold as ornamental plants and have escaped from cultivation.

Numerous invasive plant species are established in the region's beaches, dunes, sandy coastal soils, and lowland areas. Outcompeting and displacing native plant communities, these invasive species often provide inferior habitat for wildlife. Veldt grass, associated with sandy soils, can shift native shrub communities toward grasslands and is of particular concern in San Luis Obispo and Santa Barbara counties, notably at Vandenberg Air Force Base, Guadalupe Nipomo Dunes, and around Morro Bay (Bossard et al. 2000). On beaches and dunes, ice plant species, European beach grass, and Veldt grass form monocultures and dense mats of vegetation and displace native plants that provide important habitat for invertebrates like Smith's blue butterfly. Dense growth of non-native vegetation also causes unnatural stabilization of beach and dune systems. Jubata and Pampas grass are most invasive near Big Sur, Elkhorn Slough, and around the lower slopes of the Santa Cruz mountains. In timbered areas, these grasses can form dense stands that inhibit the germination of such coastal forest species as redwoods (Bossard et al. 2000). Cape ivy chokes out native vegetation with densely growing vines. Found most commonly in shady coastal lowlands, cape ivy also invades oak woodlands, riparian forests, coastal scrub, and Monterey pine forests (Bossard et al. 2000).

Aquatic systems also face a number of threats from invasive plant species. In watersheds subject to high levels of agricultural land use, such as the Salinas, Pajaro, and Santa Ynez drainages, giant reed and tamarisk species replace native riparian vegetation and provide lower-quality habitat for sensitive species such as least Bell's vireo, California red-legged frog, Western pond turtle, and kit fox. Because giant reed and tamarisk provide limited shade, proliferation of these species also results in higher water temperatures and lower levels of dissolved oxygen (Bossard et al. 2000).

Conservation Actions to Restore and Conserve Wildlife

In addition to the recommended regional actions described below, see the recommended statewide conservation actions as given in Chapter 4.

a. Wildlife agencies should establish regional goals for species and habitat protection and work with city, county, and state agency land-use planning processes to accomplish those goals.

See Statewide Action a in Chapter 4.

Priorities specific to this region include:

Areas experiencing rapid population growth and development would benefit from improved conservation planning to protect habitat values and environmental quality.

As an example, the current Monterey County General Plan Update represents an important regional opportunity to enact land-use policies that could serve as a regional and statewide model. Regionally, some of the greatest development pressures are felt in the remaining unprotected open space areas of Monterey County. Inland, rapid population growth is occurring in the Salinas and Pajaro river valleys. Along the coast, there are limited areas remaining for development. To the north, the northern portion of Santa Cruz County is largely protected by General Plan restrictions, Local Coastal Plans and State Parks and University of California management, and southern Santa Cruz County is built out to the maximum extent possible. As a result, strong development pressures are focused on the open space areas between the Santa Cruz–Monterey County line and the protected Big Sur coastline south of Yankee Point.

Monterey County's General Plan has not been updated since 1982, and the existing plan does not adequately address these strong growth pressures. A General Plan Update process has been under way for nearly a decade, three times generating draft documents, but has failed to result in the adoption of a final plan.

To preserve critical habitat areas in the county—including increasingly rare maritime chaparral and Monterey pine forest habitats, valley oak woodlands, coastal dune and grassland habitats of the endemic Smith's blue butterfly, and aquatic habitats supporting California red-legged frog—it is critical that a General Plan Update be completed to direct development to the most appropriate areas. The Monterey County Board of Supervisors should adopt a plan that incorporates strong land-use planning policies, sound conservation planning principles, and proactive implementation ideas, many of which were developed in the 2003 Draft General Plan Update document. For additional information, see Monterey County General Plan Update at the end of this chapter.

For further discussion of goals and ways to improve integration of conservation planning with land-use planning, see the Conservation Planning section in Chapter 6.

b. Federal, state, and local agencies, along with nongovernmental organizations, should work with private landowners and land managers to implement agricultural land and rangeland management practices that are compatible with wildlife and habitat conservation.

See Statewide Action h in Chapter 4.

Priorities specific to this region include:

The Central Coast Regional Water Quality Control Board and interests from the agricultural industry should continue their partnership to develop and implement the Agricultural Permit/Waiver Program that will require the agricultural landowners and managers to take courses on and implement management practices that protect environmental quality.

(See also Appendix G, Information Sources for Wildlife and Habitat Conservation on Private Lands.)

c. Federal, state, and local agencies, along with nongovernmental organizations, should work with private landowners to both continue and develop programs that help keep grazing land uses profitable.

Continued operation of private ranchlands is the most economically viable and practical way to preserve the Central Coast's wildlife diversity. At current funding and staffing levels for wildlife agencies and conservation organizations, the acquisition of sizeable rangeland parcels is rare, and large-scale restoration of native grasslands and oak woodlands is not feasible. Compared to residential and commercial development, grazing lands remain relatively open to wildlife movement and hold possibilities for future restoration efforts, if such efforts are needed. Grazing can control invasive exotic plant species and the impenetrable thatch formed by non-native annual grasses. Well-managed rangelands also provide valuable ecological services. Because they are permeable to rainfall and support vegetative cover and microbial soil communities, these rangelands contribute to aquifer recharge, erosion control, and nutrient cycling and offer resources used by insect pollinators of crops and natural vegetation.

- **Continue and expand the California Department of Fish and Game's Private Lands Management Program,** which allows private landowners to collect hunting fees if they manage their property in a wildlife-friendly manner and provide access to hunters.
- **Continue counties' efforts to enroll private ranchlands in the state Williamson Act program,** which supports private ranchers by reducing property taxes on lands in agricultural use. The state should continue to compensate counties for tax revenues lost on properties enrolled in Williamson Act contracts.

- **Develop additional tax-benefit or other financial-incentive programs at the local, state, and federal level for landowners who follow grazing management guidelines that protect wildlife habitat and rangeland health.** For example, Fish and Game's Landowner Incentive Program provides funding for management and enhancement of wildlife habitat on private lands along with annual incentive payments.

- **Support private initiatives to develop certification and labeling programs** for ecologically sustainable grazing practices for use by both private landowners and lessees on public lands.

See also Appendix G, Information Sources for Wildlife and Habitat Conservation on Private Lands.

d. Federal, state, and local agencies, along with nongovernmental conservation organizations, should work to protect large, relatively unfragmented habitat areas, wildlife corridors, and underprotected ecological community types.

Means for protection may include developing Natural Community Conservation Plans (NCCPs), establishing **conservation banks,** employing conservation easements and management agreements with landowners, and acquiring public land from willing sellers.

- **Prevent the fragmentation of large habitat areas by residential and commercial development or transportation infrastructure.**

  See Statewide Actions b and c in Chapter 4.

  Priorities specific to this region include:

  In consultation with public wildlife agencies and private resource consultants, nongovernmental conservation organizations have completed regional analyses to identify important core areas that are relatively free of roads, ecologically intact, and well buffered (Thorne et al. 2002, TNC 2005, Gallos 2005). These analyses are largely based upon wildlife agencies' data (including the California Natural Diversity Database and other sources) and incorporate Fish and Game biologists' expert opinion. Fish and Game should use and build upon these analyses to continue to clarify and prioritize conservation areas where the state's resources should be focused.

  Transportation planning should give high priority to preserving large core habitat areas, and, when possible, locate future highway or rail construction along existing transportation corridors. Current transportation proposals include several proposed roads that would bisect the Mount Hamilton area and a high-speed rail line that would bisect a number of regional State Park lands. If implemented, these proposals would fragment wildlands and important wildlife habitat areas.

- **Protect habitat linkages between large wildland areas.**

  See Statewide Action d in Chapter 4.

  Priorities specific to this region include:

Potential San Joaquin kit fox corridors running from Camp Roberts southeast along the Salinas River to the Carrizo Plain and Kern County and northeast toward the Cholame Hills are a priority for study and protection.

Ranching and other land uses that preserve unfragmented landscapes in the Cuyama Valley in southern San Luis Obispo County should be maintained to allow movement by wide-ranging species, including tule elk that have been reintroduced on the Carrizo Plain and San Joaquin kit fox.

Wildland areas in the Purisma and Soloman hills in Santa Barbara County should be protected to connect the Los Padres Forest with important habitat areas on the coast at Vandenberg Air Force Base.

Preserving a corridor along the Pajaro River and adjacent lands from the Santa Cruz Mountains to the Diablo Range and Santa Lucia Mountains is also important for wide-ranging species.

More research is needed to determine the routes currently in use by wide-ranging species. Additional resources for information about regional wildlife corridors can be found in the California Wilderness Coalition's *Guide to wildlands conservation in the Central Coast region of California* (Thorne et al. 2002), the *Conception Coast Project* (Gallos 2005), and from local land trusts.

- **Protect underprotected ecological community types.**
These include oak woodlands, serpentine habitats, maritime chaparral, riparian floodplain communities, vernal pools, native grasslands, and old-growth redwood forests (Davis et al. 1998, Thorne et al. 2002, TNC 2005). The California Gap Analysis Project prepared by the University

Tim Palmer

of California, Santa Barbara, provides useful analysis of the protection status of natural community types across the state (Davis et al. 1998).

e. Federal, state, and local public agencies should sufficiently protect sensitive species and important wildlife habitats on their lands.

Public agencies should adopt management policies that safeguard natural resources and wildlife habitat, even as they manage for multiple uses or mandates that emphasize other objectives. Management policies and practices must protect sensitive habitats from recreational uses. Recreational areas should be carefully chosen, and use restrictions should be adequately enforced, especially in fragile coastal habitats or riparian areas where there is a high potential for conflict between sensitive species and even passive recreational uses (such as hiking). Infrastructure and resource-extraction projects should be designed and sited to avoid harmful effects on sensitive species and habitats. Where grazing uses are appropriate, agencies should employ, and encourage lessees to implement, ecologically sustainable management practices.

The Los Padres National Forest encompasses 1.6 million acres in the Central Coast, including much of the Santa Lucia and Transverse ranges. The Forest Service must adopt a Resource Management Plan for the Los Padres National Forest that protects wildlife habitats and diversity, and Congress needs to appropriate adequate funds to implement the plan.

Important actions for inclusion in the forest's Resource Management Plan are:

- Protect streams and watersheds. Where alternative water sources are available to meet existing water rights, remove water diversions on forest stream systems.

- Institute protective land use designations (as Critical Biological Zones and Research Natural Areas) for areas in the forest that support sensitive species or unique or highly diverse biological communities.

- Minimize the negative effects of the grazing leases that are in place on approximately 46 percent of Los Padres National Forest lands. Careful grazing management practices are critical for sensitive habitats, including riparian areas and streams, grasslands, wildflower fields, and coastal scrub and chaparral habitats of the federally listed endangered Smith's blue butterfly.

- Institute appropriate fire management policies and practices, based on the best available science and site-specific conditions, to restore the ecological integrity of forests. Continued research is needed to better understand the fire regimes required to maintain the health of different vegetation communities.

- Prohibit new road development in roadless areas that serve as California condor habitat and in the biologically significant watersheds in the Matilija, Chumash, Dick Smith, Sespe, Ventana, and Silver Peak wilderness areas.

- Limit expansion of new roads and off-road-vehicle use areas. Close roads and prohibit off-road-vehicle use in biologically significant and sensitive areas, particularly riparian habitats. Develop areas for intensive recreational access and off-road-vehicle use in the least-sensitive forest areas so as to direct pressures away from sensitive habitats.

Bureau of Land Management lands encompass more than 310,000 acres in the region, including expansive grasslands and serpentine areas. Important management actions and issues for BLM lands include:

- Minimize the negative effects of the grazing leases that are in place on approximately 66 percent of BLM lands. Careful grazing management practices are critical for sensitive habitats, including serpentine and barrens areas on San Benito Mountain and in the Panoche, Tumey, and Kettleman hills and native grassland communities and vernal pools. Further surveys and GPS documentation are needed to locate and protect remaining patches of native or rare vegetation communities. Continue to develop and fund grazing management research at Carrizo Plain National Monument through management partnerships with Fish and Game and The Nature Conservancy.

- Restrict off-road-vehicle use in serpentine habitats. Finalize and implement the newly developed use-designations limiting off-road-vehicle use in serpentine habitats at BLM's Clear Creek Management Area. Increase funding to provide an adequate enforcement presence. Current annual funding appropriations do not fully cover even one protection officer; four to six officers are needed on busy weekends.

- Appropriately locate and plan power transmission lines and energy development projects on BLM lands to minimize impacts on sensitive resources. In particular, along the eastern slope of southern Diablo Range (from Coalinga to Los Banos), proactive conservation planning is needed to address the potential negative effects of powerline construction, proposed wind-power development, and oil exploration on sensitive kit fox habitat and serpentine areas.

Lands managed by state agencies, such as State Parks and Fish and Game, encompass more than 330,000 acres in the region. Among these are numerous coastal habitats and large blocks of natural lands, including 87,000 acres at Henry Coe State Park in Santa Clara County and an 80,000-acre easement (held jointly by the state and nongovernmental partners) on the Hearst Ranch in San Luis Obispo County. Important management actions and issues for these lands include:

- Preserving unfragmented and relatively undisturbed open space areas and wildlands within the region's state lands. This should be a priority when planning regional transportation corridors.

- Continuing to implement protective actions to prevent recreational users from disturbing sensitive species. In coastal habitats, fencing and visitor education for both hikers and off-road vehicle users are important at Western snowy plover and least tern nesting sites.

- Where grazing land uses are appropriate, employing careful prescription-grazing practices, critical to protect sensitive habitats and rare plant communities.

The region's larger military installations (U.S. Army's Fort Hunter Liggett, California Army National Guard's Camp Roberts, and Vandenberg Air Force Base) encompass more than 312,000 acres. The region also houses several smaller military bases, including Concord Naval Weapons Station and the Naval Postgraduate School in Monterey. These military lands support more than 70 sensitive species, including Western snowy plover, sage sparrow, San Joaquin kit fox, California red-legged frog, California tiger salamander, arroyo toad, and steelhead, and significant ecological communities, including oak woodlands, serpentine soils, native grasslands, vernal pools, and maritime chaparral. The military mission is often compatible with wildlife habitat needs, because large, open-space areas are preserved for training exercises, which also provide large, unfragmented habitat areas. With an average of only 10 percent to 15 percent of military lands developed, military installations provide a significant contribution to regional wildlands.

- Renew and continue to implement adequately protective Integrated Natural Resource Management Plans (INRMPs) on military installations. Currently, all of the Central Coast's installations currently have INRMPs approved or under review by Fish and Game and the U.S. Fish and Wildlife Service. State and federal wildlife agencies should continue to work with military installations to set goals for wildlife populations and habitats on military lands, update and implement INRMPs that will achieve those goals, and measure accomplishments.
- Encourage livestock operators with grazing leases on military lands to implement ecologically sustainable grazing practices.
- Increase resources for invasive plant management at Vandenberg Air Force Base and Fort Hunter Liggett.
- Continue coastal scrub and maritime chaparral restoration at Vandenberg Air Force Base.
- Continue research on oak woodland ecology at Camp Roberts and Fort Hunter Liggett; apply findings regarding fire and grazing management to address the Sudden Oak Death pathogen and to oak woodland management across the state (CAANG 2001, Zack 2002).
- Continue support for invasive species management (including bullfrogs, non-native fish, and crayfish) to secure large populations of arroyo toads on Fort Hunter Liggett and red-legged frogs on Vandenberg Air Force Base.
- Ensure protection of sensitive species and wildlife habitats if any of the region's military facilities are identified for base closures. State, federal, and local wildlife agencies and other nongovernmental conservation organizations must be well-informed about and prepared to safeguard these land's natural resource values.

f. Federal, state, and local agencies should work to restore fish passage in aquatic systems important for anadromous and wide-ranging fish populations.

Efforts to restore fish passage may require multiagency partnerships involving such state and local agencies as the State Water Resources Control Board, Caltrans, local water districts, city and county public works departments, and Fish and Game; federal agencies, such as NOAA (National Oceanic and Atmospheric Administration) Fisheries, the National Marine Fisheries Service, and the Federal Energy Regulatory Commission; and nongovernmental organizations, such as Trout Unlimited, land trusts, and watershed councils. The cooperation of private owners of dams and water supply companies will also be needed.

- Continue to inventory and assess barriers to fish passage, update and maintain the Coastal Conservancy's database of barriers, and use the database to prioritize and seek opportunities to implement fish passage improvement projects (CDFG 2004g). The Coastal Conservancy's database is available at http://www.calfish.org, under the Fish Passage Assessment link.
- Where possible, remove or modify structures and barriers to allow passage. Install fish ladders or other means of passage around dams, diversions, and other impediments, including road crossings, pipelines, and culverts. Monitor fish-passage improvement projects to assess benefits to fish populations and to document lessons learned.
- Consider removal of dams that are not structurally sound, whose reservoirs are full of sediment, or those not providing significant hydropower or water supply benefits.

g. State and local agencies should allocate sufficient water for ecosystem uses when planning for and meeting regional water supply needs. Providing adequate water for wildlife and instream uses is particularly important in systems that support sensitive species or important habitat areas.

See Statewide Action e in Chapter 4.

Planning efforts may require participation by a wide range of agencies, including state and regional water resources quality control boards; local water districts; California Department of Housing and Community Development; county and city governments; government associations; private water supply companies; and large-scale water users, such as agricultural operations.

Priorities specific to this region include:
- Conduct research to determine stream-flow needs for anadromous fish and other aquatic fauna, particularly below dams.

- Plan and scale residential, commercial, and agricultural growth according to available water resources. Utilize realistic assessments of water resources for county and city planning.

- When counties subdivide or rezone land, account for the creation of new water rights (such as new riparian rights) with mitigations or conditions to limit the expansion of water rights (CDFG 2004g).

- Improve the process for approving new water diversion and development permits or renewals.

- Maintain or increase local government, water district, and state agency funding for water conservation programs (e.g., water metering, water use restrictions, and subsidies for technologies that reduce water consumption), and allocate a major portion of the conserved water surpluses to ecosystem uses, rather than to new development that increases demand.

h. State and federal agencies should work to protect and restore biologically significant regional river systems.

Benefits to water quality and sensitive aquatic species can be achieved by preserving natural functioning in aquatic systems. To the extent possible, rivers should be managed, protected, and restored to maintain a functional connection between river and floodplain, preserve riparian vegetation and habitat, maintain natural channel courses and sediment transfer capacity, and improve water quality. Upland natural areas and vegetation buffers should also be retained or restored to the extent possible to provide water quality benefits and wildlife habitat, along with passive recreation opportunities.

- Develop and implement watershed plans in order to meet **Total Maximum Daily Load** (TMDL) standards and achieve Clean Water Act compliance. The Regional Water Quality Control Board and U.S. Environmental Protection Agency should also continue to refine TMDL standards by region to reflect natural, historical conditions.

- Where flood control requires engineering solutions and hydrologic modifications, maintain or mimic natural **fluvial** processes and flow regimes where possible. Engineers and involved agencies (e.g., U.S. Army Corps of Engineers) should work with state and federal wildlife biologists to minimize negative effects on aquatic species and habitats and to restore riparian habitats and upland buffers.

- Where gravel mining affects biologically significant watersheds, monitor mining sites to ensure that sufficient streambed gravel remains to preserve channel structure and function. Where mining has occurred historically, restore river-channel structure to allow such natural river functions as flooding and sediment transport.

i. Federal, state, and local agencies should provide greater resources and coordinate efforts to eradicate or control existing occurrences of invasive species and prevent new introductions.

See Statewide Action f in Chapter 4.

Priorities specific to this region include:

- Develop effective control methods for starthistle. Research combination treatments of burning and integrated pest management.

- Increase control efforts for tamarisk and giant reed in riparian areas, particularly along the Salinas and Pajaro rivers and in the Panoche Creek and Silver Creek drainages.

- Increase efforts to control invasive aquatic animals, including bullfrogs and crayfish, through a combination of eradication and trapping efforts and by managing aquatic systems to mimic naturally intermittent flows.

The Monterey County General Plan Update

There currently are competing ideas about the direction that Monterey County's General Plan Update should take. In 2003, after five years of preparation that included an investment of over $5 million, a third Draft General Plan Update was completed and was unanimously recommended to the County Board of Supervisors by the County Planning Commission. The Draft Plan aimed to focus development in existing urban areas, preserve the region's agricultural lands, protect air and water quality, meet the region's water supply needs, and provide affordable housing convenient to employment locations. In response to objections by development and business interests to the Draft Plan's land-use restrictions, the County Board of Supervisors rejected the Draft Plan and appointed a new General Plan Update team, which is now working on a revised Draft Plan.

A coalition of citizens and local and statewide environmental groups* has organized to preserve the proactive planning policies of the 2003 draft document. The coalition initiated its own planning process, including large-scale public meetings, to develop an alternate General Plan Update by citizen mandate. The Community General Plan document (which meets the legal requirements for a General Plan) was completed and provided to the Board of Supervisors in January 2005. This alternate General Plan Update document could provide examples of planning policies that adequately protect wildlife diversity while addressing other community needs and could inform the work of the current General Plan Update team. The document is available on the Web: http://www.co.monterey.ca.us/pbi/gpu/.

* Members of the coalition include the Planning and Conservation League; LandWatch Monterey County; Citizens for Responsible Growth; Prunedale Neighbors Group; Carmel Valley Association; Sierra Club, Ventana Chapter; California Native Plant Society; Ocean Conservancy; and others.

Conversion of Native Grasslands to Introduced Annual Grasslands

Livestock and annual forage grasses were introduced to the Central Coast more than 150 years ago, and large portions of the landscape have undergone high-intensity, year-round grazing (Barbour et al. 1993, Newman et al. 2003, Thorne et al. 2002). The pervasiveness and long history of livestock grazing have transformed large portions the region's grassland communities. Remaining native grasslands and meadows occur primarily as isolated patches within larger areas of introduced annual grasslands. Across the region, native perennial grasslands are estimated at about 30,000 acres, while non-native annual grasslands cover approximately 4 million acres and account for nearly half of the region's vegetation (Davis et al. 1998, Thorne et al. 2002). Loss of native grasses is particularly severe in the drier inland areas, where arid conditions favor the establishment of drought-tolerant, non-native species.

Records that document use of native grasslands by wildlife are limited, making it difficult to assess the affects of native grassland declines on wildlife populations. The loss of these grasslands has had a substantial impact on regional vegetation, with nearly 50 plant species of native grasslands considered rare (CNDDB, CNPS 2001). These changes in the species composition and structure of grasslands have had variable effects on wildlife species because of differences in the way these species use the landscape and habitat features. Populations of some wildlife species, including the federally and state listed endangered blunt-nosed leopard lizard, grassland nesting birds, including the grasshopper sparrow, and invertebrates associated with rare plants, have declined along with native grasslands. However, non-native grasslands provide valuable habitats for numerous regional wildlife species, including black-tailed jackrabbit, California ground squirrel, tule elk, sensitive species such as the mountain plover, and many small mammals that provide a large prey-base for raptor species. Carefully managed livestock grazing can serve as an important tool to improve habitat for some sensitive species, including San Joaquin kit fox, giant kangaroo rat, and California tiger salamander.

Many biologists consider introduced annual grasslands to be a naturalized community type, because most grasses are not invasively expanding their range, and they function as an important habitat component in the mosaic of community types across the region. Moreover, large rangeland areas provide continuous open space areas critical for wildlife movement and ecological function.

Stressors Affecting Some Major Regional River Systems and Coastal Wetlands

Salinas River Watershed

- Sediment and chemical pollutants, notably nitrate and pesticides, from agricultural runoff
- Water development and diversion, with agriculture accounting for 94 percent of total water use
- Major overdraft and seawater intrusion in the Salinas Valley groundwater basin
- Sedimentation resulting from bulldozing of river banks to control channel migration and flooding
- Removal of riparian habitat within the active floodplain for flood control
- Channelization of the mouth of the Salinas River
- Salmonid passage blocked by low instream flows and three major impoundments (the Salinas, Nacimiento, and San Antonio dams)
- Instream gravel mining
- Invasive exotic plant and animal species
- Reduction of steelhead numbers and range resulting from dams, water quality degradation, and drought; remaining steelhead are largely landlocked

Pajaro River Watershed

- Sediment and chemical pollutants from agricultural runoff
- Major overdraft and seawater intrusion in the Pajaro Valley groundwater basin
- Threats to habitat and water quality from off-road vehicle use
- Instream sand and gravel mining in one of the watershed's major tributaries (the San Benito River)
- Nearby historical mercury mining
- Invasive exotic plant and animal species
- Clearing of riparian vegetation as part of flood-control efforts along much of the river
- Channelization of the majority of the mainstem Pajaro River to provide flood protection and to facilitate agricultural drainage
- Current planning for a large-scale Army Corps of Engineers flood control project
- Declines of annual steelhead runs from between 1,000 to 2,000 fish in the 1960s to remnant runs today

cont. on next page

Stressors Affecting Some Major Regional River Systems and Coastal Wetlands, cont.

Carmel River

- Two major impoundments (San Clemente and Los Padres dams) altering natural flow regimes and impeding salmonid passage
- Critically low flows and dewatering of surface flows, broadening of the channel, and loss of riparian habitat resulting from water development
- Depletion of the lower Carmel Valley aquifer resulting from groundwater pumping beyond legal limits (exceptions to pumping limits are made annually, because water supply is needed)
- Declines of annual steelhead runs from approximately 20,000 fish in the 1920s to just a few hundred in the 1990s

Santa Maria Watershed (Cuyama and Sisquoc rivers)

- A major impoundment on the Cuyama River (Twitchell Reservoir) altering natural flow regimes and disconnecting the upper Cuyama from the Santa Maria and Siquoc rivers
- The Santa Maria Project on the Santa Maria River, capturing seasonal floodwaters and altering natural flood processes
- Reliance upon groundwater sources for irrigation resulting in severe drawdown of groundwater levels in the Cuyama Valley, eliminating cottonwood gallery forest and resulting in a river that dries up along a portion of its length and experiences flash floods
- High water demands in the upper Cuyama Valley due to the cultivation of crops grown using water-intensive overhead spray irrigation, notably broccoli, brussel sprouts, alfalfa, and carrots
- Invasive exotic plant and animal species
- Gravel mining on the mainstem of the Cuyama

Santa Ynez River

- Sediment and chemical pollutants from agricultural runoff
- Extensive clearing of riparian vegetation for flood-control efforts
- Invasive exotic plant and animal species
- Instream gravel mining
- Low flows and occasional drying up of surface flows as a consequence of groundwater pumping

cont. on next page

Stressors Affecting Some Major Regional River Systems and Coastal Wetlands, cont.

- Three major impoundments (Gibraltar, Bradbury, and Juncal dams), altering natural flow regimes and blocking salmonid passage
- Critically low flows owing to insufficient water releases below Bradbury Dam
- Near-extirpation of steelhead due to insufficient flows; historically, the Santa Ynez supported one of the largest southern steelhead runs, estimated between 12,000 to 25,000 fish

Morro Bay

- Sediment, chemical pollutants, and microbiological contaminants from agricultural runoff
- Microbiological contamination and water quality degradation resulting from septic systems

Elkhorn Slough

- Sediment and chemical pollutants from agricultural runoff
- Hydrologic alterations, including construction of a berm for a railroad and the opening of Moss Landing Harbor, resulting in the loss of 50 percent of the marsh's historical acreage

Sources: CDFG 1996, DWR 2003a, DWR 2005a, Page and Shuford 2000, TPL 2001

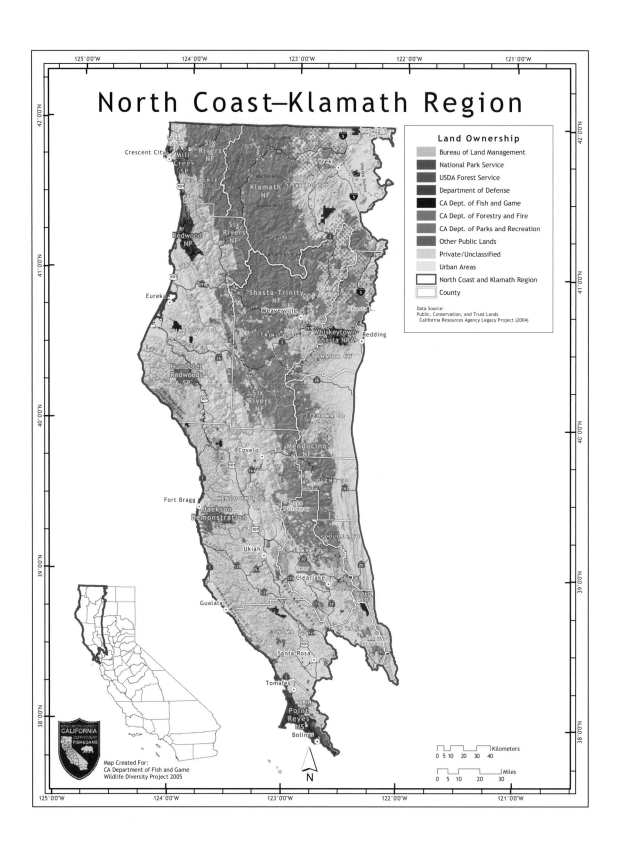

North Coast–Klamath Region

Land Ownership

- Bureau of Land Management
- National Park Service
- USDA Forest Service
- Department of Defense
- CA Dept. of Fish and Game
- CA Dept. of Forestry and Fire
- CA Dept. of Parks and Recreation
- Other Public Lands
- Private/Unclassified
- Urban Areas
- North Coast and Klamath Region
- County

Data Source:
Public, Conservation, and Trust Lands
California Resources Agency Legacy Project (2004)

Map Created For:
CA Department of Fish and Game
Wildlife Diversity Project 2005

Kilometers
0 5 10 20 30 40

Miles
0 5 10 20 30

N

11   North Coast–Klamath Region ～～

Encompassing approximately 14 million acres, the North Coast–Klamath Region extends along the Pacific coast from the California-Oregon border in the north to the San Francisco Bay watershed in the south. The region's eastern, inland boundary is formed by the Cascade ranges along the northern portion of the region and by the transition to the Sacramento Valley along the southern portion.

The region is characterized by large expanses of rugged, forested mountains that range in elevation from 3,000 feet to 8,000 feet, and includes the Klamath, Siskiyou, Marble, Trinity, and North Coast ranges. The climate varies considerably across the region, with high precipitation levels in many coastal areas and dry conditions and rain shadow effects in some inland valleys. Overall, the region has a fairly wet climate and receives more rainfall than any other part of the state, feeding more than 10 sizeable river systems.

Along the coast, sandy beaches host snowy plover, willet, and sanderling, while rocky shoreline habitats support black oystercatcher, ruddy turnstone, and surfbird. Coastal wetland communities, including estuaries, lagoons, marshes, and open-water bays, are also important for shorebirds and provide nursery habitats for **anadromous,** oceanic, and near-shore fish.

Among the region's notable coastal wetlands are the **estuary** at the mouth of the Smith River, Lake Talawa and Lake Earl, Humboldt Bay, the mouth of the Eel River, and Bodega and Tomales bays (Page and Shuford 2000).

Terrestrial communities along the coast include grasslands, coastal shrub, pine forests, mixed evergreen forests, and redwood forests. Unique, geographically limited habitats include sphagnum bogs and pygmy scrub forests. The region's coastal redwoods are among the largest, tallest, and oldest trees in the world, often exceeding 200 feet in height, 15 feet in diameter, and 2,000 years in age. Redwood groves are patchily distributed across the coastal fog belt that extends up to 40 miles inland and where winter rains and summer fog provide a persistent moist environment. Some inhabitants of coastal redwood forests include black bear, Roosevelt elk, MacGillivray's warbler, olive-sided flycatcher, marbled murrelet, Pacific giant salamander, rough-skinned newt, and the banana slug.

The region's inland Klamath-Siskiyou mountain ranges are recognized for their biological diversity; they have been designated as an area of global botanical significance by the World Conservation Union (IUCN), as one of 200 global conservation priority sites by the World Wildlife Fund, and as a proposed United Nations' biosphere reserve (Ricketts et al. 1999). These mountains harbor some of the most floristically diverse temperate coniferous forests in the world, attributable in part to the region's variable climate, geography, and soil types that create a variety of ecological communities. Unique, localized conditions have given rise to **endemic** species that have evolved to specialize in these areas, including nearly 100 plant species that are restricted to serpentine soils. Additionally, portions of the region remained unglaciated during the last ice ages and have served as centers of distribution for numerous species that sought refuge there. Finally, these mountains represent the intersection of coastal ecosystems with the inland Klamath Basin region. As a result, the inland mountains and river systems support a rich flora and fauna that include species from both regions. The Klamath river system, for instance, harbors both coastal fish, like **salmonids** and Coast Range sculpin, and fish whose ranges extend from the inland Klamath Basin, such as the tui chub.

Ecological communities of the inland mountain ranges include moist inland forests dominated by Douglas fir, ponderosa pine, and sugar pine mixed with a variety of other conifers and hardwoods; drier oak forests and savannas; serpentine soil–associated plant communities; shrublands, including such species as mountain heather-bilberry, mountain whitethorn, and manzanita; high-elevation subalpine forests dominated by white- and red fir, western white pine, and mountain hemlock; and less-widespread cranberry and pitcher plant **fens** and alpine grasslands on high peaks. More than 3,000 plant species are known from these mountains, and the area supports some 30 temperate conifer tree species, more than any other ecosystem in the world. Wildlife inhabitants include such sensitive species as the northern spotted owl, northern goshawk, Humboldt marten, and Pacific fisher, as well as common species like mule deer, black bear, and red-tailed hawk.

The region's major inland waterways are part of the Klamath River system, which includes the Klamath, Scott, Shasta, Salmon, and Trinity rivers. In the upper portions of their watersheds, these rivers are centered in **alluvial** valleys that historically supported freshwater marshes and grasslands but have now been converted to agriculture. Below these alluvial valleys, the Klamath-system rivers are generally confined between steep mountain slopes over most of their length and support fairly narrow riparian habitats. River systems draining the region's Coast Ranges include the Eel, Russian, Mattole, Navarro, Smith, Mad, and Gualala rivers. Because the Coast Range is composed of soft, easily eroded soils, these rivers have carved more extensive riparian habitats and also carry high sediment loads. Most of the North Coast–Klamath Region's large rivers widen as they approach their ocean outlets, forming alluvial floodplains and deltas. These floodplains once supported extensive black cottonwood, willow, and red alder forests but have now been largely converted to agricultural uses.

The region is known for these extensive river systems and the anadromous fish populations they support. The majority of California's river segments with state or federal Wild and Scenic river designations are in the North Coast–Klamath Region, including portions of the Klamath, Trinity, Smith, Scott, Salmon, Van Duzen, and Eel. Anadromous fish species include coho and chinook salmon, steelhead, coast cutthroat trout, green sturgeon, and Pacific lamprey. The region has seen sharp declines in its fish populations, with an 80 percent decline in salmon and steelhead between the 1950s and 1990s (California State Lands Commission 1993). These declines have resulted from degradation of river systems by forestry and other land uses; decreased instream flows resulting from water diversions and agricultural water use; overharvesting of fish (beginning in the mid-1800s and lasting until the late 1970s, at which time substantial restrictions on ocean harvest were enacted by the Pacific Marine Fisheries Council); and natural and human-influenced variation in oceanic conditions, such as plankton densities and temperatures. Nonetheless, the remaining fish populations still represent the most important anadromous fish runs in the state. The region's rivers support one-third of the state's chinook, most of the state's coho salmon and steelhead, and all of the coast cutthroat trout (California State Lands Commission 1993). Other native freshwater fish, like the Lost River sucker and shortnose sucker, have also experienced substantial population declines due to alterations of the region's freshwater river systems (CDGF 2005b).

Species at Risk

The Plan development team updated vertebrate and invertebrate species information in the California Natural Diversity Database (CNDDB) during 2004–2005. The following regional summary of numbers of wildlife species, endemic species, and **species at risk** is derived from the updated CNDDB.

The North Coast–Klamath's wide range of habitats has given rise to remarkable biological diversity. There are 501 vertebrate species that inhabit the North Coast–Klamath Region at some point in their life cycle, including 282 birds, 104 mammals, 26 reptiles, 30 amphibians, and 59 fish. Of the total vertebrate species that inhabit this region, 76 bird **taxa**, 26 mammalian taxa, two reptilian taxa, 13 amphibian taxa, and 42 fish taxa are included on the **Special Animals List.** Of these, 13 are endemic to the North Coast–Klamath Region, and nine other species found here are endemic to California but not restricted to this region (Table 11.1).

Table 11.1: State-Endemic Special Status Vertebrates of the North Coast–Klamath Region

	Ambystoma californiense	California tiger salamander
*	*Aplodontia rufa nigra*	Point Arena mountain beaver
*	*Aplodontia rufa phaea*	Point Reyes mountain beaver
*	*Arborimus pomo*	Red tree vole
	Archoplites interruptus	Sacramento perch
*	*Cottus klamathensis polyporus*	Lower Klamath marbled sculpin
	Eucyclogobius newberryi	Tidewater goby
	Geothlypis trichas sinuosa	Saltmarsh common yellowthroat
	Hydromantes shastae	Shasta salamander
*	*Hysterocarpus traski lagunae*	Clear Lake tule perch
*	*Hysterocarpus traski pomo*	Russian River tule perch
	Hysterocarpus traski traski	Sacramento-San Joaquin tule perch
*	*Lavinia exilicauda chi*	Clear Lake hitch
*	*Lavinia symmetricus navarroensis*	Navarro roach
*	*Lavinia symmetricus parvipinnis*	Gualala roach
*	*Lavinia symmetricus ssp. 2*	Tomales roach
*	*Lavinia symmetricus ssp. 4*	Clear Lake/Russian River roach
	Mylopharodon conocephalus	Hardhead

	Perognathus inornatus inornatus	San Joaquin pocket mouse
*	*Plethodon asupak*	Scott River salamander
	Rallus longirostris obsoletus	California clapper rail
*	*Zapus trinotatus orarius*	Point Reyes jumping mouse

* denotes taxon is endemic to region

The number of arthropod species is so great, and they are so poorly known taxonomically, that it is presently impossible to accurately estimate the total number of invertebrate species occurring in the state. In the North Coast–Klamath Region, however, 71 invertebrate taxa are included on the Special Animals List, including 42 arthropod taxa and 29 mollusk taxa. Of these, 38 are endemic to the North Coast–Klamath Region, and 23 other taxa found here are endemic to California but not restricted to this region (Table 11.2).

Table 11.2: State-Endemic Special Status Invertebrates of the North Coast–Klamath Region

	Andrena blennospermatis	Vernal pool bee
	Anthicus sacramento	Sacramento anthicid beetle
	Atractelmis wawona	Wawona riffle beetle
	Caecidotea tomalensis	Tomales isopod
*	*Calasellus californicus*	An isopod; no common name
*	*Calileptoneta briggsi*	A leptonetid spider; no common name
*	*Calileptoneta wapiti*	A leptonetid spider; no common name
*	*Carterocephalus palaemon magnus*	Sonoma arctic skipper
*	*Chaetarthria leechi*	Leech's chaetarthrian water scavenger beetle
	Cicindela hirticollis gravida	Sandy beach tiger beetle
	Coelus globosus	Globose dune beetle
*	*Coenonympha tullia yontocket*	Yontocket's satyr
*	*Cryptochia shasta*	Confusion caddisfly
	Desmocerus californicus dimorphus	Valley elderberry longhorn beetle
*	*Dubiraphia giulianii*	Giuliani's dubiraphian riffle beetle
*	*Hedychridium milleri*	Miller's chrysidid wasp
*	*Helminthoglypta arrosa williamsi*	Mountain bronze shoulderband snail
*	*Helminthoglypta arrosa pomoensis*	Pomo bronze shoulderband snail
*	*Helminthoglypta arrosa williamsi*	Williams' bronze shoulderband snail
*	*Helminthoglypta nickliniana awania*	Peninsula coast range shoulderband snail
*	*Helminthoglypta talmadgei*	Talmadge's shoulderband snail
*	*Hesperarion plumbeus*	A slug; no common name
	Hydrochara rickseckeri	Ricksecker's water scavenger beetle

	Hydroporus leechi	Leech's skyline diving beetle
	Icaricia icarioides missionensis	Mission blue butterfly
*	*Icaricia icarioides parapheres*	Point Reyes blue butterfly
*	*Incisalia mossii bayensis*	Marin elfin butterfly
	Lanx patelloides	Kneecap lanx
	Lepidurus packardi	Vernal pool tadpole shrimp
	Lichnanthe ursina	Pacific sand bear scarab beetle
	Linderiella occidentalis	California linderiella
*	*Lycaeides argyrognomon lotis*	Lotis blue butterfly
	Lytta molesta	Molestan blister beetle
	Megomphix californicus	Natural Bridge megomphix
*	*Monadenia callipeplus*	Downy sideband
*	*Monadenia chaceana*	Siskiyou shoulderband
	Monadenia churchi	Klamath sideband
*	*Monadenia cristulata*	Crested sideband
*	*Monadenia fidelis leonina*	A sideband snail; no common name
*	*Monadenia fidelis pronotis*	Rocky coast Pacific sideband
*	*Monadenia infumata ochromphalus*	A sideband snail; no common name
*	*Monadenia setosa*	Trinity bristle snail
	Monadenia troglodytes	Shasta sideband
*	*Nebria gebleri siskiyouensis*	Siskiyou ground beetle
*	*Nebria sahlbergii triad*	Trinity Alps ground beetle
	Nothochrysa californica	San Francisco lacewing
*	*Noyo intersessa*	Ten Mile shoulderband
*	*Ochthebius recticulus*	Wilbur Springs minute moss beetle
*	*Paracoenia calida*	Wilber Springs shore fly
	Punctum hannai	Trinity spot snail
*	*Rhyacophila lineata*	Castle Crags rhyacophilan caddisfly
*	*Rhyacophila mosana*	Bilobed rhyacophilan caddisfly
*	*Scaphinotus behrensi*	A ground beetle; no common name
*	*Speyeria zerene behrensii*	Behren's silverspot butterfly
	Speyeria zerene myrtleae	Myrtle's silverspot
	Syncaris pacifica	California freshwater shrimp
	Trachusa gummifera	A leaf-cutting bee; no common name
*	*Vespericola karokorum*	Karok hesperian (=Karok Indian snail)
*	*Vespericola marinensis*	Marin hersperian
*	*Vespericola pressleyi*	Big Bar hesperian
*	*Vespericola shasta*	Shasta hesperian

* denotes taxon is endemic to region

The Wildlife Species Matrix, including data on listing status, habitat association, and population trend for each vertebrate and invertebrate species included on the Special Animals List, is available on the Web at http://www.dfg.ca.gov/habitats/wdp/matrix_search.asp. For vertebrates, the matrix also includes links to species-level range maps. Additionally, a link to the California Department of Fish and Game's online Field Survey Form is available to assist in reporting positive sightings of species on the Special Animals List to the California Natural Diversity Database (CNDDB).

Two Species at Risk

Note: *The following discussion of two species at risk illustrates how stressors or threats affect species and highlights conservation challenges and opportunities. These species discussions are not intended to imply that conservation should have a single-species approach.*

The threats facing the marbled murrelet and coho salmon illustrate some of the most important conservation issues in the region's terrestrial and aquatic habitats.

Marbled Murrelet

The marbled murrelet is a small diving seabird that breeds along the Pacific Coast from the Aleutian archipelago and southern Alaska to central California. The murrelet has a unique life history, feeding on fish and invertebrates in the nearshore marine environment but flying up to 50 miles inland to nest in conifer forests. The marbled murrelet is the only species in the alcid family of seabirds known to nest

in trees. Murrelets utilize forests with mature- or old-growth characteristics, including large trees, a generous amount of **canopy** closure, and complex **under-** and **overstory** structure (USFWS 1997b). Nest trees must have trunk or branch formations, such as large horizontal branches, that can serve as nest platforms.

Estimates are that at least 60,000 marbled murrelets were historically present along the California coast. Current estimates are around 5,000 birds (CDFG 2005, Huff 2002). The three separate areas where the largest numbers of marbled murrelet are found in California (in coastal Santa Cruz, Humboldt, and Del Norte counties) correspond to the three largest remaining blocks of mature, uncut coastal conifer forest (USFWS 1997b).

The marbled murrelet was listed by California as endangered in 1991, and the Washington, Oregon, and California population was federally listed as threatened in 1992. The loss and alteration of nesting habitat as a result of forest management practices are the primary reasons for the bird's decline (USFWS 1997b). It is estimated that only about 4 percent of California's coastal redwood forests remains uncut (CDFG 1999, Robinson and Alexander 2002). Forest management practices in second-growth silvicultural forests favor even-aged timber stands, which are typically harvested before they attain the features needed by nesting murrelets.

Also of concern for murrelet populations is low reproductive success. Predation by common ravens and Steller's jays, which thrive in human-modified environments, is believed to contribute to nest failure. Forestry roads and recreation facilities that fragment forests allow ravens and jays access to interior forest areas, while human food sources associated with recreation areas provide favorable habitat conditions for these species. Marbled murrelets are also vulnerable to threats in the marine environment. Oil spills near Humboldt Bay have resulted in murrelet mortality (CDFG 1999, 2005b). Natural and human-influenced variation in oceanic conditions can limit the populations of fish and invertebrates that murrelets eat.

The U.S. Fish and Wildlife Service recovery plan calls for increases in the amount, quality, and distribution of suitable nesting habitat. On forestry lands, this will require management plans that promote multi-aged forests with complex forest structure and mature trees. Protecting suitable habitats and managing surrounding areas in a way that develops mature forest conditions will buffer existing habitats and provide larger areas of favorable interior forest conditions. To ensure continued genetic exchange, the plan suggests restoring forest habitats between the most southerly occurrences of murrelets in California and those on the North Coast. To minimize potential nest disturbance or predation, the construction or modification of any facilities on protected park lands should be carefully planned. The plan also recommends research to improve information on population size and trends, including annual at-sea surveys. Finally, the plan notes the importance of protecting large areas of suitable nesting habitat.

Coho Salmon

In California, coho salmon occupy coastal drainages from the Oregon border south to Santa Cruz County. Historically, smaller populations also occurred as far south as Big Sur and Santa Barbara County (CDFG 2004b).

Coho have an anadromous life cycle. Hatching in freshwater streams, they migrate to live for two years in the ocean and then return to breed, or spawn, in freshwater, almost always returning to the same river in which they were born. Returning adults typically enter freshwater rivers in the late fall, and spawning occurs throughout the fall and winter. Eggs hatch in the early spring, and juveniles then live in the river-bottom gravel for 10 weeks before emerging. After maturing for about a year in freshwater, coho migrate downstream to coastal estuaries and enter the ocean in the spring.

www.brandoncole.com

Because coho use a variety of habitat features and depend on many different parts of the watershed, from upper freshwater reaches to estuaries, they are an indicator of watershed health. Each stage in a coho's life requires specific environmental conditions for it to survive; the river conditions affecting its life cycle include flows, **substrate**, channel structure, water quality conditions such as temperature and nutrient and oxygen levels, and prey availability.

Increased flow in the fall and winter signal ocean-dwelling coho salmon to move into inland waterways. High flows to breach sand bars that have formed at river mouths are sometimes needed to allow fish to enter. High flows can also allow passage over obstacles that may be insurmountable during lower flows. Suitable flow and substrate characteristics are needed to provide nesting sites (known as **redds**). Females usually build nests where flows are adequate to ensure good circulation of oxygenated water and elimination of wastes. Spawning gravel must be of a size that provides spaces for the eggs and juvenile fish and be free of excessive fine sediments that can reduce oxygen and inhibit movement of newly hatched fish.

Pools and large woody debris offer areas with slow flows and cool temperatures needed by migrating coho to rest and escape predation. Because they are not strong swimmers, juvenile coho in particular require protected and slow-flow areas to escape predation and to avoid being swept out of rivers during high flows. Important habitat areas for juveniles include slow-flowing tributaries, pools, and sloughs, along with backwaters and side channels that can form in alluvial floodplains. Appropriate water temperatures are also critical; excessively high temperatures can increase susceptibility to disease and reduce vigor during competitive interactions with other fish species. Changes to natural temperature regimes can also result in accelerated development of juvenile fish and premature emigration of large numbers of fish at times when ocean conditions are not suitable.

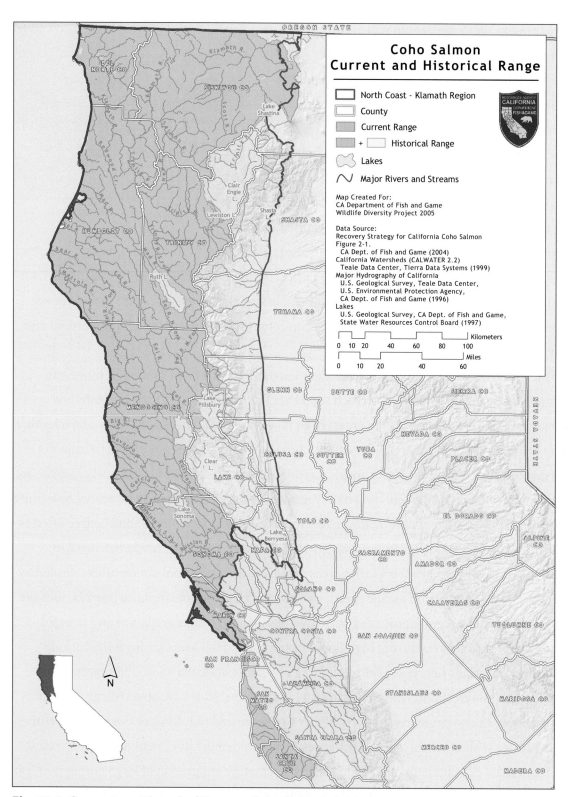

Fig. 11.1: Current vs. Historical Range of the Coho Salmon

In the southern portion of their range, coho salmon have been entirely eliminated from tributaries of the San Francisco Bay. Coho are still found throughout most of North Coast–Klamath Region, but their numbers have declined to a small fraction of their historical populations.

Human activities that alter watershed functioning can disrupt this complex life history that has evolved in response to natural cycles. The principal threats to coho habitats are dams, water diversions, gravel mining in river channels, and agricultural and forestry land uses. Dams can restrict coho migration, alter temperature and flow regimes, and affect sediment transport. Water diversions also alter the amount and timing of water in streams, affecting water temperature. Gravel mining operations can alter substrate availability, channel shape, and flow characteristics. Agriculture and forestry can reduce riparian vegetation, limit woody debris in streams, reduce shade, elevate temperatures, and increase the influx of sediment. In agricultural valleys, channelization and berm construction have simplified river channels, resulting in channels with relatively uniform depths and rapid flows. These channels lack features like backwaters and braided structure that historically provided important coho habitat.

The effects of human activities have reduced the range and population numbers of California's coho salmon. Although coho are still found in most major river systems in the northern portion of the state, coho runs have been eliminated from many tributaries, including some streams in the Klamath and Eel river basins (NMFS 1995). Overall, from Humboldt County north, coho are now found in roughly two-thirds of the streams identified as historical habitat (CDFG 2004g). In the southern portion of their range, coho have been eliminated from all tributaries of the San Francisco Bay (CFDG 2004g).

More dramatic than the coho's range reductions have been population declines. California's coho population has declined by 60 percent since the 1960s and is now estimated to be between 6 percent and 15 percent of 1940s levels (CDFG 2004g). California's coho are federally listed as threatened, and California lists coho south of Punta Gorda in Humboldt County as endangered and, north of that, as threatened.

In 2003, Fish and Game completed the *Recovery Strategy for California Coho Salmon*. The recovery strategy's recommendations include planning and regulating water supply development and water rights to ensure adequate stream-flow levels and timing; elimination of barriers to fish passage where possible; and restoration and land management practices that improve habitat conditions. The recovery strategy also provides specific recommendations for individual watersheds and rivers, prioritizes watersheds according to restoration and management potential, and prioritizes the tasks needed to achieve the plan's goals. Recovery of this species will also continue to rely on protecting the fishery through adequate laws and regulations concerning sport and commercial harvest. Recovery of this species will also continue to rely on protecting the fishery through adequate laws and regulations concerning sport and commercial harvest.

Stressors Affecting Wildlife and Habitats

- Water management conflicts
- Instream gravel mining
- Forest management conflicts
- Altered fire regimes
- Agriculture and urban development
- Excessive livestock grazing
- Invasive species

Water Management Conflicts

With relatively high precipitation levels across most of the region, the North Coast–Klamath Region produces about 40 percent of California's total natural runoff (DWR 2004). Large-scale dams and diversions on many of the region's major river systems supply water and hydropower, most of which is exported out of the region. The region's water resources are also taxed by smaller-scale water diversions for local use and by groundwater extraction.

Dams and diversions reduce the amount of water in regional rivers and change the timing of seasonal high- and low flows. In shallow waters, temperatures can rise to levels unsuitable for aquatic species, and important habitat features such as deep pools may be eliminated. Some river reaches dry out, severing the connectivity between different sections of a river basin and limiting fish movement. Fish can be stranded in isolated river sections without access to tributaries or river reaches that provide cool temperatures or important habitat features like pools and cover. Additionally, without flood flows, willow trees and other vegetation can encroach into river channels—as has occurred in portions of the Klamath basin and below the Trinity Dam—resulting in narrower channels and reduced instream habitat.

Dams and diversion structures also restrict fish movement. (See Fig. 11.2.) For the region's anadromous species, such as Pacific lamprey, steelhead, chinook and coho salmon, and green sturgeon, these structures can hinder migration and block access to important spawning and rearing habitats. For other regional fish species that move widely within rivers, such as redband and rainbow trout, Klamath River lamprey, and Klamath smallscale sucker, dams can isolate population segments and disrupt gene flow. Sediment movement is also blocked by dams. Coupled with altered flows, restricted sediment supply can result in substantial alteration of channel structure and degradation of instream and riparian habitats downstream of dams.

Reduced flows and reservoir conditions can contribute to water quality problems. In the Klamath system, for example, agricultural runoff in the upper basin, including fertilizers and animal wastes, favors algae growth and depletes oxygen levels in reservoirs. Flow levels below dams are not sufficient to flush away or dilute these poor water quality conditions. Low flows also diminish aquatic systems' capacity to transport and discharge sediment, sometimes resulting in increased turbidity or sediment deposition. In fall 2002, on the Klamath River below Iron Gate Dam, low flows coupled with poor water quality conditions contributed to the deaths of more than 33,000 fish, largely chinook salmon (CDFG 2003c).

Large Scale Diversions and Impoundments

Four major hydroelectric dams are located on the mainstem of the Klamath River in California and Oregon. These dams block migratory fish access to hundreds of miles of historical habitat (Hamilton et al. 2005, TPL 2001). On the Shasta River, a major tributary to the Klamath, the Dwinnell Dam blocks approximately 100 miles, or 17 percent, of the river basin. On the Trinity River, another major tributary to the Klamath, the Lewiston and Trinity dams block 109 miles, or 24 percent, of the upper river basin. Moreover, over the last 40 years, a large proportion of the Trinity's annual flow has been diverted to the Sacramento River to provide domestic and agricultural water supply as part of the Central Valley Project (prior to 1986, as much as 90 percent of the Trinity's flow was diverted at the Lewiston diversion). The river's reduced and altered flow regime adversely affected the river's fish and wildlife, and, in 1984, Congress passed the Trinity River Basin Fish and Wildlife Restoration Act, which required the Secretary of Interior to develop and implement a program to restore fish and wildlife to levels existing before the construction of the Trinity River division of the Central Valley Project. In spite of this legislation, operation of the diversion continued to cause substantial reductions in flow, and, by the early 1990s, the Trinity's anadromous fisheries had been reduced to about 10 percent of historical numbers (California State Lands Commission 1993). In response to these continued declines, in 2000, the U.S. Department of the Interior issued a Record of Decision to substantially increase instream flows and to undertake several other actions to restore the Trinity River to a more naturally functioning system. These increased flow regimes went into effect in spring 2005.

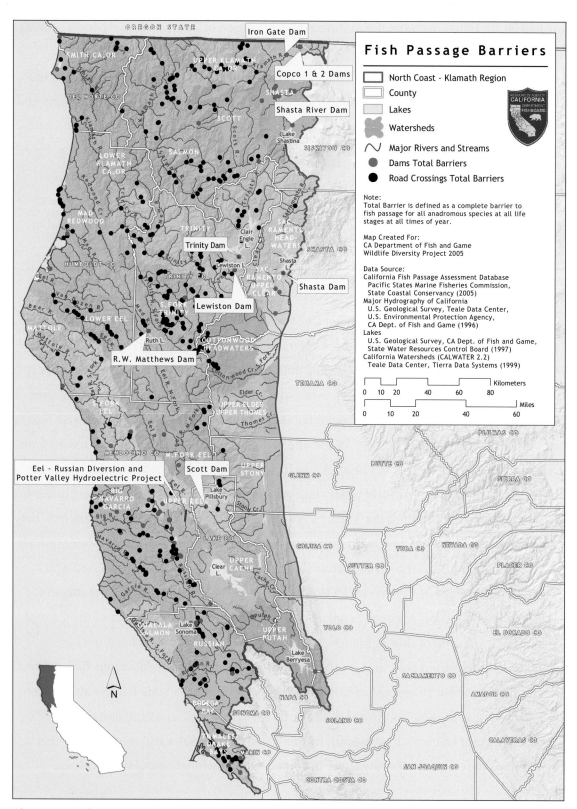

Fig. 11.2: Fish Passage Barriers

Large-scale dams and smaller structures like road crossings can fragment watersheds. As shown above, more than 200 dams and roads create complete barriers to fish passage.

On the Eel River, steelhead, chinook, and coho salmon access to the upper watershed is blocked by the Scott Dam and the Pillsbury Reservoir. Estimates of the total river miles above Scott Dam that historically provided spawning habitat range from 30 to 100 miles (Brown 2005 pers. comm., TPL 2001). From the reservoir, a substantial proportion of the Eel's annual flow is diverted to generate power at the Potter Valley Hydroelectric Project and is then exported to the Russian River for domestic water supply in Mendocino, Sonoma, and Marin counties (DWR 2004).

Refer to the section on Hydropower Project Operations in Chapter 13, Sierra Nevada and Cascades Region, for additional discussion of the effects of hydropower projects and opportunities to seek operational changes through the Federal Energy Regulatory Commission (FERC) relicensing process.

Small-scale Diversions and Groundwater Use

The cumulative effects of small-scale surface water diversions have substantial consequences for some of the region's river systems. Agricultural and domestic water use has resulted in low flows and has dried up river segments. Increasing numbers of groundwater wells are being used to supply water for expanding agricultural and residential development, further contributing to lower flows and drying. Small-scale diversions to provide livestock water sources have depleted instream flows in some waterways, such as the Mad River watershed. These changes will be compounded by longer, drier summers brought on by the effects of climate change.

Instream Gravel Mining

Over the past century, the river channels of the North Coast–Klamath Region have supplied millions of tons of gravel for such aggregate-dependent industries as road building and construction. Historically, gravel mines operated with virtually no environmental regulation. In the 1990s, Fish and Game worked with the mining industry to develop operational standards that minimize its consequences for the environment. They also established monitoring and reporting requirements to document mining activities and the negative effects that do occur. Today, in order to receive county mining permits, gravel operations must comply with these standards, along with federal regulations (administered by the Army Corps of Engineers and the National Oceanic and Atmospheric Administration), and ultimately take

Fig. 11.3: Photograph and Aerial Spot Imagery of Trinity Dam

The Trinity Dam, on the Trinity River in the Klamath River system, is one of the region's large-scale dam and diversion projects. Dams create a dramatic difference in a river's structure. Upstream of the dam, natural instream and riparian habitats are replaced by impounded lake-like conditions. Downstream, natural habitats are altered by regulated and reduced flows.

Klamath River Lampreys

The Klamath River system is a global center of diversity for lamprey species, which are an ancient and little-studied group of fish. Elongated and lacking prominent fins, lampreys resemble eels but are not related to them. About one-fifth of the world's 38 known lamprey species occur here, including the Pacific lamprey and the endemic Klamath River lamprey and Pit-Klamath brook lamprey. Current survey efforts and genetic research will likely lead to identifying additional species within the Klamath River.

Historically, the Pacific lamprey was abundant in coastal streams and provided an important food source for many birds, fish, and mammals, especially seals and sea lions. In some rivers, lamprey abundance reduced predation pressures on salmonids. Today, however, populations of the Pacific lamprey are substantially lower than they were historically, and numbers of other lamprey species are believed to have declined, as well (Kostow 2002).

Lamprey species are affected by the same factors that reduce habitat availability and quality for other aquatic species. Because many lamprey species are anadromous or wide-ranging within freshwater rivers, dams and other fish-passage obstructions negatively affect them. Lampreys also have an unusually long larval life stage; the wormlike larvae spend as long as four to seven years living and traveling widely in stream-bottom substrates (Kostow 2002). This may make lampreys especially vulnerable to gravel mining, sedimentation, and other streambed disturbances. Research is needed to assess populations and understand habitat needs of this unusual and ecologically important species group. Current studies and survey efforts are under way by wildlife agencies and Native American tribes, including the Karuk and Yurok.

actions to reclaim or restore mining sites (CDFG 2004g). Nonetheless, many rivers continue to suffer the effects of channel degradation from historical gravel mining (and gold mining), and, even with improved regulation, removal of river substrate inevitably has the potential to alter aquatic habitats and river morphology.

Gravel extraction has a number of effects on river channels, including increased bank erosion; depletion of gravel supply (sometimes resulting in deepening and incision of the channel); alteration of channel shape, braiding, and gravel-bar features; creation of deep pits that change flow patterns; increased turbidity; and reduction of riparian vegetation and instream debris (CDFG 2004g). Species that depend on stream-bottom habitats may be particularly vulnerable to gravel mining impacts. These include invertebrates, which form a food base for many fish and amphibian species; salmonids, which require gravel for spawning and as habitat for juveniles; and lampreys. (See Klamath River Lampreys, above.)

Some of the most substantial regional aftereffects of gravel mining have occurred on the Mad and Russian rivers, where gravel extraction has resulted in extensive downcutting and deepening of the Russian River channel and widening of the Mad. Gravel mining is also common near the ocean outlets of many of the region's large rivers, including the Eel and the Smith.

Forest Management Conflicts

Forestry is the most widespread land use in the North Coast–Klamath Region, which is one of the state's leading timber-producing regions (FRAP 2003). There are 1.9 million acres of privately owned timber production lands in the region, the majority located in the coastal portion of the region and owned by large private timber companies (USFWS September 2005). Timber harvest on private lands is governed by California's Forest Practice Rules, and timber harvest plans are reviewed and approved by the State Board of Forestry. Inland, a large proportion of the region's forest lands are in public ownership. The region's five national forests (Six Rivers, Klamath, Shasta-Trinity, Mendocino, and a small portion of the Siskiyou) comprise 4.8 million acres (34 percent of the region) and are managed by the Forest Service and the Bureau of Land Management.

Historical forest management practices resulted in significant impacts on the region's forest habitats and waterways. Regulations governing current logging practices and advances in technology have substantially improved timber-harvest practices. However, some ongoing management practices continue to adversely affect the vegetation communities and wildlife habitats of forest systems.

Shaped by natural disturbances and variable ecological conditions, forests are characterized by a mosaic of different habitat types, including stands of trees of different ages, shrub-dominated habitats, numerous open meadows containing grasses and **forbs,** and wet fens. In recently disturbed areas, saplings, shrubs, and herbaceous understory vegetation are abundant. Other forest areas are dominated by large trees several centuries old and support complex habitat features like large, standing dead trees and decaying, fallen trees.

Wildlife species evolved to make use of this diverse forest landscape. Some species, like Northern goshawk and Pacific fisher, depend on large, old trees for nesting or denning but forage in more open areas where herbaceous vegetation supports abundant prey species (Campbell et al. 2000, DellaSalla et al. 2004, Smith 2001). Many songbird species nest in open-canopy mixed grass and shrub habitats (Smith 2001), while cavity-nesting birds, like the pileated woodpecker and Vaux's swift, depend on dead trees hollowed by fire (Robinson and Alexander 2002).

Over the last century and a half, forest management practices have included cultivation of even-aged timber stands, clear cutting, fire suppression, clearing of dead trees and downed wood, and road building for forest access and timber transport. Herbicide use to reduce shrub growth and short harvest rotations have also been employed.

The cumulative effects of these practices have resulted in substantial changes in the forest habitats of the North Coast–Klamath Region, often making these forests less suitable for some wildlife communities. There are fewer old forest areas, and second-growth forests are simplified, with reduced structural diversity and less varied habitats. Forests managed for timber harvest are often characterized by even-aged stands of trees dominated by a single species, while the early grass-, forb- and shrub-dominated stages of forest growth are cut short in order to quickly establish tree crops. Fire suppression and lack of harvest or thinning in areas planted for timber production result in unnaturally dense growth. This dense, woody growth can displace open-forest habitats like meadows and prevent sunlight from reaching the forest floor to support herbaceous vegetation.

Timber harvest can fragment forest lands, sometimes with adverse effects on wildlife and ecosystems. Forest roads can introduce invasive plant and animal species (Lindenmayer and Franklin 2002), and some species, like the varied thrush, depend on unfragmented forest interior habitats (George 2000, Strittholt and DellaSala 2001).

Poorly constructed or maintained roads and ground disturbance resulting from timber harvest can also result in soil- and surface-water runoff. High rainfall levels, steep topography, and erodible soils make many parts of the region particularly vulnerable to increased erosion and landslides. Erosion and sedimentation can have substantial consequences for aquatic systems, leading to **turbidity** and fine-sediment deposition that smothers spawning gravels and invertebrate habitats (CDFG 2004g, USFWS 2002c). The addition of coarse sand, gravel, and cobble to waterways can raise stream bed levels and alter channel shape, resulting in shallower waterways and elevated temperatures. Under standards established by the National Clean Water Act, many regional rivers (including the Big, Gualala, Russian, Navarro, Mattole, Eel, Mad, Scott, and Trinity rivers and Redwood Creek) are considered impaired due to excessive sediment loads and elevated temperatures that are at least partially attributable to timber harvest (SWRCB 2002a).

Natural and human-caused disturbances (including timber harvest) also can benefit forest communities by creating canopy gaps that allow for the growth of understory vegetation and **edge-habitats** that are important to some of the region's wildlife species.

Altered Fire Regimes

Wildfire is an ecologically important natural disturbance in the North Coast–Klamath Region. In forest communities, fires promote a mix of habitat types and successional stages. Some regional vegetation species and communities are adapted to fire; ceanothus and some other montane shrubs, for example, need fire to germinate. Fires create important habitat features like downed wood and hollow logs and tree bases that serve as dens for bears and other mammals and as nesting cavities for birds. Fires also create and maintain open forest habitats and meadows.

Climate, fuels, and terrain determine the extent, frequency, and intensity of wildfires. Owing to the moist coastal climate, redwood forests are believed to have naturally infrequent fire events. Inland, many forest types found in the Klamath mountains, including ponderosa pine and mixed conifer forests, are characterized by fairly frequent, low- to moderate-intensity fire regimes (DellaSala et al. 2004, Wills and Stuart 1994). Some of the Klamath region's forests also experience highly variable fire patterns because of the many different microclimates, geographical features, and soil types (Odion et al. 2004).

Over the last century, forest management and land development activities have altered the role of fire in the region. Fire suppression has had important effects on the region's forest ecosystems. Because fires have not been allowed to burn, many areas of today's forests are denser than early 20th-century forests, and many meadow habitats have been filled in by forest growth. In other places, however, human activities have contributed to an increased frequency or severity of fires. Roads and rural residential development that expand the wildland-urban interface can lead to an increased incidence of human-caused fire. Additionally, some tree plantations experience more frequent severe fires than multi-aged forests (Odion et al. 2004).

Climate is also a major factor in determining fire patterns. Climate scientists project warmer and drier conditions in the coming century (Hayhoe et al. 2004, Schneider et al. 2002). These changes will add another variable to efforts to develop management measures that can approximate the historical role of fire in maintaining the mosaic of habitats and multi-aged forests naturally found across this landscape.

Agriculture and Urban Development

When compared to other areas of California, the North Coast–Klamath Region is sparsely populated. Rugged topography has limited urban and agricultural development across much of the region. Currently, urban land use occurs on about 2 percent of the region's area, and low-density rural residential development is found on less than 2 percent (DWR 2004, FRAP 2003). Agriculture occupies about 7 percent (CDC 2002). However, in flatter coastal areas and valleys, urban and agricultural land uses are widespread and have substantially reduced and altered wildlife habitats.

The region's population centers include coastal cities (Eureka, Arcata, Fort Bragg, and Crescent City) and, inland, Santa Rosa and Redding. In the interior portions of the region, residential growth has closely followed agricultural development in the major valleys. Some areas, like Humboldt and Siskiyou counties, are seeing increasing subdivision of large land-holdings into smaller parcels for second-home and rural residential development. The most significant population pressures are felt in the southern portion of the region and in the Russian River basin, with population growth in Napa and Sonoma counties beginning to expand to Mendocino and Lake counties.

Agricultural development has occurred primarily in the major river valleys, where common crops are alfalfa and irrigated pasturelands. Agricultural uses also occur on coastal grasslands, where dairy operations are widespread, and on alluvial plains formed at the coastal outlets of large rivers. Some southern portions of the region support wine grapes, nursery stock, and orchards. Vineyard acreage, in particular, is expanding from Napa and Sonoma counties to Mendocino and Lake counties.

In some river valleys, agricultural use of alluvial plain and delta areas has virtually eliminated native riparian black cottonwood, willow, and red alder forests, limiting habitat for riparian species like willow flycatcher (RHJV 2004). In these areas, berms and canals prevent flooding of agricultural fields and pastures, which disconnects the rivers from their natural floodplains and eliminates such benefits of natural flooding regimes as deposition of river silts on valley-floor soils, recharging of wetlands, and flushing flows that prevent clogging of coastal outlets. Braided channel structure and backwaters are eliminated, resulting in higher-velocity flows. These changes lower habitat suitability for salmon, which need low-flow refuges to keep from being flushed out of river channels during flood flows.

Many of the region's coastal agricultural lands, as well as coastal lands in urban use, were created by draining and diking wetlands and salt marshes, particularly around Humboldt Bay, where more than 90 percent of the historical tidal marshlands have been lost. The resulting coastal grasslands are extensively used for grazing, especially by dairy cattle. Creating these grasslands reduced marsh and wetland habitats used by shorebirds and estuarine nursery areas important for anadromous and marine fish. (However, these agricultural grasslands now provide valuable habitats for many bird species [Page and Shuford 2000].) If improperly managed, livestock uses can result in eutrophication of wetlands and coastal waters.

In agricultural river valleys, substantial habitat alteration results from river diversions and water use. Many small-scale irrigation diversions deplete the flows of regional river systems, sometimes resulting in rivers completely drying up. In livestock production areas, water is also diverted to provide cattle-watering sources.

In the southern portion of the region, irrigated vineyards use large amounts of water during the grape-production season, sometimes resulting in streams completely drying up. Stream habitats are also adversely affected by sedimentation, because some irrigated vineyards tend to be erosion-prone, especially if located on hillsides. Vineyards also fragment habitats and restrict wildlife movement to a greater degree than do pasturing or the cultivation of alfalfa.

Excessive Livestock Grazing

Livestock grazing on private lands is prevalent in many portions of the region. Livestock also graze on public lands; approximately 39 percent of the 4.8 million acres of national forest lands (USFS 2005b) within the region and about 10 percent of the 646,000 acres of BLM land are leased for grazing (BLM 2005a).

The effects of grazing on wildlife vary from beneficial to detrimental, depending upon how grazing is managed, including the seasonality and duration of grazing and the type and number of livestock. These effects also depend on the relative sensitivities of individual wildlife species, since not all species respond the same way to grazing. Well-managed livestock grazing can benefit sensitive plant and animal species, particularly by controlling annual grasses and invasive plants where these have become established. These working lands are an essential part of the solution to conserving the state's wildlife.

While recognizing the values of appropriate grazing practices, this plan is required to focus on stressors affecting wildlife species at risk. Thus, the following discussion describes those situations where excessive grazing practices stress those species. Excessive grazing, as used here, refers to livestock grazing at a frequency or intensity that causes degradation of native plant communities, reduces habitat values for native wildlife species, degrades aquatic or other ecosystems, or impairs ecosystem functions. (The term "overgrazing" has a different meaning; it is usually used in referring to the productivity of the forage crop and range condition).

The effects of grazing depend largely on rangeland management practices, including the seasonality and duration of grazing and the type and number of livestock. Livestock grazing in riparian areas can be a cause for concern because cattle will congregate in these habitats, using them as water sources. Livestock trampling of stream channels results in collapse of stream banks and erosion of soils. In heavily grazed areas, cattle trails and reduced plant cover also contribute to erosion. Increased sediment in waterways can shade out aquatic plants, fill important pool habitats, and scour away or smother stream-bottom sediments that are important spawning sites and invertebrate habitats. Livestock consume and trample riparian plants, which decreases shade and can increase water temperatures, reducing habitat for species that depend on cool water (CDFG 2004g). In the coastal portion of the region, more than 40 percent of the river miles listed as impaired under the Federal Clean Water Act list grazing as one of the causes of pollution (FRAP 2003). The effects of grazing on the water quality and temperature of spring-fed seeps and waterways can also be of concern, because these spring-fed systems often support many snail species that can be very sensitive to water quality conditions (Ricketts et al. 1999).

Excessive grazing also contributes to changes in plant communities. Annual forage grasses replace native perennial grasses, and livestock can aid the spread of invasive weeds. In the region's coniferous forest lands, grazing reduces grasses and other understory plants, eliminating habitat for some wildlife species, including small mammals and birds like chipping sparrow and fox sparrow that require herbaceous cover (Robinson and Alexander 2002). Where forest understory plants are consumed by livestock, woody species may increase in density in the absence of competition. Dense woody growth limits habitat for species requiring more open-forest habitats, such as Nashville warbler and mountain bluebird (Robinson and Alexander 2002).

Invasive Species

As in other regions of California, invasive species present a noteworthy threat to the region's biodiversity. In addition to introduced invasive species, some native species have been favored by human activity to the point where they have become pests, threatening sensitive native species.

Coastal beach and dune habitats are threatened by a number of invasive plant species. These habitats support unique plant and animal communities, including sensitive species like Western snowy plover and beach layia, a small succulent plant endemic to the region. Dune habitats are naturally dynamic, with dune migration serving as a natural disturbance that keeps early successional dune and beach habitat available. Because coastal development and urbanization have occurred along many of the region's sandy beach areas, dunes are limited in their ability to migrate. This problem is exacerbated by colonization by non-native plants, including European beach grass and yellow bush lupine, which form dense monocultures of vegetation and result in unnatural stabilization of beach and dune systems (Bossard et al. 2000). These invasive plants also displace native vegetation, including short-grass areas, degrading the habitat of such sensitive species as western lily and hippolyta fritillary. In salt marshes and coastal estuaries, particularly around Humboldt Bay, native plant communities are threatened by introduced dense-flowered cordgrass.

Inland areas of the region are being invaded by such noxious weeds as yellow starthistle, spotted knapweed, and Scotch broom (Bossard et al. 2000). Most of these invasive exotic plants spread via roadways and river corridors and then invade surrounding lands as a consequence of disturbance by fire, forest management practices, or agricultural practices and livestock grazing.

Other species causing problems in the region include brown-headed cowbirds, European starlings, common ravens, and jays. Native brown-headed cowbirds thrive in grazing lands, where they are attracted to livestock droppings and feed. With the growth of regional grazing lands, cowbirds have greatly expanded their range and undergone population increases. Cowbirds can lower the reproductive success of native birds by laying their eggs in other birds' nests, causing them to raise the cowbird nestlings at the expense of their own. Native common ravens, Steller's jays, and introduced European starlings also thrive in human-altered environments, including recreational areas. Starlings compete with native birds, while ravens and jays prey on many native bird species.

Conservation Actions to Restore and Conserve Wildlife

In addition to the recommended regional actions described below, see the recommended statewide conservation actions as given in Chapter 4.

a. For regional river systems where insufficient or altered flow regimes limit populations of salmon, steelhead, and other sensitive aquatic species, federal and state agencies and other stakeholders should work to increase instream flows and to replicate natural seasonal flow regimes.

See Statewide Action e in Chapter 4.

Planning efforts to meet these goals require participation by private landowners and a wide range of agencies, including state and regional Water Resources Quality Control Boards, the Department of Water Resources, local water districts, wildlife agencies, county and city governments, watershed councils, and resource conservation districts.

Priorities specific to this region include:

- Agencies and partners should develop water-use and supply plans that meet minimum flow and seasonal flow-regime requirements for sensitive aquatic species (CDFG 2004g). In determining flow regimes, the suitable range of variability in flow, rate of change, and peak- and low-flow events should be considered (Richter et al. 1997).

- Water trusts or other forums that provide a structured process for willing participants to donate, sell, or lease water dedicated to instream use should be pursued (CDFG 2004).

- Innovative ways to manage small-scale water diversions should be developed, such as agreements to alternate diversion schedules (so that all water users do not withdraw water at once) and the use of off-stream reservoirs to store winter water and limit diversion during the dry season. Incentives should be established for water users to participate in these efforts (CDFG 2004g).

- Agencies and partners should encourage water conservation practices and use of technologies that reduce water consumption by residential and agricultural water users through incentives and education (CDFG 2004g).

b. Federal, state, and local agencies and private landowners should work to restore fish passage in aquatic systems important for anadromous and wide-ranging fish populations.

Efforts to restore fish passage will require cooperative efforts by private owners of dams and water supply companies and partnerships among a wide range of agencies, including such state and local agencies as the State Water Resources Control Board, Caltrans, local water districts, city and county public works departments, and Fish and Game; federal agencies, such as NOAA (National Oceanic and Atmospheric Administration) Fisheries and the Federal Energy Regulatory Commission; other stakeholders, such as Native American tribes; and nongovernmental organizations, land trusts, and watershed councils.

- Agencies and partners should continue to update and maintain the Coastal Conservancy's database of barriers to fish passage and use the database to seek and prioritize opportunities to implement fish passage improvement projects. (A link to the database is available at http://www. calfish.org, under the sidebar heading Fish Passage Assessment.)

- Where feasible, fish barriers should be removed or modified. Fish ladders or other means of passage around dams, small-scale diversions, and other impediments should be installed (CDFG 2004g).

c. Through the Federal Energy Regulatory Commission (FERC) relicensing process, the state should pursue changes in operations of hydropower projects to provide more water for aquatic species and ecosystems and require that flows be managed to approximate natural flow regimes.

- Ensure that Fish and Game is adequately staffed over the next decade to be a fully engaged participant in all FERC proceedings affecting rivers and watersheds and aquatic species of the North Coast–Klamath Region.

- Through the partnered efforts of Fish and Game and the State Water Resources Control Board, seek provisions in the new license agreements that will improve habitat conditions and environmental quality and allow the region's river systems to support healthy populations of fish and wildlife. Renewed FERC permits should also contain provisions to reduce the adverse effects of hydropower operations on terrestrial species.

d. Fish and Game should continue fisheries restoration and watershed assessment efforts.

The Fisheries Restoration Grant Program funds projects to restore habitat for declining salmonid populations. Since 1981, the program has provided more than $120 million and supported approximately 2,100 restoration projects. Projects include removal of barriers to fish passage, riparian restoration, and protection and enhancement of existing rearing habitat for juveniles and instream complexity.

Continued funding and staffing are critical to enable the program to continue its work to:

- collect and synthesize data to prioritize locations for recovery efforts based on importance to fish populations, restoration potential, and extent of regulatory control and public lands.

- expand monitoring programs to evaluate the effectiveness of past grant projects and finalize new protocols to assess both physical habitat and fish populations following restoration projects.
- review and gather information from regional watershed plans that were created by watershed councils and nongovernmental environmental groups.

The Coastal Watershed Planning and Assessment Program utilizes multidisciplinary data to evaluate ecological conditions and determine limiting factors for fish populations. This includes compiling current data on geology, land use history, historical and present fish populations, and habitat conditions. The resulting Assessment Reports document a watershed's ability to support fish populations and provide recommendations for protection and restoration efforts. (For additional information, see http://www.ncwatershed.ca.gov.)

Regional watershed assessments have been completed for the Mattole and Gualala rivers and Redwood Creek. The program is currently employing the watershed prioritization system established in the Recovery Strategy for California Coho Salmon (CDFG 2004g) to determine the order in which watershed assessments should be undertaken. The assessment reports are being used by government agencies and stakeholder groups to guide and prioritize conservation efforts. For example, a coalition of watershed groups used the Mattole River assessment to determine that the southern sub-basin of the watershed had the greatest restoration potential and successfully applied for grant funds from Coastal Conservancy, Wildlife Conservation Board, and the Fisheries Restoration Grant Program to undertake restoration activities.

The Coastal Watershed Planning and Assessment Program should:

- continue monitoring watershed conditions and land-use activities and update the watershed assessment reports as changes occur. Tracking and documenting ecological changes and land-use activities will help build a dataset from which to develop a greater understanding of cumulative and synergistic effects of human activities as well as the effects of restoration activities; and
- complete currently planned assessments for the Shasta, Scott, Albion, Salt, and Big rivers, the south fork and lower Eel River, and the lower Van Duzen River.
- expand assessment activities beyond the river itself and integrate with upland assessment activities and needs.

e. Fish and Game should work to complete and implement recovery strategies and plans for listed species and develop and implement statewide or regionwide recovery plans to benefit multiple species.

The Fish and Game's *Recovery Strategy for California Coho Salmon* represents a 16-month effort to assemble all existing information on historical and current status, habitat needs and availability, and threats to coho salmon; additional field studies were conducted where needed.

- Agencies should build on the Recovery Strategy to develop a regional multispecies conservation plan that focuses on preserving and restoring aquatic systems' health. Such a plan would incorporate population and distribution data for numerous species and species groups and bring together conservation assessments for target species to highlight actions benefiting multiple species and habitats.

f. Where historical or active gravel mining has had substantial effects on river systems that are important for sensitive aquatic species, federal, state, and local agencies should continue monitoring and restoration efforts to minimize the negative effects of mining. Active mining operations should employ the most ecologically sensitive practices possible.

Active mining operations should limit the volume of gravel extracted to the amount of replacement gravel that will naturally enter the river reach from upstream, obtain gravel from upland and inactive floodplain areas as far from active wet channels as possible, and establish adequate monitoring plans for reclamation efforts.

g. Public forest lands should be managed to maintain healthy ecosystems and wildlife diversity. State and federal forest and wildlife managers should work cooperatively to develop a vision for future forest conditions.

Management of national forests and other public forestry lands should incorporate the following principles:

- Restoration and maintenance of habitat diversity across the landscape.
- Restoration of vegetation communities historically present within forest landscapes.
- Restoration and maintenance of structural complexity in forest stands, including dead trees, snags, and fallen logs.
- Restoration and maintenance of connectivity in the forest landscape.
- Retention of remaining mature and late-successional forests.
- Restoration and maintenance of the integrity of riparian and aquatic ecosystems.

h. On public lands, post-fire and post-harvest treatments and forest management should be designed to achieve the principles listed in Action g, above.

i. Federal and state agencies should work to understand the natural fire regimes of different ecosystems and how the ecological role of wildfire can be replicated with prescribed fire and other forest management practices.

- Federal forest managers and state and federal wildlife biologists should also work cooperatively to design forest-thinning and prescribed-fire treatments that can restore forest habitat diversity. These treatments should be designed and implemented in such a way as to maintain soils, water- and air quality, and the health of forest ecosystems in accordance with the principles in Action g.
- Agencies should develop fire management policies specific to different forest types (DellaSala et al. 2004) and support the efforts of the national, multiagency Fire Regime Condition Class (FRCC) program to develop science-based fire management policies for different forest types. (See http://www.frcc.gov/ for additional information.)
- The complex and dynamic ecological communities that have evolved with natural wildfire should be conserved so as to favor the fire regimes that have historically maintained those communities.
- Fuel-control treatments and fire-suppression efforts should be focused on the interface between residential areas and wildlands.

j. State and federal forest and wildlife managers should work cooperatively with private landowners and timber companies to develop timber-harvest cumulative-impact standards for watersheds in the North Coast–Klamath Region to protect ecosystem health and wildlife habitat.

- Using the best-available science, forest and wildlife managers should determine the extent, pattern, and pace for timber harvest in a forest watershed that will conserve ecosystems and wildlife habitat and prevent excessive sedimentation. Forest management practices will have to be tailored to different ecosystem types.
- State and federal forest managers should coordinate to ensure that cumulative effects of timber-harvest plans for public and private lands meet ecologically based standards for each watershed.

k. State and federal agencies should work with private forestry operators and landowners to implement forest management practices that are compatible with wildlife and habitat conservation.

- Agencies should develop nonregulatory policies and incentive programs at the state and federal level so that those landowners who follow guidelines for ecologically sustainable forest management qualify for tax benefits or other financial incentives.
- Agencies and nongovernmental organizations should support certification and labeling programs that increase the market value of timber produced and harvested using such

ecologically sustainable practices as the Forest Stewardship Council program. (For information, see http://www.fscus.org.)

See also Appendix G, Information Sources for Wildlife and Habitat Conservation on Private Lands.

l. **The state should coordinate the development of a model ordinance and building codes for new or expanding communities in fire-adapted landscapes to make those communities more fire compatible and reduce the state's liability for fire suppression.**

Counties need to consider adopting development restrictions that require planning and accommodation for wildfire consistent with the local historical fire regime, and such measures should be incorporated into the public-safety elements of the county General Plans. In addition, specific ordinances should be adopted:

- The model ordinances should address the design of new development to ensure new communities are safer and compatible with natural forest fires.
- The model ordinances should address maintenance of existing residential and commercial areas to ensure firebreaks are maintained to improve compatibility with forest fires.
- Model building codes should specify that all new construction employ materials and design features to make them more fire resistant.
- The state should encourage adoption of the model fire ordinances and building codes by cities and counties in forested areas.

m. **Federal, state, and local agencies and nongovernmental organizations should work with regional landowners to develop and implement agricultural and rangeland management practices that are compatible with wildlife and habitat conservation.**

See Statewide Action h in Chapter 4.

Priorities specific to this region include:

- In agricultural river valleys, agencies and nongovernmental partners should develop water-conservation practices and create educational and incentive programs to encourage landowner participation. Examples of such practices include development of alternate livestock watering facilities and water storage facilities to reduce dry-season diversions; changes in cropping types or practices that reduce water consumption; reuse of irrigation runoff water; and water conservation through efficient water transport, such as lined ditches and pipes. Restoration of river-channel shape and riparian and floodplain areas through levee and berm setbacks is also an important management practice in agricultural areas.

• Rangeland management practices to protect such sensitive habitats as riparian areas and springs should be developed.

See also Appendix G, Information Sources for Wildlife and Habitat Conservation on Private Lands.

n. Federal, state, and local agencies should provide greater resources and coordinate efforts to eradicate or control existing occurrences of invasive species and to prevent new introductions.

See Statewide Action f in Chapter 4.

Priorities specific to this region include:

• Staffing and funding resources should be increased for active control and eradication programs for invasive plant species. Priority areas include fragmented forest habitats, coastal beach and dune systems, and other areas that are vulnerable to invasion because of natural or human-caused disturbances. Highly noxious weed species invading inland areas are also a priority for control efforts.

• Forest fragmentation should be reduced to limit the expansion of invasive and nuisance species into interior forest habitats.

• Agencies and partner organizations should conduct active management in coastal beach and dune systems to mimic natural disturbances that limit the expansion of invasive species.

o. Federal, state, and local agencies, nongovernmental conservation organizations, and private landowners should protect and restore underprotected and sensitive habitat types such as riparian forests and coastal dunes.

• Historically, riparian forests of cottonwood, willow, and red alder occurred in the alluvial floodplains formed where the region's large rivers approach their ocean outlets and along inland valleys. These riparian forests have been almost entirely eliminated by agricultural land uses. Remaining mature forests should be protected, and restoration efforts should be undertaken to expand this habitat type. For example, Fish and Game should continue protection and restoration efforts on the Eel River, where mature riparian forests occur.

• Coastal beaches, dunes, and estuaries are threatened by exotic plant species and by urban land uses that restrict dunes' natural ability to migrate. Active management and restoration are needed to control invasive species and to mimic the effects of natural disturbances.

Modoc Plateau Region

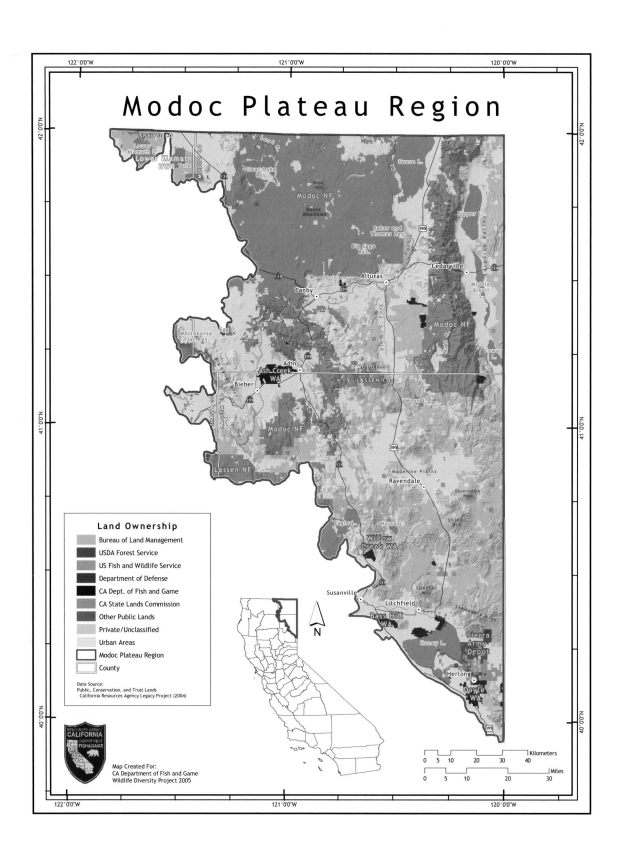

Land Ownership

- Bureau of Land Management
- USDA Forest Service
- US Fish and Wildlife Service
- Department of Defense
- CA Dept. of Fish and Game
- CA State Lands Commission
- Other Public Lands
- Private/Unclassified
- Urban Areas
- Modoc Plateau Region
- County

Data Source:
Public, Conservation, and Trust Lands
California Resources Agency Legacy Project (2004)

N

Kilometers
0 5 10   20   30   40

Miles
0   5   10   20   30

CALIFORNIA
DEPARTMENT
FISH&GAME

Map Created For:
CA Department of Fish and Game
Wildlife Diversity Project 2005

12   Modoc Plateau Region ~~~~~~~~~

David Bunn

The Modoc Plateau Region is located in the northeastern corner of the state, framed by and including the Warner Mountains and Surprise Valley along the Nevada border to the east and west to the edge of the southern Cascades Range. The region extends north to the Oregon border and south to include the Skedaddle Mountains and the Honey Lake Basin.

A million years ago, layered lava flows formed the 4,000–5,000-foot elevation Modoc Plateau, separating the watersheds of the region from the Klamath drainage to the northwest. The waters of the western slope of the Warner Mountains and the Modoc Plateau carved a new course, the Pit River, flowing to the southwest through the Cascades and joining the Sacramento River.

Situated on the western edge of the Great Basin, the Modoc Plateau historically has supported high desert plant communities and ecosystems similar to that region—shrub-steppe, perennial grasslands, sagebrush, antelope bitterbrush, mountain mahogany, and juniper woodlands. Sagebrush plant communities are characteristic of the region, providing important habitat for sagebrush-dependent wildlife. Conifer forests dominate the higher elevations of the Warner Mountains and the smaller volcanic mountain ranges and hills that shape the region. Wetland, spring, meadow, vernal pool, riparian, and aspen communities scattered across the rugged and otherwise dry desert landscape support diverse wildlife. The region has varied aquatic habitats, from high mountain streams to the alkaline waters of Goose Lake and Eagle Lake to clear spring waters of Fall River and Ash Creek.

Northeastern California is an outstanding region for wildlife, providing habitat for mountain lion, mule deer, pronghorn, Rocky Mountain elk, greater sage-grouse, and the colorful waterfowl of the **Pacific Flyway** that funnel through the area during their annual migrations. Golden eagles, peregrine and prairie falcons, northern goshawks, sandhill cranes, and American white pelicans nest and hunt or forage in the region. The varied aquatic habitats and natural barriers along the Pit River and its tributaries have allowed the evolution of several unique aquatic communities that include **endemic** fish and invertebrates.

Sixty percent of the region is federally managed; the Forest Service manages 30 percent, BLM manages 26 percent, and the Fish and Wildlife Service and the Department of Defense each manage about 2 percent of the lands. State Fish and Game manages 1 percent of the region as wildlife areas. About 37 percent of the lands are privately owned or belong to municipalities.

Only 9 percent of the forests and rangelands of the Modoc region are designated as reserves, such as wilderness areas, less than is protected in any other region of the state except the Central Valley. The wilderness areas and refuges in the region are grazed by livestock (CDFFP 2003). The combined total of lands managed by State Parks and the National Park Service is about 2,500 acres.

Many of the region's plant communities and ecosystems have been substantially altered or degraded over the last 120 years by a combination of stressors. Despite being in one of the least-developed regions of the state, the sagebrush, perennial bunchgrass, aspen, bitterbrush, and mountain mahogany habitats of the Modoc Plateau are among the most threatened ecosystems of North America (TNC 2001). Aspen stands are in sharp decline (Di Orio et al. 2005). Many of the meadow and riparian areas are overgrazed or are suffering from encroachment by juniper, pine, fir, and invasive plants (Loft et al. 1998, USFS 2001, 1991b).

The major stressors negatively affecting terrestrial wildlife on the Modoc Plateau are a combination of livestock and feral horse grazing, invasive annual grasses, the expansion of native western juniper, and altered frequencies of fire. Together, these stressors have combined to alter the region's sagebrush and forest habitats and ecosystems (Miller et al. 1994, Schaeffer et al. 2003). Today, extensive season-long grazing continues to degrade and prevent recovery of riparian habitats, streams, and creeks. In the Warner Mountains, most riparian areas are not in good ecological condition (USFS 2000b). In the forested areas, the additional effects of timber-management practices that emphasize single species and even-aged tree stands negatively affect wildlife habitat. Aquatic ecosystems throughout the region are affected by water diversions, erosion from logging roads, grazing activities, and introductions of non-native fish and invertebrates.

Private land owners, state and federal land management agencies, resource conservation districts, watershed groups, and fishing and hunting organizations, working through various partnerships, are involved in stream, riparian, wetland, and upland restoration and conservation projects across the region.

Species at Risk

Northeastern California is particularly noted for its charismatic large mammals, sagebrush-dependent species, and waterfowl. By the 1920s, however, widespread hunting for marketable game and for predator control that occurred in the years following the Gold Rush eliminated California bighorn sheep, elk, gray wolf, and grizzly bear. Pronghorn herds were decimated but not eliminated. The local extinction of sharp-tailed grouse is attributed to the conversion of lands to farming and ranching and the subsequent loss of riparian habitat (Shilling et al. 2002, Williams 1986). Native species once abundant in the region, like greater sage-grouse and other sagebrush-associated species, have declined dramatically over the last several decades (McAdoo et al. 2002, Monsen and Shaw 2000). Native fish and aquatic invertebrates, including endemic Modoc sucker, the Lost River sucker, shortnose sucker, redband trout, and Shasta crayfish, are affected by sediment runoff and altered river flows and are displaced by introduced species through predation or ecological competition.

These are the more well-known species affected by human activities. Unfortunately, due to lack of interest and lack of information, less is known about how hundreds of other animal species have fared over the past decades.

The Plan development team updated vertebrate and invertebrate species information in the California Natural Diversity Database (CNDDB) during 2004–2005. The following regional summary of numbers of wildlife species, endemic species, and **species at risk** is derived from the updated CNDDB.

There are 399 vertebrate species that inhabit the Modoc Plateau region at some point in their life cycle, including 235 birds, 97 mammals, 23 reptiles, six amphibians, and 38 fish. Of the total vertebrate species that inhabit this region, 57 bird **taxa**, 21 mammalian taxa, three reptilian taxa, one amphibian taxon, and 20 fish taxa are included on the **Special Animals List.** Of these, three are endemic to the Modoc Plateau region, one is endemic to California but introduced to this region, and three species found here are endemic to California but not restricted to this region (Table 12.1).

Table 12.1: State-Endemic Special Status Vertebrates of the Modoc Plateau Region

+	*Archoplites interruptus*	Sacramento perch
	Cottus asperrimus	Rough sculpin
	Cottus klamathensis macrops	Bigeye marbled sculpin
*	*Gila bicolor ssp. 1*	Eagle Lake tui chub
*	*Gila bicolor vaccaceps*	Cow Head Lake tui chub
	Mylopharodon conocephalus	Hardhead
*	*Oncorhynchus mykiss aquilarum*	Eagle Lake rainbow trout

* denotes taxon is endemic to region
+ denotes taxon is endemic to California but introduced in this region

The number of arthropod species is so great, and they are so poorly known taxonomically, that it is presently impossible to accurately estimate the total number of invertebrate species occurring in the state. In the Modoc Plateau region, however, 11 invertebrate taxa are included on the Special Animals List, including one arthropod taxon and 10 mollusk taxa. Of these, one is endemic to the Modoc Plateau region, and four other taxa found here are endemic to California but not restricted to this region (Table 12.2).

Table 12.2: State-Endemic Special Status Invertebrates of the Modoc Plateau Region

	Colligyrus convexus	Canary duskysnail
	Lanx patelloides	Kneecap lanx
	Pacifastacus fortis	Shasta crayfish
*	*Pyrgulopsis cinerana*	Ash Valley pyrg
	Pyrgulopsis eremica	Smoke Creek pyrg

* denotes taxon is endemic to region

The Wildlife Species Matrix, including data on listing status, habitat association, and population trend for each vertebrate and invertebrate species included on the Special Animals

List, is available on the Web at http://www.dfg.ca.gov/habitats/wdp/matrix_search.asp. For vertebrates, the matrix also includes links to species-level range maps. Additionally, a link to the California Department of Fish and Game's online Field Survey Form is available to assist in reporting positive sightings of species on the Special Animals List to the California Natural Diversity Database (CNDDB).

Two Species at Risk

Note: *The following discussion of two species at risk illustrates how stressors or threats affect species and highlights conservation challenges and opportunities. These species discussions are not intended to imply that conservation should have a single-species approach.*

The story of the greater sage-grouse illustrates how the alteration by multiple stressors of native plant communities in the region has caused the decline of species associated with those native plant communities. The struggle to reintroduce bighorn sheep to northeastern California highlights how multiple uses of wildlands may not be compatible with wildlife and healthy ecosystems.

Greater Sage-Grouse

The colorful and charismatic greater sage-grouse is sought by birders and is a popular game bird. Its long-term survival is a high priority for wildlife managers in northeastern California. A long-lived upland bird with a low reproductive rate, the greater sage-grouse is completely dependent on the sagebrush habitats of western states.

Paul Ippolito

The greater sage-grouse has specific habitat requirements. It needs open areas among sagebrush and other shrubs, away from tall trees, utility poles, or other features that offer perches to predators like ravens and raptors (Connelly et al. 2004, BLM 2000). Seasonally, they gather in leks, or breeding display sites. Leks are very specific locations and typically occur in open areas surrounded by sagebrush. Lek sites are used year after year, unless the habitat is altered or destroyed. Each lek has from 10 to 100 or more male birds that will exhibit brilliant strutting displays to attract females for breeding.

Sage-grouse were once abundant on the Modoc Plateau, but owing to habitat degradation, it is a species of concern in the region. Sage-grouse have declined in numbers as sagebrush habitat has been transformed by livestock grazing, the invasion of exotic grasses, increased

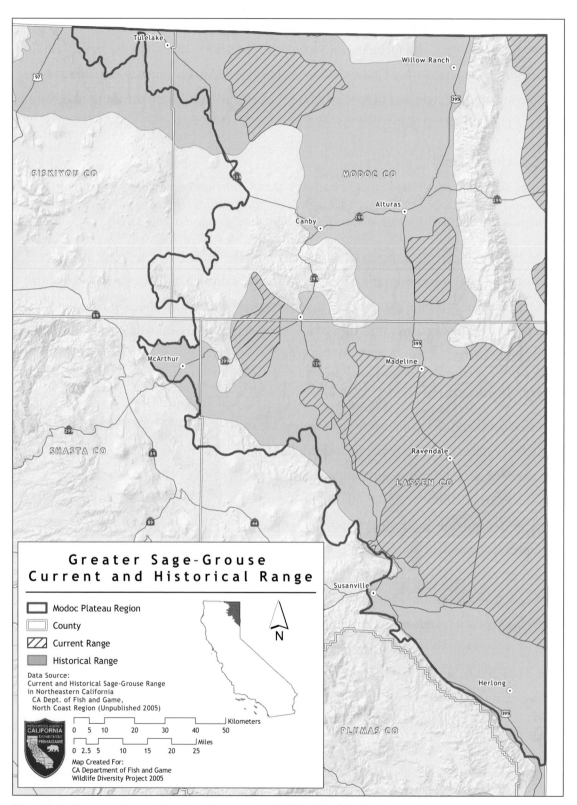

Legend:
- Modoc Plateau Region
- County
- Current Range
- Historical Range

Greater Sage-Grouse Current and Historical Range

Data Source:
Current and Historical Sage-Grouse Range
in Northeastern California
  CA Dept. of Fish and Game,
  North Coast Region (Unpublished 2005)

Map Created For:
CA Department of Fish and Game
Wildlife Diversity Project 2005

Fig. 12.1: Greater Sage-Grouse Current and Historical Range
Greater sage-grouse range has declined as sagebrush habitat has been transformed by livestock grazing, the invasion of exotic grasses, changes in fire frequency, and expansion of western juniper.

fire frequency at lower elevations, and expansion of western juniper at higher elevations. Grouse habitat also has been degraded by roads, fences, utility poles, and land development (Connelly et al. 2004, Dobkin 1995, NDOW 2004, Nelle et al. 2000). Lek sites are abandoned where western juniper has become dominant. Sage-grouse are also sensitive to disturbances such as off-road vehicles and development. (See Fig. 12.1, Greater Sage-Grouse Current and Historical Range.)

In the 1940s there were 46 active leks and thousands of sage-grouse utilizing Devil's Garden—the rugged lava-rock-strewn shrub-steppe between Goose Lake and Tule Lake. In 2002, there were only two leks with just 16 male birds in the Devil's Garden (Hall 2002).

The greater sage-grouse is the flagship species of the multi-state effort to restore sagebrush habitats of the West. The Greater Sage-Grouse Conservation Plan for Nevada and Eastern California, published in June 2004, is the result of a four-year cooperative effort by stakeholders in California and Nevada (NDOW 2004). Its purpose is to ensure that, to the greatest extent feasible, sage-grouse populations and their habitat are maintained, enhanced, or restored on public lands and that such activities are promoted on private lands. Restoration of sagebrush habitats would benefit numerous other sagebrush-dependent species as well, like the sage sparrow, sage thrasher, the Brewer's sparrow, the pygmy rabbit, and the pronghorn. Each will benefit from a plan that conserves and protects complex sagebrush-dominated habitats (McAdoo et al. 2002). Also, BLM has produced the Greater Sage-Grouse and Sage-Steppe Ecosystems Management Guidelines as a guide for land managers (BLM 2000).

California Bighorn Sheep

California bighorn sheep are native to northeastern California but were extirpated from the region by 1922. Domestic sheep-grazing on public lands and on adjacent private lands has defeated efforts to reestablish bighorn sheep in the Modoc Plateau Region. The threat of disease transmitted from domestic sheep is the primary reason bighorn sheep have not been reestablished in several ranges of northeastern California (Bleich et al. 1996, Krausman et al. 1996, NCBSIAG 1991).

Fish and Game has attempted to reintroduce bighorn sheep to the area. In 1971, 10 sheep were captured in British Columbia and released in the Lava Beds National Monument, a site near the western edge of the Modoc Plateau Region. For nine years, the Lava Beds bighorn progressed well, expanding their numbers to 43 by 1979. In the winter of 1980, four bighorn sheep were moved from the Lava Beds to the Warner Mountains to join 10 bighorn sheep transferred from the southern Sierra. The Warner Mountains turned out to be particularly good habitat for bighorn sheep. Between 1980 and 1987, no lamb mortality was documented, and by 1987 the Warner's bighorn numbers had grown to about 60 animals. But exposure to domestic sheep on public grazing allotments and on adjacent private lands led to a complete die-off of bighorn sheep at both sites. In the summer of 1980, the remaining sheep in the Lava Beds succumbed to pneumonia, attributed to contact with domestic sheep. The complete die-off of the Warner bighorn herd in 1988 was also attributed to disease derived from domestic sheep (Bleich et al. 1996, NCBSIAG 1991, Siperek 2004 pers. comm., USFS 1991a).

The historical range of the Warner Mountains and the Lava Beds provides ideal habitat for bighorn sheep. However, the continued presence of domestic sheep on public and private lands in or adjacent to these areas makes new efforts to reintroduce bighorn sheep to these areas not practical at this time. The Amedee and Skedaddle Mountains, 25 miles east of Susanville, have also been identified as excellent range for bighorn sheep in northeastern California. While under consideration for two decades, the reintroduction of bighorn sheep to the Amedee and Skedaddle Mountains has not been implemented largely because of continued grazing of domestic sheep in this area (Armentrout 2004 pers. comm., Bleich 2004 pers. comm., NCBSIAG 1991).

Stressors Affecting Wildlife and Habitats

- Excessive livestock grazing
- Excessive feral horse grazing
- Altered fire regimes
- Western juniper expansion
- Invasive plants
- Forest management conflicts
- Water management conflicts and degradation of aquatic ecosystems

Excessive Livestock Grazing

The effects of grazing on wildlife vary from beneficial to detrimental, depending upon how grazing is managed, including the seasonality and duration of grazing and the type and number of livestock. These effects also depend on the relative sensitivities of individual wildlife species, since not all species respond the same way to grazing. Well-managed livestock grazing can benefit sensitive plant and animal species, particularly by controlling annual grasses and invasive plants where these have become established. These working lands are an essential part of the solution to conserving the state's wildlife.

While recognizing the values of appropriate grazing practices, this plan is required to focus on stressors affecting wildlife species at risk. Thus, the following discussion describes those situations where excessive grazing practices stress those species. Excessive grazing, as used here, refers to livestock grazing at a frequency or intensity that causes degradation of native plant communities, reduces habitat values for native wildlife species, degrades aquatic or other ecosystems, or impairs ecosystem functions. (The term "overgrazing" has a different meaning; it is usually used in referring to the productivity of the forage crop and range condition).

Livestock production is a major economic activity of northeastern California. The Modoc Plateau and the adjacent forested lands have been grazed since the late 1800s. While livestock grazing practices have improved over the last few decades, excessive grazing continues to degrade riparian plant communities and aquatic ecosystems in the region (USFS 1991b, 2000b, 2001b). Today, there are very few areas in the region that are not grazed; grazing allotments cover nearly all public forest and rangelands that can support large herbivores. (See Fig. 12.2.) For example, the Warner Mountain range is currently managed as rangeland for cattle and sheep, with 28 grazing allotments covering nearly the entire landscape, including much of the South Warner Wilderness Area (USFS 2000b). Livestock in the region are typically grazed on private lands in the winter and moved to BLM and Forest Service lands in the spring and summer (Roush 2005 pers. comm.). In the Modoc National Forest, there are 122,000 **Animal Unit Months** (AUMs) allocated for livestock, 20,000 AUMs for wildlife, and 4,000 AUMs for horses. (An Animal Unit Month is the amount of forage necessary to support one horse, one steer or a cow and calf, or five sheep for one month). On BLM land in the region there are about 55,000 AUMs allocated for livestock.

Excessive livestock grazing has both short-term and long-term impacts. Seasonally, grazing reduces available herbaceous vegetation required by native herbivores, and it reduces nesting- and escape cover for birds and other wildlife. As upland grasses and forbs dry in the summer, livestock grazing intensifies around riparian and meadow habitats, and browsing shifts to other higher-protein sources such as bitterbrush, mountain mahogany, and aspen; annual bitterbrush leaders and willow and aspen shoots are consumed (Loft et al. 1998,

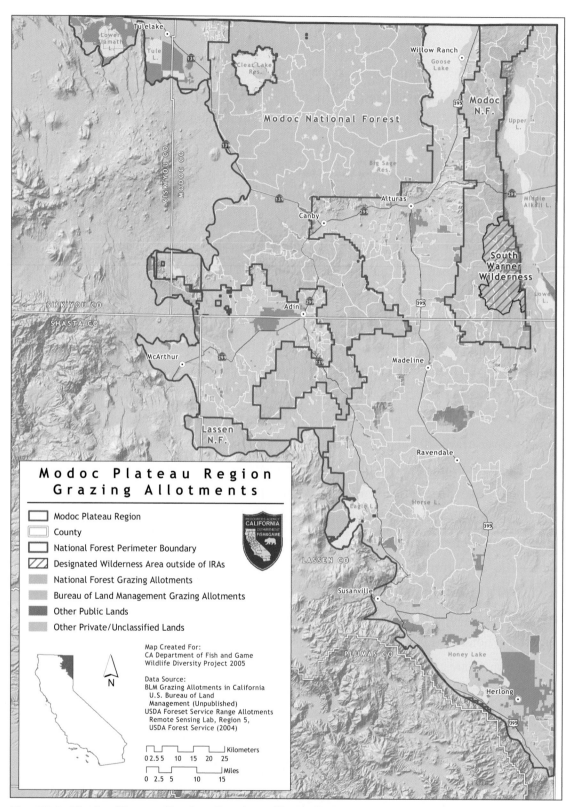

Fig. 12.2: Modoc Plateau Region Grazing Allotments
Livestock grazing allotments cover nearly the entire Modoc Plateau Region. Very little area is managed primarily for the benefit of wildlife and habitat.

Menke et al. 1996, USFS 1991b, Young and Clements 2002b). Heavy grazing removes vegetation and causes erosion along springs, creeks, meadows, and riparian corridors of the Modoc Plateau Region (Hall 2004 pers. comm., Moyle 2002).

Decades of excessive livestock grazing have also contributed to long-term ecosystem and habitat changes in the region. Since the late 1800s, overgrazing has triggered changes in composition and abundance of grasses, herbs, shrubs, and tree species. Livestock carried seeds of invasive species into the region. Grazing pressure created conditions for invasive grasses to outcompete native species and facilitated shrub growth over perennial grasses. Exotic annual grasses, particularly cheatgrass, carpet the landscape with fine fuels conducive to more frequent fires in shrub-grass plant communities (Pellent 1996 and 2002). Intentional clearing of sagebrush stands to improve range conditions for livestock also contributed to the transformation of shrub habitats. This combination of grazing-associated stressors has caused landscape-level changes, resulting in steep declines in the sagebrush, bitterbrush, and mountain mahogany plant communities that once supported abundant populations of greater sage-grouse and other shrub-dependent species. Grazing has also degraded wildlife habitat in areas like the sagebrush steppe on the Devil's Garden, the forestlands of the Warner Mountains, and the forest meadows throughout the region, reducing habitat values for native species (Menke et al. 1996, Miller et al. 1994, Schaeffer et al. 2002, Young and Clements 2002b).

Reduced fire frequency and livestock grazing throughout the growing season have contributed to the decline of aspen communities in the region. Livestock, along with deer and elk, consume aspen suckers and shoots and compact soft soils, preventing the successful regeneration of aspen stands. Like riparian habitats, aspen stands represent a small area of the landscape, but they are very important for supporting wildlife diversity. The multilayered vegetative aspen understory of herbs, shrubs, and woody debris provides abundant food and shelter for wildlife. Cottontail rabbit, snowshoe hare, porcupine, beaver, mule deer, blue grouse, quail, flycatchers, bluebirds, and Northern goshawk are among the animals that utilize and rely on aspen communities (Burton 2002, Loft et al. 1987).

Riparian and aquatic ecosystems are particularly affected by livestock grazing today (USFS 1991b, 2001b). These impacts are discussed under the Water Management Conflicts and Degradation of Aquatic Ecosystems section.

Excessive Feral Horse Grazing

David Bunn

While grazing by feral horses is very limited compared to cattle and sheep grazing in the region, it adds to the total impact of livestock and wildlife grazing. Since the arrival of settlers in the late 1800s, horses have escaped or been released, and today horses roam as feral herds throughout the Modoc Plateau Region. More than 2,300 feral horses graze year-round in northeastern California and border areas of Nevada on BLM and Forest Service land in eight Herd Management Areas (HMAs). Feral horses graze riparian and aquatic plant communities in late season, when these habitats are most vulnerable to damage (Beever 2003). One of the largest herds in the region is on the Modoc National Forest's 236,000-acre Devil's Garden Wild Horse Territory (WHT), overlapping 10 livestock-grazing allotments. Many of the Devil's Garden horses are descendants of draft horses, large animals with big hooves (Pasero 2004 pers. comm.). The heavier animals consume more forage and likely cause more trampling damage to delicate soils and creek beds than smaller horses.

For each Herd Management Area and the Wild Horse Territory, BLM and the Forest Service have established an "Appropriate Management Level" (AML), the target number of animals that the land management agencies have decided is appropriate for an area to achieve a "thriving natural ecological balance" (BLM July 2004). However, a "thriving natural ecological balance" has not been defined based on scientific principles or ecological criteria. Nor have ecological indicators been identified that could be monitored to assess when "natural ecological balance" is achieved.

The BLM and the Forest Service committed significant resources to maintain horse numbers within the AMLs. However, feral horse numbers have routinely exceeded, sometimes by two- or threefold, the AMLs for the herd management units and the Wild Horse Territory. In August 2004, horse herd sizes in the eight herd management units in Northern California exceeded the AMLs by an average of 68 percent (BLM 2004a). The excessive horse numbers contribute to overgrazing in the region, leaving less forage for wildlife, degrading range condition, and adding to grazing impacts on seeps, springs, riparian habitat, and aspen stands.

For the past 30 years, the Forest Service, with the help of BLM, has struggled to maintain horse numbers in the Wild Horse Territory within the appropriate management levels.

Horses are captured and adopted out. Some horses that are not adopted are returned to the public lands. The feral horse herds have been very productive, increasing in numbers by nearly 20 percent annually (Beever 2003, Pasero 2004 pers. comm., USFS July 2004). Horses must be gathered year after year to maintain herds within their AML. For example, the AML for the Wild Horse Territory is 305 horses. Thus, 60 to 75 animals must be permanently removed from the herd annually to maintain the herd near the target size of 305 animals. Costs for gathering horses have skyrocketed. From 1990 to 2002, the cost per horse for capture and adoption increased from $350 to $1,500. If horse numbers were within the target range for all the herds of northeastern California, it would require the capture and permanent removal of nearly 300 horses annually to maintain them within the BLM- and Forest Service-established appropriate management levels.

In August 2004, more than 800 horses grazed Devil's Garden, exceeding the AML by 500 animals. Contracted by the Forest Service, BLM launched a two-week effort, employing a helicopter, large stock trucks, and hired wranglers in an attempt to gather 500 horses. Despite a very determined effort, only 174 horses were gathered. Additional weeks of helicopter flight-time, livestock truck rental, and hired crews would be required to reduce the herd size below 305 animals.

The lack of resources to maintain limited horse herd sizes means horses contribute to overgrazing of the region; thus, the combined grazing of livestock and horses far exceeds grazing levels that are compatible with maintaining wildlife diversity and abundance.

Table 12.3: Chronology of Horse Gathering in Devil's Garden Wild Horse Territory

1974	500 animals in WHT
1976–78	260 horses removed from WHT
1978–1979	Horse population rebounded to 1,000 animals
1979	Forest Service contracted BLM—388 excess horses were removed.
1985–1990	BLM removed 60 horses annually
1990	469 horses counted in WHT
1992–93	Rough winters reduced herd to 200 animals
1995–2001	BLM gathered 100 horses annually
2002	Herd exceeded 700 animals; BLM gathered 260, adopted out about 70 percent, and returned rest to WHT
2004 (August)	More than 800 horses in WHT; BLM gathered 174

Altered Fire Regimes

Fire is an ecologically important disturbance that shapes and maintains native plant communities and wildlife habitats. Fire frequency and intensity are determined by the pattern and density of vegetation (fuel loading), landscape topography, fuel moisture, and long-term weather trends. In turn, fire affects ecological processes, the vegetative mosaic of the landscape, the structural diversity of habitats, and the accumulation of organic material. Specific plant communities or habitats have evolved within ranges of fire-return intervals. At higher elevations, natural wildlife habitats of northeastern California are adapted to specific fire-return intervals of between 12 and 30 years. At lower elevations and drier sites dominated by shrubs, with less dense fuel, natural fire return intervals may be 30 to 100 years (Brooks and Pyke 2001, Chang 1996, Young et al. 1988). However, for the past 150 years, land-use activities, native and non-native plant invasions, and fire suppression have increased or decreased fire frequencies, upsetting fire regimes and degrading habitat for native species (Arno and Fiedler 2005).

For example, in native shrub-grass communities, overgrazing in the years between the 1860s and the 1930s reduced native perennial grasses, providing conditions more beneficial to invasive annual grasses and to shrub expansion (Menke 2005 pers. comm.). The proliferation of flammable annual grasses led to increased fire frequency in many areas, reducing less fire-tolerant shrubs, such as big sagebrush, mountain mahogany and lower-elevation bitterbrush. More-frequent fire disturbance has facilitated additional invasions of non-native plants, further transforming the plant community, which is now dominated by invasive grasses less suitable for native wildlife (Brooks and Pyke 2001, Hall 2004 pers. comm., McAdoo et al. 2002).

For other plant communities of the region, such as pine and fir forests, fire is critical for maintaining healthy ecosystems and habitat for native wildlife. These plant communities have evolved with fire, and, through adaptation, have developed traits that require fire. Some plants, like deerbrush, need fire for germination (Perry 1994). Other plants have accelerated their life cycles to complete development between fire intervals. Species have developed fire-resistant buds, twigs, and bark. Fire facilitates sprouting in some plants and seed release and flowering in others. Wildlife species are dependent on many plant species that require fire (Chang 1996, McKelvey et al. 1996, Skinner and Chang 1996).

Western Juniper Expansion

Livestock grazing between 1880 and 1930 likely facilitated the expansion of native western juniper. Grazing consumed fine fuels, decreasing fire frequency and reducing competition from herbaceous species. (This process began 30 to 50 years before invasive grasses increased fire frequencies in the early 1900s.) The reduced fire frequency allowed western juniper to expand its coverage into sagebrush, bitterbrush, mountain mahogany, riparian, and aspen plant communities (BLM 2000, Miller and Rose 1999). Juniper has flourished by outcompeting other vegetation for water and nutrients and altering ecosystems to such an extent that other once-abundant native plants and wildlife are now scarce in these areas. In the last 130 years, juniper has increased its coverage in the plant communities tenfold and now covers more than 2.5 million acres of northeastern California (EOARC 2004, USFS July 2004). (See Fig. 12.3.) The expansion and increased density of this tree reduces shrubs, herbaceous cover, and plant diversity, decreasing habitat for shrub-affiliated native wildlife (Miller et al. 2000, Miller 2001). As juniper crowds out shrubs and **forbs**, ground- and shrub-nesting birds are absent or in low numbers. With the increase in juniper dominance and the decline of sagebrush communities on the Modoc Plateau, greater sage-grouse populations have plummeted.

There have been limited efforts to reduce western juniper to encourage the growth of shrubs and grass for forage. The Big Sage Fire Management Unit, which overlies portions of the Devil's Garden and Doublehead Forest Districts, has a fire plan that allows lightning-caused fires to burn with minimum suppression effort. This practice has reduced juniper on several hundred acres. Since 1980, the Doublehead Ranger District of the Modoc National Forest has removed about 150 acres per year of western juniper through firewood sales (USFS 1991a). The Cooperative Sagebrush Steppe Restoration Initiative, launched by a coordinated effort of BLM and the Forest Service, is preparing plans for landscape treatments to re-establish the shrub communities that are more important for wildlife. Reestablishing native shrubs and grasses where juniper now dominates is not as simple as cutting down or burning acres of juniper. Invasive annual grasses, rather than native plant communities, are likely to replace the juniper unless conditions are appropriate to benefit the native plants. Conversion of juniper to alternate native plant communities will require careful field testing and analysis of results, followed up with **adaptive management** (Belsky 1996, Miller 2001).

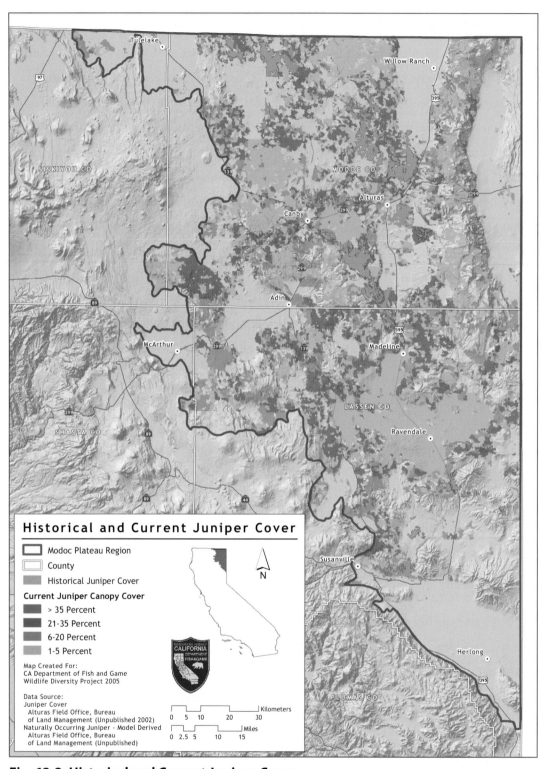

Historical and Current Juniper Cover

- Modoc Plateau Region
- County
- Historical Juniper Cover

Current Juniper Canopy Cover
- > 35 Percent
- 21-35 Percent
- 6-20 Percent
- 1-5 Percent

Map Created For:
CA Department of Fish and Game
Wildlife Diversity Project 2005

Data Source:
Juniper Cover
Alturas Field Office, Bureau
of Land Management (Unpublished 2002)
Naturally Occurring Juniper - Model Derived
Alturas Field Office, Bureau
of Land Management (Unpublished)

Fig. 12.3: Historical and Current Juniper Cover

The expansion of western juniper is replacing sagebrush and other plant communities. Naturally occurring western juniper was derived from a predictive model (using soil types, range boundaries, and topography) and is estimated to have covered 196,000 acres. Present-day extent of western juniper is estimated to be over 2.5 million acres.

Invasive Plants

Numerous exotic grasses and plants, like perennial pepper weed, annual medusahead, red brome, and various non-native thistles and aquatic weeds such as Eurasian watermilfoil, have displaced native plants and altered local plant communities. One species, cheatgrass, has had a particularly dramatic impact on native shrub and grassland communities. Native to southern Europe, North Africa, and southwestern Asia, cheatgrass was first dispersed in northeastern California sometime in the early 1900s, probably via contaminated grain seeds. Cheatgrass displaces native grasses and forbs by more effectively tapping soil moisture and hinders seedling establishment of native shrubs by reducing moisture and nutrients in surface soils (Norton et al. 2004). Once established and abundant, cheatgrass facilitates frequent fires by providing a carpet of fine fuels, which carries fire more efficiently than well-spaced native perennial grasses and native shrubs (Pellant 1996). Plant species slow to recolonize following fire, like bitterbrush and sagebrush, decline with increased fire frequencies. Cheatgrass has converted native vegetation to fire-prone grasslands, destroying sagebrush, bitterbrush, and mountain mahogany plant communities. The invasion of cheatgrass and other exotic plants has contributed to the wholesale conversion of thousands of acres of sagebrush, bitterbrush, and mountain mahogany plant communities to annual grasslands less supportive of native wildlife (Henstrom et al. 2002, Miller et al. 1994, Schaefer et al. 2003, Young 2000).

Forest Management Conflicts

Forest management practices, including even-aged tree production, road building, and fire suppression, significantly affect forest ecosystems and wildlife in the Modoc Plateau Region, as they do in the Sierra Nevada and Cascades. The U.S. Forest Service Sierra Nevada Framework Plan included the forests of the Modoc Plateau Region within its analysis of wildlife and habitat resources. Rather than repeat the forest discussion here, forest management stressors and conservation efforts in the Modoc region are discussed in Chapter 13, Sierra Nevada and Cascades Region.

Water Management Conflicts and Degradation of Aquatic Ecosystems

Many of the stressors affecting terrestrial habitats also combine to impact the aquatic ecosystems and species of northeastern California. Unique fish communities, native trout, amphibians, and invertebrates are at risk in aquatic systems throughout the region.

The 3-million-acre Pit River **watershed** is the major drainage of the Modoc Plateau, providing 20 percent of the water to the Sacramento River. The upper reaches of the watershed are in creeks of the Warner Mountains that drain into Goose Lake. The north fork of the Pit River flows from Goose Lake southwest and merges with the south fork of the Pit River, which drains the southern Warner Mountains. The Pit River meanders across the plateau and farmlands, receiving the drainage of Ash Creek and the flows of Fall River and Hat Creek before weaving west across the southern Cascades range. The river is checked and held by several dams and reservoirs along the way but eventually drains into Lake Shasta. Unique fish and invertebrates have evolved in isolated springs and segments of the Pit River watershed. Fourteen native fish species are found in various associated fish communities in segments of the watershed's rivers and creeks. Endemic aquatic species inhabit the watershed, including the Modoc sucker, the Goose Lake redband trout, Goose Lake tui chub, Goose Lake lamprey, Cow Head Lake tui chub, and the Shasta crayfish (Ellis and Cook 2001, Moyle 2002).

Creeks of the northern Modoc Plateau (or Lost River watershed) drain to Clear Lake. The outlet of Clear Lake is the Lost River, which circles north into Oregon farmland and then joins the Klamath River system. The Lost River watershed has its own endemic aquatic fish and invertebrates.

In these watersheds, the effects of timber management practices (particularly erosion from logging roads), livestock grazing, and nutrient runoff from farms have degraded creeks and rivers, negatively affecting ecosystems that support aquatic and riparian species. Dams and diversions for hydroelectric power and agricultural diversions have disrupted normal flow patterns, increased water temperatures, and blocked spawning migrations. Dams have fragmented creeks and rivers, permanently isolating subpopulations of aquatic species such as the Shasta crayfish.

These stressors have degraded the main stem and tributaries of the Pit River. The State Water Resources Control Board lists the Pit River and Fall River as impaired—failing to meet state water quality standards; 123 miles of the Pit River fail to meet those standards. Grazing and farm waste runoff have increased water temperature and polluted the river with excessive nutrients, lowering dissolved oxygen. Many Pit River tributaries suffer similar degradation from land-use practices (SWRCB 2002b).

Fall River emerges as spring water in the southern Cascades, receives the Bear Creek drainage, and then joins the Pit River. Fall River is known for its premiere wild trout fishery. However, sediment runoff from past land-use practices in the Bear Creek watershed has polluted Fall River (SWRCB 2002b).

The introduction of exotic aquatic species (e.g., largemouth bass and non-native trout to lakes, and bullheads, catfishes, and signal crayfish to rivers and streams), has reduced or extirpated populations of native amphibians and fish and affected invertebrates in many segments of the rivers, creeks and lakes of the region.

Restoring and protecting aquatic, riparian, meadow, and aspen habitats is among the highest priorities to maintain wildlife diversity for northeastern California. Both the Sierra Nevada Ecosystem Project and the Sierra Framework recommended action to protect these key habitats (SNEP 1996, USFS 2001b).

Various public and private efforts are under way in the region to restore stream habitats or to prevent further damage from livestock. The Central Modoc Resource Conservation District and the Pit River Watershed Alliance are working with land owners on stream restoration projects. The Forest Service has fenced some streams to protect the endangered Modoc sucker and other species. Rotational grazing systems that provide rest on a regular basis have been implemented to restore riparian habitats on many grazing allotments on the Modoc National Forest. The Goose Lake Fishes Working Group has been working on public and private lands to restore native fishes of the Goose Lake Basin (USFS 2000a, Yamagiwa 2005 pers. comm.).

Conservation Actions to Conserve and Restore Wildlife

In addition to the recommended regional actions described below, see the recommended statewide conservation actions as given in Chapter 4.

a. **Federal land management agencies should more effectively manage forest, shrub, aspen, meadow, and riparian habitat to enhance ecosystems and conditions for wildlife.**

Management actions may include the use of timber harvest, livestock grazing, and fire as tools to restore degraded habitats and improve ecosystem function.

b. **Federal land management agencies should implement modifications to grazing management on public lands that are conducive to recovery of key habitats for restoring and conserving wildlife.**

Changes in management practices should modify or discontinue livestock grazing in areas where habitats have been significantly degraded.

c. The Bureau of Land Management should update the Resource Management Plans (RMPs) to include provisions to restore and conserve wildlife diversity.

BLM has begun the process to develop RMPs for its three field offices of northeastern California. This is a good opportunity for BLM to modify guidelines for resource stewardship to restore and maintain wildlife diversity on BLM lands.

U.S. Fish and Wildlife Service, the California Department of Fish and Game, and conservation organizations should be active participants in the development of management guidelines, strategies, and practices to support wildlife diversity for incorporation into the RMPs.

The RMPs should incorporate the work agreed upon in other planning, restoration, and recovery efforts. For example, pursuant to BLM's own National Conservation Strategy for Sage-Grouse, local sage-grouse conservation planning efforts are already under way through the USFWS with multi-agency oversight. Previously adopted bighorn sheep management guidelines should be functionally integrated into the RMPs as well.

d. Feral horse numbers should be maintained at levels that meet the constraints imposed by law, and funds should be provided for BLM and the Forest Service to meet the standards in place for the protection of meadows and riparian areas.

BLM does not have the resources to conduct horse gatherings with adequate frequency to prevent the populations of horse herds from expanding to levels that damage wildlife habitats and ecosystems. However, BLM could adequately manage horses if animals were maintained at much lower numbers in northeastern California. Studies are under way to evaluate the use of fertility control in feral horse herds (Daels and Hughes 1995). If these techniques prove effective and economically practical, they may assist efforts to maintain herds at levels that do not cause damage in the future. Until new control methods have been proven successful, however, it is necessary to reduce herd numbers to a manageable level (at achievable levels with allocated resources) to prevent degradation of wildlife habitats.

e. The Cooperative Sagebrush Steppe Restoration Initiative and the National Resource Conservation Service (NRCS) should design juniper-removal projects to benefit wildlife diversity and ecosystem health.

Working with state and federal wildlife agencies, the Cooperative Sagebrush Steppe Restoration Initiative should ensure that tree-removal projects will improve conditions for recovery of native wildlife species. Monitoring and ongoing evaluation of wildlife habitats should be an essential part of the entire initiative.

The NRCS should implement "wildlife friendly" juniper-removal guidelines and conduct post-removal monitoring to restore shrub and forb components to juniper-dominated private lands.

f. Public forest lands should be managed to maintain healthy ecosystems and wildlife diversity, including thinning to restore diverse habitats and reducing the risk of catastrophic wildfire. State and federal forest managers and wildlife agencies should work cooperatively to develop a vision for the future forest condition.

See Statewide Action f, Chapter 4.

g. Regarding forest management conservation actions, see Conservation Actions d, e, f, and g in Chapter 13, Sierra Nevada and Cascades Region.

h. Land management and wildlife agencies and conservation NGOs should develop an aquatic multispecies conservation plan for the Pit River watershed.

Various agencies and private parties involved in partnerships to implement restoration projects in selected areas of the watershed need to direct restoration projects and management efforts to the actions of greatest priority and ensure that conservation actions are not in conflict.

The Goose Lake Fishes Conservation Strategy was developed in 1996 to restore habitat for the native fishes of the Goose Lake Basin. This strategy and associated goals and objectives should be updated to reflect changes in habitat conditions throughout the Goose Lake Basin. The Pit River Watershed Alliance is actively restoring habitats in the Pit River watersheds.

Moyle and Yoshiyama (1994) have developed a five-tier approach to protect aquatic biodiversity. The tiered approach recommends action in the following order: 1) protect threatened and endangered species; 2) protect clusters of co-occurring native species; 3) create a system of Aquatic Diversity Management Areas (ADMAs), in which maintaining aquatic diversity is the first goal of management; 4) implement conservation plans at the watershed level, in which protection of aquatic biodiversity is an important goal; and 5) implement regional plans for integrated use by humans and other organisms. The aquatic multispecies conservation plan should include elements similar to this five-tiered approach. A core element should include implementing ADMAs and key projects beneficial to maintaining aquatic wildlife diversity in the region.

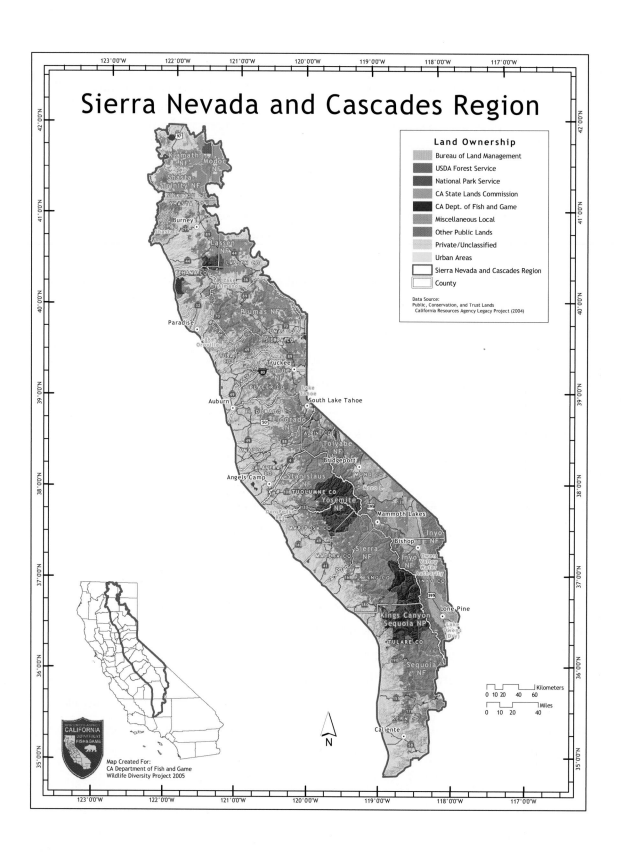

Sierra Nevada and Cascades Region

Land Ownership

- Bureau of Land Management
- USDA Forest Service
- National Park Service
- CA State Lands Commission
- CA Dept. of Fish and Game
- Miscellaneous Local
- Other Public Lands
- Private/Unclassified
- Urban Areas
- Sierra Nevada and Cascades Region
- County

Data Source:
Public, Conservation, and Trust Lands
California Resources Agency Legacy Project (2004)

Map Created For:
CA Department of Fish and Game
Wildlife Diversity Project 2005

CALIFORNIA
DEPARTMENT
FISH&GAME

Kilometers
0 10 20 40 60

Miles
0 10 20 40

N

13   Sierra Nevada and Cascades Region

Tim Palmer

Extending approximately 525 miles from north to south, the Sierra Nevada and Cascade ranges form the spine of the California landscape. The mostly volcanic southern Cascades stretch from north of the Oregon border southeastward, merging just south of Mt. Lassen with the northern reaches of the predominantly granitic Sierra Nevada. To the south, the Sierra Nevada range embraces the Mojave Desert to the east and curves south to link with the Tehachapi Mountains. The region includes the oak woodland foothills on the western slopes of the Sierra and Cascade ranges and, on the east, the Owens Valley and edges of the Great Basin.

On the west side, the slope of the Sierra Nevada and Cascades rises gradually from near sea level at the floor of the Central Valley to ridges ranging from 6,000 feet in the north to 14,000 feet in the south, then drops off sharply to the east. In contrast, the east side of the Cascades slopes gradually. As the Sierra elevation increases from west to east, life zones transition from chaparral and oak woodlands to lower-level montane forests of ponderosa and sugar pine to upper montane forests of firs, Jeffrey and lodgepole pine and, above timberline, to alpine plant communities.

Federal agencies manage about 61 percent of the Sierra Nevada and Cascades: 46 percent by the Forest Service, 8 percent by the National Park Service, and 7 percent by the Bureau of Land Management. About 2 million acres are wilderness areas, mostly in the eastern and southern Sierra, managed by the Forest Service. Lands managed by the National Park Service include Lassen Volcanic, Sequoia, Kings Canyon, and Yosemite national parks and Devils Postpile National Monument. State parks and wildlife areas account for 1 percent of the region, and the remaining, approximately 36 percent of the Sierra and Cascades, is privately owned. Most of the higher elevations and the eastern Sierra are public lands, whereas most of the oak woodlands and lower mixed conifer forests and rangelands below 3,000 feet on the western slope are in private ownership. There is a checkerboard ownership pattern of private and public lands in areas of the northern half of the Sierra that lie near historical railway routes (CRA 2004, SNEP 1996).

About 40 percent of the state's surface-water runoff flows to the Central Valley from the Sierra and Cascades. These flows are critical to meet California's hydropower demands and agricultural and drinking water needs. Much of the water is stored in reservoirs and is conveyed by aqueducts to irrigate agriculture from Redding to Bakersfield and to provide drinking water for most of urbanized California, including the San Francisco Bay Area and Southern California (DWR 1998).

The hundreds of creeks and streams of the western slope of the Sierra and Cascades drain via a dozen major river basins to merge with the Sacramento River in the north and the San Joaquin River in the south, eventually joining at the San Francisco Bay Delta. The southern forks of the Kings River and streams farther south drain into the Tulare basin. The streams east of the Sierra crest flow into the Great Basin via the Lahontan, Mono, and Owens drainages. Many of the springs and creeks of northeastern California drain via the Pit River, which winds through the Cascades and joins the Sacramento River at Lake Shasta. Maintaining and restoring the ecological health of these watersheds and aquatic systems is important to ensure clean water.

Bold topography, the large elevation gradient, and varied climatic conditions of the Sierra and Cascades support diverse plant communities. Fifty percent of California's 7,000 vascular plants are found in the region, and more than 400 plant species are endemic (Shevock 1996). The varied conditions and floristically and structurally diverse plant communities provide a large array of habitats important for maintaining California's wildlife diversity and abundance.

Several major stressors have altered aquatic ecosystems and transformed forest structure and habitats on both public and private lands. Dramatic human population growth and development in the western Sierra foothills, forest management practices, fire suppression, and livestock grazing have altered ecosystems and continue to affect wildlife habitats. Hydropower facilities and agricultural and municipal water diversions have disrupted natural river flow regimes. Eroding access roads in forested and other habitats and excessive livestock grazing have resulted in the conversion of wet meadows to drier lands and have degraded streams and aquatic habitat. The introduction of trout has caused declines in native species. In the central Sierra, historic mining severely altered watersheds and water courses, and those effects persist.

The altered forest ecosystems of the Sierra and Cascades largely lack the qualities of old-growth forests or late-**seral** stage forests (forests that are in the later stages of development with large-diameter trees, snags, and logs) that are important for diverse and abundant wildlife (Franklin and Fites-Kaufman 1996, USFS 2001b). Species that depend on old-growth or late-seral stage forest habitat, like the Pacific fisher, have been negatively affected. The degradation of mountain meadows and loss of willows and other riparian woody plants have affected the endangered willow flycatcher and other species that have similar habitat requirements.

New conservation challenges and opportunities will affect the Sierra and Cascade ranges in the next few decades. How new development is managed will determine the extent of wildlife habitat fragmentation. Changing global climate will alter depth and seasonality of snowpack, further modifying river flow regimes and ecosystems. The relicensing of hydropower projects provides an opportunity to change hydropower operations to reduce their effects on fish and wildlife.

Concerned about the decline of old forests and associated wildlife species of the region, Congress funded, in 1993, the Sierra Nevada Ecosystem Project (SNEP), based at UC Davis, for the "scientific review of the remaining old growth in the national forests of the Sierra Nevada in California, and for the study of the entire Sierra Nevada ecosystem by an independent panel of scientists, with expertise in diverse areas related to this issue." The forests of the Sierra, Cascades, and the Modoc Plateau were evaluated by a multidisciplinary team of scientists from many organizations. SNEP completed its work and published a three-volume report in 1996. Based on the work of dozens of scientists, the report analyzed the status of conifer forests, rangelands, meadow and riparian plant communities, and aquatic ecosystems, and suggested alternatives to restore ecosystems.

Aquatic and riparian systems are believed to be two of the most altered and impaired habitats of the Sierra Nevada. Among other critical findings, SNEP found that key causes of the decline of mammals, birds, and other vertebrates in the Sierra, Cascades, and Modoc regions include the loss and degradation of riparian areas, foothill woodlands, and diverse old forest habitats (including large trees, snags, fallen logs, and layered vegetative structure).

Meanwhile, a 1992 technical report by the Forest Service's Pacific Southwest Research Station highlighting at-risk California spotted owl populations triggered challenges and debate. That debate prompted the Forest Service to initiate a multiyear planning process that resulted in the Sierra Nevada Framework for Conservation and Collaboration (Sierra Framework), which evolved into the Sierra Nevada Forest Plan Amendment Final Environmental Impact Statement (SNFPA) covering the national forests of the Sierra, Cascades, and Modoc regions. In January 2001, Forest Service announced the SNFPA Record of Decision, describing chosen management options. In January 2004, the SNFPA was amended, reducing livestock-grazing and timber-harvest restrictions and giving the Forest Service greater management discretion.

Numerous watershed groups, private landowners, local conservancies, resource conservation districts, and state and federal programs are engaged in habitat conservation and restoration work on public and private lands throughout the region. The legislatively created Sierra Nevada Conservancy, established in January 2004, is a new collaborator and a potential source of funding for conservation and restoration of habitats for species at risk in the Sierra.

Species at Risk

The Plan development team updated vertebrate and invertebrate species information in the California Natural Diversity Database (CNDDB) during 2004–2005. The following regional summary of numbers of wildlife species, **endemic** species, and **species at risk** is derived from the updated CNDDB.

There are 572 vertebrate species that inhabit the Sierra Nevada and Cascades region at some point in their life cycle, including 293 birds, 135 mammals, 46 reptiles, 37 amphibians, and 61 fish. Of the total vertebrate species that inhabit this region, 83 bird **taxa**, 41 mammalian taxa, 12 reptilian taxa, 23 amphibian taxa, and 31 fish taxa are included on the **Special Animals List**. Of these, 26 are endemic to the Sierra Nevada and Cascades Region, two are endemic to California but introduced in this region, and 26 other species found here are endemic to California but not restricted to this region (Table 13.1).

Table 13.1: State-Endemic Special Status Vertebrates of the Sierra Nevada and Cascades Region

	Ambystoma californiense	California tiger salamander
	Ammospermophilus nelsoni	Nelson's antelope squirrel
+	*Archoplites interruptus*	Sacramento perch
	Batrachoseps campi	Inyo Mountains slender salamander
*	*Batrachoseps diabolicus*	Hell Hollow slender salamander
*	*Batrachoseps kawia*	Sequoia slender salamander
*	*Batrachoseps regius*	Kings River slender salamander
*	*Batrachoseps relictus (=pacificus)*	Relictual slender salamander
	Batrachoseps robustus	Kern Plateau salamander
*	*Batrachoseps simatus*	Kern Canyon slender salamander
*	*Batrachoseps sp. 1*	Breckenridge Mountain slender salamander
*	*Batrachoseps stebbinsi*	Tehachapi slender salamander
*	*Bufo canorus*	Yosemite toad
*	*Catostomus fumeiventris*	Owens sucker
	Charina umbratica	Southern rubber boa
	Cottus asperrimus	Rough sculpin
	Cottus klamathensis macrops	Bigeye marbled sculpin
+	*Cyprinodon nevadensis amargosae*	Amargosa pupfish
*	*Cyprinodon radiosus*	Owens pupfish
*	*Dendragapus obscurus howardi*	Mount Pinos blue grouse
	Diadophis punctatus modestus	San Bernardino ringneck snake
	Dipodomys heermanni dixoni	Merced kangaroo rat
	Dipodomys panamintinus argusensis	Argus Mountains kangaroo rat
	Elgaria (=Gerrhonotus) panamintinus	Panamint alligator lizard
	Ensatina eschscholtzii croceator	Yellow-blotched salamander
*	*Gila bicolor snyderi*	Owens tui chub
*	*Hydromantes brunus*	Limestone salamander
*	*Hydromantes platycephalus*	Mount Lyell salamander
	Hydromantes shastae	Shasta salamander
*	*Hydromantes sp. 1*	Owens Valley web-toed salamander
	Hysterocarpus traski traski	Sacramento-San Joaquin tule perch
	Lavinia symmetricus ssp. 1	San Joaquin roach
*	*Lavinia symmetricus ssp. 3*	Red Hills roach
	Microtus californicus vallicola	Owens Valley vole

	Mylopharodon conocephalus	Hardhead
*	*Oncorhynchus clarki seleniris*	Paiute cutthroat trout
*	*Oncorhynchus mykiss aguabonita*	Volcano Creek golden trout
*	*Oncorhynchus mykiss gilberti*	Kern River rainbow trout
*	*Oncorhynchus mykiss ssp. 2*	McCloud River redband trout
*	*Oncorhynchus mykiss whitei*	Little Kern golden trout
	Onychomys torridus tularensis	Tulare grasshopper mouse
	Perognathus alticolus inexpectatus	Tehachapi pocket mouse
	Perognathus inornatus inornatus	San Joaquin pocket mouse
*	*Perognathus longimembris tularensis*	No common name
	Perognathus parvus xanthonotus	Yellow-eared pocket mouse
	Rhinichthys osculus ssp. 2	Owens speckled dace
*	*Rhinichthys osculus ssp. 5*	Long Valley speckled dace
*	*Sorex lyelli*	Mount Lyell shrew
	Spermophilus mohavensis	Mohave ground squirrel
	Tamias speciosus speciosus	Lodgepole chipmunk
*	*Thomomys bottae operarius*	Owens Lake pocket gopher
*	*Xantusia vigilis sierrae*	Sierra night lizard

* denotes taxon is endemic to region
\+ denotes taxon is endemic to California but introduced in this region

The number of arthropod species is so great, and they are so poorly known taxonomically, that it is presently impossible to accurately estimate the total number of invertebrate species occurring in the state. In the Sierra Nevada and Cascades Region, however, 96 invertebrate taxa are included on the Special Animals List, including 68 arthropod taxa and 28 mollusk taxa. Of these, 57 are endemic to the Sierra Nevada and Cascades Region, and 23 other taxa found here are endemic to California but not restricted to this region (Table 13.2).

Table 13.2: State-Endemic Special Status Invertebrates of the Sierra and Cascades Region

*	*Ammonitella yatesi*	Tight coin (=Yates' snail)
	Andrena blennospermatis	Vernal pool bee
	Andrena macswaini	An andrenid bee
	Andrena subapasta	An andrenid bee
*	*Aphrastochthonius grubbsi*	Grubbs' cave pseudoscorpion
*	*Argochrysis lassenae*	Lassen chrysidid wasp
*	*Artemia monica*	Mono brine shrimp
	Atractelmis wawona	Wawona riffle beetle

*	*Banksula californica*	California banksula harvestman
*	*Banksula galilei*	Galile's cave harvestman
*	*Banksula grubbsi*	Grubbs' cave harvestman
*	*Banksula martinorum*	Martins' cave harvestmen
*	*Banksula melones*	Melones Cave harvestman
*	*Banksula rudolphi*	Rudolph's cave harvestman
*	*Banksula tuolumne*	Tuolumne Cave harvestman
*	*Banksula tutankhamen*	King Tut Cave harvestman
	Branchinecta mesovallensis	Midvalley fairy shrimp
*	*Caecidotea sequoiae*	An isopod; no common name
*	*Calasellus longus*	An isopod; no common name
*	*Calicina cloughensis*	Clough Cave harvestman
*	*Calicina conifera*	A harvestman; no common name
*	*Calicina dimorphica*	A harvestman; no common name
*	*Calicina macula*	A harvestman; no common name
*	*Calicina mesaensis*	Table Mountain harvestman
*	*Calicina piedra*	Piedra harvestman
*	*Ceratochrysis gracilis*	A chrysidid wasp; no common name
	Colligyrus convexus	Canary duskysnail
*	*Cryptochia denningi*	Denning's cryptic caddisfly
*	*Cryptochia excella*	Kings Canyon cryptochian caddisfly
	Desmocerus californicus dimorphus	Valley elderberry longhorn beetle
*	*Desmona bethula*	Amphibious caddisfly
*	*Ecclisomyia bilera*	Kings Creek ecclysomyian caddisfly
*	*Euphilotes battoides comstocki*	Comstock's blue butterfly
*	*Euphydryas editha monoensis*	Mono checkerspot butterfly
*	*Euproserpinus euterpe*	Kern primrose sphinx moth
*	*Farula praelonga*	Long-tailed caddisfly
*	*Helminthoglypta allynsmithi*	Merced Canyon shoulderband
*	*Helminthoglypta concolor*	White fir shoulderband
	Hydrochara rickseckeri	Ricksecker's water scavenger beetle
*	*Hydroporus hirsutus*	Wooly hydroporus diving beetle
	Hydroporus leechi	Leech's skyline diving beetle
*	*Hygrotus fontinalis*	Travertine band-thigh diving beetle
*	*Juga occata*	Scalloped juga
	Lanx patelloides	Kneecap lanx
*	*Larca laceyi*	Lacey's cave pseudoscorpion
*	*Lepidostoma ermanae*	Cold Spring caddisfly
	Lepidurus packardi	Vernal pool tadpole shrimp

	Linderiella occidentalis	California linderiella
	Lytta moesta	Moestan blister beetle
	Lytta molesta	Molestan blister beetle
*	*Megaleuctra sierra*	Shirttail Creek stonefly
	Megomphix californicus	Natural Bridge megomphix
	Monadenia churchi	Klamath sideband
*	*Monadenia circumcarinata*	Keeled sideband
*	*Monadenia mormonum buttoni*	Button's Sierra sideband
*	*Monadenia mormonum hirsuta*	Hirsute Sierra sideband
	Monadenia troglodytes	Shasta sideband
*	*Monadenia tuolumneana*	Tuolumne sideband
*	*Monadenia yosemitensis*	Yosemite Mariposa sideband
*	*Nebria darlingtoni*	South Forks ground beetle
*	*Neothremma genella*	Golden-horned caddisfly
*	*Oravelia pege*	Dry Creek cliff strider bug
*	*Orobittacus obscurus*	Gold Rush hanging scorpionfly
	Pacifastacus fortis	Shasta crayfish
*	*Parapsyche extensa*	King's Creek parapsyche caddisfly
	Parnopes borregoensis	Borrego parnopes chrysidid wasp
*	*Philotiella speciosa bohartorum*	Bohart's blue butterfly
*	*Pseudogarypus orpheus*	Music Hall Cave pseudoscorpion
	Punctum hannai	Trinity spot
*	*Pyrgulopsis aardahli*	Benton Valley (=Aahrdahl's) springsnail
	Pyrgulopsis eremica	Smoke Creek pyrg
*	*Pyrgulopsis perturbata*	Fish Slough springsnail
*	*Pyrgulopsis rupinicola*	Sucker Springs pyrg
	Pyrgulopsis wongi	Wong's springsnail
*	*Rhyacophila spinata*	Spiny rhyacophilan caddisfly
*	*Stygobromus gradyi*	Grady's cave amphipod
*	*Stygobromus harai*	Hara's cave amphipod
*	*Stygobromus wengerorum*	Wengerors' cave amphipod
	Talanites moodyae	A gnaphosid spider; no common name
*	*Tetrix sierrana*	Sierra pygmy grasshopper

* denotes taxon is endemic to region

The Wildlife Species Matrix, including data on listing status, habitat association, and population trend for each vertebrate and invertebrate species included on the Special Animals List, is available on the Web at http://www.dfg.ca.gov/habitats/wdp/matrix_search.asp. For vertebrates, the matrix also includes links to species-level range maps. Additionally, a link to the California Department of Fish and Game's online Field Survey Form is available to assist in reporting positive sightings of species on the Special Animals List to the California Natural Diversity Database (CNDDB).

Three Species at Risk

Note: *The following discussion of three species at risk illustrates how stressors or threats affect species and highlights conservation challenges and opportunities. These species discussions are not intended to imply that conservation should have a single-species approach.*

Three species at risk are discussed here to illustrate the effects of stressors in the region on species and the opportunities for conservation. The Sierra willow flycatcher (two of the three subspecies of willow flycatcher) and other species have declined as mountain meadows and riparian habitats have been drained or degraded. The case of the Sierra willow flycatcher illustrates the result of habitat degradation and the challenge ahead to make the land-use changes necessary to restore meadow and riparian ecosystem health and wildlife populations.

The status of the Pacific fisher is one indicator of the status of forest conditions of the Sierra, particularly the old-growth component. The fisher requires specific features of mature forest, such as large trees with cavities for nesting, within a forest mosaic that contains areas of open canopy and layered groundcover supportive of squirrels and other prey species. Conservation of the Pacific fisher is dependent upon the approaches to and success of restoring healthy and diverse forest ecosystems along the Sierra range.

The mountain yellow-legged frog, once abundant in aquatic habitats throughout much of the Sierra, is absent from many areas of its historical range, and several stressors are implicated in its decline.

Sierra Willow Flycatcher

The willow flycatcher (*Empidonax traillii*) has declined to low numbers and is still declining in the Sierra, where it occurs primarily on federally managed lands (Green et al. 2003). It is designated as endangered by the state. Two subspecies of the willow flycatcher, the little willow flycatcher (*E.t. brewsteri*) and the Great Basin willow flycatcher (*E.t. adastus*), are found in the Sierra Nevada, with combined total  numbers estimated between 300 and 400 birds; *brewsteri* is found on the western slope, and *adastus* inhabits the east side. For the purposes of this discussion, these two subspecies are collectively referred to as Sierra willow flycatcher. One estimate is that since 1982, individual male territories of the Sierra willow flycatcher have declined 26 percent (Green et al. 2003). *E.t. brewsteri* was also historically prevalent in the Central Valley but has been **extirpated** there owing to habitat loss and cowbird nest parasitism.

The Sierra willow flycatcher is dependent on riparian thickets and wet mountain meadows skirted with willows and alders. For over a century, the browsing and grazing of vegetation by domestic sheep and cattle, combined with the carving of roads for timber and mining operations and ditches for diversion of water for various uses, have had an effect on the vegetation and caused drying of montane meadows (SNEP 1996, USFS 2001b). Livestock grazing has facilitated the invasion of the cowbird, a brood parasite that causes willow flycatcher nest failure. Cowbirds have a **commensal** association with livestock and have invaded the Sierra in the last 60 to 70 years; in the central Sierra, cowbird brood parasitism has been documented at several sites ranging from 8 percent to 47 percent of willow flycatchers' nests (Green et al. 2003). The drier conditions have led to increased nest predation of willow flycatchers by enabling the encroachment of trees and brush that, in turn, provide perches for predators, including squirrels, chipmunks, hawks, and ravens. Road building, water diversions, and inappropriate grazing continue to occur in some areas of willow flycatcher habitat.

The precarious condition of the Sierra willow flycatcher was highlighted in the Sierra Framework. The U.S. Forest Service described the willow flycatcher as the highest-priority land bird in the Sierra Nevada, because it had the highest probability of being extirpated there. The 2001 Record of Decision declared the intent of the Forest Service to produce a conservation assessment of the willow flycatcher in the Sierra. Completed in March 2003, the Assessment identifies the needs of the willow flycatcher and the urgent need to reduce or curtail land uses that negatively affect riparian and meadow habitats and the need to restore degraded habitats (Blankenship 2004 pers. comm., USFS 2001b).

The causes of the degradation of willow flycatcher habitat are now well-enough understood to enable actions that will contribute to the recovery of the species. The critical status of the willow flycatcher warrants reducing or excluding livestock grazing and other land uses adversely affecting montane meadows and riparian habitat, particularly where there are known flycatcher territories, unless new research can show the land uses have no detrimental effects on the flycatcher and other species (USFS 2001b). The Forest Service Conservation Assessment concludes that "regardless of causes, meadow condition must be improved." The species-recovery benefit of eliminating a stressor of riparian habitat is dramatically exhibited on Lee Vining and Rush creeks, tributaries to Mono Lake. Reestablished flows and restoration work on these creeks, which had dried up due to water diversions to Los Angeles, are credited with the return of willow flycatchers to the creeks (Heath 2004 pers. comm.).

Pacific Fisher

The fisher inhabits mountain forests across much of North America. In California, the Pacific subspecies lives in the Klamath region and the Sierra Nevada. Historically, in the Sierra Nevada, the Pacific fisher ranged from Lassen National Forest in the northern Sierra to Sequoia National Forest in the southern Sierra. Today, the only known fisher populations in the region are in the southern Sierra; surveys to date suggest they may be absent from 240 miles of their former range in the Sierra to the north. More surveys are needed to confirm the distribution status of the fisher (Campbell et al. 2000, USFWS 2004e, Zielinski et al. 1995).

The Pacific fisher is long-lived, has low reproductive rates, and occurs in low densities with large home ranges. With these life characteristics, the fisher is vulnerable to extirpation and will be slow to recover when conditions improve. The fisher requires specific habitat features associated with older conifer or hardwood-conifer forests and riparian forests (Campbell et al. 2000). Suitable habitat is well-shaded forest containing small areas of open canopy along with thick vegetative layers mixed with snags and fallen logs. Large-tree forests provide denning and resting habitat and an open canopy areas of herbs and shrubs to support prey of small mammals and birds. Our understanding of the broader home range is less well developed.

The fisher inhabits the lower and mid-elevations of the Sierra. These are also the areas where development pressures are greatest. The apparent extirpation of the fisher from the northern and central Sierra is attributed to the loss of forest complexity, itself attributable to logging of larger trees and older forests, forest management for even-aged forests (including tree farming), removal of fallen logs and snags, fire suppression, and the fragmentation of forest landscapes by roads and residential development (Campbell et al. 2000, USFS 2001b, USFWS 2004e).

Today, the fisher is a rare **species of special concern.** The U.S. Fish and Wildlife Service (USFWS) has been petitioned three times to list the West Coast population of the fisher as endangered or threatened. In 2004, USFWS concluded that listing was warranted. But due to a backlog of other species-listing issues, USFWS recognized Pacific fisher as a candidate species for listing, to be further considered at a later date (USFWS 2004e).

Restoring and managing preferred forest habitats throughout the Sierra are essential to conserve the fisher. Maintaining connectivity of habitats is important to enable the fisher to recolonize the central and northern Sierra from the fisher populations in the south. Conservation of the fisher also necessitates protecting and restoring the black oak woodlands component of mixed-conifer forest ecosystems, conserving large deformed trees, and reestablishing patches of lush layered ground vegetation, snags, and fallen logs to provide conditions for abundant prey.

The SNFPA highlighted the precarious status of the Pacific fisher in the Sierra, selecting it as a focal species for special protection as part of its old-forest ecosystems and associated species conservation strategy (USFS 2001b).

Mountain Yellow-Legged Frog

William Flaxington

The mountain yellow-legged frog exists in two regions of the state, in the higher elevations of the Sierra and in the mountains of Southern California. Few frogs exist today where they were once common in the San Gabriel and San Jacinto mountains. In 2002, the Southern California population of mountain yellow-legged frog was federally listed as endangered. The mountain yellow-legged frog was widespread throughout the Sierra range above 4,500 feet and abundant in some areas, in lakes and slow-moving streams, until the 1960s (USFS 2001b). In the early 1990s, field studies found that mountain yellow-legged frog numbers had dramatically declined and were absent from more than 80 percent of their historical range. The mountain yellow-legged frog in the Sierra is a state and federal species of concern and a candidate for listing under the federal Endangered Species Act.

The mountain yellow-legged frog is a highly aquatic frog, found in lakes and larger streams. It seeks warmer nearshore areas for cover and reproduction during the short summer season and overwinters in deep lake waters and in deep crevices near shore. It moves short distances over land between aquatic habitats. The Sierra mountain yellow-legged frog evolved in historically fishless habitats and is very vulnerable to predation by introduced trout, because in higher elevations it has a multiple-year tadpole stage (Knapp 1996, Knapp and Mathews 2000). One study found that while the tadpole has a prey response to native predatory snakes, it shows no such response to predatory non-native fish.

The introduction of predatory non-native trout over the last 100 years is considered the primary cause of decline of the mountain yellow-legged frog in the Sierra. Exposure to pesticides from upwind agricultural applications and chytrid fungal infection are also considered contributing factors to their decline.

Field studies have found frogs to be extirpated from most lakes where trout exist. However, the frog has rapidly repopulated lakes following the removal of trout (Milliron 1999, 2005, Milliron et al. 2004). Fish and Game and the Pacific Southwest Research Station of the Forest Service have conducted extensive field surveys of trout and frogs throughout the high Sierra in recent years. The field studies identified sub-basins protected by natural trout barriers, such as waterfalls, where frogs are likely to recover and thrive after the removal of trout. Based on this work, Fish and Game has developed basin plans to restore mountain yellow-legged frogs and other aquatic species while maintaining quality trout fishing opportunities at selected lakes. (Basin plans have been prepared for the southern Sierra; the central and northern Sierra basin plans are not yet prepared).

While further studies are needed to understand all the significant stressors affecting native amphibians and other aquatic species in the Sierra, immediate restoration of mountain yellow-legged frog populations appears feasible through the establishment of trout-free sub-basins across the high Sierra.

Stressors Affecting Wildlife and Habitats

Stressors Affecting Upland Habitats

- Growth and land development
- Forest management conflicts
- Altered fire regimes
- Excessive livestock grazing
- Invasive plants
- Recreational pressures
- Climate change

Stressors Affecting Aquatic and Riparian Habitats

- Water diversions and dams
- Watershed fragmentation and fish barriers
- Hydropower project operations
- Excessive livestock grazing
- Water diversion from the Owens Valley
- Introduced non-native fish

Stressors Affecting Upland Habitats

Growth and Land Development

The Sierra Nevada underwent population growth of 130 percent between 1970 and 1990, compared to the state's average of 49 percent growth over the same period, and growth in the region is expected to continue at a pace exceeding the state average, adding about 175,000 new residents every decade (Duane 1998, SNEP 1996).

The greatest growth and development have occurred in the mostly privately owned western foothills, particularly in the watersheds of the Yuba, American, and San Joaquin rivers, in the Lake Tahoe Basin, and around Lake Almanor. Development pressure is strong in the foothills adjacent to the metropolitan centers of Redding, Sacramento, Stockton, Merced, Fresno, and Bakersfield, particularly along the foothill river corridors near these cities. (See Fig. 13.1, Development Along Highway Corridors.) On the Sierra Nevada's east side, growth pressure is greatest between Reno and Susanville and near Bishop.

Ranchette and residential communities are expanding from metropolitan areas of Reno and Redding along highways 395, 299, and 44 along the eastern foothills and across the northern Sierra and Cascades (Laudenslayer 2004 pers. comm., Rickman 2004 pers. comm.). New development along these highway corridors is displacing wildlife habitat and creating barriers in important wildlife migration areas. For example, development along Highway 395 south of Susanville hinders the seasonal migration of deer across the Bass Hill Wildlife Area. Key wildlife corridors in the region are crossed by highways. Highway 299 descends the Cascades between Mount Lassen and Mount Shasta and winds northeast across the Modoc Plateau (Penrod et al. 2000). As development expands on the private lands adjacent to Highway 299, migrating mule deer, elk, and antelope will be less able to move between seasonal ranges. Without conservation planning, future development along these corridors will likely have a significant impact on the region's wildlife.

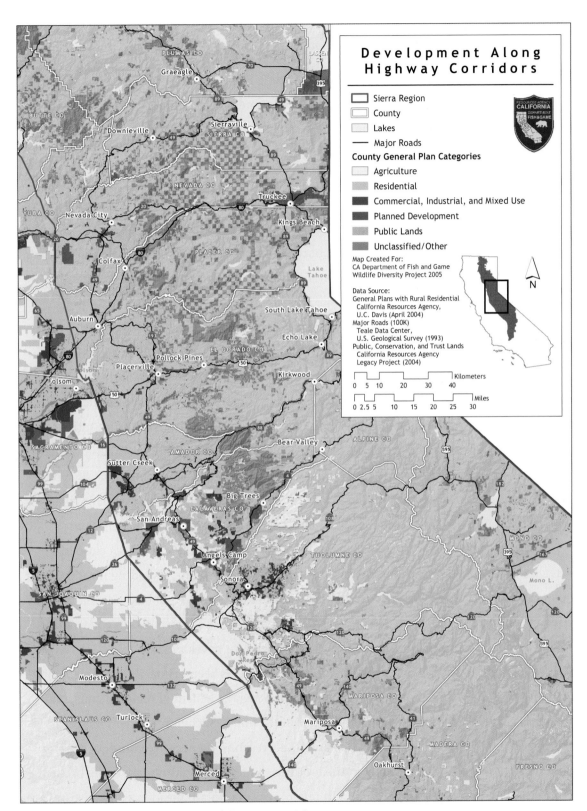

Fig. 13.1: Development Along Highway Corridors

Development pressure in the Sierra Nevada is anticipated to be particularly strong along highway corridors extending from urban centers in the Central Valley.

In the Sierra and Cascades, development is also expanding into the forest. New golf courses, scattered single-family homes, commercial properties, ski resorts, industrial sites, and new roads are replacing and fragmenting wildlife habitat. Where development occurs, fire is suppressed, preventing regeneration of fire-dependent vegetation and altering plant communities. Development also requires new water diversions and creates new sources of pollution. Mountain meadows, oak woodlands, and riparian streams are places of high wildlife diversity, and they are also preferred sites for development.

As seasons change, the survival of many mammal, bird, and fish species depends on their ability to migrate between higher and lower elevations in both the Sierra and Cascades. But opportunities to migrate successfully have been compromised by dams, reservoirs, highways, altered stream flows, residential community development, and predation by free-roaming domestic pets.

For 150 years, the west-slope foothills have been the most seriously affected area of the Sierra, with cattle ranching having the greatest presence. Western foothill development has fragmented riparian corridors and other habitats (Kattelman 2000). Much of the development on the western slope of the Sierra has degraded oak woodlands, lower mixed conifer forests, and similar habitats that support more wildlife diversity than other plant communities of the region. More than 350 species of birds, mammals, reptiles, and amphibians inhabit the oak woodlands (CalPIF 2002). The Sierra Nevada Ecosystem Project documented that 85 terrestrial vertebrate species require west-slope foothill savanna, woodland, chaparral, or riparian habitats to retain population viability, and 14 of these species are at risk of extinction.

Many early homestead settlements in the high Sierra clustered in level areas close to water, areas that are also particularly important for wildlife habitats, including meadows and along rivers and streams. While most higher-mountain habitats are public lands managed by federal agencies, these older settled areas remain largely in private ownership. Today, these private lands, surrounded by national forests, are prized for development.

Development in the Sierra over the last three decades has been primarily via incremental single-home and small commercial development, lacking the benefit of regional conservation planning. Low-density development has been the norm. Such development has resulted in greater fragmentation of the landscape and its corresponding negative consequences for wildlife. In many locations throughout the foothills, larger land holdings are being broken up into smaller parcels for single homes. In other areas, mountain meadows and pastures are being converted to golf courses and residential communities.

Development also exacerbates existing stresses on wildlife and habitats. **Invasive** plant species are often introduced along new roads and with new landscaping. Invasive species outcompete native species in development-disturbed lands. Additional domestic water use further reduces water available for aquatic ecosystems.

Growth has also increased the need to suppress fire, thereby expanding the conflict with efforts to restore more natural fire regimes in these fire-adapted ecosystems. Adding residents to the region will likely result in more citizen resistance to prescribed fire and more objections to the smoke it generates.

The severity of future development's effects on species at risk will depend on whether conservation planning is embraced and if growth allowed by counties is designed to account for fire, to protect ecosystems, and to minimize further fragmentation of habitats.

Forest Management Conflicts

[This discussion applies to the forests of the Sierra Nevada and Cascades Region and the Modoc Plateau Region.]

Using narrative descriptions by explorers and pioneers of the 1800s, in conjunction with the requirements of native forest species and what is known of land use activities over the past 150 years, scientists have developed descriptions of forests as they were before Euro-American settlement. The forests were a mosaic of stands of conifer trees with an understory of herbaceous plants and shrubs, open meadows, aspen stands, and riparian plant communities. Mixed conifer forests were patchy, with stands of trees in all stages of development, from recently burned areas yielding young saplings among shrubs and herbaceous vegetation to mature forests of scattered large trees several centuries old. Stands of middle-aged and older trees were broken up by natural disturbances like fire, disease, or avalanche, leaving areas of fallen trees where understory vegetation was abundant.

Wildlife species evolved to make use of the diverse forest landscape. Some species use the older tree stands for nesting or resting but require forage in the more open areas of the forest mosaic, where the herbaceous vegetation supports prey species. For example, raptors such as the northern goshawk and the California spotted owl nest in mature forests but hunt for prey in open areas near their nest sites. Fisher and marten select older trees for den sites, but some of their prey are more abundant where the tree canopy is open, fallen logs are common, and shrubs and herbs carpet the ground. Aspen stands dispersed along streams and meadows provide habitat for many mammals, birds, reptiles, and amphibians. Mule deer use the cover in which to hide, and songbirds often use nest sites provided by the shrubs and trees of aspen stands.

For the last century, forest management practices have adversely affected wildlife and plant communities of the Sierra Nevada, Cascades, and the Modoc Plateau regions. The cumulative effects of even-aged timber-harvest practices, elimination of older trees, snags and brush, logging-road construction, and fire suppression have changed forest plant communities. While some of these stressors have been reduced in recent years, they all continue to affect the forests' ecosystems and wildlife.

The SNEP project found that old-forest conditions (old-growth and late-seral forest) exist on 17 percent of national forest lands and on 47 percent of national park lands. On national forest lands outside of wilderness areas, remaining old-growth forest is likely less than 8 percent (Franklin and Fites-Kaufman 1996, USFS 2001b). Old-forest conditions exist primarily as small patches. Large areas of old forest are uncommon in national forests, and only remnant areas of old-forest conditions exist on private lands. Fire-tolerant old forests, often with open canopies, have been replaced by dense, even-aged forests that lack diverse wildlife habitat features and are prone to devastating wildfires.

Maintaining diverse wildlife requires forests that contain, in adequate distribution, all sizes and ages of trees, areas of open and closed canopies, and a varied landscape shaped by natural disturbance. Conserving biological diversity also requires maintaining connections between diverse habitats, ecosystem functions (e.g., energy cycling, food webs, and fire regimes), and the integrity of aquatic ecosystems (Franklin 2005 pers. comm., Lindenmayer and Franklin 2002, Moyle 1996a, Rickman 2004 pers. comm., Smith 2001). Protecting the remnant stands of old-growth and late-seral forests and generally conserving older, larger trees are important components of maintaining forest diversity in the Sierra, Cascades, and Modoc regions. Nevertheless, the harvesting of large trees continues.

Much of the Sierra Nevada, Cascades, and Modoc mixed-conifer forests needs to be thinned to restore complex forest structure, improve conditions for wildlife, and reduce the risk of catastrophic fires (Rickman 2004 pers. comm., Smith 2001). The design of forest thinning projects requires input from wildlife biologists and forest ecologists to ensure that the forest treatments contribute to wildlife habitat restoration.

Tremendous volumes of small and medium trees must be harvested over the next several decades to appropriately thin Sierra, Cascades, and Modoc forests. Currently, California does not have adequate wood-product processing infrastructure to handle these volumes of timber.

Thus, the economic feasibility of thinning forests is dependent on development of new forest products and processing facilities.

In addition to treatments of forest stands, regeneration practices following timber harvests or fire are very important in shaping the future forest structure. While timber harvest strategies on public lands are beginning to incorporate wildlife and habitat needs, regeneration practices have generally not made similar changes (Franklin 2005 pers. comm.). In some national forests, regeneration treatments clear shrubs and herbaceous vegetation to promote growth of tree species (Britting 2004 pers. comm., Buckley 2005 pers. comm.). Yet shrubs and herbaceous vegetation are particularly important for wildlife. These kinds of post-harvest treatments are more common on private forest lands. The National Forest Management Act and federal regulations prescribe the method and speed of reestablishing the next generation of trees on federal lands (Tappeiner and McDonald 1996). State Forest Practice Rules have similar prescriptions for private forest lands. These regeneration prescriptions are generally designed to enhance timber production and do not generally support regeneration practices specifically to benefit wildlife and restore diverse native plant communities. For example, if a land owner wishes to restore aspen stands following the removal of conifers, to do so may be in conflict with regeneration rules.

The rules governing forest management decisions, and the processes for arriving at those decisions, are different depending on the forest jurisdiction. Within the Sierra-Cascades and Modoc Plateau regions, the U.S. Forest Service manages the 11 national forests, the National Park Service manages forested national park lands, and BLM manages a very limited area of forested lands in the northern Sierra and Modoc regions. Timber harvest on private lands is governed by State Forest Practice Rules, and timber harvest plans are reviewed and approved by the State Board of Forestry.

Altered Fire Regimes

Most of California's forest ecosystems have evolved with recurring fire, and each plant community of the Sierra and Cascades has evolved with some range of frequency of wildfire. The plant communities, topography, elevation, and climatic conditions influence the "fire regime," the frequency and intensity of fire for a specific plant community (McKelvey et al. 1996). In turn, the extent and intensity of fire influence ecological processes, shape plant communities, and affect wildlife.

Declining Aspen

Quaking aspen are scattered across the Sierra Nevada, the southern Cascades, and the Warner Mountains of the Modoc National Forest, usually in stands of fewer than five acres and usually adjacent to streams, springs, lake shores, and meadows. Aspen is found within a wide range of elevation in the Sierra, from the lower elevations of western juniper on the east side to higher zones of fir and lodgepole pine, generally along creeks or meadows. Like other riparian communities, aspen communities comprise only a small portion of the landscape but provide habitat for many species. The multilayered herbaceous vegetation and shrubs that thrive beneath aspen canopy provide nesting, denning, and foraging habitat for insects, birds, amphibians, and mammals. The fruits produced by this diverse plant life and the insects that are abundant in the moist aspen environment provide food for a wide variety of birds. Northern goshawks, owls, and other raptors rest in the upper canopy and hunt adjacent habitats. Cavity-nesting songbirds make use of all layers of the canopy and brush of aspen stands. Large mammals also use aspen stands. Deer forage and hide in the layers of vegetation; black bears forage on the berry bushes. Rabbits, voles, and other small animals thrive here, too (Burton 2002, Loft et al. 1987, Romsos 2000).

Across the West, including in the Sierra Nevada and Modoc Plateau, aspen are in decline. Heavy livestock grazing, reduced fire frequency, historically high numbers of foraging deer in the 1950s and 1960s, the drying of meadows, and conifer encroachment have all contributed to the decline of aspen stands. Less-frequent fire over the past century has limited the regeneration of aspen trees. Aspen regenerate primarily by clonal production of suckers. Fire reduces conifer encroachment, opens up the canopy, removes shrub cover, and stimulates sucker release. Historic grazing consumed vegetation around aspen stands, reducing fuel available for fire. Also, under conditions of moderate-to-heavy livestock grazing, both livestock and wildlife graze more heavily on vegetation in aspen stands, including any emerging aspen shoots. The soil water tapped by conifers has contributed to the drying of meadows, reducing water available for aspen. Pine and fir trees eventually tower over the aspen stands, shading them from sunlight.

The U.S. Forest Service and Fish and Game have launched programs to inventory, restore, and conserve aspen plant communities. Aspen conservation efforts involve prescribed fire, removal of encroaching conifers, and restoration of meadow and riparian wet conditions.

A continuum of fire regimes has evolved in the various forest types. For example, historically, ponderosa pine-dominated mixed conifer forests of the Sierra had a fire regime of frequent, low- to moderate-intensity fires. Before fire suppression, such a fire regime along with other conditions maintained a plant community of large, well-spaced trees. At higher elevations, lodgepole pine communities evolved with less-frequent but more-severe fires (McKelvey et al. 1996). Wildfire is such an influential ecological element that the regeneration of some plant communities and the survival of many plant species require fire (Kilgore 1973). Coupled with selective harvest of large trees, road building, and intensive grazing, suppression of fire over the last 100 years has affected fire frequency and intensity and thus dramatically reshaped forest structure and altered ecosystems throughout the region.

In the early 1900s, the nature and role of wildfire was not understood and was generally viewed as damaging to forests. As a result, state and national policy for the last century has been to aggressively suppress forest fires and to put them out quickly, minimizing fire on the landscape of the West (van Wagtendonk 1995). The Forest Service's "Smokey Bear" campaign was highly successful, training generations of Americans that wildfire was synonymous with waste and destruction and that it was everyone's duty to prevent forest fires (Dombeck et al. 2004, Kaufman 2004).

To restore native plant communities, forest ecologists generally agree that fire needs to be returned to forests at intervals consistent with historical fire regimes. But a century of fire suppression has created an enormous backlog of forest acreage with dense tree stands and high fuel loads (Husari and McKelvey 1996). The 1964 federal Wilderness Act recognized the ecological role of fire and established a policy allowing natural fires to burn in national parks. The National Park Service has implemented prescribed fires for many years. However, most of the forests needing fire are lower in elevation than most of the wilderness areas. In 1971, Forest Service policy was amended to allow prescribed fires on national forest lands, as well (Caprio and Swetnam 1993, Chang 1996, Kilgore 1973, Skinner and Chang 1996). The results of prescribed fires in the Sierra have shown excellent ecological benefits (Keifer et al. 2000). Yet, while prescribed fire is considered a necessary tool to restore ecosystems and reduce the risk of catastrophic wildfire, and its use is increasing, it is currently applied to very few forested acres of the Sierra.

Returning fire to the forests presents great challenges. The fire threat to people and expanding communities in the forests, excessive fuel loads created by fire suppression and past forest management practices, effects on air quality and conflicts with clean-air laws, and liability all impose difficult constraints on the increased use of prescribed fire and allowing natural fires to burn. Even with the best efforts to reduce fire conflicts and risks, in many areas, reintroducing fire will not be practical or politically possible, at least as a first treatment. Certainly in some locations, selective timber harvest may have to serve as the surrogate for natural fire to begin the process of restoring ecological diversity to forests. Mechanical thinning, however, will not provide all of fire's ecological benefits.

Excessive Livestock Grazing

The effects of grazing on wildlife vary from beneficial to detrimental, depending upon how grazing is managed, including the seasonality and duration of grazing and the type and number of livestock. These effects also depend on the relative sensitivities of individual wildlife species, since not all species respond the same way to grazing. Well-managed livestock grazing can benefit sensitive plant and animal species, particularly by controlling annual grasses and invasive plants where these have become established. These working lands are an essential part of the solution to conserving the state's wildlife.

While recognizing the values of appropriate grazing practices, this plan is required to focus on stressors affecting wildlife species at risk. Thus, the following discussion describes those situations where excessive grazing practices stress those species. Excessive grazing, as used here, refers to livestock grazing at a frequency or intensity that causes degradation of native plant communities, reduces habitat values for native wildlife species, degrades aquatic or other ecosystems, or impairs ecosystem functions. (The term "overgrazing" has a different meaning; it is usually used in referring to the productivity of the forage crop and range condition).

Over the past 150 years, grazing on forests, shrublands, and grasslands of the Sierra Nevada, the southern Cascades, and Modoc Plateau has been characterized as excessive and unsustainable, destroying native vegetation and degrading meadows and streams (Menke et al. 1996). At one time, millions of sheep and cattle grazed throughout the Sierra, Cascades, and Modoc forests, on private and public lands of oak woodlands of the western foothills to high mountain meadows and the east-side high-desert slopes. Sheep and cattle grazing were unregulated on public lands until after the establishment of the Forest Service in 1905, and livestock numbers continued to exceed sustainable levels and reduce forage quality as late as the 1960s. On the western foothills and on higher forest lands, shrubs were often cleared with fire or herbicides to expand rangelands or to respond to brush encroachment on overgrazed lands (Burcham 1982, Menke et al. 1996).

Today, livestock numbers have been lowered to levels that are more sustainable for forage for livestock production (Kondolf et al. 1996, Menke et al. 1996). However, grazing continues to have negative consequences for forage, cover, and nest sites for dozens of wildlife species throughout much of the Sierra and Cascades Region. Plant communities and ecosystems that are particularly important for sustaining wildlife diversity, including riparian, aspen, meadow, aquatic, and oak woodland habitats, continue to be subject to livestock grazing.

The 1996 Sierra Nevada Ecosystem Project (SNEP) found that "over-grazing in mountain meadows is a threat to many rare species that are restricted to these habitats." Sierra and Cascades high mountain meadows and plant communities evolved without the kind of grazing pressure caused by livestock. Yet, as described by the Forest Service, "the riparian and meadow systems are the key livestock forage areas within allotments above 4,000-foot elevations. Studies have shown that 50 percent to 80 percent of the herbage used comes from these meadow systems, which constitute a small percentage (generally less than 5 percent) of the allotment area. In the Sierra Nevada forests, the meadow systems cover an estimated 2 percent of the allotment areas" (USFS 2001b).

The SNEP and the SNFPA also found that aquatic and riparian habitats are particularly affected by livestock grazing. Cattle are attracted to the lush forage, water, and shade of riparian habitat. In late summer and fall, especially when upland habitats have dried out, cattle can decimate riparian plant communities, grazing and trampling meadows, converting meandering meadow streams into eroded channels, and stripping forage and cover needed by wildlife. The erosion increases sediment runoff, degrading aquatic ecosystems.

Livestock grazing is affecting the composition of plant communities important for wildlife diversity. Where livestock grazing is excessive, forage often becomes scarce, and both livestock and deer consume young aspen shoots, hindering the regeneration of aspen stands. Excessive grazing is a factor in reducing the regeneration of blue oak and many other plant species throughout the predominantly privately owned foothill region (McCreary 2001, Mitchell 2005 pers. comm.). Livestock compact soils and remove leaf litter, making conditions less than optimal for germination of acorns and new growth. Livestock also consume acorns and young oak saplings.

Several aquatic, riparian, and meadow-dependent species are at risk in the Sierra region (USFS 2001b). Half of the occupied willow flycatcher nest sites in meadow and riparian areas in the Sierra Nevada continue to be grazed by cattle or sheep. Wet meadow and stream areas for the Yosemite toad, a species of special concern, are also grazed (USFS 2004b). The SNEP project concluded that "livestock grazing has been implicated in plant compositional and structural changes in foothill community types, meadows, and riparian systems, and grazing is the primary negative factor affecting the viability of native Sierran land bird populations" (SNEP 1996).

Livestock grazing also negatively affects native species by transmitting diseases to wild animals. *Pastuerella*, a bacteria transmitted from domestic sheep, has had a devastating effect on bighorn sheep in the Sierra, Cascades, and Modoc regions. Efforts to reintroduce bighorn sheep to the Lava Beds National Monument and the Warner Mountains have failed as a result of disease transmission (Bleich et al. 1996, NCBSIAG 1991).

For the last decade, a major multiagency effort has implemented a recovery program for the Sierra Nevada bighorn sheep. Currently, there are 300–350 bighorn sheep in seven herds along the steep terrain of the eastern Sierra. The greatest threat to the survival of these endangered bighorn sheep is domestic sheep grazing nearby on public and private lands. (See Fig. 13.2, showing proximity of bighorn sheep to domestic sheep.) The domestic sheep are still permitted to graze on allotments within the range of the wild bighorn sheep. If the California bighorn are exposed to these domestic sheep, pastuerellosis could wipe out the contacted wild sheep population within a few weeks (Boyce 2005 pers. comm.).

Invasive Plants

Invasive plants have transformed plant communities and contributed to the decline of native species in ecosystems of the Sierra and Cascades. Foothill oak woodlands and riparian plant communities, so important for maintaining wildlife diversity, have been particularly affected by invasions of exotic grasses and shrubs. High desert shrublands on the Sierra and Cascades' east side have also been altered by invasive grasses. Sub-alpine and alpine plant communities, however, are relatively intact, with few invasive plants (Schwartz et al. 1996).

The understory of foothill woodlands of blue oak, interior live oak, valley oak, and gray pine are now dominated by wild oats, fescue, cheatgrass, and other invasive non-native grasses. Scotch broom and yellow starthistle have also degraded the Sierra Nevada and Cascades foothills (Bossard et al. 2000, DiTomaso and Gerlach 2000). Both weed species displace native species and are toxic to grazing wildlife. Saltcedar, Russian olive, giant reed, eucalyptus, and English ivy are among the invasive plants that have intruded into low- and mid-elevation riparian habitats. On the east side of the Sierra and Cascades, the combined effects of invasive cheatgrass, which outcompetes native perennial and annual grasses, and livestock grazing have contributed to changes in fire regimes and transformed desert scrub and grassland communities.

Generally, invasive plants that replace native plants degrade habitat quality for native species. Some wildlife species are dependent on specific native plants. Other animal species become stressed when the invasive plants offer inferior nutrition or nesting or prey habitat.

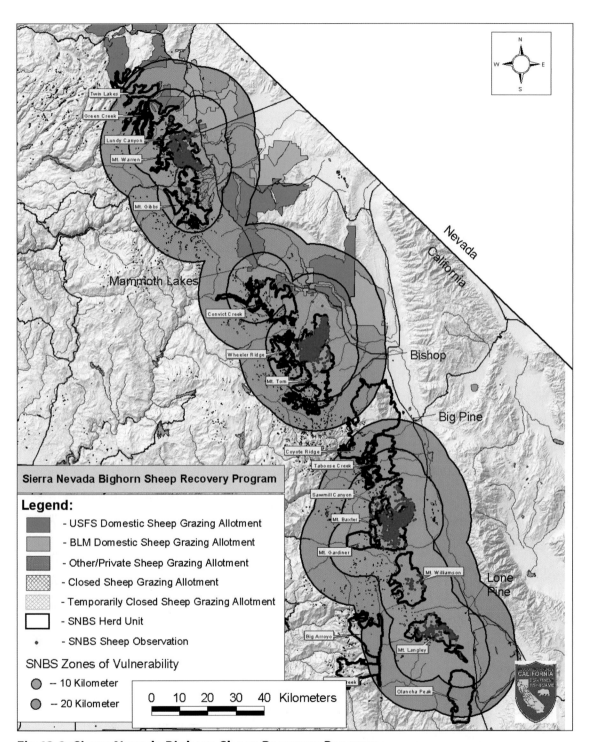

Fig 13.2: Sierra Nevada Bighorn Sheep Recovery Program
Sheep grazing allotments overlap the ranges of endangered Sierra Nevada bighorn sheep, potentially exposing the bighorn sheep to a deadly disease that is transmitted from domestic sheep.
(Locations as of May 2005.)

In some areas, invasive annual grasses make for greater fuel loads compared to native vegetation, which increases the intensity of fires and causes further ecological changes.

Recreational Pressures

The mountains and wildlands of the Sierra and Cascades are very popular recreation destinations. National parks, wilderness areas, and wildlife areas provide recreational opportunities while also providing greater protection for wildlife. The public develops a better understanding and appreciation for wildlife by visiting these natural areas.

Recreational activities are diverse, from traditional ones like fishing, hiking, and backpacking to those requiring more infrastructure and visitor services, such as fixed camps, ski resorts, golf courses, and off-road vehicle areas. Some types of recreation have grown significantly in the last few decades, such as mountain biking and off-road vehicle use; the numbers of off-road vehicle users have risen several-fold over the past 30 years.

Accordingly, the effects of recreation on wildlife and ecosystems are diverse and are increasing in many areas. Ski-resort runs and infrastructure crisscross steep mountains, and golf courses have replaced some mountain meadows. Vegetation is removed and soils are eroded along creeks in popular camping areas, and more land is cleared for recreation infrastructure. Recreation technologies, such as all-terrain vehicles, snowmobiles, and lighter, warmer, and waterproof camping gear and clothing, have allowed people to drive, mountain bike, ski, camp, and hunt in wild areas that years ago were natural refuges, too remote to be affected by recreation activities.

Recreation has consequences for soils, vegetation, wildlife, and aquatic resources. Soils become compacted or eroded, and habitat is cleared in areas that are heavily used by motorized vehicles, packhorses, and campers. A number of recreation activities inadvertently cause nest- or den abandonment, displace wildlife from important foraging or watering sites, and interfere with migratory corridors (Leung and Marion 2000).

Providing more recreational opportunities while protecting wildlife habitats and aquatic ecosystems requires that sufficient resources be devoted to planning, management, and enforcement. Federal and state land agencies construct parking lots and restrooms, establish information kiosks, build and sign roads and trails, and manage garbage and sewage to accommodate recreational visitors. And there is an increased need for wildlife agencies to provide wildlife education to keep visitors safe and minimize their effects on species at risk.

Climate Change

While climate change will undoubtedly affect all regions of the state, the consequences for vegetation, wildlife, and water resources will likely be most dramatic in the Sierra Nevada. Depending on the model and assumptions, scientists project the average annual temperature in California to rise between 4 and 10.5 degrees F above the current average temperature by the end of the century (Hayhoe et al. 2004, Schneider and Kuntz-Duriseti 2002, Turman 2002). Within 50 years, average wintertime temperatures are expected to rise between 2 and 2.5 degrees. A rise in this range would substantially reduce annual snowpack and increase fire frequency and intensity. By mid-century, the Sierra snowpack could be reduced by 25 percent to 40 percent and by as much as 70 percent at the end of the century (duVair 2003). Snow season would be shortened, starting later and melting sooner, while fire season would be longer and hotter. The reduction of snowpack and more extreme fire conditions would have cascading effects on water resources, plant communities, and wildlife.

The average annual Sierra snowpack is roughly equal to half the storage capacity of the state's reservoirs, holding water until the melt in late spring and early summer. Rising temperature would reduce the total snowpack and melt it earlier in the year, further shifting stream- and river flow regimes throughout the Sierra (Stewart et al 2004, Vanrheenen et al. 2004). As the runoff comes earlier, spring and summer stream flow is projected to decline by 10 percent to 25 percent by 2050 and decline by potentially as much as 40 percent to 55 percent by the end of the century (duVair 2003). The changing flow regimes will alter riparian and aquatic ecosystems. Streams may be reshaped by different timing and intensity of flood conditions, while some perennial streams may dry up and transition to ephemeral streams no longer supportive of many aquatic species (Turman 2002). One strategy to alleviate these effects would rely on maintaining and restoring healthy mountain meadows, which act like sponges and would help to hold water later into the dry season.

Average annual temperature is a key element that determines plant communities found across the elevation gradient of the Sierra Nevada and Cascades. As temperature rises, alpine and sub-alpine plant communities will shrink as mixed conifer forest expands higher in the range. Alpine and sub-alpine plant communities may decline by 40 percent to 50 percent by mid-century. Oak woodlands may move higher, replacing pine and fir forest. At the lower elevations, the longer, warmer dry season could lead to increased fire frequency, likely converting some shrub communities to grasslands (du Vair 2003, Turman 2002). The expected changes in fire regimes will likely alter the abundance and distribution of plant communities, affecting habitats for wildlife (McKenzie et al. 2004, Miller and Urban 1999).

As climate change shifts annual average temperatures along the elevation gradient, as fire reshapes plant communities, and as stream flow regimes change, habitats and wildlife populations will be substantially affected. So far, very little research has evaluated the consequences of projected climate change on species at risk in the Sierra and Cascades.

Stressors Affecting Aquatic and Riparian Habitats

The Sierra Nevada Ecosystem Project and the Sierra Framework highlighted aquatic and riparian ecosystems as vital to the sustenance of wildlife diversity. Aquatic and riparian ecosystems provide diverse and rich habitats for wildlife in the Sierra and Cascades (Moyle 1996a). There are 67 aquatic habitat types in the region. Major riparian habitats include valley foothill riparian, montane riparian, wetland meadow, and aspen. Numerous invertebrate and vertebrate species are associated with these moist habitats. Other wildlife species, including some raptors and numerous songbirds, live in drier plant communities and rely on nearby aquatic and riparian habitats for hunting, foraging, cover, and resting.

SNEP concluded that aquatic and riparian systems are the most altered and impaired habitats of the Sierra. Of the 67 aquatic habitat types, nearly two-thirds are in decline. Ecosystem functions have been disrupted in thousands of riparian areas, particularly in mountain meadows (Kattelman and Embury 1996). Riparian corridors are fragmented, and more than 600 miles of river habitat have been submerged under reservoirs.

Deterioration of the aquatic and riparian habitats has contributed to the decline of native fish and amphibians. Wildlife species that depend on these habitats, including the Sierra willow flycatcher, foothill- and mountain yellow-legged frog, California red-legged frog, Cascade frog, Northern leopard frog, and Yosemite toad, are at risk of extinction (USFS 2001). In the Sierra, of the 83 terrestrial species dependent on riparian habitat, 24 percent are at risk (Graber 1996). Aquatic insects and other invertebrates, important prey for fish and amphibians, have also been affected by habitat changes. Six of the 40 native fish of the Sierra are listed as threatened or endangered. Only half of the 40 species have secure populations (Moyle et al. 1996). Among the fish species at risk in the region are several of California's native trout, including the Little Kern golden trout and Lahontan and Paiute cutthroat trout. Half of the 29 native amphibian populations of the region are at risk of extinction (Jennings 1996).

Multiple stressors have negatively affected rivers, streams, and wet meadows in the region. Dams and water diversions throughout the region have profoundly altered stream-flow patterns, increased water temperatures, and degraded aquatic ecosystems. Dams and reservoirs have also blocked animal migration routes. Livestock grazing, eroding forest roads, timber harvest activities, development, and recreational activities have also contributed to the fragmentation of riparian habitats, caused bank erosion, and increased sediment and nutrient runoff into aquatic ecosystems. (See Fig. 13.3).

Water Diversions and Dams

Among the 24 major river systems of the Sierra and Cascades, all but a few rivers have multiple dams or diversions. Flows are managed for hydropower generation, for water for irrigation and domestic uses, and for flood control (DWR 1998). A few small dams were developed and are still maintained for instream flow protection and management downstream, and/or for wet meadow habitat maintenance. Others were constructed by fisheries managers to provide barriers between sensitive native fish populations and introduced fishes with capability to interbreed or prey upon the native species. The unnatural managed flows disrupt and degrade aquatic and riparian ecosystems. Below dams, river flows are ramped up and down and water temperatures are changed, often creating lethal conditions for aquatic species. Dams and diversions of the rivers that flow into the Sacramento and San Joaquin drainages have been particularly detrimental to **anadromous** chinook salmon, steelhead trout, and Pacific lamprey. Each of these species historically spawned in Sierra mountain rivers and streams, their young swimming to the sea and returning a few years later as adult fish to spawn. The construction of dams and water diversions blocked fish passage, causing dramatic declines in salmon and steelhead populations of the Sacramento and San Joaquin drainages. Fewer anadromous fish also means fewer eggs, young fish, and fish carcasses that provide nutrients for numerous other aquatic species. Historically, 1 million to 3 million chinook salmon spawned each year in the western Sierra. Today, dams block salmon access to upstream spawning habitat in all but a few creeks. Late fall, winter, and spring runs of salmon have collapsed. Steelhead and the winter and spring runs of salmon are endangered, and the late fall run salmon are taxa of special concern. The hatchery-supported fall run of salmon ranges between 100,000 to 200,000 fish and continues to support a commercial and sport fishery. Many other aquatic species also are affected by the migration impediments imposed by dams and their associated reservoirs.

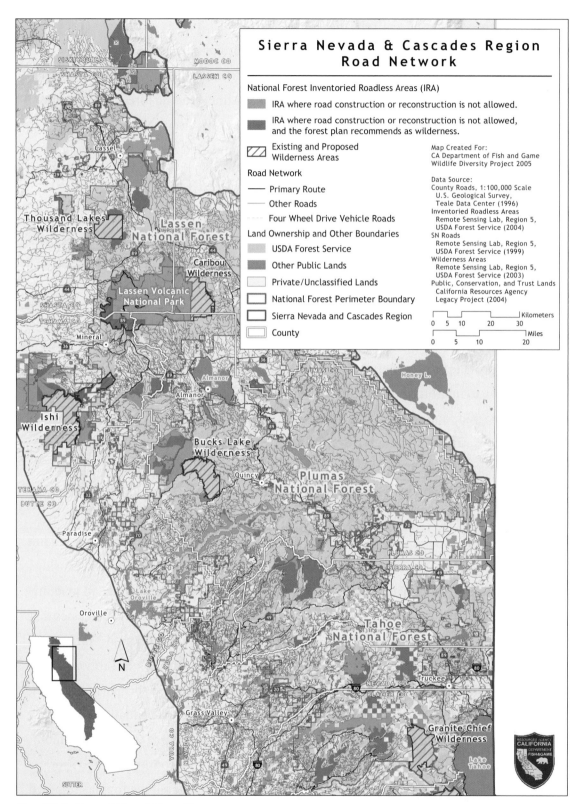

Fig. 13.3: Forest Road Density

One of the major effects of forest management practices on wildlands and aquatic ecosystems is the erosion and runoff associated with forest roads.

Native Fish of the Sierra Nevada and Cascades Region

The native fish of the region evolved in four hydrologically separated areas: the west side Sacramento–San Joaquin drainage; Lahontan drainage, consisting of the Susan, Truckee, Carson and Walker Rivers; Eagle Lake drainage; and the Owens drainage (Moyle et al. 1996). Diverse assemblages of native fish inhabited the rivers and creeks of the western slope of the Sierra and Cascades, which flowed into the Sacramento–San Joaquin system. These assemblages included 22 native taxa of fish, including abundant runs of Chinook salmon, steelhead, and Pacific lamprey. Ten native fish species were abundant in the low- to middle elevations in the Lahontan rivers and lakes. Lahontan cutthroat trout was so abundant that in the 1800s it had supported commercial fisheries in Lake Tahoe and Pyramid Lake, Nev. Five native fish resided in Eagle Lake, including the endemic Eagle Lake rainbow trout. Four unique fish species are found in the Owens Valley: the Owens pupfish, Owens tui chub, Owens sucker, and Owens speckled dace (Moyle 2002).

In the foothills, residential development continues to add "river wells" located directly on stream aquifers. Increased water drafting has turned some year-round streams into seasonal creeks and dried up other streams (Mitchell 2005 pers. comm.). Native fish (such as hitch and hardhead), amphibians, and native invertebrate populations are adversely affected where streams have receded. Similarly, the development of springs for domestic water supply on private and public lands has degraded riparian habitats for native amphibians and invertebrates.

Watershed Fragmentation and Fish Barriers

Aquatic species depend upon the ability to move within watersheds as a way to survive temperature changes and catastrophic events and to access different habitats at different stages in their lives. Upstream tributary habitats offer breeding and rearing grounds, and downstream habitats usually provide expanded nurseries with an abundance of nutrients. This annual mixing and migration allows recolonization of tributary or downstream habitats following catastrophic events such as floods or fires. Aquatic connectivity is an important part of overall watershed function, one that has been disrupted by many activities. Present populations of numerous fish species are confined below or above dams or separated by other fish barriers such as poorly designed culverts. These artificial barriers prevent genetic mixing between populations and block recolonization of areas within the watershed. Within the fragmented watersheds, native minnows and other fish and amphibian populations are listed either as threatened or endangered or as species of special concern.

Hydropower Project Operations

Dams and reservoir levels are operated to meet their primary purposes: generating hydropower, storing water for domestic or agricultural uses, and providing flood protection. California hydropower projects generate about 15 percent of the electricity used in the state, and they provide critical peaking capacity, giving the electrical system flexibility. However, hydropower project operations have major consequences for rivers and riverine ecosystems of the Sierra Nevada and Cascades, contributing to the decline of endangered salmon, steelhead, and other fish populations. Similar to the barriers mentioned above, hydropower operations affect water from rivers and streams, changing natural flow regimes of rivers, altering water temperature, and blocking fish passage and migration (McKinney 2003).

The daily fluctuation in river water levels caused by hydropower operations affects fish, reptiles, amphibians, invertebrates, and plants. Rapid changes in water flows strand spawning salmon and trap young salmon in pools on their journey to the sea. Thousands of miles of rivers and streams no longer support salmon and steelhead because migration is blocked by hydropower dams. Radical stream flow fluctuations and higher-than-normal flows from peaking hydropower projects can drown deer and other animals if high-flow releases are improperly timed with migratory or reproductive seasons.

The Federal Energy Regulatory Commission (FERC) licenses 119 of California's hydropower projects, accounting for 85 percent of the state's hydroelectric capacity. FERC licenses generally have terms from 30 to 50 years. Thirty-seven percent of the state's hydropower system is up for relicensing by 2015. (See Fig. 13.4.) Most of these projects were first licensed before 1970 and typically do not reflect today's generally accepted environmental considerations and standards. FERC relicensing of so many of California's hydropower projects presents a prime opportunity to reduce the consequences of hydropower operations on fish and wildlife. The full engagement of state biologists and enforcement officials in the FERC relicensing processes over the next decade would likely yield major benefits for river and stream ecosystems of the Sierra Nevada and Cascades.

The consideration of improvements for flow regimes and aquatic connectivity through the FERC relicensing process has had a project-by-project approach. Consideration of aquatic systems conservation across watersheds may yield greater restoration benefits for ecosystems

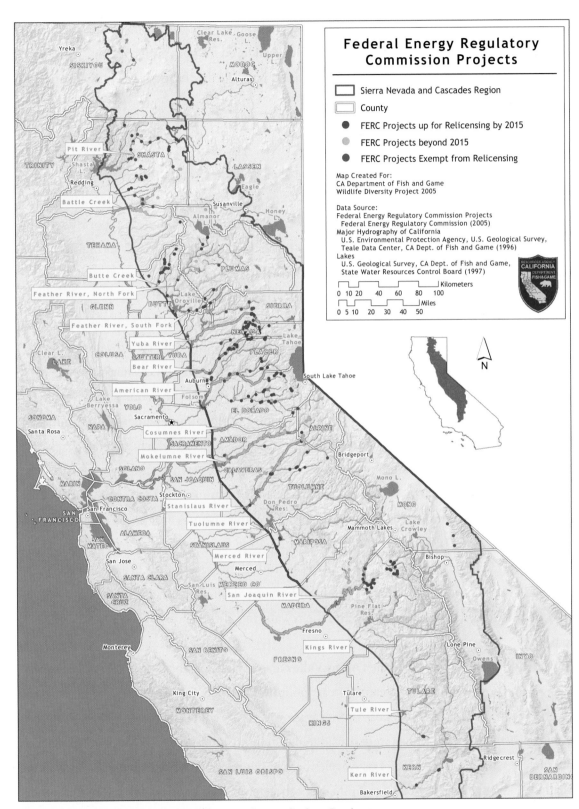

Fig. 13.4 Federal Energy Regulatory Commission Projects
Dozens of hydropower projects affect rivers and aquatic ecosystems throughout the Sierra Nevada and Cascades. The relicensing of these projects is an opportunity to make hydropower-project operational changes that benefit wildlife resources.

and wildlife. For example, projects that generate little power but greatly affect salmon and steelhead and other aquatic resources should be considered for decommissioning. The decommissioning could be negotiated as a mitigation trade for hydropower operation impacts in adjacent watersheds.

Water Diversion from the Owens Valley

The Owens Valley is the ecological beneficiary of the cold mountain creeks draining watersheds east of the Sierra crest and of the dozens of artesian springs that bubble up in the valley. These waters commingled in the Owens Basin and as wetlands and pools and the Owens River flowing south to Owens Lake. Historically, these wetlands and springs, the miles of lush riparian habitat, and the alkaline, shallow lake and mud flats supported tens of thousands of shorebirds, waterfowl, and neotropical migratory birds.

The city of Los Angeles diverts creek water that flows to Owens Valley into two aqueducts. Along with diverting creek flows, Los Angeles has relied on pumping groundwater in the Owens Valley. The environmental consequences of the increased groundwater pumping led Inyo County to file suit against the city of Los Angeles in 1972. The county and the city contended in the courts for a dozen years before jointly conducting research on groundwater, soils, and the effects of groundwater pumping on native vegetation, which served as background for the Environmental Impact Report completed in 1991. Inyo County, the city of Los Angeles, Fish and Game, the California State Lands Commission, the Sierra Club, and the Owens Valley Committee executed an MOU resolving disputes and proposing the Lower Owens River Project (LORP) as compensatory mitigation for the effects of groundwater pumping. The LORP would return water flows to and restore riverine and riparian habitat along 62 miles of river and restore wetlands and other wildlife habitats. Implementation of the LORP has been delayed, however, and the rewatering of the lower Owens River has yet to occur.

The diversion of water from the Owens Valley also turned Owens Lake into a dry lakebed, with a salty, powdery surface, creating an air pollution problem for the valley. Pursuant to the federal Clean Air Act, in 2000, Los Angeles was ordered to reduce the blowing dust from the dry lake surface. Three options were considered—shallow flooding, revegetation, or covering the surface with gravel. To date, Los Angeles has shallow-flooded the lake bed to control dust. Shallow flooding has restored some of the wet ecosystems, providing brine shrimp and other invertebrates for feeding shorebirds and other species, and bird numbers in the valley have increased. These ecological improvements are contingent upon continuing to shallow-flood Owens Lake lakebed year after year.

Introduced Non-Native Fish

The introduction of non-native fish to lakes and streams has significantly affected the aquatic life of the region, particularly in the sub-alpine and alpine ecosystems and in the Owens Valley. Decades of stocking fish for recreational fishing have contributed to the decline of native fish and frog species in the region. Stocking of trout into historically fishless high mountain lakes has contributed to the extirpation of native amphibians in some basins, with particularly severe consequences for the once-common mountain yellow-legged frog (Knapp 1996, Milliron 1999, Milliron et al. 2004, Vredenburg 2004). By consuming the native amphibians and aquatic insects, the predatory trout also are negatively affecting the western terrestrial garter snake and some birds and bats that depend on these prey species (Knapp 2005 pers. comm., Mathews et al. 2001, Milliron 2005 pers. comm.).

Stocking non-native rainbow trout (hatchery-raised or not native to a particular watershed), brook trout, and brown trout into native trout waters has degraded native trout populations through predation and interbreeding. The introduced eastern brook trout outcompetes the native Lahontan cutthroat trout. Introduced rainbow trout have interbred with and altered the genetics of golden trout and Little Kern golden trout in portions of their historical ranges. Along the eastern Sierra in the Owens Valley, the endangered Owens pupfish and Owens tui chub have been extirpated from the river, creeks, and pools where non-native largemouth bass are present (USFWS 1998b). In western foothill streams, introductions of non-native sunfishes and other exotic species have seriously threatened the continued existence of native minnow and amphibian populations. Many of these are now either listed as threatened or as species of special concern (Mitchell 2005 pers. comm.)

Fish and Game recently conducted a Sierra-wide field study of amphibians, trout, and other fauna in the high mountain lakes. The multiyear project, begun in 1998, has collected data on three-quarters of the Sierra's 10,000 high-mountain lakes. The results of the study are serving to inform Aquatic Biodiversity Management Plans that are being prepared for the high mountain watersheds of the Sierra. The goal of these plans is to protect and restore native amphibians and other fauna while maintaining thriving recreational fisheries. The results of the field studies have yielded information needed to design management plans that will achieve both of these goals. Lakes isolated by fish barriers and where exotic trout reproduction is absent have been identified for restoring native fauna. Lakes identified as popular with anglers or where reproduction of exotic trout is uncontrollable will be managed to improve their fisheries. Implementation of the completed aquatic biodiversity management plans and the completion of additional plans are contingent upon future funding and staffing.

In the Owens Valley, Fish and Game has conducted numerous projects over the last two decades to restore populations of pupfish and tui chub. Eliminating non-native predatory fish from the river and streams and pools of the Owens Valley is unlikely. Thus, the best strategy for the long-term conservation and restoration of Owens pupfish and tui chub is to introduce them to numerous small springs and creeks of the valley that do not have largemouth bass and other predators (Parmenter 2005 pers. comm.). However, introducing endangered fish to springs and waters that currently have none creates land management challenges for the landowners, in this case the Los Angeles Department of Water and Power. The long-term survival of these two Owens Valley native fish may well depend on a special agreement that permits LADWP to continue normal canal clearing and maintenance, even if such activities kill some fish. In exchange, the endangered fish would be introduced to numerous isolated waters, where it is expected they will flourish, free of predatory non-native species.

Conservation Actions to Restore and Conserve Wildlife

In addition to the recommended regional actions described below, see the recommended statewide conservation actions as given in Chapter 4.

a. **The state should provide scientific and planning assistance and financial incentives to local governments to develop and implement regional multispecies conservation plans for all of the rapidly developing areas of the Sierra Nevada and Cascades.**

The western foothills, the Lake Tahoe Basin, and the highway corridors of the Sierra Nevada are experiencing rapid development without the conservation planning necessary to minimize its negative consequences for wildlife and plant communities. Key wildlife habitats will be unnecessarily destroyed, degraded, and fragmented unless conservation planning is supported by the state and fully embraced by cities and counties.

The state should increase conservation science and planning assistance and economic incentives to counties to develop regional multispecies conservation plans and to incorporate conservation plans into county and city General Plans.

b. **The Sierra Nevada Conservancy should develop a program, closely coordinated with federal, state, and local wildlife conservation planning efforts, that prioritizes areas for acquisition and easements based on the needs of wildlife.**

- The Sierra Nevada Conservancy should consult with state and federal wildlife experts and wildlife conservation nongovernmental organizations to identify priority areas for acquisition and easements.

- The Sierra Nevada Conservancy should be a key funder for the implementation of conservation plans. Developing Natural Community Conservation Plans for the Sierra will depend on capital funding from, among other sources, the Sierra Nevada Conservancy, to be used for conservation easements and acquisitions of habitat reserves.

c. **In areas where substantial development is projected, the state and federal land management and wildlife agencies should identify and protect from development those critical wildlife migration or dispersal corridors that cross ownership boundaries and county jurisdictions.**

See Statewide Action d, Chapter 4.

Knowledge of important wildlife migration or dispersal corridors will help conservation planners and local governments prevent fragmentation of wildlife habitat and avoid creating barriers to wildlife movements, thereby maintaining conditions for the long-term survival of some species.

d. **Public forest lands should be managed to maintain healthy ecosystems and wildlife diversity, including thinning to restore diverse habitats and reducing the risk of catastrophic wildfire. State and federal forest managers and wildlife agencies should work cooperatively to develop a vision for the future forest condition.**

Watersheds, or a group of adjacent watersheds, may be the appropriate organizing unit for collaborative forest management.

Management of national forests and other public forest lands should incorporate the following principles:

- Retention of the remaining old-growth and late-successional forest stands
- Restoration of vegetative communities historically present within forest landscapes
- Restoration and maintenance of connectivity in the forest landscape
- Restoration and maintenance of habitat diversity across the forest landscape
- Restoration and maintenance of structural complexity in forest stands, including dead trees, snags, and fallen logs
- Restoration and maintenance of the integrity of riparian and aquatic ecosystems

e. On public lands, post-fire and post-harvest treatments and forest management should be designed to achieve the principles listed in Action d, above.

For example, natural regeneration or tree-stocking following fires, timber harvest, and other forest disturbances should be determined based on what will contribute to achieving the principles in Action d.

f. State and federal forest managers and state and federal wildlife managers should cooperatively develop timber-harvest cumulative-impact standards for each watershed or group of adjacent watersheds of the Sierra, Cascades, and Modoc regions to protect aquatic ecosystems and conserve wildlife habitat.

Using the best-available science, forest and wildlife managers should determine the extent, pattern, and pace for timber-harvest in a forest watershed or cluster of watersheds. Ecologically based standards or limits should be set for timber-harvest. State and federal forest managers should coordinate to ensure that cumulative effects of timber-harvest plans for public and private lands meet the standards for each watershed.

Federal forest managers and state and federal wildlife biologists should also work cooperatively to design forest-thinning and prescribed-fire treatments.

g. The California Resources Agency should coordinate the development of a model ordinance and building codes for new or expanding communities in fire-adapted landscapes to make those communities more fire compatible and reduce the state's liability for fire suppression.

Counties need to consider adopting development restrictions requiring planning and accommodation for wildfire consistent with the local historical fire regime, and such measures should be incorporated into the public-safety elements of the county General Plans. In addition, specific ordinances should be adopted:

- The model ordinances should address the design of new development to ensure new communities are safer and compatible with natural forest fires.
- The model ordinances should address maintenance of existing residential and commercial areas to ensure firebreaks are maintained to improve compatibility with forest fires.
- Model building codes should specify that all new construction employ materials and design features to make them more fire resistant.
- The California Resources Agency should encourage adoption of the model fire ordinances and building codes by cities and counties in forested areas.

h. Federal, state, and local agencies and fire-safe councils should work cooperatively to expand the use of prescribed fire and natural-burn programs.

- Prescribed fire should be based on criteria for protecting watersheds, aquatic ecosystems, water quality, and achieving the principles in Action d.

- Limited resources available to implement prescribed fire dictate that, where feasible, programs should be designed to prioritize reintroduced fire according to areas of greatest ecological need.

- State and federal agencies should implement a coordinated campaign to educate the public about the ecological benefits of fire and to promote prescribed fire.

i. State and federal wildlife agencies and federal land managers should jointly develop and implement grazing strategies for the Sierra Nevada and Cascades Region to reduce or eliminate livestock grazing on sensitive habitats to restore the condition of meadow, riparian, aspen, and aquatic habitats.

Restoring and protecting meadow, riparian, aspen, and aquatic ecosystems habitats is essential to protect wildlife diversity.

In areas where livestock grazing is maintained, wildlife- and land-management agencies should encourage or require practices to reduce negative ecological consequences.

Actions to reduce or eliminate livestock grazing on important habitats for at-risk wildlife species should include strategies or programs to reduce the economic impact on grazing allotment permit-holders affected by new restrictions.

j. Federal, state, and local agencies should provide greater resources and coordinate efforts to eradicate or control existing occurrences of invasive species and to prevent new introductions.

See Statewide Action f, Chapter 4.

k. In their conservation planning and ecosystem restoration work, state and federal wildlife agencies and land managers should consider the most current projections of the effects of global warming.

Global warming is expected to have major consequences for the Sierra and Cascades' snowpack and aquatic ecosystems. Projected changes are important factors to consider when planning long-term conservation or restoration projects.

l. **Fish and Game should be allocated the resources to monitor and enforce the distribution of sensitive fish and other aquatic species populations and to engage effectively in water-rights decision processes, water diversion issues, land-management planning, and conservation planning actions to restore and enhance aquatic systems.**

m. **Through the FERC relicensing process, the state should pursue changes in operations of hydropower projects that will provide more water for wildlife, mandate that water flows be managed as close to natural flow regimes as possible, and ensure that the new license agreements provide the best possible conditions for ecosystems and wildlife.**

   • Over the next decade, Fish and Game should be staffed adequately to be a full partner in all FERC proceedings affecting river systems and aquatic species of the Sierra Nevada and Cascades.

   • Partnering with the State Water Resource Control Board, Fish and Game should seek provisions in the new license agreements that provide the best possible conditions for aquatic ecosystems and wildlife.

   • The state should consider an alternative hydropower-project relicensing strategy that trades mitigation credits across watersheds. Under this strategy, the state would identify those systems most important for hydropower and those systems most important for aquatic resources. Rather than making only marginal improvements to all major river systems, some systems would focus on hydropower generation, while diversions would be eliminated on other systems, making dramatic improvements for salmon, steelhead, and other aquatic resources.

   • All hydropower projects up for relicensing should be evaluated for the costs and benefits of decommissioning. The amount of energy generated versus environmental-impact costs and benefits should be thoroughly reviewed. Where appropriate, the state should seek decommissioning of hydropower projects.

n. **The state, Inyo County, and the city of Los Angeles should fully implement the Lower Owens River Project (LORP), restoring riparian and aquatic habitat along 62 miles of the lower Owens River.**

o. **The city of Los Angeles should reach long-term agreement with Inyo County and the state to use shallow flooding to control dust on the Owens Lake lakebed.**

In addition to controlling dust, the shallow flooding has restored aquatic and mudflat habitat on Owens Lake, benefiting tens of thousands of shorebirds and other species.

p. Fish and Game and the U.S. Fish and Wildlife Service should seek an agreement with the Los Angeles Department of Water and Power (LADWP) to establish Owens pupfish and Owens tui chub in springs and creeks of the Owens Valley on LADWP lands as part of a strategy to recover these two endangered fish and ensure their long-term survival.

An agreement to establish new populations of the two endangered fish on LADWP lands will require provisions that allow LADWP to continue its normal operations and maintenance of canals and ponds.

q. Fish and Game should establish trout-free sub-basins and lakes across the high Sierra and Cascades to restore amphibians and other native species while concurrently improving trout fisheries in other lakes.

Introduced non-native trout are a major stressor of aquatic ecosystems in high mountain lakes of the Sierra and Cascades, and some native amphibians have recovered where trout were removed. The six completed Aquatic Biodiversity Management Plans, prepared by Fish and Game, provide good guidance for where conditions for native species can be restored and where trout fisheries may be improved.

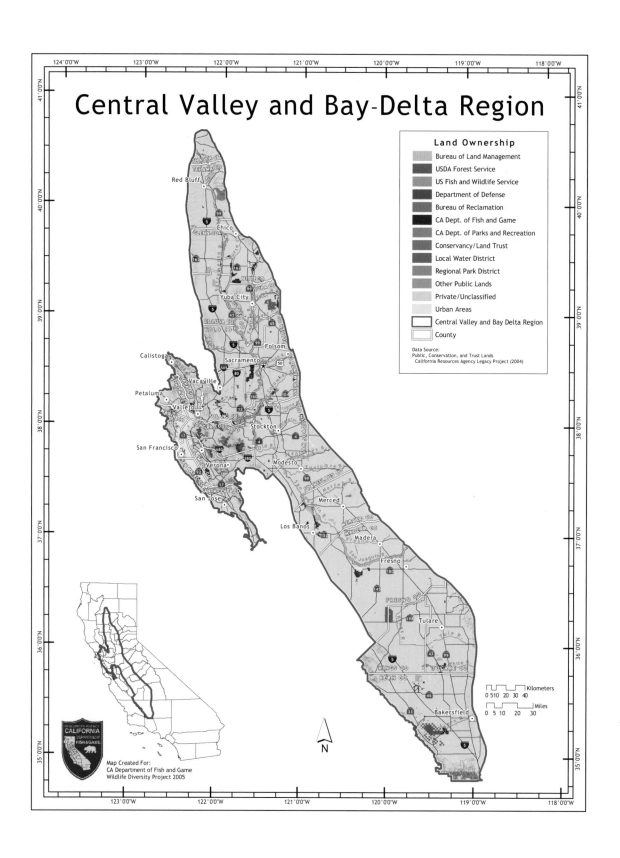

Central Valley and Bay-Delta Region

Land Ownership

- Bureau of Land Management
- USDA Forest Service
- US Fish and Wildlife Service
- Department of Defense
- Bureau of Reclamation
- CA Dept. of Fish and Game
- CA Dept. of Parks and Recreation
- Conservancy/Land Trust
- Local Water District
- Regional Park District
- Other Public Lands
- Private/Unclassified
- Urban Areas
- Central Valley and Bay Delta Region
- County

Data Source:
Public, Conservation, and Trust Lands
  California Resources Agency Legacy Project (2004)

Map Created For:
CA Department of Fish and Game
Wildlife Diversity Project 2005

Kilometers
0 5 10 20 30 40

Miles
0 5 10 20 30

N

14 *Central Valley and Bay-Delta Region*

The Central Valley and Bay-Delta Region comprises most of the low-lying lands of Central California. Much of the region is part of a vast hydrological system that drains 40 percent of the state's water. This water, falling as either rain or snow over much of the northern and central parts of the state, drains along the Sacramento and San Joaquin rivers into the

Delta. In the Delta, freshwater from these rivers mixes with saltwater from San Francisco Bay, creating a rich and diverse aquatic ecosystem. Encompassing 1,600 square miles of waterways, the San Francisco Bay and Delta together form the West Coast's largest estuary and the second-largest estuary in the nation.

The region has four distinct subregions: the San Francisco Bay Area, the Delta, the Sacramento Valley, and the San Joaquin Valley. Each has unique combinations of climate, topography, ecology, and land-use patterns.

The San Francisco Bay Area subregion, the most densely populated area of the state outside of the Southern California metropolitan region, consists of the low-lying baylands, aquatic environments, and watersheds that drain into San Francisco Bay. It is bounded on the east by the Delta subregion, on the north by the North Coast Region, on the south by the Central Coast Region, and on the west by the Pacific Ocean. Low coastal mountains

333

surround San Francisco Bay, with several peaks rising above 3,000 feet. The region receives 90 percent of its surface water from the major Central Valley rivers via the Delta. Other major rivers draining into the Bay include the Napa and Petaluma rivers and Sonoma, Petaluma, and Coyote creeks. The Bay Area has relatively cool, often foggy summers and cool winters, strongly influenced by marine air masses. Rain falls almost exclusively during the winter season (October to April) and averages 15–25 inches annually, with occasional snowfall at higher elevations. Rainwater runs off rapidly, and most of the smaller streams are dry by the end of the summer.

The topography allows for a variety of different habitats. The Bay itself has both deep and shallow estuarine (mixed freshwater and saltwater) environments. In addition to estuarine species, the Bay also supports many marine species, including invertebrates, sharks, and even, on occasion, whales. Along the shoreline are coastal salt marsh, coastal scrub, tidal mud-flats, and salt ponds. Freshwater creeks and marshes, especially those that still have patches of riparian vegetation, are home to aquatic invertebrates and freshwater fish. Upland areas support a mixture of grasslands, chamise chaparral, and live oak and blue oak woodlands. Small stands of redwood, Douglas fir, and tanoak grow in moister areas.

The Great Central Valley of California contains the other three subregions: the Sacramento Valley, the San Joaquin Valley, and the Sacramento–San Joaquin Delta. Together, they form a vast, flat valley, approximately 450 miles long and averaging 50 miles wide, with elevations almost entirely below 300 feet. The Sutter Buttes, a circular set of 2,000-foot-high hills that rises from the middle of the valley floor (promoted locally as the "Smallest Mountain Range in the World"), is the only topographic feature that exceeds that height. The Central Valley is surrounded by the Sierra Nevada on the east, the coastal ranges on the west, the Tehachapi Mountains on the south, and the Klamath and Cascade mountains on the north. Less influenced by marine air than San Francisco Bay, the valley's climate has hot, dry summers and foggy, rainy winters. Annual rainfall averages from 5 inches to 25 inches, with the least rainfall occurring in the southern portions and along the west side (in the rainshadow of the coastal mountains).

Agriculture dominates land uses in the Central Valley, with very few remnants of natural land remaining. The major natural upland habitats are annual grassland, valley oaks on floodplains, and vernal pools on raised terraces. The more arid lands of the southern San Joaquin Valley also contain alkali sink and saltbush shrublands. Slow-moving rivers along the valley floor provide habitat for fish and invertebrates and help maintain adjacent riparian, wetland, and floodplain habitats.

Hydrology is the main difference between the three Central Valley subregions. The Delta is a low-lying area that contains the tidally influenced portions of the Sacramento, San Joaquin, Mokelumne, and Cosumnes rivers. The Delta was once a huge marsh formed by the confluence of the Sacramento and San Joaquin rivers. Once described as a "terraqueous labyrinth of such intricacy that unskillful navigators have been lost for days in it" (Bryant 1848), it has been extensively drained and diked for flood protection and agriculture. Exposure of the rich, organic soils behind these levees has increased oxidation rates to such an extent that the land is breaking down and much of the surface has now subsided below sea level. Due to its natural patterns of flooding, the Delta is relatively less populated than the other subregions.

The second subregion, the Sacramento Valley, contains the Sacramento River, the largest river in the state. This river historically overflowed into several low-lying areas, particularly in its lower reaches. The lower 180 miles of the river, below Chico Landing, are now constrained by levees, and excess floodwaters are diverted into large bypasses to reduce risks to human populations.

The third subregion of the Central Valley, the San Joaquin Valley, has two distinct, or separate, drainages. In the northern portion, the San Joaquin River flows north toward the Delta. It captures water via several major rivers that drain the central Sierra Nevada. The southern portion of the valley is isolated from the ocean and drains into the closed Tulare Basin, which includes the beds of the former Tulare, Buena Vista, and Kern lakes. These lakes and vast wetlands historically were fed by the rivers that drain the southern Sierra Nevada (the Kings, Kaweah, Tule, and Kern). These lakes are now dry most of the time because water has been diverted to upland agriculture. Runoff during the wettest years will occasionally flood out of river channels and temporarily refill some of these lakebeds. The California Aqueduct extends along the entire western edge of the valley, delivering water from the Delta to farmers in the Tulare basin and over the Tehachapi Mountains to Southern California.

The wildlife of this region is beset by a wide variety of stressors, described below. The major problem has been the loss, degradation, and fragmentation of habitats, both terrestrial and aquatic, due to the development of agriculture and urban areas. Many of the streams have been dammed, blocking fish migration, or have been so severely degraded that they are no longer usable by salmon. Flood control structures, such as dikes, levees, and hardened embankments (**riprap**), have altered floodplain habitats like riparian forests and wetlands throughout the region. This loss of habitat has led to the extirpation of several species, including elk and pronghorn from the Central Valley and yellow rail and grizzly bear from

California (TNC 1987). Many other species that persist on the remaining habitat fragments are at risk of local or rangewide extinction. Ninety-five percent of the historic Central Valley salmon habitat has been lost (CDFG 1993).

This region is primarily in private ownership, and the role of private landowners is very important for conservation. More than 75 percent of the known California locations of 32 animal species of concern occur predominately on private lands. Examples of these species include Swainson's hawk, burrowing owl, San Pablo vole, and Buena Vista Lake shrew.

Species at Risk

The Plan development team updated vertebrate and invertebrate species information in the California Natural Diversity Database (CNDDB) during 2004–2005. The following regional summary of numbers of wildlife species, **endemic** species, and **species at risk** is derived from the updated CNDDB.

There are 490 vertebrate species that inhabit the Central Valley and Bay-Delta Region at some point in their life cycle, including 279 birds, 88 mammals, 40 reptiles, 18 amphibians, and 65 fish. Of the total vertebrate species that inhabit this region, 80 bird **taxa**, 38 mammalian taxa, 11 reptilian taxa, six amphibian taxa, and 25 fish taxa are included on the California Department of Fish and Game's **Special Animals List**. Of these, 20 are endemic to the Central Valley and Bay-Delta Region, and 28 other species found here are endemic to California but not restricted to this region (Table 14.1).

Table 14.1: State-Endemic Special Status Vertebrates of the Central Valley and Bay-Delta Region

	Ambystoma californiense	California tiger salamander
	Ammospermophilus nelsoni	Nelson's antelope squirrel
	Anniella pulchra pulchra	Silvery legless lizard
	Archoplites interruptus	Sacramento perch
	Charina umbratica	Southern rubber boa
*	*Dipodomys californicus eximius*	Marysville California kangaroo rat
	Dipodomys heermanni berkeleyensis	Berkeley kangaroo rat
	Dipodomys heermanni dixoni	Merced kangaroo rat
	Dipodomys ingens	Giant kangaroo rat
	Dipodomys nitratoides brevinasus	Short-nosed kangaroo rat
*	*Dipodomys nitratoides exilis*	Fresno kangaroo rat
*	*Dipodomys nitratoides nitratoides*	Tipton kangaroo rat
	Dipodomys venustus venustus	Santa Cruz kangaroo rat

	Ensatina eschscholtzii croceator	Yellow-blotched salamander
	Eucyclogobius newberryi	Tidewater goby
	Gambelia sila	Blunt-nosed leopard lizard
	Geothlypis trichas sinuosa	Saltmarsh common yellowthroat
*	*Hypomesus transpacificus*	Delta smelt
	Hysterocarpus traski traski	Sacramento-San Joaquin tule perch
*	*Lampetra hubbsi*	Kern brook lamprey
*	*Lavinia exilicauda exilicauda*	Central Valley hitch
	Lavinia symmetricus ssp. 1	San Joaquin roach
	Masticophis flagellum ruddocki	San Joaquin whipsnake
	Masticophis lateralis euryxanthus	Alameda whipsnake
*	*Melospiza melodia maxillaris*	Suisun song sparrow
*	*Melospiza melodia pusillula*	Alameda song sparrow
*	*Melospiza melodia samuelis*	San Pablo song sparrow
*	*Microtus californicus sanpabloensis*	San Pablo vole
	Mylopharodon conocephalus	Hardhead
*	*Neotoma fuscipes riparia*	Riparian (=San Joaquin Valley) woodrat
	Onychomys torridus tularensis	Tulare grasshopper mouse
	Perognathus alticolus inexpectatus	Tehachapi pocket mouse
	Perognathus inornatus inornatus	San Joaquin pocket mouse
	Perognathus inornatus neglectus	McKittrick pocket mouse
*	*Pogonichthys macrolepidotus*	Sacramento splittail
	Rallus longirostris obsoletus	California clapper rail
	Reithrodontomys raviventris	Salt-marsh harvest mouse
*	*Scapanus latimanus insularis*	Angel Island mole
*	*Scapanus latimanus parvus*	Alameda Island mole
*	*Sorex ornatus relictus*	Buena Vista Lake shrew
*	*Sorex ornatus sinuosus*	Suisun shrew
*	*Sorex vagrans halicoetes*	Salt-marsh wandering shrew
*	*Sylvilagus bachmani riparius*	Riparian brush rabbit
	Tamias speciosus callipeplus	Mount Pinos chipmunk
*	*Thamnophis gigas*	Giant garter snake
	Thamnophis sirtalis tetrataenia	San Francisco garter snake
*	*Toxostoma lecontei macmillanorum*	San Joaquin Le Conte's thrasher
	Vulpes macrotis mutica	San Joaquin kit fox

* denotes taxon is endemic to region

The number of arthropod species is so great, and they are so poorly known taxonomically, that it is presently impossible to accurately estimate the total number of invertebrate species occurring in the state. In the Central Valley and Bay-Delta region, however, 63 invertebrate taxa are included on the Special Animals List, including 58 arthropod taxa and five mollusk taxa. Of these, 26 are endemic to the Central Valley and Bay-Delta Region, and 32 other taxa found here are endemic to California but not restricted to this Region (Table 14.2).

Table 14.2: State-Endemic Special Status Invertebrates of the Central Valley and Bay-Delta Region

	Adela oplerella	Opler's longhorn moth
	Aegialia concinna	Ciervo aegilian scarab beetle
	Andrena blennospermatis	Vernal pool andrenid bee
	Andrena macswaini	An andrenid bee
	Andrena subapasta	An andrenid bee
	Anthicus sacramento	Sacramento anthicid beetle
*	*Apodemia mormo langei*	Lange's metalmark butterfly
*	*Banksula incredula*	Incredible banksula harvestman
*	*Branchinecta conservatio*	Conservancy fairy shrimp
	Branchinecta longiantenna	Longhorn fairy shrimp
	Branchinecta mesovallensis	Midvalley fairy shrimp
	Caecidotea tomalensis	Tomales isopod
*	*Calicina breva*	A harvestman; no common name
*	*Calicina diminua*	A harvestman; no common name
	Chrysis tularensis	Tulare chrysidid wasp
*	*Cicindela hirticollis abrupta*	Sacramento Valley tiger beetle
*	*Cicindela tranquebarica n. ssp.*	San Joaquin tiger beetle
	Coelus gracilis	San Joaquin dune beetle
	Desmocerus californicus dimorphus	Valley elderberry longhorn beetle
*	*Dufourea stagei*	Stage's dufourea bee
*	*Efferia antiochi*	Antioch efferian robberfly
*	*Elaphrus viridis*	Delta green ground beetle
	Euphydryas editha bayensis	Bay checkerspot butterfly
*	*Helminthoglypta callistoderma*	Kern shoulderband snail
*	*Helminthoglypta nickliniana bridgesi*	Bridges' coast range shoulderband snail
	Hydrochara rickseckeri	Ricksecker's water scavenger beetle
	Hydroporus leechi	Leech's skyline diving beetle
*	*Hygrotus curvipes*	Curved-foot hygrotus diving beetle
	Icaricia icarioides missionensis	Mission blue butterfly
*	*Idiostatus middlekauffi*	Middlekauff's shieldback katydid
	Incisalia mossii bayensis	San Bruno elfin butterfly

*	*Ischnura gemina*	San Francisco forktail damselfly
	Lanx patelloides	Kneecap lanx
	Lepidurus packardi	Vernal pool tadpole shrimp
	Lichnanthe ursina	Bumblebee scarab beetle
	Linderiella occidentalis	California linderiella
	Lytta hoppingi	Hopping's blister beetle
	Lytta moesta	Moestan blister beetle
	Lytta molesta	Molestan blister beetle
	Lytta morrisoni	Morrison's blister beetle
*	*Metapogon hurdi*	Hurd's metapogon robberfly
	Microcina homi	Hom's micro-blind harvestman
*	*Microcina jungi*	Jung's micro-blind harvestman
*	*Microcina leei*	Lee's micro-blind harvestman
*	*Microcina lumi*	Lum's micro-blind harvestman
*	*Microcina tiburona*	Tiburon micro-blind harvestman
*	*Myrmosula pacifica*	Antioch multilid wasp
	Nothochrysa californica	San Francisco lacewing
*	*Perdita scituta antiochensis*	Antioch andrenid bee
*	*Saldula usingeri*	Wilbur Springs shorebug
*	*Speyeria callippe callippe*	Callippe silverspot butterfly
	Speyeria zerene myrtleae	Myrtle's silverspot
*	*Sphecodogastra antiochensis*	Antioch sphecodogastra bee
	Syncaris pacifica	California freshwater shrimp
	Talanites moodyae	Moody's gnaphosid spider
*	*Talanites ubicki*	Ubick's gnaphosid spider
	Trachusa gummifera	A megachilid bee; no common name
	Tryonia imitator	Mimic tryonia (=California brackishwater snail)

* denotes taxon is endemic to region

The Wildlife Species Matrix, including data on listing status, habitat association, and population trend for each vertebrate and invertebrate species included on the Special Animals List, is available on the Web at http://www.dfg.ca.gov/habitats/wdp/matrix_search.asp. For vertebrates, the matrix also includes links to species-level range maps. Additionally, a link to the California Department of Fish and Game's online Field Survey Form is available to assist in reporting positive sightings of species on the Special Animals List to the California Natural Diversity Database (CNDDB).

Three Species at Risk

Note: *The following discussion of three species at risk illustrates how stressors or threats affect species and highlights conservation challenges and opportunities. These species discussions are not intended to imply that conservation should have a single-species approach.*

Central Valley spring-run chinook salmon provides a good example of a species that faces many interacting stressors, that depends on a variety of complementary conservation approaches, and that represents the aquatic environment. Like the chinook, Swainson's hawk represents another wide-ranging, migratory species that can persist in a matrix of natural and agricultural lands. As a terrestrial species, the hawk faces a different set of stressors and helps highlight the loss of native grasslands and riparian habitats. Both species illustrate the important role of regional planning, private land conservation, and coordination among adjacent landowners. The third species, the Tulare grasshopper mouse, contrasts considerably with the previous two species in several ways and illustrates the variety of conservation situations in which at-risk species find themselves. This mouse requires native habitat exclusively and cannot live in disturbed lands. It is representative of a habitat that may lack the public appeal of riparian and other habitats but one that is nonetheless host to many at-risk species. Moreover, it also illustrates the lack of available knowledge about a given species, knowledge that is essential for making wise conservation decisions.

Spring-run Chinook

Peter Moyle

Central Valley spring-run chinook salmon is one of five distinctive "runs" or "stocks" of chinook in California, each recognized by differences in genetics and life history characteristics. Although four chinook runs use the Central Valley river system, they do so at distinctly different times of the year (fall run, late-fall run, winter run, and spring run), which prevents them from interbreeding (CALFED 2000, CDFG 1998c, 2004h, Moyle 2002).

Spring-run chinook migrate between freshwater streams of the Central Valley and the ocean, entering the rivers in the spring or early summer. They historically occupied approximately 2,000 miles of river habitat in headwaters of all major river systems in the Central Valley, and fish were able to ascend the Sacramento River as far as Mt. Shasta City and Fall River, north of Mt. Lassen. Until 1940, the Central Valley run was as large as 600,000 fish, and the San Joaquin River once supported a population of 50,000 fish, which at times may have exceeded 200,000 fish.

Spring-run chinook need deep, cold pools in headwater streams to wait in until they spawn in the early fall. Successful spawning depends on gravelly river bottoms for water circulation around eggs. Juvenile survival depends on cool water temperature and adequate dissolved oxygen in the water. As river flows increase during the winter and spring, turbidity increases, water temperatures drop, and juveniles move downstream. Once on the valley floor, fish historically moved into floodplains during high water, where they found warmer temperatures, greater food for rapid growth, and protective cover from predators. Most of the juveniles migrate to the ocean in spring, where they stay from one to five years. Their complicated life history makes it challenging to detect the success of conservation actions over shorter periods.

The single biggest cause for the decline of this fish has been the construction of dams and diversions. By the 1940s, completion of Shasta and Friant dams had blocked access to many upper headwater spawning areas. Water diversion in the San Joaquin River eliminated the run of spring-run chinook in that river. By 1997, spring-run chinook populations had declined to fewer than 1 percent of their historic population levels. Approximately 80 percent of historical spring-run habitat is now no longer accessible, and the fish's current distribution is the Feather River below Oroville Dam, the Yuba River, and Clear, Mill, Deer, and Butte creeks.

In addition to blocking access to upstream habitats, dams and diversions alter river flows, increase water temperatures, trap and kill fish (entrainment), and change the hydrological dynamics needed to maintain gravel beds and channel configurations. In the south Delta, juvenile fish are also exposed to altered river flows and salinity gradients resulting from strong pumping action in the southern Delta for large water exports to Southern California. This reverse flow confuses fish attempting to reach the ocean or natal streams and diverts them toward the major pumps.

Other factors that have contributed to the decline include loss of floodplain, riparian, and estuarine habitat due to diking, draining, and flood-control actions, increased predation on juveniles (particularly by introduced predatory fish), and regional climatic fluctuations in the Pacific Ocean.

Many actions are under way to improve conditions for spring-run chinook and for the river systems overall. The California Bay-Delta Authority has a lead role in coordinating many agencies to modify the operations of Delta pumps and major dams to improve conditions and habitat for chinook and other aquatic species. This Authority, based out of the California Resources Agency, oversees a broad, interagency effort to address water-related issues called the CALFED Bay-Delta Program. The California Department of Fish and Game is the lead agency for implementing this program's Ecosystem Restoration Plan.

Recovery actions, including habitat restoration and screening of diversion pumps, are also under way by the Central Valley Project Improvement Act Program (CVPIA—Anadromous Fish Restoration Program) and National Oceanic and Atmospheric Administration's (NOAA) Fisheries Service (previously the National Marine Fisheries Service). Restoration activities address stream flows, water temperatures, gravel supply, floodplains, meander zones, riparian habitat, wetlands, and the direction and velocity of flows in the Delta.

Ecological research on the Bay-Delta ecosystem is being carried out by many agencies. One key program is the Interagency Ecological Program, which has been conducting such research in the Delta for several decades.

Other types of conservation actions are benefiting spring-run chinook, which was state listed as a threatened species in 1998 and federally listed in 1999. Improved regulations on ocean harvest and inland fishing now provide greater legal protection for the fish. Watershed planning that involves agencies and local groups is starting to improve water quality, riparian habitat, and fish passage in headwaters. Technical assistance programs are helping farmers to minimize soil erosion and toxic discharges in drainage water.

Despite the progress being made by these efforts, more work is still needed to restore spring-run chinook populations to self-sustaining levels. This work should include:

- continuing to remove passage barriers, such as dams and other structures;
- reestablishing natural flow and temperature regimes in rivers;
- restoring riverine and floodplain habitats and ecological processes;
- improving and enforcing fishing regulations and hatchery practices;
- reducing **nonpoint** source pollution from cities and agricultural areas;
- controlling predators where chinook are most vulnerable; and
- restoring runs to streams where they have been eliminated.

Swainson's Hawk

Richard Hall

The Swainson's hawk is unusual among hawks in the West in that it feeds on insects much of the year, is gregarious, and migrates long distances between North and South America. This hawk historically bred throughout much of California, as well as other places in the West, with California population estimates ranging as high as 17,000 pairs. By the 1940s, however, researchers began to document population declines of this hawk, and, by

1979, the species was nearly extirpated throughout large parts of its former range. By 1994, their population statewide had declined by more than 95 percent to approximately 800 pairs. Additional surveys are needed to document current population levels (CDFG 2005b).

Swainson's hawks in California now breed primarily in the Sacramento/Davis/Stockton region of the Central Valley and the Modoc Plateau of northeastern California. These birds require large, open grasslands with abundant prey in association with suitable nest trees. Suitable foraging areas include native grasslands or lightly grazed pastures, alfalfa and other hay crops, and certain grain and row croplands. Unsuitable foraging habitat includes vineyards, orchards, certain row crops, rice fields, corn, and cotton fields (CDFG 2005b).

The majority of Swainson's hawk territories in the Central Valley are on private lands and in riparian systems adjacent to suitable foraging habitats. Swainson's hawks often nest in proximity to riparian systems as well as in lone trees or groves of trees in agricultural fields.

The loss of agricultural lands to various residential and commercial developments is the primary threat to Swainson's hawk populations throughout California. Additional threats are loss of nesting habitat due to riverbank protection projects; conversion from agricultural crops that provide abundant foraging opportunities to crops such as vineyards and orchards, which provide fewer foraging opportunities; shooting; pesticide poisoning of prey animals and hawks on foraging and wintering grounds; competition from other raptors; and human disturbance at nest sites (CDFG 2005b).

Recent die-offs of several thousand Swainson's hawks and other raptors in Argentina wintering grounds have been attributed to pesticide use at agricultural fields. California birds, however, winter primarily in Mexico, rather than Argentina, and at a time of year when few or no pesticides are used on croplands (Woodbridge 1998). Thus, the risk from pesticides on the wintering grounds is substantially lower than for hawks that breed in other states.

In 1983, the Swainson's hawk was state listed as a threatened species. Conservation actions to date include regional conservation planning, habitat mitigation guidelines, and other habitat protection and restoration activities.

Regional conservation planning includes Habitat Conservation Plans and Natural Community Conservation Plans. These plans are currently under way in six counties within the Swainson's hawk range and focus on conservation of both the Swainson's hawk and other species.

Mitigation for habitat loss is covered under the California Endangered Species Act and the California Environmental Quality Act. This protection does not cover some of the primary impacts to the hawks, such as loss of agricultural foraging areas. Mitigation guidelines exist to improve conservation efforts, but these are often not sufficiently implemented. Rather than being enforceable regulations, these guidelines are advisory only, and they are not inclusive enough to cover effects on the quality (as compared to extent) of bird's habitat. A more effective Department of Fish and Game mitigation policy is needed to address the continued loss of habitat and disturbance of nest sites, particularly in the Central Valley where most of the population still exists.

The Swainson's hawk Technical Advisory Committee, an independent group made up of experts from public agencies and private organizations, provides a forum for advising and implementing conservation actions for this species. It conducts research, sponsors scientific symposia, and provides expert advice on land-use issues that affect these hawks and has developed some of the elements of a draft recovery strategy. The important conservation needs for this species include protecting suitable nesting and foraging habitat, maintaining compatible agricultural practices within 10 miles of nest sites, and eliminating major disturbances near nests during breeding periods (CDFG 2005b).

In addition to the regional conservation plans mentioned above, several other projects are conserving riparian habitat that will benefit these hawks. These include the California Bay-Delta Authority's Ecosystem Restoration Program as well as conservation and restoration at the Cosumnes River Preserve, along the American River Parkway, in state and federal wildlife refuges, and at a variety of state and local parks (Natural Resources Project Inventory 2005). Wintering grounds in Mexico are also receiving conservation attention by Partners in Flight, a public-private partnership dedicated to maintaining healthy bird populations in the United States and throughout the Western Hemisphere (Geupel 2005 pers. comm.).

This conservation attention is starting to reap benefits. The range of nesting Swainson's hawks has expanded over the past decade into the southern San Joaquin Valley, with some of the nest sites occurring on new conservation lands (Saslaw 2005 pers. comm.).

Tulare Grasshopper Mouse

As mentioned above, the Tulare grasshopper mouse is a rare species that is not listed under either the state or federal Endangered Species Act. It lives in the saltbush scrub of the southern San Joaquin Valley, along with many other at-risk species. It and other southern grasshopper mice are known as "wolves of the mouse world" because of their carnivorous diet and their "howling" to keep competing males away.

The Tulare grasshopper mouse historically ranged across the central and southern San Joaquin Valley, from the vicinity of San Benito and Madera counties south to the Tehachapi

Mountains. Currently, Tulare grasshopper mice are known to occur only in scattered locations across this range. Despite the presence of several large blocks of historical habitat on the floor of the Tulare Basin and extensive trapping efforts in several of these areas, no Tulare grasshopper mice have been captured. The only recent record is the capture in 1994 of a grasshopper mouse at Allensworth Ecological Reserve.

Little is known about these mice, and much is inferred from other southern grasshopper mice. They eat mostly small animals, with insects forming the bulk of their diet. They are nocturnal and active year round. No information is known about their reproduction, mating systems, demography, or dispersal.

Tulare grasshopper mice typically inhabit arid shrubland communities in hot, arid grassland and shrubland associations, but they also occur in alkali scrub dominated by saltbush, iodine bush, mesquite, and grassland habitats. There is little information about the habitat requirements of this mouse, and there are no current overall estimates of population size for this subspecies (USFWS 1998h).

Habitat reduction, fragmentation, and degradation accompanying settlement and development of the Central Valley for agriculture are the principal causes of decline of Tulare grasshopper mice, and these continue to be major stressors. Random catastrophic events (e.g., floods, fire, and drought) combined with their low reproductive rate and other demographic indicators probably are the most significant factors in elimination of fragmented populations. However, use of insecticides (first DDT and then others, now mainly malathion) on natural lands to control beet leafhoppers could have contributed to the disappearance of grasshopper mice from fragmented islands of natural land on the Valley floor, both from direct and indirect poisoning and the reduction of insects, their staple food (USFWS 1998h).

The Tulare grasshopper mouse is not a candidate for federal listing but is considered a species of concern (USFWS 1998h). Conservation of this mouse is likely to be a part of an overall effort to conserve its habitat, which is also home to several listed kangaroo rats, the blunt-nosed leopard lizard, and the San Joaquin kit fox. The apparent elimination of this mouse from the valley floor is of greatest concern because it suggests relatively high vulnerability to extinction by random catastrophic events or from use of pesticides on even relatively large habitat areas.

Habitat protection needs for Tulare grasshopper mice are essentially the same as those for Nelson's antelope squirrels and the three subspecies of the San Joaquin kangaroo rat (USFWS 1998h). These include:

- Inventorying and assessing existing natural land (known and potential habitat) within the historical range of these species to locate populations and assess population status;

- Managing publicly owned lands and conservation lands to benefit these species;

- Protecting additional land supporting key populations;

- Regularly monitoring all populations throughout their range, or at least populations that represent the range of variation in populations, habitat conditions, and environmental variation;

- Improving understanding of the relationships and taxonomic identity of isolated populations; and

- Conducting research on habitat management and restoration, focusing primarily on how different habitat management prescriptions and restoration approaches affect the population dynamics.

Additional measures of highest priority for conservation of the Tulare grasshopper mice (USFWS 1998h) are:

- Determining the current distribution and population status of Tulare grasshopper mice on isolated blocks of historical habitat on the valley floor of the Tulare Basin;

- Analyzing the environmental features of inhabited and uninhabited fragmented islands of natural land on the Central Valley floor to determine factors, including pesticide use, that might be associated with survival and elimination;

- Establishing a rangewide monitoring program at sites representative of the range of occupied communities and areas;

- Restoring habitat and reintroducing Tulare grasshopper mice as agricultural lands are retired to natural lands;

- Including Tulare grasshopper mice in studies of management and land uses on habitat of other species of the same community associations; and

- Reevaluating the status of the Tulare grasshopper mouse within three years of recovery plan approval.

Stressors Affecting Wildlife and Habitats

- Growth and development (including urban, residential, and agricultural)
- Water management conflicts and reduced water for wildlife
- Water pollution
- Invasive species
- Climate change

Each of these stressors is significant in the loss or degradation of habitat and ecosystem processes. In aquatic environments, including wetlands and riparian, the overall amount and quality of habitat has been reduced by water management and water pollution. Invasive species are important stressors in both upland and aquatic areas. Climate change has only recently been recognized as a major stressor that is likely to have significant, long-term effects on the human and natural environment in the next few decades.

Growth and Development

The main underlying cause of habitat loss and degradation is the increasing human population and its high demand for a limited supply of land, water, and other natural resources.

Up until the last few decades, much of the terrestrial habitat loss in the region has been due to agricultural land conversion. Fig. 14.1 illustrates this historical loss of habitat, using the San Joaquin Valley as an example. Recent land-use trends show a more mixed set of pressures from both urban and agricultural land conversion, depending on the habitat, topography, and proximity to major highways. Some habitats, such as wetlands and floodplains, are receiving increased environmental protection and thus less development pressure than other habitats (Landis and Reilly 2003). On the floor of the Central Valley, urbanization occurs mostly on previously cultivated lands, where much of the habitat has already been lost or highly degraded (Fig. 14.2). In these areas, particularly in rural lands, the remaining fragments of habitat continue to be converted to intensive agriculture. In the eastern uplands and foothills of the Central Valley, urban and rural residential development has had a greater impact on habitat because it occurs generally on grasslands and other naturally vegetated lands.

The rate of population growth in the Central Valley is remarkable. Fifteen of the top 20 fastest-growing counties in California between 1990 and 2003 were in the Central Valley, all exceeding the statewide average growth rate. This pattern is likely to remain the same during the next 50 years. Between 1990 and 2003, the Central Valley gained 1.8 million residents, nearly 30 percent of the total gain statewide. By comparison, the San Francisco Bay Area gained 974,000 residents, and the Southern California coastal region gained 3 million. By 2050, the Central Valley will gain an additional 7.4 million people, exceeding the 7.1 million-person gain for Southern California and the 3.2 million-person gain of the Bay Area (CDOF 2000, 2003, 2004; Sanders 2004).

Natural habitats of this region have been converted to a variety of different land uses, including weedy pastureland, dryland farming, irrigated cropland, relatively permanent orchards and vineyards, large dairies, rural residential, and high-density urban. Wildlife species have different tolerances for each of these conversions, with many of them unable to adapt to the more-developed land uses. Beyond direct habitat loss, converting land to more intensive human-related uses brings additional stressors, including invasive species, human

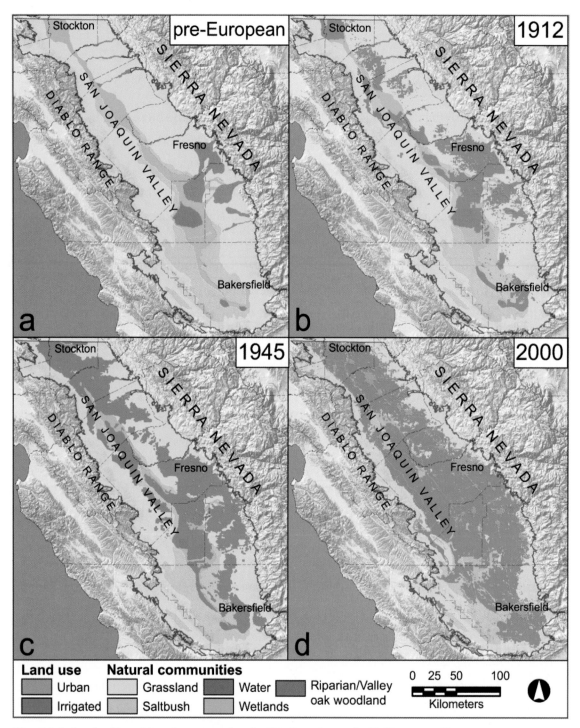

Land use

- Urban
- Irrigated

Natural communities

- Grassland
- Saltbush
- Water
- Wetlands
- Riparian/Valley oak woodland

0 25 50 100
Kilometers

Fig. 14.1: Agricultural land conversion in the San Joaquin Valley, pre-European settlement to 2000 (Kelly et al. 2005)

disturbance, fire suppression, and insect control, that further degrade ecosystem health and wildlife viability.

Examples of habitat conversions include:

- In the Central Valley, 99.9 percent of the historic native grasslands, 99 percent of valley oak savanna, about 95 percent of wetlands, 89 percent of riparian woodland, 66 percent of vernal pools, and 67 percent of San Joaquin Valley shrublands are gone (CVHJV 1990, Hickey et al. 2003, Kelly et al. 2005, TNC 1987, 1995, 1998). Habitat conversion has continued since these analyses were made.

- In the Bay Area, development has removed or significantly altered 88 percent of the original moist grasslands, 84 percent of riparian forest, 80 percent of the original tidal marshes, and 40 percent of the mudflats and vernal pool complexes. Much of the loss of tidal habitats was caused by diking and filling. The bay itself has shrunk 30 percent in the last 150 years due to filling of tidal and subtidal lands (Goals Project 1999).

Growth and development fragment habitats into small patches, which cannot support as many species as larger patches can. These smaller fragments often become dominated by species more tolerant of habitat disturbance, while less-tolerant species decline. Populations of less-mobile species often decline in smaller habitat patches due to reductions in habitat quality, extreme weather events, or normal population fluctuations. Natural recovery following such declines is difficult for mobility-limited species. Such fragmentation also disrupts or alters important ecosystem functions, such as predator-prey relationships, competitive interactions, seed dispersal, plant pollination, and nutrient cycling (Bennett 1999, ELI 2003).

Growth and development, along with associated linear structures like roads, canals, and power lines, impede or prevent movement of a variety of animals. This is generally less significant than habitat loss but makes it more difficult for those species that need to move large distances in search of food, shelter, and breeding or rearing habitat and to escape competitors and predators. Animals restricted to the ground, like mammals, reptiles, and amphibians, face such obstacles as roads, canals, and new gaps in habitats. Attempts to cross these obstacles can be deadly, depending on the species and the nature of the gap (four-lane highways with concrete median barriers compared to narrow, rural two-lane roads, for example). Fish and other water-bound aquatic species attempting to move either upstream or downstream are blocked by lack of water resulting from diversions, physical barriers like dams, and by entrainment in diverted water. Even the movement of highly mobile species like birds and bats can be impeded by such features as transmission lines and wind energy farms, particularly in focused flight corridors like Altamont Pass, and 50 new wind energy sites are currently proposed throughout the state on land managed by the Bureau of Land Management (Bolster

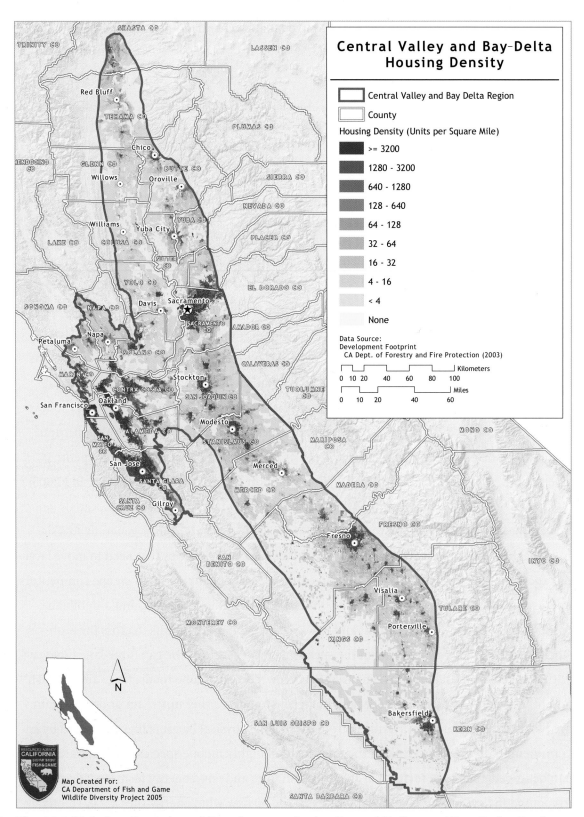

Fig. 14.2: Existing Growth and Development in the Central Valley and Bay-Delta Region
Although most of this region is in agriculture, much of it has also developed into either urban or rural residential uses, as shown by U.S. Census housing density data.

2005 pers. comm.) Such species either cannot see or do not avoid these structures, and many die as a result. The actual extent of bird fatalities due to power-line collision in California is unknown. However, the California Energy Commission estimates that fatality rates due to Central Valley power-line collisions alone could reach as high as 300,000 birds per year (CEC 2002a, 2002b).

Water Management Conflicts and Reduced Water for Wildlife

Water management stressors include water diversions, dams, flood control structures (e.g., levees and bank protection), groundwater pumping, stream and river crossings (e.g., culverts, bridges), and dredging. Managing these stressors is a major element of the California Bay-Delta Authority's Ecosystem Restoration Program (CALFED 2000, 2004a).

Water diversions are found throughout the Central Valley's rivers and tributaries, the Delta, and San Francisco Bay. Water is diverted for agriculture, municipal and industrial uses, and managed wetlands. Up to 70 percent of the freshwater flow that would naturally enter San Francisco Bay is now diverted (Steere and Schaefer 2001). Dams are located on all of the major rivers in the Central Valley and on many of their tributaries (Fig. 14.3).

Dams and diversions have dramatically affected the aquatic ecosystems of the Central Valley, altering historical flooding regimes, erosion, and deposition of sediments that maintain floodplains. They also decrease riparian habitats and coarse gravel supplies needed for salmon reproduction. Dam operations create rapid changes in flow rates that have led to the stranding of fish and exposure of fish spawning areas (Brown 2004 pers. comm.).

Dams reduce the amount of water remaining in the river that is needed by fish at critical times, and they alter the flow regimes in ways that are detrimental to aquatic life. Less water in the rivers also means less water for managed wetlands. Reduced river flows downstream also allow saltwater intrusion into the Delta, increasing the salinity levels in the San Francisco estuary and bay beyond the tolerance levels of many species (Steere and Schaefer 2001).

Agricultural diversions usually get the highest-quality water, discharging salty water that is then used in wildlife areas. By the time it is discharged from some wildlife areas, its salinity triggers concerns about water quality by regulatory agencies, particularly in the San Joaquin Valley. Efforts to correct this problem are complicated, owing to a poor understanding of the historic elements of salinity and the naturally saline wetlands of the San Joaquin drainage (Single et al. 2004 group interview).

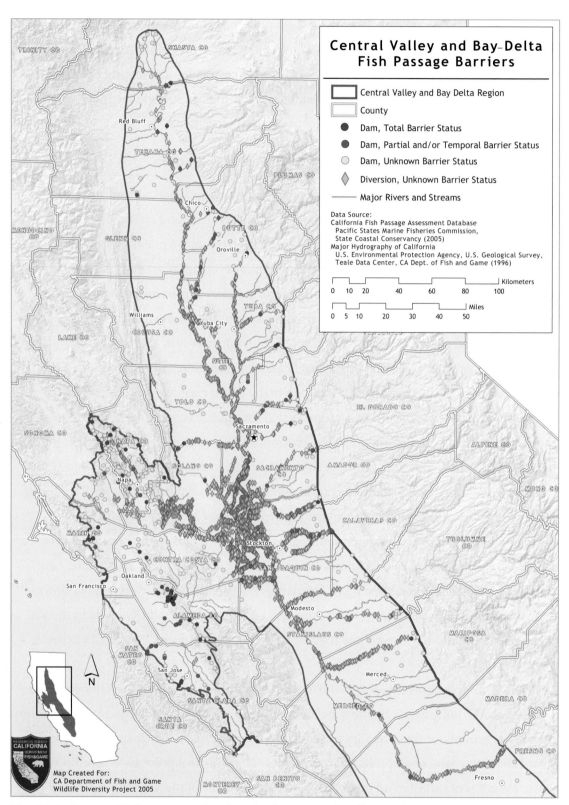

Fig. 14.3: Known Fish-passage Barriers in the Central Valley and Bay–Delta
All of the major creeks and rivers in the Central Valley and Bay Area are either dammed or diverted.
Diversions are more abundant along rivers in the valleys. Dams are more common at the edge of the
Central Valley, where topography more easily allows the creation of reservoirs.

Dams and diversions also block fish movement to upstream habitat, remove fish and wildlife habitat, alter water quality (i.e., temperature and flow), and kill fish through entrainment and entrapment. Dams have cut off salmon access to 95 percent of their historical range (State Lands Commission 1993, TPL 2001). The diversion of water through powerful pumps from the Delta to the canals heading to Southern California reverses Delta flows and confuses migrating fish trying to find their way to the ocean. At times, the young fish swim with the flowing waters toward the pumps rather than toward the open ocean.

Levee, bridge, and bank-protection structures are present along more than 2,600 miles of rivers in the Central Valley and in the Delta (DWR 2005a). These structures prevent flood flows from entering historic floodplains and eliminate or alter the character of floodplain habitats, such as shaded riverine habitat, and floodplain ecosystem processes. Constrained flood-level flows increase scouring and incision of river channels and reduce or halt the formation of riparian habitat, channel meanders, and river oxbow channels.

These changes in water supply also stress many upland species. Most of the resident terrestrial animals need to find adequate water for drinking during California's long, dry summer months. As human demand for water increases, there is less water available for resident wildlife species, and thus they experience greater physiological stress. In some cases, though, water management has led to sustained year-round flows in streams that historically dried up in the summer.

One important difference between the Bay Area and the Central Valley is the geographic drainage areas of watersheds and the role of water transfers. Except for estuarine habitats that are influenced by flows from the Delta, most of the habitats in the Bay Area depend on relatively small, local watersheds. Central Valley habitats rely on a much larger and complex drainage, involving snowmelt and land use up to 300 miles away and water imports from and exports to other major river basins. Thus, although local watershed efforts are important in both subregions, they can have a more direct influence on reducing water-related stressors in the Bay Area for the same level of effort.

Current water management practices exemplify how several of these stressors interact. As urban development expands, it creates more impermeable surfaces like concrete, asphalt, and the roofs of buildings. Subsequent rainfall is then less able to soak into the ground and runs off quickly. Rapid runoff reduces the recharge of groundwater reservoirs and reduces later summer stream flows. Combined with water diversions, this reduction in groundwater causes streams to dry up more quickly, thus reducing the availability of water to wildlife during summer months. Increased urban runoff also is a major source of water pollution (described below). It washes various pollutants out of urban areas, depositing them into creeks, rivers, and other water bodies, adding to wildlife stress.

Water Pollution

Up to 40,000 tons of contaminants enter the Bay-Delta annually. Four types of water contaminants affect wildlife in the Bay-Delta:

- inorganic compounds such as heavy metals, phosphates, and nitrates from municipal wastewater, industrial effluent, agricultural and mine drainage, and urban runoff;
- organic compounds such as polychlorinated biphenyls (PCBs), pesticides, fertilizers, and detergents from urban and agricultural runoff;
- biological contaminants, such as viruses and bacteria from sewage, farm, dairy, and feedlot runoff, and from urban runoff; and
- other toxins that originate from a variety of sources, some of which are unknown.

The most significant toxins are diazinon, mercury, PCBs, chlorpyrifos, and boron. These pollutants or conditions are present in hundreds of miles of streams and most estuarine waters throughout the Bay, Delta, and Central Valley (see Fig. 14.4). Other important factors that impair water quality include increased levels of nutrients, pathogens, low levels of dissolved oxygen in water, and sedimentation (SWRCB 2002a).

Mercury contamination has become a major concern for wildlife conservation in the Bay-Delta region, and high mercury concentrations in Bay fish pose a human health risk. The pathways of mercury uptake from the environment are poorly understood, which exacerbates the problem. Ongoing inputs from the watershed and historical deposits of mercury from the gold-mining days are of concern, particularly as ecosystem restoration efforts proceed. The primary concern is that large-scale wetland restoration may transform residual mercury into a chemical form more easily taken up by clams, fish, birds, and other estuarine life, with potential sublethal effects for them and health risks for any humans consuming contaminated fish (CALFED 2003).

Pollutants reduce dissolved oxygen in Delta waterways, stressing aquatic species. One source of low dissolved oxygen levels is water that drains from some of the managed wetlands, such as in the Suisun Marsh. These operations flood fields for waterfowl, and the floodwaters then soak up organic matter. The resulting "black water" that drains out of the fields is very low in dissolved oxygen and causes fish kills in some localized areas. Although this problem has been known for many years, little action has been taken to correct it (Moyle 2002). Similar to the salinity issue mentioned above, too little is known about historic base-

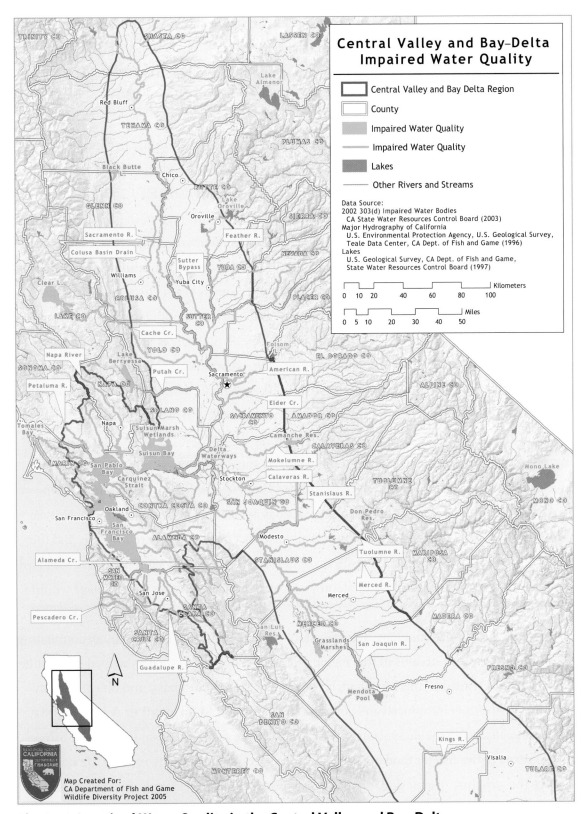

Fig. 14.4: Impaired Water Quality in the Central Valley and Bay-Delta
Water contaminants include organic and inorganic compounds, biological contaminants, and other toxins.

line conditions of dissolved oxygen in Delta waterways, and coherent decisions on integrated land and water management have not been made. The overall system of actions and conditions affecting water quality is quite complex and is only beginning to be understood.

Invasive Species

Invasive plant and animal species are an important stressor on wildlife in this region, just as they are in other regions throughout the state (CALFED 2000, CalIPC 1999, CDFG 2005, Goals Project 1999, Hickey et al. 2003, Jurek 1994, Lewis et al. 1993, RHJV 2004).

Invasive plants can be found in many different habitats in this region. In grasslands, some of the more challenging plant invaders include eucalyptus, fountain grass, gorse, medusahead, tree of heaven, and yellow starthistle. In riparian and wetland areas, invading plants include edible fig, giant reed or arundo, Himalayan blackberry, pampas grass, Russian olive, tamarisk (or saltcedar), pennyroyal, peppergrass and tree of heaven. Smooth cordgrass is a major concern in salt marshes. Oak woodlands are invaded by plants such as Scotch broom and French broom. Coastal habitats face alien species such as gorse, iceplant, and pampas grass.

Introduced plants also invade aquatic habitats. These aquatic invaders include Brazilian waterweed, egeria, Eurasian watermilfoil, hydrilla, water hyacinth, water pennywort, and parrot feather.

Introduced animals have invaded both terrestrial and aquatic environments. Sixty-four non-native terrestrial animal species have invaded California wildlands, including brown-headed cowbirds, European starlings, domestic dogs and cats, introduced red foxes, Norway rats, and feral pigs (Grenfell et al. 2003). Not all introduced vertebrates are invasive, and they have varying effects on wildlife. The species of most concern in the region parasitize songbird nests, dominate limited nesting habitat, prey on native species, or otherwise damage wildlife habitats.

Fifty-one new fish species have become established in California (Moyle 2002), dominating most of the rivers and streams in this region. These include species such as striped bass, white catfish, channel catfish, American shad, black crappie, largemouth bass, and bluegill. Many fish were historically introduced and continue to be introduced (planted) by federal and state resource agencies to provide sport fishing or forage fish to feed sport fish. Introduced fish out-compete native fish for food or space, prey on native fish (especially in early life stages), change the structure of aquatic habitats (increasing turbidity, for example, by their behaviors), and may spread diseases (Moyle 2002). Several of the introduced predatory fish have increased predation levels on chinook salmon (CALFED 2000).

In addition to introduced fish, native aquatic species are stressed by introduced bullfrogs, red-eared sliders (a turtle), and invertebrates. Introduced invertebrates, such as Asian clam, zebra mussel, Chinese mitten crab, and mysid shrimp, are causing significant problems for native species in rivers, streams, sloughs, and the San Francisco estuary. The introduction of species via discharge of ship ballast water in San Francisco Bay has created one of the most invaded estuaries in the world (CALFED 2000). Most of the clams, worms, and other bottom-dwelling invertebrates presently inhabiting the Bay-Delta have been introduced from other estuaries. This biological invasion continues, with a new species introduced roughly every 14 weeks (CALFED 2000). While not all of the introduced aquatic species are invasive or have significant consequences for native species, biologists are concerned about the sheer dominance of these new species and their current and potential effects on the structure and function of the estuarine ecosystem.

Climate Change

Although climate change is already affecting wildlife throughout the state (Parmesan and Galbraith 2004), and its effects will continue to increase, it has particular significance for this region's major river and estuarine systems.

In general, California winters will likely become warmer and wetter during the next century. Instead of deep winter snowpacks that nourish valley rivers through the long, dry summer, most of the precipitation will be winter rain that runs off quickly. For the Central Valley and the Bay, this means more intense winter flooding, greater erosion of riparian habitats, and increased sedimentation in wetland habitats (Field et al. 1999, Hayhoe et al. 2004).

Hotter, drier summers, combined with lower river flows, will dramatically increase the water needs of both people and wildlife. This is likely to translate into less water for wildlife, especially fish and wetland species. Lower river flows will allow saltwater intrusion into the Bay and Delta, increasing salinity and disrupting the complex food web of the estuary. Water contaminants may accumulate during the summer as the natural flushing action decreases.

Sea level worldwide during the past 100 years has been rising from 1 to 2 millimeters per year, 10 times faster than the rate over the past 3,000 years. Gauges along the California coast have already measured 4-inch to 6-inch increases in sea level since 1900 (NOAA 2005). By 2100, sea levels might rise as high as 3 feet above their present levels (ACIA 2004, IPCC 2001).

This is especially significant in the San Francisco Bay Area and the Delta, where much of the land has subsided to below sea level and is currently protected from flooding by levees. Fig. 14.5 shows those lands that are fewer than 3 feet above sea level in the Bay and Delta area.

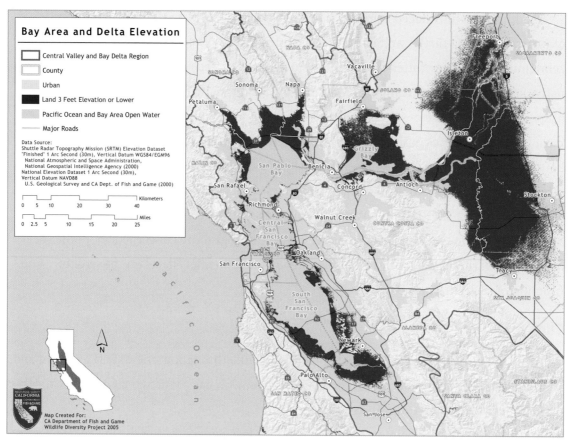

Fig. 14.5: Lands in the Delta below 3 Feet of Elevation

Much of the Delta and large sections along the San Francisco Bay shoreline are below 3 feet of elevation. Sea level rise due to climate change could flood these areas with saltwater. Existing levees and other flood barriers that protect lands below sea level are too small to display at this map scale. Anomalies in digital elevation data may overestimate or underestimate the actual acreage of these lands by up to 15 percent in some areas.

Continuation of current farming practices will worsen this subsidence throughout much of the Delta. This increased subsidence, combined with higher sea level, increased winter river flooding, and more intense winter storms, will significantly increase the hydraulic forces on the levees. Given their current state, a powerful earthquake in the region could collapse levees, leading to major seawater intrusion and flooding throughout the Delta (Mount and Twiss 2005).

Even without levee collapse, the sea-level rise alone could make conditions unsuitable for pumping freshwater through the Delta channels for the major water-export pumps. Continued water exports might need an alternative freshwater conveyance facility for the Delta to circumvent this saltwater intrusion. The consequences of sea-level rise are also likely to occur in the Bay Area, where tidal wetlands that are currently squeezed between urban lands and the sea will no longer be able to persist (CEC 2005, DWR 2004, Field et al. 1999, Shaw 2002).

The ecological functioning of upland habitats is likely to be disrupted as individual species respond differently to climatic changes. Some species will likely adapt in place, others will probably move to better climates, and the rest will experience different rates of population or health declines. Movement to other habitats will be more challenging as the few remaining habitat patches shrink and the gaps between habitats grow.

Conservation Actions to Restore and Conserve Wildlife

In addition to the recommended regional actions described below, see the recommended statewide conservation actions as given in Chapter 4.

a. The California Resources Agency, Fish and Game, the U.S. Fish and Wildlife Service, public land managing agencies, and local governments need to develop multicounty regional habitat conservation and restoration plans.

See Statewide Actions a and c in Chapter 4.

Much of the conservation planning in this region occurs either at the county scale or smaller or focuses on only a subset of wildlife issues (e.g., bird conservation plans, recovery plans) with little integration among them.

Regional conservation plans need to integrate with state-level or regional plans for housing, transportation, energy, water, and other infrastructure that provide opportunities or constraints for conservation.

Many of the recommendations elsewhere in this chapter need to be part of this regional planning, including managing across ownership boundaries, targeting landowner assistance programs, restoring habitats, ensuring reliable water for wildlife use, and controlling invasive species.

The Baylands Ecosystem Habitat Goals report (Goals Project 1999) provides a good example of regional assessment and planning; it created the basis for the bayland conservation efforts of the San Francisco Bay Joint Venture and its many partners. Conservation interests in the Bay Area have started to build upon this type of approach to cover upland habitats and wildlife needs, although this effort currently lacks sufficient funding. Similar goal-setting efforts need to be developed in other watersheds throughout the region to form a stronger foundation for conservation decisions (Collins 2005 pers. comm.).

The California Bay-Delta Authority's Ecosystem Restoration Program views integrated regional plans as its next important phase. The most developed of these is the Delta Regional Ecosystem Restoration Implementation Plan. Plans are being initiated in Suisun Marsh and along the Sacramento River. Other regions under consideration include the Bay Area and the San Joaquin Valley (Jacobs 2004 pers. comm.). The California Bay-Delta Authority needs to ensure that these plans go beyond the organization's aquatic focus and integrate its recommendations with other, overlapping upland conservation plans.

b. **While numerous private landowners are leaders in conservation, Fish and Game, the U.S. Fish and Wildlife Service, the USDA Natural Resources Conservation Service, and local resource conservation districts need to improve conservation and restoration on private lands by assisting private landowners.**

See Statewide Action h in Chapter 4.

The vast majority of land in the Central Valley and Bay Area is in private ownership. Agencies and conservation organizations are unlikely to protect all of the important areas for wildlife in this region by use of acquisition, easements, and regulatory approaches alone. Landowners need to be encouraged to provide wildlife habitat on their lands and reduce their cumulative stresses on wildlife through voluntary programs. Assisting private landowners requires recognizing the varied types of landowners in this region, understanding the major challenges to private land conservation, and finding ways to overcome these challenges (see Fig. 14.6, Conservation Assistance to Private Landowners).

While the participation of willing landowners is critical for success, assistance programs need to target their efforts in areas with high wildlife values and where enhancements are technically feasible, rather than simply being opportunistic. These programs are likely to be most successful in rural areas, away from cities. In rapidly urbanizing areas, development pressures increase land values so dramatically that assistance programs are often poor competitors for landowner attention (Chamberlin 2004 pers. comm., Environmental Defense 2000, Fischer 2004, Hummon and Casey 2004, Shaffer 2004 pers. comm.).

State and federal agencies need to strengthen, improve, and increase publicity for their existing private-landowner assistance programs. They need to better integrate these programs with one another to improve their overall effectiveness and develop state Safe Harbor-type agreements (USFWS 2002b). Safe Harbor Agreements are voluntary arrangements between the U.S. Fish and Wildlife Service or National Marine Fisheries Service and cooperating nonfederal landowners. The agreements benefit endangered and threatened species while

Fig. 14.6. Conservation Assistance to Private Landowners

Landowners have differing interests, face differing challenges, and have differing needs for conservation assistance.

Types of private landowners

- Conservation-focused
  (land trusts, environmental groups)
- Recreation-focused
- Farmers and ranchers
  (small to industrial-sized operations)
- Public utilities
- Residential
  (urban, suburban, small rural,
  large rural)
- Land or resource investors

Level of interest by landowner in both conservation and receiving assistance

- None
- Low
- Moderate
- High

Most appropriate type
of assistance

Challenges facing landowners

- Inadequate owner awareness of land's
  biological significance
- Insufficient knowledge about wildlife needs
- Uncertainty about how to meet both
  wildlife needs and other objectives for
  the land
- Complex regulatory environment; concern
  about increased regulatory burden
  following voluntary wildlife enhancements
- Insufficient resources (time, technical,
  funding) to take conservation action
- Lack of motivation or incentives to
  encourage action
- Poor experiences with or trust of
  government programs

Types of assistance

- Basic information about what to
  conserve and how
- Public recognition
  (awards, signage, press)
- Technical assistance:
  ◊ Permitting and regulations
  ◊ Conservation practices
- Market-based approaches
  (conservation trading, ecotourism)
- Financial
  ◊ Tax benefits or credits
  ◊ Direct funding for
    habitat improvement

Sources: Defenders of Wildlife 2002, Environmental Defense 2000, Fischer 2004, Henson 2004, Hummon and Casey 2004, Sustainable Conservation 2004, USFWS 2002b, USFWS 2002f, USFWS 2004a

giving the landowners assurances from additional restrictions. Following development of an agreement, the agency issues an "enhancement of survival" permit to authorize any necessary future incidental take and provide participating landowners with assurances that no additional restrictions will be imposed as a result of their conservation actions.

Public and private agencies should encourage conservation of grassland and shrubland habitats on private lands by promoting economically and ecologically sustainable grazing as a compatible land use. There are several important programs that provide support for working landscapes including the Environmental Quality Improvement Program, the Wildlife Habitat Improvement Program, the Grasslands Reserve Program, and Conservation Security Program.

A related form of private landowner assistance is the nurturing and support of local land conservancies and watershed groups, which can work effectively with private landowners at the local and regional level. For example, with funding from the California Resources Agency and The David and Lucile Packard Foundation, the nonprofit Sequoia Riverlands Trust purchased the Homer Ranch near the Kaweah River in the San Joaquin Valley. The land remains a working cattle ranch, but it also provides public access, public education, protection for riparian wildlife, and one of the largest remaining sycamore alluvial woodland communities in the state (Sequoia Riverlands Trust 2005).

c. Public land managers need to continue improving wildlife habitat for a variety of species on public lands.

Although this region has a relatively small public land base, public land managers have an important role to play in protecting and restoring wildlife populations and habitats. Simply because habitat is in public ownership does not necessarily mean that these lands are receiving adequate protection or management. Many additional activities beyond the initial real estate action are necessary to meet the needs of wildlife on those lands. To improve the contribution of public lands to protecting wildlife, the following actions are needed:

- Adequately fund operation and management of public lands that were established specifically for wildlife conservation. Dedicated endowments for long-term management of properties would help ensure that management funds remain available and not subject to other competing agency priorities.

- Manage wildlife areas for the full variety of habitats and species found in the area. Managers should be funded to evaluate and, where feasible, adopt the habitat management recommendations given in existing species- or habitat-specific conservation plans, which include such actions as monitoring, research, and restoration. Managers should adopt approaches that manage for both ecosystems and species of special interest or concern.

- Improve the management of large rural public lands to support functioning ecosystems and enhanced wildlife populations. In this region of limited public land, every piece of such land with native vegetation is valuable for wildlife. These lands include state and federal wildlife areas, large rural parks (national, state, or local), water-district and utility-district lands, military lands, and other public lands. Land managers should develop and implement management prescriptions that benefit wildlife, sustain populations, and reduce the effects of invasive species.

d. Public agencies and private organizations need to work with the San Francisco Bay Joint Venture to protect and restore the Bay's tidal habitats and baylands.

The most important habitats of concern around the shore of San Francisco Bay are deep and shallow bay and channel environments, tidal baylands, and diked baylands. Tidal bayland habitats include tidal flats, marshes (both salt and brackish), and lagoons. Diked bayland habitats include diked wetland, agricultural lowlands, salt ponds, and storage ponds.

Recommendations listed elsewhere in this chapter also apply to tidal and bayland habitats in San Francisco Bay, including improved easements, private landowner assistance, improved public land management, invasive species control, and improved water quality. Continued and expanded support is needed for implementing the San Francisco Bay Joint Venture's (SFBJV) detailed strategy for conserving baylands (Steere and Schaefer 2001). Building on the San Francisco Baylands Ecosystem Habitat Goals report, the SFBJV strategy provides acreage objectives for acquiring, restoring, and enhancing these habitats in each of five subregions of the Bay. It also provides recommendations for managing these habitats on both public and private lands, strengthening funding, and collaborating with other conservation programs. The SFBJV strategy needs to continue and to expand its collaboration with the San Francisco Estuary Project's Comprehensive Conservation and Management Plan for the Bay and Delta (SFEP 1993).

e. Public agencies and private organizations need to collaboratively protect and restore habitat connectivity along major rivers in the Central Valley.

See Statewide Actions d and g in Chapter 4.

Several collaborative efforts have already started to protect and restore riparian, flood-plain, and other habitat along Central Valley rivers, including the Central Valley Habitat Joint Venture, the Riparian Habitat Joint Venture, the CALFED Ecosystem Restoration Program, and the Sacramento River Conservation Area Forum. Individual state, federal, and local agencies and private conservation organizations are also engaged in these types of conservation actions.

More action and funding are needed to complete or initiate conservation and restoration projects along these major rivers. The set of actions varies, depending on the location and the specific habitat or species needs, but includes habitat restoration, modification of flood control structures, acquisition or easements, and private landowner assistance. Some of the important rivers and tributaries include:

- Main stems of the Sacramento, Feather, and San Joaquin rivers;
- Tributaries of the Feather and Sacramento rivers that link the valley floor to Sierra Nevada foothills and coastal foothills;
- The Cosumnes, Calaveras, and Mokelumne rivers, linking the Delta to the Sierra Nevada foothills;
- Tributaries of the San Joaquin River that link the valley floor to Sierra Nevada foothills and coastal foothills;
- The Kings and Kern rivers and their tributaries.

f. Public agencies and private organizations need to collaboratively protect and restore upland linkages among protected areas in the San Joaquin Valley.

See Statewide Action d in Chapter 4.

Important linkages for conservation attention include:

- Linkages among protected areas of the Grasslands Ecological Area (including the San Luis National Wildlife Refuge complex and Los Banos Wildlife Area) in central Merced County;
- Linkages in the Tulare Basin among Kern and Pixley National Wildlife Refuges, Allensworth Ecological Reserve, northern Semitropic Ridge, and the western foothills;
- Linkages along the western edge of the San Joaquin Valley, including the Carrizo Plain National Monument and the Lokern Natural Area northwards to the Panoche Hills and the foothills of the Diablo Range near Tracy.

g. Public agencies and private organizations need to collaboratively protect and restore lowland linkages in San Francisco Bay.

See Statewide Action d in Chapter 4.

Important lowland linkages include:

- Linkages between tidal marshes, salt ponds, and other bayland habitats along the margin of San Francisco Bay;
- Stream corridors connecting low baylands (tidal marshes, salt ponds, etc.) throughout San Francisco Bay with upland areas, where possible. These baylands have been significantly isolated from upland areas by roads and urban development.

h. Public agencies and private organizations need to collaboratively protect upland linkages and reduce the risk of habitat isolation in the eastern and northern San Francisco Bay area.

See Statewide Action d in Chapter 4.

The rapid urbanization of the eastern and northern portions of the Bay Area is beginning to create at least four major "islands" of natural vegetation and public lands. These areas are at risk of being completely isolated from one another due to land development along major highways. As with the areas above, planners need to evaluate these areas to determine species conservation needs and appropriate types of connections to either maintain or reestablish them. Land-use planning and habitat-protection actions are needed to keep these lands connected with other natural areas. Based on a simple map-based inspection of existing patterns of natural vegetation, land use, and transportation routes, the main constriction zones are:

- Interstate 80 between Fairfield and Vallejo, where development pressure may isolate Suisun Marsh from upstream areas north of the freeway;
- Interstate 580 between Dublin and Castro Valley, where development pressure may isolate natural lands on the north (including Las Trampas Regional Park and Chabot Regional Park) from lands to the south (including Pleasanton Ridge Regional Park);
- Interstate 680 between Fremont and Pleasanton, where development pressure may isolate natural lands on the north (Pleasanton Ridge Regional Park) from natural lands to the south;
- Interstate 580 near Altamont Pass (between Livermore and Tracy), where development pressure may isolate natural lands on the north (including Mt. Diablo State Park and the Los Vaqueros watershed lands) from natural lands to the south.

i. Water management agencies need to secure dependable and adequate amounts and quality of water for wildlife.

See Statewide Action e in Chapter 4.

As California's population increases, the demand for water increases and reduces the amount left for wildlife, particularly species that are dependent on rivers and wetlands.

Wildlife areas that support wetlands (on both private and public lands) have a high demand for sufficient quantities of unpolluted water. The amount of water available to refuges varies each year and is commonly not delivered at times most needed for wetland management. Typically, refuges receive water only after all other agricultural, municipal, and industrial demands are fulfilled.

Although water for wildlife was agreed to in the Central Valley Project Improvement Act, it is insufficient to meet the needs of wildlife areas, especially as those areas strive to meet the needs of a greater variety of species. Much of the water goes for fisheries management, with inadequate amounts left over to meet the needs of other species. Additionally, water amounts have to be agreed upon in time-consuming, year-to-year negotiations (Shaffer 2004 pers. comm., Single et al. 2004 group interview).

As water prices increase, wildlife agencies and private wetland managers often cannot afford to purchase enough water and convey it to where it is needed. They have to compete against cities and agricultural interests that are able to pay higher prices in the water market. The Central Valley Habitat Joint Venture has a report that examines this issue in more detail (Shaffer 2004 pers. comm.). The Central Valley Habitat Joint Venture Implementation Plan provides more specific recommendations about water needs (CVHJV 1990), and a major update of this plan is scheduled for 2005.

- Secure legal rights for water for wildlife in perpetuity with long-term agreements. Secure sufficient amounts of adequate-quality water for wildlife areas at the appropriate seasons using long-term multiple-year contracts. One possibility is to include this as a requirement of long-term agricultural water contracts or to include in mitigation efforts (CDFG 1995, Shaffer 2004 pers. comm.).
- Reduce large water exports out of the Central Valley so that more water is available for wildlife.
- Design water-banking projects within the region to provide wetland and upland habitats for wildlife.

j. Water management agencies need to reestablish and maintain more natural river flows, flooding patterns, water temperatures, and salinity conditions to support wildlife species and habitats.

See Statewide Action g in Chapter 4.

River flows, particularly in the major rivers of the Central Valley, need to be of sufficient frequency, timing, duration, and magnitude to restore and maintain functional natural flood-plain, riparian, and riverine habitats. Such flows should be able to:

- mobilize gravel bed transport;
- allow for channel migration, river meanders, and complex channel patterns; and
- provide suitable aquatic conditions, including river water temperature and estuarine salinity, for viable populations of native aquatic species.

Restoring natural flow regimes can both favor native aquatic species and reduce the impacts of invasive aquatic species.

Adequate freshwater flows in Central Valley rivers are also one of the essential components to restore and maintain a healthy and diverse estuary in the Bay Area (SFEP 1993). One of its major influences is on salinity conditions in the estuary. The saltiness of the water, and particularly its seasonal and year-to-year patterns of variability, affects which aquatic species live where within the estuary. Salinity also determines where water can and cannot be diverted for human consumption and irrigated agriculture and plays a role in determining the capacity of the estuary to cleanse itself of wastes.

k. Water management agencies need to restore gravel supply in sediment-starved rivers downstream of reservoirs to maintain functional riverine habitats.

One of the major negative effects of dams is the capture of coarse sediments that naturally would move to downstream areas. As a result, the downstream reaches become coarse-sediment starved, hardening (armoring) streambeds with fine sediments to the point where they are largely unsuitable for spawning salmon and other anadromous fish. The CALFED Ecosystem Restoration Plan (CALFED 2000) describes several important actions that are needed to improve gravel supply for fish habitat, including:

- Protecting existing natural sediment sources in river floodplains from such disturbances as bank protection, gravel mining, levees, dams, changes in stream flow, and changes to natural stream meanders;
- Artificially maintaining sediment supplies below dams;
- Increasing the availability of sediment stored in banks and riverside floodplains;
- Enhancing and restoring natural stream-bank erosion and stream meander processes;
- Increasing gravel passage through small reservoirs;
- Removing non-essential or low-value dams;
- Eliminating instream gravel mining on channels downstream of reservoirs;
- Developing incentives to discourage mining of gravel from river channels and adjacent floodplain sites;
- Developing programs for comprehensive sediment management in each watershed;
- Developing ecologically based stream-flow regulation plans.

l. Public agencies and private organizations should conserve and restore water-dependent habitats (including wetland, riparian, and estuarine) throughout the region. Design of these actions should factor in the likely effects of accelerated climate change.

See Statewide Action g in Chapter 4.

Conserving water-dependent habitats is especially important in this region because they are among the most significant wildlife areas left. These habitats include tidal habitats, shallow water sloughs, rivers and creeks, wetlands and vernal pools. Much of the water that flows through these habitats drains from uplands. Poor land-use in these higher areas can unnaturally accelerate runoff and increase sediment and contaminant loading downstream. Thus regional and watershed-based conservation actions are an essential part of the overall solution.

Conservation planning for riverine and estuarine habitats also needs to factor in the likely effects from rapid climate change. Tidal habitat conservation efforts need to include upslope room for marshes to migrate as sea level rises. Rising sea levels could obliterate current successes in tidal marsh habitat restoration. Riparian restoration along tightly controlled rivers could be washed away as the intensity of winter rains and floods increase.

Restoration is also needed to reestablish significant portions of wetlands and aquatic communities in the Tulare Lake Basin, building on the efforts of the Central Valley Habitat Joint Venture and local initiatives.

Actions to conserve and restore rivers and floodplains include:

- Discourage permanent development, such as urban uses, and encourage wildlife-compatible land uses in lands that are near sea level (within 6 feet of high tide line) and near rivers and streams. This is especially important in areas immediately upslope or inland of important tidal habitats. Acquisition of fee-title or conservation easements should be encouraged in these areas to give tidal lands room to migrate as sea level rises.

- Expand information about flood-prone areas in the California Dept. of Water Resource's nonregulatory Awareness Floodplain Mapping Program database to include all flood-prone developing areas in California. Its data need to be improved to account for future build-out and the resulting expected increase in runoff downstream. Such floodplain maps should be prepared on a watershed basis, rather than on political boundaries, using consistent mapping standards throughout each watershed. These maps should also account for current and future build-out (DWR 2002).

- Avoid development of permanent buildings in floodplains. Existing flood maps used by local government should be based on the improved Water Resources database described above.

- Expand conservation zones by setting back levees and removing riprap along all rivers and major creeks so they can freely meander and safely overflow existing channels. This will help create and maintain complex channel morphology, in-channel islands, and shallow water habitat in the Delta and Suisun Marsh; increase the extent of freely meandering reaches; promote the natural cycle of channel movement, sediment deposition, and scouring needed for a diversity of riparian vegetation types; and restore coarse sediment supplies to sediment-starved rivers downstream of reservoirs.

- Use nonstructural approaches, such as bypasses and managed floodplains, to control flooding along rivers and major creeks. An example of successful multi-objective floodplain management is in the Yolo Bypass. Although initially established for use as a floodwater corridor, it is also intensively cultivated outside the flood season, provides habitat for native fish, waterfowl and wading birds, and provides important outdoor recreation, including wildlife viewing, hunting, and fishing. (DWR 2004, Sommer et al. 2001).

- Manage floodplains and bypasses to maximize ecosystem protection, habitat restoration, and wildlife use while still providing for public safety and flood-damage reduction. The California Floodplain Management Task Force report (DWR 2002) provides a comprehensive list of recommendations for improving floodplain management.

- Provide agricultural buffers upslope of areas likely to be damaged by changes related to climate change, including sea level rise and more catastrophic flood events.

- Maintain, restore, and improve the functional hydrological connections between upper watersheds and downstream habitats (such as wetlands, estuaries, and marine environments). Elevate roadways (an example is the Yolo Causeway) where they divide wetlands from upper watersheds to reduce habitat fragmentation between these connected habitats. Design river and stream crossings to convey sediment as well as water; this will reduce upstream flooding and downstream erosion and thus help maintain aquatic and riparian habitats. Restore surface and groundwater sources, stream channels, and natural storage places for sediment and water; this will help sustain base flows, wet meadows, and transitional habitats between rivers and tidal systems.

m. Water management agencies, state and federal wildlife agencies, and other public agencies and private organizations need to collaboratively improve fish passage by removing or modifying barriers to upstream habitat.

In some cases, improving fish passage is a matter of providing adequate water flow in streams. In other cases, it may mean modification or complete removal of dams and other obstacles to make passage easier.

The statewide inventory of barriers to fish passage (CalFish 2005) needs to be improved to identify the relative significance of different barriers and barrier types. It also needs to be expanded to include the locations of all other existing passage barriers.

State government needs to develop a comprehensive program to remove these barriers, building on the work of Water Resources' Fish Passage Improvement Program and the interagency Fish Passage Forum. Partnerships with nongovernmental organizations can leverage and extend the effectiveness of these programs.

Opportunities for improving fish passage exist on large rivers (e.g., the Red Bluff Diversion Dam on the Sacramento River) as well as on smaller streams. Collectively, actions on both rivers and streams can make a big contribution. These actions need to focus on strategic areas in which to make the best contribution with limited resources.

n. To support healthy aquatic ecosystems, public agencies and private organizations, in collaboration with the California Bay-Delta Authority, need to improve and maintain water quality in the major river systems of this region.

The California Bay-Delta Authority has two program elements that are interactively addressing water quality in the Sacramento and San Joaquin river systems: the Drinking Water Quality Program and the Ecosystem Restoration Program. Both programs need to implement their current multiyear plans to improve water quality conditions. The multiyear plan for the Drinking Water Quality Program (CALFED 2004b) recommends a Delta Improvements Package to address salinity problems in the San Joaquin River, improve agricultural drainage, and modify levees and water circulation in the Delta. The plan also calls for actions beyond the Delta to improve land management practices related to irrigated agriculture, managed wetlands, grazing, and urban runoff. The Ecosystem Restoration Program's multiyear plan (CALFED 2004a) recommends a variety of actions, including remediating mercury contamination, identifying and focusing on watersheds with the greatest toxic risk to wildlife, improving dissolved oxygen conditions in the Delta, and improving contamination-data systems. One approach that both improves water quality and provides wildlife habitat is the use of artificial wetlands as initial wastewater treatment filters.

Improving water quality in these Central Valley river systems is integrally linked to improving water quality in San Francisco Bay, which receives much of the contaminants. Other important actions for these river systems are described in the San Francisco Bay water quality section.

o. Regional water quality boards, in collaboration with other public agencies and private organizations, need to improve and maintain water quality in streams and tidal waters of San Francisco Bay.

The number and variety of contaminants entering the rivers and estuary is poorly known, as are their toxic effects, in part because the amounts and kinds are constantly changing. Reducing concentrations of contaminants is difficult, because it requires broad changes in land management practices and pest control practices in agricultural and residential areas.

Efforts to improve water quality need to account for residual contamination from past practices. Some resident wildlife species already contain high levels of contaminants in their tissues that are passed on to predators. Some contaminants, such as mercury, are difficult to remove because they are stored in river and bay sediments and gradually released over long periods into the water.

One of the main sources for water quality impairments in San Francisco Bay is drainage from the Central Valley. Thus, an integral part of addressing Bay water quality problems is the improvement of Central Valley water quality.

Other major sources of water pollution are from the lands around San Francisco Bay itself. To address this problem, state and federal agencies need to continue implementing the Comprehensive Conservation and Management Plan for the Bay and Delta (SFEP 1993). This plan includes actions such as watershed assessment, researching the effects of toxins on wildlife, reducing pesticide loads, supporting watershed management efforts, improving agricultural practices, reducing urban runoff, modifying wetlands flooding and drainage practices, and cleaning up environmental contaminants.

p. Fish and Game should expand funding and coordinate efforts to prevent the establishment of invasive species and to reduce the damage of established invasive species.

See Statewide Action f in Chapter 4.

An example program within this region that can be used as a model for implementing those recommendations is the San Francisco Estuary Invasive Spartina Project (2005).

The importance of river and estuarine systems makes aquatic invasive species of particular concern in this region. In addition to the statewide actions mentioned above, efforts are also needed to implement the California Bay-Delta Authority's Non-native Invasive Species Implementation Plan. This plan provides more specific actions related to collaborative partnerships, education, monitoring and assessment, research, technology transfer, and enforcement.

q. State and federal agencies should expand law enforcement funding and staffing and coordinate efforts to enforce regulations to prevent the degradation of rivers and streams and to detect, prevent, and take actions to protect water quality.

Adequate resource and water quality protection is an important element of river and estuarine system conservation. Agencies need to have sufficient staffing and funding to be proactive in identifying and detecting problems before they become significant environmental issues. Officers need the time and ability to monitor general compliance with environmental regulations, in addition to their duties in responding to specific service calls and related work. Such ongoing monitoring can prevent the degradation of these vital areas.

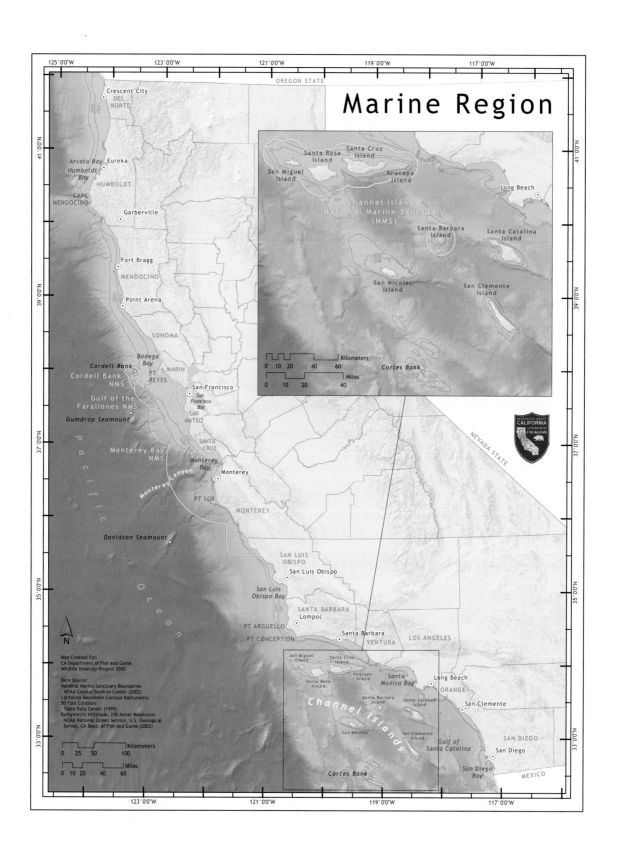

Marine Region

Map Created For:
CA Department of Fish and Game
Wildlife Diversity Project 2005

Data Source:
National Marine Sanctuary Boundaries
  NOAA Coastal Services Center (2002)
California Nearshore Contour Bathymetry
50 Foot Contours
  Teale Data Center (1999)
Bathymetric Hillshade, 200 Meter Resolution
  NOAA National Ocean Service, U.S. Geological
  Survey, CA Dept. of Fish and Game (2002)

15   Marine Region ～～～～～～～～～～～～～

Darrell Deuel

Along the western edge of California lies a stretch of wilderness that ranks as one of our planet's most productive ecosystems, with a plant and animal mass far exceeding that of the world's tropical rainforests. Comprising mountains, canyons, and forests, it supports some of the most diverse assemblages of wildlife found anywhere in the world. California's economy is in large part driven by it, the livelihoods of many Californians depend upon it, and one could argue that this particular region is what makes California an ultimate destination for people from all over the world.

This wilderness is the Pacific Ocean, its waves breaking along 1,100 miles of California's coastline. The Pacific's California Current, which flows down the North American Pacific Coast from Alaska to Central America, drives one of the most biologically important ocean upwelling systems in the world, where cold water, rich with nutrients, rises up from the depths of the ocean to the surface just off the coast. These nutrient-rich waters flow over, under, through, and past a diversity of coastal and underwater habitats, supporting abundant marine wildlife both in and above the water. Eelgrass beds, kelp forests, subtidal reefs, seamounts, canyons, vast expanses of featureless muddy or sandy bottom, and the **pelagic** zone create a complexity of habitats that maintains a dazzling level of biodiversity under water. Above the high-tide line, sandy beaches, headlands, estuaries, rocky shorelines, intertidal zones, offshore rocks, and islands provide critical habitat for marine birds and mammals and are what make the California coast spectacular. California's marine region is home to millions of mammals, birds, fish, sharks, turtles, urchins, clams, crabs, and worms; to grasses, algae, and other plants; and to trillions of microscopic plants and animals that float in the water, contributing to the planet's carbon- and oxygen cycles and feeding millions of other ocean organisms.

At the same time, the 220,000 square miles of combined state and federal waters off the coast of California support some of the busiest shipping lanes and ports in the world, multimillion-dollar commercial and recreational fisheries and tourism industries, and unparalleled opportunities for wildlife viewing and recreation. The coast's ecological and economic amenities offer compelling reasons to want to live in California. Indeed, 80 percent of the state's 36.8 million residents live within 30 miles of the coastline; not surprisingly, this isn't without its ramifications for the health and integrity of California's marine region and the wildlife it supports. Under pressure are the largest concentrations of breeding seabirds in the lower 48 states, the most diverse assemblage of marine mammals anywhere in the world, and the critical feeding and breeding grounds of dozens of threatened and endangered species, including the southern sea otter, the Northern elephant seal, the leatherback sea turtle, the white abalone, the Western snowy plover, and many others.

The pressures on wildlife resources that exist at the interface between urban development and oceans are similar the world over. Resource extraction, loss of habitat, pollution, invasive species, and global climate change threaten marine species off the coast of California just as they threaten marine wildlife in other parts of the Pacific and the world. That said, issues of wildlife management and conservation in California's marine region are unique in a few key respects. Because California's marine region is of global importance as an area of intense productivity and biodiversity, what happens here has ramifications for marine wildlife living throughout the Pacific Ocean, and the ever-increasing population of California confers a rising level of pressure on this system and the wildlife that depend upon it.

California Marine Policy

Conservation of marine biodiversity will require both a significant advancement in our understanding of marine ecosystems and the development and implementation of new and innovative tools for managing and conserving habitats and the marine life they support. Two reports on the status of oceans and ocean management in the United States, one produced by the Pew Oceans Commission, the other by the United States Commission on Ocean Policy, were released in spring 2003. These two independent and nearly simultaneous publications essentially came to the same conclusion: The nation's oceans are in trouble, and radical changes are essential in the way federal and state governments manage them.

Upon the release of these reports, California was already at the forefront in recognizing that the conservation of marine life diversity and abundance largely depends on the development and implementation of new marine policy. The Marine Life Management Act (MLMA), effective January 1999, marked a new era in fisheries management in California. The MLMA focuses on managing for long-term sustainability over short-term economic gain, acknowledges that marine resources have nonconsumptive value to the public as a whole, and recognizes that healthy and intact marine habitats are essential for sustaining life in the ocean. It represents a radical departure from previous approaches to marine management, in that it calls for a science-based, multispecies, ecosystem-level approach to managing living marine resources.

Under the MLMA, the California Department of Fish and Game is charged with developing fishery management plans (FMPs), which are the primary basis for management. They are to be based on the best available science, fairly allocate increases or restrictions on harvest between commercial and recreational sectors, and involve stakeholders and constituents in the management planning process. Pursuant to the MLMA, Fish and Game developed FMPs for the white seabass, nearshore finfish, and market squid fisheries. The nearshore finfish plan exemplifies the application of an ecosystem-based approach: it focuses on 19 species (including several rockfish and greenling species, California sheephead, and cabezon) and makes recommendations for sustainably managing these populations through seasonal and area closures; restricted access to the fishery; regionally specific management to address variability in distribution and abundance of these species; and precautionary approaches to both the commercial and recreational fisheries. The nearshore finfish FMP also calls for research to generate data that will enable managers to adaptively manage the fishery as knowledge improves.

California's Marine Life Protection Act, effective in 1999, also set the precedent for new marine policy. In the early 20th century, about the time that President Theodore Roosevelt was establishing the country's national park system to protect vast stretches of wild lands, a fisheries biologist from Southern California noted that fish populations around Santa Catalina Island had declined dramatically due to "… lack of protection and overfishing"

(McArdle 2002). Nearly a century later, with just 0.006 percent of state and federal waters off California's coast designated as areas completely off-limits to fishing, the state of California passed the Marine Life Protection Act (MLPA). Establishing marine protected areas that limit human extraction of resources and alteration of habitats allows populations of fish and invertebrates to remain viable through the vagaries of environmental variation and oscillation. California's MLPA mandates a process for the establishment of a network of marine protected areas (MPAs) to help conserve the diversity and abundance of marine life and the integrity of marine ecosystems in California and requires that those areas be designed and sited according to sound science. (See Fig. 15.1.)

Most recently, in 2004, California heeded the call to action as laid out in the Pew Oceans Commission's and the U.S. Commission on Ocean Policy's reports by enacting the California Ocean Policy Act, which aims to better coordinate marine resource management across agencies by establishing the California Ocean Protection Council. Chief among this council's mandates is identifying a steady and sustainable source of revenue to support marine management and conservation in the state.

At the federal level, the Magnuson-Stevens Fishery Conservation and Management Act (1976, amended in 1996) guides the management of fisheries in federal waters, from 3 to 200 nautical miles offshore, via eight management councils around the country that address regionally specific issues pertaining to the sustainability of federally managed fisheries. The Pacific Fishery Management Council advises the National Marine Fisheries Service on the management of fisheries for salmon, groundfish (e.g., rockfish, lingcod, cabezon, Pacific cod, sole, flounder), sharks and skates, highly migratory species (e.g., tuna, billfish, dorado) and coastal pelagics (e.g., sardines and mackerel) off the coasts of California, Oregon, Washington, and Alaska. The council regulates these fisheries by implementing management plans calling for periodic stock assessments and controlling harvest of these species through seasonal and area closures, reductions in allowable **take**, and in the number of permits allowed for each fishery. Fish and Game works with the council and the National Marine Fisheries Service to manage those fisheries guided by a federal FMP for species caught or landed in California waters (e.g., rockfish, salmon, and sharks).

Species at risk

The Plan development team updated vertebrate and invertebrate species information in the California Natural Diversity Database (CNDDB) during 2004–2005. The following

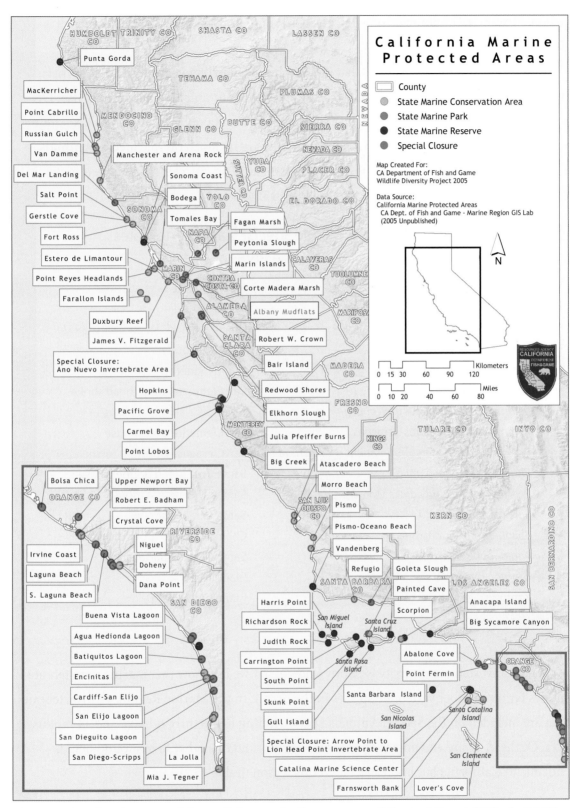

Fig. 15.1: Marine Protected Areas Prior to the Enactment of Central Coast MPAs in 2007

regional summary of numbers of wildlife species, **endemic** species, and **species at risk** is derived from the updated CNDDB.

There are 638 vertebrate species that inhabit the Marine Region at some point in their life cycle, including 163 birds, 62 mammals, 15 reptiles, four amphibians, and 394 fish. Of the total vertebrate species that inhabit this region, 38 bird **taxa**, 17 mammalian taxa, four reptilian taxa, two amphibian taxa, and 26 fish taxa are included on the **Special Animals List**. Of these, 15 are endemic to the Marine Region, and one species found here is endemic to California but not restricted to this region (Table 15.1).

Table 15.1: State-Endemic Special Status Vertebrates of the Marine Region

*	*Amphispiza belli clementeae*	San Clemente sage sparrow
*	*Aphelocoma insularis*	Island scrub-jay
*	*Batrachoseps pacificus pacificus*	Channel Islands slender salamander
	Eucyclogobius newberryi	Tidewater goby
*	*Lanius ludovicianus anthonyi*	Island loggerhead shrike
*	*Lanius ludovicianus mearnsi*	San Clemente loggerhead shrike
*	*Peromyscus maniculatus anacapae*	Anacapa Island deer mouse
*	*Peromyscus maniculatus clementis*	San Clemente deer mouse
*	*Pipilo maculatus (=erythrophthalmus) clementae*	San Clemente (spotted) towhee
*	*Pituophis catenifer pumilis*	Santa Cruz Island gopher snake
*	*Reithrodontomys megalotis santacruzae*	Santa Cruz harvest mouse
*	*Sorex ornatus willetti*	Santa Catalina shrew
*	*Spilogale gracilis amphiala*	Channel Islands spotted skunk
*	*Thamnophis hammondii ssp*	Santa Catalina garter snake
*	*Urocyon littoralis*	Island fox
*	*Xantusia riversiana*	Island night lizard

* denotes taxon is endemic to region

Marine invertebrate diversity is poorly known, but we do know that marine invertebrate species far outnumber vertebrate species in the ocean. In the Marine Region, 19 invertebrate taxa are included on the Special Animals List, including five arthropod taxa and 14 mollusk taxa. Of these, 17 are endemic to the Marine Region, and one other taxon found here is endemic to California but not restricted to this region (Table 15.2).

Table 15.2: State-Endemic Special Status Invertebrates of the Marine Region

*	*Ashmeadiella chumashae*	A megachilid bee
*	*Binneya notabilis*	Santa Barbara shelled slug (=slug snail)
	Cicindela hirticollis gravida	Sandy beach tiger beetle
*	*Coenonycha clementia*	San Clemente coenonycha beetle
*	*Haplotrema catalinense*	Santa Catalina lancetooth
*	*Haplotrema duranti*	Durant's snail
*	*Helminthoglypta ayresiana sanctaecrucis*	Ayer's snail
*	*Lasioglossum channelense*	Channel Island halictid bee
*	*Micrarionta facta*	Santa Barbara islandsnail
*	*Micrarionta feralis*	San Nicolas islandsnail
*	*Micrarionta gabbi*	San Clemente islandsnail
*	*Micrarionta opuntia*	Pricklypear islandsnail
*	*Pristiloma shepardae*	Shepard's snail
*	*Radiocentrum avalonense*	Catalina mountainsnail
*	*Sterkia clementina*	San Clemente Island blunt-top snail
*	*Trigonoscuta stantoni*	Santa Cruz Island shore weevil
*	*Xerarionta intercisa*	Horseshoe snail
*	*Xerarionta redimita*	Wreathed islandsnail

* denotes taxon is endemic to region

The Wildlife Species Matrix, including data on listing status, habitat association, and population trend for each vertebrate and invertebrate species included on the Special Animals List, is available on the Web at http://www.dfg.ca.gov/habitats/wdp/matrix_search.asp. For vertebrates, the matrix also includes links to species-level range maps. Additionally, a link to the California Department of Fish and Game's online Field Survey Form is available to assist in reporting positive sightings of species on the Special Animals List to the California Natural Diversity Database (CNDDB).

Two Species at Risk

Note: *The following discussion of two species at risk illustrates how stressors or threats affect species and highlights conservation challenges and opportunities. These species discussions are not intended to imply that conservation should have a single-species approach.*

The plight of each of these species is an example of the myriad challenges facing marine wildlife in California. The histories of abalone and common murre populations in California are quintessential stories of how stressors affect marine wildlife and diversity.

Abalone

Mark Cortright

Prized for their meat and their brilliant shells, abalone have been harvested in California for as long as humans have lived here. Native Americans and European settlers gathered them from beaches and intertidal zones, while southern sea otters preyed upon them in deeper water. Despite human and otter predation, abalone populations were able to sustain themselves because large adults, capable of producing millions of larvae, hid in inaccessible crevices, out of reach of predators. There were enough of these reproductive adults, and they were close enough together, that each year when they spawned millions of eggs and sperm into the water, enough embryos would develop into planktonic larvae that, during years when the oceanographic conditions were right for **recruitment**, the larvae managed to settle onto appropriate habitat, where they developed into juveniles and then adult animals.

When, as a result of the fur trade, southern sea otters all but disappeared in the 19th century, abalone populations flourished. The "abnormal" abundance of abalone in the 20th century drove a lucrative commercial and recreational fishery for several of the abalone species living along the coastline. In Southern California, fishermen first focused their efforts on red abalone and pink abalone, then greens, then whites, and finally they harvested black abalone. This serial depletion of abalone species helped drive a near-total collapse of abalone populations in Southern California (Karpov et al. 2000). In 1997, a moratorium was placed on all abalone fishing south of San Francisco Bay; today, only red abalone may be taken, only by recreational fishermen without the aid of scuba gear, and only north of San Francisco. Red abalone populations in Northern California appear to be stable (although there is some concern about recruitment), in part because the Fish and Game Commission has placed more stringent controls on how many abalone may be harvested each year by licensed recreational fishermen and also because free divers simply cannot descend far enough to collect the ones that live at depth (Karpov et al. 1998). The red abalone population in Southern California, on the other hand, is still at critically low densities.

Theoretically, the ban on all fishing for abalone south of San Francisco should have resulted in the steady improvement of abalone numbers, but their populations continued to decline after the fishery was closed. This is in part due to disease; black abalone, in particular, were hard-hit beginning in the mid-1980s by a disease called withering syndrome, and this emerging disease resulted in dramatic declines in this species both in the Channel Islands and on the mainland. But the inability of abalone populations to recover on their own in the absence of fishing pressure may also be due to the "Allee effect": Remaining breeding-age adults are now simply too few and far between to successfully reproduce. When they broadcast spawn, they are so far apart that their sperm and eggs do not mingle in the water column. The result is too few larvae and juveniles drifting in the pelagic zone, ready to take advantage of prime ecological conditions for development into adults. Most abalone populations have simply become so small that many scientists and resource managers believe they will never recover to the point of again sustaining a fishery. In May 2001, the National Marine Fisheries Service listed the white abalone as an endangered species under the Endangered Species Act, making it the first marine invertebrate whose listing was largely due to human take.

Common Murre

The common murre is a striking black-and-white bird that nests on offshore rocks and islands from British Columbia to Baja California. It feeds by ducking below the surface and "flying" underwater to catch fish and invertebrates and has been recorded as diving to depths exceeding 500 feet in pursuit of prey. When common murre chicks are just a few weeks old and still small, weighing only 25  percent of their adult body weight, they head out onto the water with one of their parents (usually the male), where they are attended and fed by that parent until well after they learn how to fly. In mid-to-late summer off California's coast, these adult-chick pairs, along with nonbreeding juveniles and adults, form vast rafts of birds sitting on the water.

The common murre is the most abundant breeding seabird off the coast of California, and, overall, their populations in the North Pacific are relatively stable. However, because these are ground-nesting, surface-dwelling birds that dive underwater to feed, they are uniquely sensitive to certain types of human activities. As a result, historically they have suffered huge declines in California at the hands of humans. In the early 1800s, there were likely close to 3 million birds nesting on the Farallon Islands in Central California (Manuwal et al. 2001). However, hunting and egg collecting by European settlers in the early 19th century had devastating and cumulative effects, and, by 1930, the colony was pushed to near-extinction. Over this same period, the southernmost colonies of common murres in the Channel Islands also disappeared.

Fortunately, the disallowing of egg collecting and increased levels of government protection for nesting habitat allowed common murres to begin rebounding. But between 1979 and 1989, the Central California common murre population plummeted once again, declining by almost 10 percent a year; by 1989, the total state population was half of what it was in 1980 (Manuwal et al. 2001). This decline was in part due to the 1982–1983 El Niño season, when many young birds starved due to the collapse of their prey base. But the population's ability to recover from this natural climatic event was severely hampered by oil pollution and gill net fisheries. More than 75,000 common murres died between 1979 and 1987 as a result of entanglement in gill nets in Monterey Bay, the Gulf of the Farallones, and Bodega Bay (Mills and Sydeman 2004). During this same period, two major oil spills occurred, each of which killed several thousand murres.

While common murre populations are increasing once again in Central California, in part due to bans placed on gillnetting in the 1980s and 1990s, they still have not recolonized the Channel Islands, and they remain susceptible to oil from spills statewide. Indeed, common murres continue to be the most susceptible of seabirds species in California to the consequences of oil contamination of the marine environment; just recently, oil leaking from the *Jakob Luckenbach*, which sank in 1954 in the Gulf of the Farallones, killed an estimated 20,000 seabirds throughout the winter of 2003, most of them common murres (Hampton et al. 2003a).

Stressors Affecting Marine Wildlife and Habitats

The diversity and abundance of marine wildlife in California are profoundly affected by human activities in, on, and alongside the water, and the focus of this report is on those stressors and how to address them.

It is important, however, to consider marine stressors in the context of the natural variation that occurs as a result of large-scale shifts in oceanographic conditions, which create a background of natural change that has a profound impact on marine diversity. For example, the distribution and abundance of marine species very much depend on the strength and temperature of the California Current, which itself varies on a scale measured in decades. When atmospheric pressure in the far northern Pacific is high, the California Current is stronger, the water temperature is colder, and significant upwelling drives high productivity of the ecosystem, allowing populations of many species to flourish under these conditions of plentiful food. When atmospheric pressure in the far northern Pacific is lower, the California Current weakens, water temperatures rise, and there is less upwelling of nutrient-laden water. As a result, the planktonic biomass shrinks, as do the size and range of populations of marine wildlife positioned higher in the food web.

Another oceanographic process that affects the distribution and abundance of marine species is the El Niño–Southern Oscillation (ENSO), when the temperature of the equatorial ocean off the coast of South America rises. When ENSOs are particularly strong, warming of ocean water extends further north of the equator than usual, affecting the California Current. Warmer ocean temperatures off our coast favor the presence of more of the species that prefer warmer water and are less hospitable for the coldwater species, which then typically move offshore. The opposite occurs the year after a strong ENSO, when the waters off our coast become cooler than usual. Strong El Niño–Southern Oscillation events appear to be increasing in frequency, possibly due to global climate change.

These regime shifts in oceanographic conditions mean that, over billions of years, marine organisms have evolved life-history strategies—growth processes, feeding preferences, movement patterns, reproductive behaviors—that enable populations of species to survive periods of low food availability or years when ocean temperatures or ocean current characteristics do not favor the successful production of next year's generation of organisms. The distribution and abundance of marine species naturally fluctuate over time with shifts and changes in the ocean, and populations and ecosystems remain intact because they are large and resilient enough to make it through the tough years.

The challenge for many marine species now, however, is that humans have disrupted the intricacies of this dynamic system such that human activities in and on the ocean cause additional stress for marine species in California. Major stressors affecting marine wildlife and their habitats in California are:

- Overfishing
- Degradation of marine habitats

- Invasive species
- Pollution
- Human disturbance

Overfishing

Commercial and recreational fishing can be an important stressor affecting marine wildlife diversity in California. While fishing is of significant socioeconomic value in the state's coastal communities, every year it results in the removal of large numbers of fish from the ocean. Fishing directly reduces the abundance of fish and may indirectly affect the abundance and diversity of other species, including birds and mammals, that share the marine ecosystem with fish.

The direct effect of fishing is a matter of numbers; millions of fish are harvested every year. In 2003, 274 million pounds of fish were commercially landed in California (CDFG 2004d). Between 1998 and 1999, recreational fishermen caught 17.8 million fish, of which 9.6 million were harvested whole, 7.1 million were returned live to the water, and 1.2 million were used as bait, filleted at sea, or discarded dead (Leet et al. 2001). The Southern California commercial-passenger fishing-vessel fleet alone caught an average of 4.25 million fish a year between 1963 and 1991; notably, despite a consistent fleet size of approximately 200 boats since 1991, this figure has decreased to 2.5 million fish a year (Dotson and Charter 2003).

The level of harvest that occurred in the last century in California—indeed, throughout the world (Jackson et al. 2001)—was largely the result of a general sense that the ocean's bounty was limitless, an attitude shared equally by both the fishermen and the fisheries managers. Regulations placed on fisheries were often not precautionary, and commercial and recreational fishermen had the equipment and technology to catch whatever the regulators would allow.

The lack of a precautionary approach in some cases has contributed to the decline of some populations to very low numbers. As of 2003, 36 percent of United States' commercially harvested stocks (those for which we have enough information with which to assess their status) are officially categorized as overfished; another 21 percent are classified as "experiencing overfishing" (NMFS 2004). Information isn't available on the status of most stocks of fish caught in California to make a similar evaluation of their status, but for species for which stock assessments have been completed relatively recently, such as for cowcod (Piner et al. 2005), stocks are lower than target levels.

In the 1990s, state and federal governments began to realize that some populations of species caught off this country's coasts, including in California, were in decline. In addition, the overall fishing capacity of some commercial fleets was too large compared to the stocks that they were harvesting. In response to these conditions, California began implementing restricted-access policies in some commercial fisheries.

The number of permits in the nearshore fishery, for example, has been reduced from roughly 1,300 to approximately 200 over the last several years. Many of California's fisheries have undergone one, if not more, reductions in the number of permits given to fishermen in order to reduce fishing pressure on stocks that could not sustain the higher level of fishing effort. Other management actions taken in recent years due to declining stocks have included area closures, such as prohibiting bottom fishing over much of the continental shelf to allow several species of depressed rockfish to recover, which has resulted in significant economic hardship to both commercial and recreational sectors.

Harvesting one species can have ripple-like effects on other organisms in the marine ecosystem and can result in the decline of nonharvested species (Dayton et al. 2002). For example, heavily fishing one species can disrupt food webs; approximately 360 million of the 425 million pounds of fish commercially harvested in California in 1999 were coastal pelagic fish, such as market squid, anchovy, mackerel and sardines (Leet et al. 2001)—principal prey species for fish-eating fish, as well as seabirds and marine mammals.

By the same token, fishing one species can also allow another species to flourish unnaturally, thereby disrupting delicate balances among predator and prey that have evolved over eons. Such imbalances are classically illustrated in California by sea otters, sea urchins, and kelp forests. After sea otters were hunted to the brink of extinction in the late 19th century, populations of their favored prey item, sea urchins, grew exponentially. These unnaturally large populations of urchins overgrazed kelp forests, reducing this highly biodiverse habitat and thereby indirectly disrupting the life cycles of other fish species that depend upon kelp forests for habitat. Today, careful management and conservation of a remnant population of sea otters on the Central Coast has allowed the southern sea otter to rebound—at the "cost" of a sea urchin population size that some consider not large enough to sustain an urchin fishery in this part of the coast but to the benefit of healthy, intact kelp forest habitat.

Fishing can result in significant mortality to nontargeted species through unintended harvest (or "bycatch"). California lacks adequate data with which to evaluate the ecological consequences of bycatch in our marine waters. A preliminary assessment of bycatch in the spot prawn trawl fishery in 2000 and 2001 documented a significant level of bycatch and also demonstrated that, compared to trawls, spot prawn traps significantly reduced bycatch of finfish. Entanglement in fishing gear is also a significant fishing-related cause of mortality for nontarget species, including seabirds and marine mammals. Injury or death resulting from entanglement has been identified as one of the most serious threats to seabirds in California (Mills and Sydeman 2004). In Central and Northern California, most of the set gillnet fisheries were closed between 1982 and 1987, with the last few remaining set gillnet fisheries in Central California shut down in 2002, when they were determined to be drowning large numbers of seabirds and marine mammals. The set gillnet fishery was in part responsible for a 50 percent decline in the state's population of common murres in the 1980s and the bycatch of numerous other seabird species (Manuwal et al. 2001).

Degradation of Marine Habitats

Unlike terrestrial wildlife species that tend to complete their entire lifecycles within a single or perhaps a few habitat types, the life histories of most marine wildlife species involve different parts of the ocean at different stages. Many of these essential marine habitats in California have been significantly changed, either by outright loss or by degradation of the quality of what habitat remains. Habitat loss, whether quantitative or qualitative, limits the capacity of marine species to complete critical parts or even all of their life cycle. Humans have altered marine habitats in many ways, including shoreline development (in the form of bulkheads, sea walls, jetties, and marinas), fishing (via bottom trawling and deposition of debris and derelict gear), and dredging (for navigation channels and underwater cable routes).

Giant kelp forests are a globally important, highly biodiverse habitat—sometimes called the "rainforests of the sea." Numerous species of marine invertebrates, fish, and mammals are associated with giant kelp forests, which offer a broad web of food in part derived from kelps. More importantly, the kelp-forest habitat offers nursery areas and protection from predators for many marine species. The size and shape of kelp forests are determined by season, ocean temperatures, nutrient availability in the surface waters, and grazing by marine herbivores. Some kelp forests were degraded by pollution and deposition of sediments from the land (especially in Southern California), and currently, giant kelp forests are being altered by the loss of species that live in and shape the kelp forest ecosystem.

The influence of sewage and industrial outfalls on marine wildlife has been documented since the 1970s, when coastal communities began monitoring the effects of these discharge operations, and the Clean Water Act of 1972 began requiring industrial plants and regional sanitation districts to monitor and minimize the consequences of their outfalls on the marine environment. Such monitoring has significantly reduced the inflow of particulate matter and chemicals into the ocean. Nevertheless, some chemical contaminants dumped in the marine environment persist for decades, and not all sewage outfalls in California operate at the highest levels of effluent treatment. And input of solid and liquid waste and contaminants into the ocean from uncontrolled sources like storm drains—called **nonpoint** source pollution—continue to pollute coastal waters. The effects of coastal power plants on marine life are also of ongoing concern to resource managers and scientists. Twenty-one power plants, from Eureka to San Diego, are permitted to either withdraw or discharge nearly 17 billion gallons of seawater per day. These cooling intakes and warm-water outfalls raise the temperature of the seawater around the plant, trap fish and eggs against intake screens, and draw small aquatic organisms like eggs and larvae into the plant. This latter effect—called "entrainment"—is believed to have the greatest harmful effect on marine resources and has led the state to require several of these plants to invest in marine enhancement projects as a mitigation measure (Richins 2005).

Bays, estuaries, and lagoons sit at the land-sea interface, functionally buffering the ocean from inflows of sediments from land. Because these waters are shallow (so sunlight penetrates easily) and relatively protected from strong wind action and currents, they are highly vegetated, supporting large underwater meadows of eelgrasses and extensive tidal salt marshes. These vegetated areas function as protective and nutrient-rich nursery grounds for large numbers of marine fish and invertebrates (Beck et al. 2003). However, of all marine habitats, bays, lagoons, and estuaries are probably the hardest hit by human activity. Shoreline development, intentional draining to make way for development, and destruction of upland watersheds have all contributed to erosion and sediment runoff, damaging these shallow underwater habitats and affecting their quality as habitat for marine organisms and plants. Deposition of sediments suffocates eelgrass beds; contaminants accumulate in sediments, creating toxic microenvironments for plant roots and for larval organisms; and dredging for navigation channels digs up plants and animals, transforms bottom contours, and suspends toxic sediments and benthic organisms. Shoreline armoring (bulkheads, seawalls, jetties) and diversion of rivers and streams flowing into the ocean disrupt the normal deposition of sand onto beaches that occurs through natural erosion and transfer of suspended sands by wave action. Declines in beach quality and quantity have negative consequences for species that depend upon sandy beach habitat for reproduction, like shorebirds, sea turtles, and California grunion.

Invasive Species

The unintended introduction of invasive species to marine habitats, both underwater and on shore, is a stressor to native marine species. These non-native invaders quickly and successfully establish residency and expand their range, adversely affecting native species by preying upon them or outcompeting them for critical habitat or food. Non-native species in the marine environment tend to be a more critical issue in bays and estuaries, where they are more likely to be introduced and to gain a foothold. Once an invasive species is established in a bay or estuary, it is generally there to stay—with few exceptions, eradication of marine invasives is exceedingly difficult.

California's coastal marine ecosystem has been invaded by hundreds of non-native species; in fact, San Francisco Bay ranks as one of the most-invaded bodies of water in the world, with an estimated 225 introduced species (SFEI 2004). Estimates are that a new species is unintentionally introduced and becomes established in San Francisco Bay every 14 weeks. Well-known non-native species invasions in California's marine environment include the

Caulerpa taxifolia Eradication

In June 2000, a patch of an aggressive non-native alga called *Caulerpa taxifolia* was discovered in a small coastal lagoon called Agua Hedionda, near Carlsbad in northern San Diego County, and shortly thereafter in Orange County's Huntington Harbor. Dubbed "killer algae," this alga was well known; accidentally introduced into the Mediterranean Sea in 1984, in 13 short years it had blanketed the sea's northern coastline, displacing numerous native marine plants and animals and disrupting commercial fisheries and coastal tourism. *Caulerpa* likely showed up in Agua Hedionda Lagoon via storm drains containing discarded water from hobbyists' saltwater aquariums. Because it is capable of living in a wide range of ocean temperatures and habitats and spreads easily if pieces of the plant are torn off by anchors or stormy weather, the *Caulerpa* invasion posed an immediate and dire threat to the nearshore marine ecosystem of Southern California, especially to native eelgrass beds, which are critical habitat for numerous marine species. Upon its discovery, federal, state, and local agencies waged a no-holds-barred effort to eradicate *Caulerpa* by sealing each patch of *Caulerpa* under a tarp and treating it with chlorine. To date, this appears to have been effective; the sites remain covered with the tarps, and, so far, no new patches of *Caulerpa* have appeared in the area. And while the experience in Carlsbad prompted the state to pass legislation in September 2001 to ban the sale and possession of nine different species of *Caulerpa*, it is still available for sale via various Web sites. Most marine resource managers agree that it is just a matter of time before *Caulerpa* invades other parts of the California coast.

European green crab, the Chinese mitten crab, the Asian clam, the yellowfin goby, and aggressive plants and algae like *Spartina alterniflora*, *Undaria*, and *Caulerpa taxifolia* (see "*Caulerpa taxifolia* Eradication," above). The yellowfin goby has become one of the most abundant species in San Francisco Bay and other bays and estuaries in California and is still increasing its range (Allen et al., in prep.). The European green crab, an underwater predator, was first detected in San Francisco Bay in 1989 and has since scurried up the Pacific coast all the way to Washington. Upon its arrival in California, the green crab reduced populations of native crabs and clams, and laboratory experiments showed that it was a voracious predator of juvenile Dungeness crabs (Grosholz et al. 2000). The population of another invader, the Asian clam, is so large that it has effectively knocked out the summer phytoplankton bloom in the northern part of San Francisco Bay, depriving hundreds of endemic marine organisms of an important food source (Grosholz 2002).

The brown alga *Undaria pinnatifida*, native to Japan, was first seen in Southern California harbors in 2000. By 2001, populations of *Undaria* had established themselves in harbors as far north as Monterey and even on the open coast of Santa Catalina Island. This alga likely first arrived in ballast water but may now be spreading via the movements of small boats, to which microscopic forms of the alga have attached. The cordgrass *Spartina alterniflora*, native to the Atlantic coast, was intentionally planted years ago in San Francisco Bay because it was thought to be an effective method for restoring the estuary. However, it has since invaded many of Northern California's tidal wetlands, rapidly engulfing tidal mudflats. Its consequences for wildlife have been well studied in San Francisco Bay, where it has devastated important foraging habitat for the millions of shorebirds that migrate through the Bay Area and depend upon open mudflats for foraging (PRBO 2004b). The presence of *Spartina alterniflora* is even implicated in the decline of the California clapper rail; the plant has altered tidal habitats to such an extent that the bird is now more vulnerable to terrestrial predators.

Above the high-tide line, California's marine wildlife are also threatened by non-native terrestrial predators. Rats and cats, especially, threaten nesting seabirds in California (Mills and Sydeman 2004). Cats have been introduced to five of the Channel Islands, where they drove the Cassin's auklet to extinction on Santa Barbara Island, and black rats significantly reduced the nesting population of Xantus's murrelets on Anacapa Island. Thanks to concerted eradication efforts, cats have been removed from most of the smaller islands, including Anacapa and Santa Barbara islands, but still remain on Santa Catalina, San Nicolas, and San Clemente islands. Black rats have been removed from Anacapa Island (K. Faulkner pers. comm.) but are still present on San Miguel, San Clemente, and Santa Catalina islands. Seabirds are threatened by non-native herbivores like feral pigs, which trample nesting burrows and significantly alter native habitat by grazing on native vegetation and causing erosion. Feral pigs have been eradicated from Santa Rosa and San Clemente islands and are being eradicated on Santa Catalina and Santa Cruz Islands (Mills and Sydeman 2004, G. Davis, pers. comm.).

Pathogens have the potential to act as invasive non-native species in California's marine wildlife. For example, a significant percentage of southern sea otters that wash ashore dead are infected with a brain parasite, *Toxoplasma gondii*, which normally infects cats. Some of the dead otters are also infected with another central nervous system parasite, *Sarcocystis neurona*, which is carried by Virginia opossums and causes a well-recognized disease in horses. The exact mode of transmission of these parasites to sea otters is being investigated but is likely related to inadequate treatment of sewage effluent in some coastal areas such as Morro Bay (Kreuder et al. 2003). Pathogen pollution is of most concern where it may potentially affect populations of threatened or endangered species, like the southern sea otter, which, after a century of population growth, has recently shown signs of decline, in part due to infectious disease. Along these same lines, a parasitic marine sabellid worm native to South Africa was accidentally introduced into California's abalone aquaculture industry, where it devastated culture stocks. Fortunately, Fish and Game successfully eradicated this parasite from culture facilities, and it never escaped into the open water, where it might have had devastating effects on abalone species, one of which is federally endangered.

Pollution

The most well-recognized and uniformly feared form of pollution in the marine environment is oil. Whether from a catastrophic spill, a natural seep, or from a non-point source like run-off from land, oil most notably affects marine birds and marine mammals. Oil pollution also exerts damaging effects on numerous other organisms, including microscopic plankton, either by the directly toxic effects of oil exposure or by sublethal, chronic effects that limit population viability or that damage critical underwater and shoreline habitats.

Oil spills can affect thousands of birds at a time. The *Apex Houston* spill off Central California in 1986 is estimated to have killed more than 10,000 birds (Mills and Sydeman 2004). The *Jakob Luckenbach* spill, which oiled birds in the Gulf of the Farallones throughout the winter of 2003, is estimated to have killed 20,000 seabirds. The *Luckenbach* had likely been leaking oil for decades since sinking in 1954 and is now believed to have been a major source of chronic oil pollution in Central California, causing numerous "mystery" spills that have occurred year after year, especially during the 1990s (Hampton et al. 2003a). Over the last 20 years, significant numbers of seabirds have been affected by 12 major oil spills off the coast of California (Hampton et al. 2003b).

Oil in the marine environment may affect only a few individuals or whole populations, depending upon its location and whether it is present in a place or season when significant numbers of seabirds are in the area wintering, breeding, or molting. In California, the seabird species most frequently affected is the common murre, in part because, at certain times of the year, murres spend much of the time sitting on the water, where they are easily oiled. The size of an oil spill doesn't necessarily correlate with the amount of damage it can do. Even small spills can have big consequences for birds if the oil contaminates an area where large numbers of seabirds are rafting or foraging.

Human Disturbance

As coastal communities grow, and tourism continues to bring millions of visitors every year to the California coast, more and more people seek opportunities to make their livelihoods or recreate, whether onshore, in, or on the water, bringing people and marine wildlife into closer and more-frequent proximity to one another. Disturbance, whether from light and noise produced by human activity or simply by the presence of humans themselves, can cause marine animals to alter their behaviors in ways that reduce their survival on an individual basis or disrupt breeding efforts of populations.

Hikers, boaters and kayakers, and low-flying aircraft can cause breeding birds to temporarily or permanently leave their nests, leaving the egg or chick vulnerable to exposure to weather or predation by other seabirds. People and their dogs walking on the beach startle and distress beach-feeding or -nesting shorebirds and seabirds, which then either abandon their feeding grounds or nests or simply stop establishing breeding colonies where they once did. The loss of undisturbed roosting sites was a cause of the decline of brown pelicans in the 1980s; Scorpion Rock, which sits near the main entry harbor for Santa Cruz Island, was historically an important roosting site for brown pelicans but is no longer used by the birds because the rock is so heavily used by kayakers (K. Faulkner pers. comm.). Both the Pacific population of the Western snowy plover and the California least tern have suffered population declines in California, in part because increasing numbers of people and their pets recreate in their nesting habitat on sandy beaches and in sand dunes.

Another disturbance having the potential to negatively affect California's marine wildlife populations is the increased level of noise and light produced by at-sea industries, including fishing, drilling, and underwater engineering. The Southern California market squid fishery, for instance, uses light boats to catch squid. The amount of light produced by these boats, as much as 30,000 watts per boat (described by some as providing enough light to read a newspaper from a mile away) disrupts the ability of night-foraging birds like the state-listed Xantus's murrelet to navigate to and from foraging grounds and has resulted in nest abandonment and low reproductive success for brown pelicans (Mills and Sydeman 2004; K. Faulkner pers. comm.). The bright lights also render seabirds more vulnerable to predation by gulls and raptors. Fish and Game has worked with the market squid fishing fleet to modify their lighting equipment by shielding the bulbs (so that light is directed down onto the water surface) and limiting the maximum wattage and is working with other resource agencies and fishermen to educate vessel operators about keeping nighttime on-deck light levels low when anchored offshore of seabird islands.

Underwater noise from large ship engines, military activity, engineering, and oil and gas exploration may disturb marine mammals. Biologists have described aberrant behavior of whales and dolphins during the use of underwater sonar by naval vessels, and noise-related damage to sensory organs has been postulated as a contributor in several mass stranding events in other parts of the country. As a result, the federal government is currently conducting research on hearing thresholds of marine mammals in order to make recommendations on underwater noise levels that will minimize their effects on marine mammals.

Conservation Actions to Restore and Conserve Wildlife

a. The state should fully implement the Marine Life Management Act to ensure that marine fisheries and the marine ecosystem are managed sustainably.

> • **The state should commit financial and personnel resources to developing and implementing fishery management plans.**
> Full implementation of the Marine Life Management Act (MLMA) will ensure that fisheries are managed more sustainably and with less impact on other species and habitat. However, a lack of adequate funding and personnel to support the process has resulted in a disconnect between the admirable principles and requirements within the Act and the reality of implementing it. A full rollout of the MLMA has been the responsibility of Fish and Game's Marine Region, but

since the legislation's enactment six years ago, the financial and staff resources dedicated to implementing it, inadequate to begin with, have been further reduced by 25 percent. The MLMA Master Plan itself states that "Funding required for [fishery management plans] is a fundamental issue needing resolution." While the state has succeeded in developing plans under the MLMA for nearshore finfish, white seabass, and market squid, it lacks sufficient funding and staff resources to develop them for other high-priority species identified in the FMP Master Plan.

- **The state should support and conduct more fish and invertebrate stock assessments.**
  Along with adequate funding and resources for developing science-based fishery management plans, the state at the same time needs to fully assess the size, age structure, or recruitment rates of the stocks of species of fish and invertebrates caught in state waters. Currently, too few such assessments are conducted by Fish and Game, again, in part, because the department has been inadequately funded and staffed to do so. Without adequate assessments, the ability of resource agencies to create and implement fishery management plans is hampered.

- **The state should expand monitoring of recreational fisheries.**
  The MLMA applies to all species caught in California, both commercially and recreationally. At present, the state lacks a complete understanding of the scale and scope of recreational fisheries on par with its understanding of commercial fisheries. This lack of information impairs the state's ability to incorporate appropriate measures for sustainability into fishery management plans. Fish and Game currently monitors the annual recreational take by surveying the commercial passenger fishing vessel fleet and private fishermen, using the California Recreational Fishing Statistical Survey (CRFSS). Fish and Game has tripled its surveying effort in the last year to obtain better estimates of recreational take of rockfish; the result has been more accurate data on species and total fish taken. The CRFSS applies to finfish only; thus, there is no information on recreational take of invertebrates. Along with expanding the CRFSS program, the state should look for ways to share with recreational fishermen the responsibility for monitoring catch. One possible method would be to establish angling management organizations for recreational fishing that would place monitoring and reporting responsibility on the local recreational fishing communities (Sutinen and Johnston 2003).

- **The state should support and conduct more scientific research and long-term monitoring to enable adaptive management of fisheries.**
  A core tenet of the Marine Life Management Act is that fisheries management plans must be based on the best available science. Furthermore, the Act mandates that the state adaptively manage fisheries; i.e., that fishery management plans be continually reassessed and revised based on new information. The state should commit more resources to support and conduct research that generates both fishery-dependent and non-fishery-dependent data essential to carrying out that mandate. Fish and Game has taken steps to address the current lack of personnel and financial resources by implementing the Cooperative Resource Assessment of Nearshore Ecosystems (CRANE) project with university scientists and other resource agencies. This highly collaborative program started in 2002 and is collecting habitat, biological, and oceanographic data by means of scuba diver- and remotely operated-vehicle surveys in shallow rocky reef habitats up and down the coast. This innovative program will, however, require new funds in order to continue over the long term. Given the current availability of financial and personnel resources, the state should continue to develop innovative ways of conducting

research, including programs that involve fishermen in data collection, and programs that utilize technologically advanced systems for collecting data and monitoring remotely. Fundamentally, however, the state needs to adequately fund and conduct marine research and resource monitoring and not rely solely on organizing others to do the critical work that is inherently governmental and core to the state's public responsibility for resource stewardship.

- **The state should evaluate bycatch.**
  Because it has the potential to affect marine biodiversity, the state needs to get a better handle on the extent of bycatch in the state-managed fisheries, on par with federal oversight of bycatch effects in federally managed fisheries. The state should collect data on the harvest of nontarget species in major fisheries and develop recommendations to address bycatch concerns through the fishery management plan process and through enforcement of regulations designed to protect nontarget species. This could be accomplished with fishery observers—individuals placed on commercial fishing vessels to independently record data on catch and bycatch and on interactions between the fishing vessel and sea turtles, sea birds, and marine mammals. Observer programs are a reliable independent source for this type of detailed data but potentially costly; other data collection methods, such as remote-monitoring technologies, should be considered.

b. **The state should move forward in implementing the Marine Life Protection Act by establishing a network of marine protected areas.**

- **The state should implement the Marine Life Protection Act statewide.**
  One of the best actions the state can take to ensure marine biodiversity is establishing a network of marine reserves. California recognized the need for such areas when it enacted the Marine Life Protection Act in 1999. Currently, the state is implementing the act through the Marine Life Protection Act Initiative, a public-private partnership that provides essential financial and personnel resources to the planning process in Central California. It is imperative that the state commit the financial and personnel resources to this planning process statewide, enabling a scientifically defensible network of marine protected areas to be established for the benefit of marine life diversity.

- **The state should take a habitat approach to marine protected area (MPA) planning.**
  For the most part there is not enough fundamental biological and ecological data available to support sound decisions regarding MPA designation to be based on those criteria alone. A habitat approach to MPAs allows preservation of ecological linkages among species. To site MPAs that protect key habitats, the state should invest in the creation and distribution of a statewide detailed map of critical marine habitat upon which to base consideration of alternatives for protecting them. The habitat approach to MPA designation could apply to above-water species, as well. For example, some closures around sensitive seabird colonies have taken place through the establishment of the Channel Islands Marine Protected Areas network, but the state should consider additional protected areas around these colonies to preserve their foraging habitat during the nesting season.

- **The state should evaluate and consider marine bird and mammal migration and feeding areas in the coastal and pelagic zones as marine protected areas, and**

consideration should be given to protecting parts of the ocean not necessarily contiguous with a land mass.

Initial planning for pelagic reserves in California has begun (Pelagic Working Group 2002); the state should facilitate moving this process forward.

- **The state should develop a program to provide greater protection for intertidal habitats (tidepools).**

Human recreational exploration of intertidal areas (tidepooling) may damage microscopic plants and animals that live on the rocks. Scientific studies have documented significant negative consequences for the intertidal zone from tidepooling activity in Southern California (Guang-yu Wang pers comm.), and other scientists have conjectured that full recovery from human damage to the intertidal zone could require decades of complete protection from human use. The state should assess whether intertidal habitats statewide need a higher level of protection from human use, so that this habitat remains intact and undamaged. An assessment will require both scientific studies and a socioeconomic analysis of tidepool use for recreation and education.

- **Federal and state agencies should partner to advance marine stewardship in areas of jurisdictional overlap, especially with regard to marine protected areas.**

Multiple federal and state agencies, with varying mandates, have jurisdictional authority over marine waters off California. For example, the National Oceanic and Atmospheric Administration manages fisheries via the National Marine Fisheries Service's Pacific Fishery Management Council and regulates the use of vast tracts of coastal ocean via the National Marine Sanctuaries program. Additionally, the National Park Service is charged with protecting and conserving marine species on land and in the nearshore marine environment. The Bureau of Land Management manages the California Coastal Monument, composed of more than 20,000 offshore rocks. On the state level, the Dept. of Fish and Game manages and conserves marine resources within state waters; the California Coastal Commission regulates and oversees development and use of the coastal zone; the California State Coastal Conservancy promotes public access to the coastline and protection and enhancement of marine resources; State Parks operates several coastal protected areas; and the State Water Resources Control Board protects ocean water quality. To implement stronger, more well-coordinated and sustainable policies, all agencies with jurisdiction in California's coastal waters should promote and engage in multiagency partnerships where jurisdictions overlap and missions are complementary.

- **The state should enforce the protection of established marine protected areas.**

Concurrent with the designation of marine protected areas in California must be a financial commitment on the part of the state to enforce their protected status. The state should dedicate resources to investigating, developing, and implementing new and economical ways of enforcing the protected status of these areas. Options may range from simply clearly marking the boundaries, both on the water and on maps, to on-the-water patrolling of protected-area boundaries to advise user groups of their proximity to such areas and citing users who are violating rules and regulations. Marine reserves, areas off limits to fishing, will require an on-site enforcement approach. The state should also take a close look at the feasibility of developing technologically advanced ways of remotely monitoring protected areas; e.g., using satellite technology to monitor the proximity of fishing vessels to marine protected areas or to track boats. Ideally, such remote-monitoring programs would also enable the state to cite violators.

c. The state should secure Tidelands Revenues for implementation of the California Ocean Protection Act.

The California Ocean Protection Act (COPA), effective October 2004, has further advanced marine management in California by establishing a California Ocean Protection Council and allocating $10 million from the state's fiscal 2004–2005 budget to form the Ocean Protection Trust Fund, facilitating implementation of ocean and coastal research and management projects and policies. The act also authorizes the creation of an innovative Fisheries Revolving Loan Fund that would enable fishermen to implement projects aimed at improving commercial fisheries' financial and conservation performance, stabilizing coastal economies, increasing cost-sharing by industry, and freeing up state funds. The California Ocean Protection Act will make possible numerous additional programs and projects aimed at improving coastal water quality, enhancing coastal stewardship, and developing a long-term funding strategy for ocean and coastal protection and management. Having initially funded the California Ocean Protection Council with a one-time allocation in 2004–2005 to establish the Ocean Protection Trust Fund, it is imperative that the state ensure a long-term, permanent source of revenue to the Council in order to achieve these important marine conservation goals.

d. The state should increase efforts to restore coastal watersheds.

This recommended action is discussed extensively in the South Coast, Central Coast, and North Coast region sections of this plan, and the reader is directed to those sections for detail. However, this recommended action warrants mention in the Marine section, as well, because of its importance for restoring and maintaining healthy underwater habitat for marine life in California. The level of damage done to estuarine and shallow bay habitats from massive diversions of freshwater flow, along with the deluge of sediment washing down degraded and channelized rivers and streams, has had a significant negative effect on the health of key marine habitats like seagrass beds and kelp forests, which serve as nursery grounds for numerous marine species. From the Klamath River to the Tijuana River, it is imperative that the state continue to commit resources to the restoration of watersheds, so that they may once again act as natural buffers between land and sea.

e. The state should adopt a "no net loss" policy for critical marine habitat.

The state recognizes that coastal wetlands are a mere fraction of what they once were, that every last remaining acre must be protected, and that, to the extent feasible, concerted efforts should be made to restore wetlands to their historical status. The state should adopt a similar "no net loss" policy toward other critical habitats essential for sustaining marine diversity, such as kelp forests, seagrass beds, and beaches. When permanent damage to these essential habitats is unavoidable, the state should require that a similar amount of that habitat, or the enhanced quality or functionality of remaining habitat, is restored or created. When eelgrass beds are damaged by dredging, construction or heavy boat use, the state should require the purposeful enhancement of these beds, along the lines of the Southern California Eelgrass Mitigation Policy (NMFS 1991), and/or permanent protection of the integrity of other beds. Where kelp forests are damaged by underwater outflows, the state should continue to support the restoration of that kelp forest.

f. The federal and state resource agencies should expand efforts to eradicate introduced predators from all seabird colonies.

The state and federal resource agencies with authority to manage mainland areas and islands that support seabird colonies (the National Park Service, California Department of Fish and Game, California State Parks, and the U.S. military) should expand their collective efforts to completely eradicate all introduced terrestrial predators (primarily rats and cats) from the seabird colonies and roosting areas. The agencies should dedicate the personnel and financial resources necessary to make the long-term commitment required for these types of eradication efforts, which typically take years to achieve, and then require a commitment to maintain permanent vigilance against reinvasion. The resource agencies should also continue to control predators around mainland colonies of endangered species, such as beach-nesting colonies of Western snowy plovers and California least terns.

g. The state should systematically review and monitor the distribution and abundance of nonharvested marine fish and invertebrates.

Management and conservation of nonharvested marine fish and invertebrates is currently based on very little science. There is a paucity of historical and current data on distribution and abundance or on stressors to population sustainability. It is quite likely that many marine species native to California marine waters remain relatively or wholly undescribed by science. The state should conduct an in-depth, systematic review of the distribution and abundance of nonharvested marine fish and invertebrates within state waters, collating and collecting essential data on their distribution and abundance and on their reproductive strategies and prey preferences. The state should then assemble this data into an overall assessment of marine biodiversity and habitat in California. Where these species may be directly or indirectly affected by fisheries or habitat use, such data can then inform management and conservation plans that aim to reduce or minimize where necessary ecosystem-level effects of human activities. These data also can serve as a guide for resource agencies and the nonprofit sector in allocating their time, energy, and funding towards marine life conservation.

h. Federal and state resource agencies and institutions should foster and facilitate interstate collaborative research on marine species whose ranges cross jurisdictional boundaries.

Numerous marine species—including mammals, birds, turtles, and highly migratory fish species like tuna—range vast distances to and from breeding and feeding grounds. In some cases, species like the western sandpiper or the gray whale migrate from wintering grounds in Central America through or past California to feeding grounds in the Arctic. Improving strategies for the management and conservation of these species in California will depend upon a concerted effort on the part of all West Coast states, provinces, and countries to seek and engage in collaborative, cross-jurisdictional research and management. Whenever appropriate, the state should foster and facilitate interstate and international projects and initiatives. For some species, normal ranges can be so wide—in some instances, the entire North American Pacific coast—that, by necessity, a transjurisdictional collaborative approach will be needed to gain meaningful distribution and abundance data on which to base management decisions. Species like the gray whale and the black oystercatcher are good examples of broadly distributed species that warrant multistate collaborative research and cooperative management.

i. Federal and state resource agencies should foster and facilitate interstate collaborative enforcement efforts on marine species whose ranges cross jurisdictional boundaries.

Multiple federal and state agencies, with varying mandates, have enforcement authority over marine waters off California. For example, the National Oceanic and Atmospheric Administration enforces federal marine regulations via the National Marine Fisheries Service and regulates the use of vast tracts of coastal ocean via the National Marine Sanctuaries program. Additionally, the National Park Service is charged with protecting and conserving marine species on land and in the nearshore marine environment. The Bureau of Land Management manages the California Coastal Monument, composed of more than 20,000 offshore rocks. On the state level, the Department of Fish and Game enforces state marine regulations within state waters; State Parks operates and enforces regulations in several coastal protected areas; and the State Water Resources Control Board protects ocean water quality. To implement stronger, more well coordinated and sustainable enforcement policies, all agencies with jurisdiction in California's coastal waters should promote and engage in multi-agency partnerships where jurisdictions overlap and missions are complementary.

Appendices

Appendix A
Required Report Elements and Compliance

California Wildlife: Conservation Challenges, California's Wildlife Action Plan, addresses the eight required elements and subelements (as described in the NAAT Review Reference Guide) either in the plan document or its affiliated Web publications. The eight required elements are listed below with a description of where and how the elements are addressed.

1. Information on the distribution and abundance of species of wildlife, including low and declining populations, that is indicative of the diversity and health of the state's wildlife as the state fish and wildlife agency deems appropriate.

This element is addressed in Chapter 2, in the Species at Risk section of each regional chapter, and in the online Wildlife Species Matrix (http://www.dfg.ca.gov/habitats/wdp/matrix_search.asp).

The California Department of Fish and Game has a designated Special Animals List, also referred to as "species at risk" or "special status species." The Department uses this list to identify the species in greatest need of conservation. This list includes approximately 800 species, representing marine, aquatic, and terrestrial habitats, and includes birds, mammals, reptiles, amphibians, fish, and invertebrates. It focuses on threatened and endangered species and species of special concern, as well as species that are rare or declining in numbers. The Special Animals List is routinely updated, and species are added to list based on the criteria of state and federal wildlife and land management agencies. More information about this list is provided in Chapter 3 (Species at Risk) and Appendix D (Department of Fish and Game Species and Habitat Information Sources).

The Wildlife Action Plan team updated information for the nearly 800 special status species statewide on the Special Animals List. This task was accomplished by conducting literature searches for each species (including vertebrates and invertebrates), entering new-occurrence information from journal articles, consulting species experts for opinions regarding the inclusion of additional rare or threatened species, and entering data from the California Natural Diversity Database backlog of field survey forms and reports. The Wildlife Action Plan team then developed the Wildlife Species Matrix that includes information about those 800 species.

The Wildlife Species Matrix lists the species at risk and provides the rarity ranking status, associated habitat, population trends, and range maps for each, where available. The range maps indicate the distribution of the species at risk. New or updated range maps were prepared for vertebrates. The California Department of Fish and Game will continue to update range maps as new information becomes available. To the extent data is available, abundance information is provided in the Natural Diversity Database and in Fish and Game's Threatened and Endangered Species and Species of Special Concern reports. These reports are routinely updated every few years. More information about these reports is provided in Appendix D (Department of Fish and Game Species and Habitat Information Sources).

The Species at Risk section in each regional chapter summarizes the numbers of species, endemic species, and species at risk that are associated with the region and included on the Special Animals List.

2. Descriptions of locations and relative condition of key habitats and community types essential to conservation of species at risk.

This element is addressed in the Stressors Affecting Wildlife and Habitats section of each regional chapter. The regional scale, such as a portion of a county or the bay-delta, is appropriate because it is the scale at which many of the stressors act and affect habitat condition, and it is the scale at which most resource agencies are organized for conservation management.

The Wildlife Action Plan team conducted regional scoping meetings and consulted regional experts to identify the major stressors affecting wildlife and habitats in each region. In the California Wildlife Action Plan, the key habitats and community types important for species at risk are discussed in the context of the major stressors affecting wildlife and habitats.

The California Department of Fish and Game has an ongoing program to collect habitat distribution and condition information for priority habitats and regions. The Vegetation Classification and Mapping Program conducts many of the habitat surveys and produces the habitat and condition maps for priority conservation regions or areas. (See the Vegetation Classification and Mapping Program on the Web at http://www.dfg.ca.gov/bdb/html/vegcamp.html.) The program is currently focused on western Riverside County (the area of a new NCCP), the Sierra Nevada western foothills (an area of significant biodiversity and great development pressures), and the San Francisco Bay Delta (an area with major water management concerns and essential habitats).

Detailed habitat information is typically compiled as part of major conservation planning efforts such as development of a Natural Community Conservation Plan (NCCP) or Fish and Game's high mountain lakes program. Habitat location and condition studies will continue as part of these kinds of large-scale regional conservation efforts.

Habitat location and condition information is also collected with species sighting records for the Natural Diversity Database. Additionally, available habitat location and condition information is imported into the California Wildlife Habitat Relationships System for use by biologists and conservation practitioners. (See http://www.dfg.ca.gov/bdb/html/wildlife_habitats.html.)

The key habitats and their condition and community types important for species at risk are discussed at the regional level in the context of the major stressors affecting wildlife and habitats. For example, riparian habitats and condition are addressed and the stressors affecting riparian habitats are discussed in several of the regional chapters. In addition, a workshop on conserving riparian habitats was held to discuss the condition and conservation of riparian habitats (workshop results are in Appendix F). Oak woodlands and aquatic habitats are other examples of key habitats, the conditions of which are addressed in the regional chapters.

Numerous ongoing efforts in California gather information on vegetation and habitat condition. The most detailed habitat condition analyses are done in conjunction with regional habitat conservation planning efforts. Among many other regional habitat analyses efforts, the following are examples of California projects or programs that have compiled detailed habitat information:

- Natural Community Conservation Programs in Southern California
- The San Francisco Bay Area Wetlands Ecosystem Habitat Goals Project
- The CalFed Ecosystem Restoration Program
- Fish and Game's High Mountain Lakes Surveys
- The North Coast Watershed Assessment Program
- Habitat Joint Ventures (there are five Joint Ventures in California)
- The Sierra Nevada Ecosystem Project (completed in 1996)

3. Descriptions of problems and threats that may adversely affect species at risk or their habitats, and priority research and survey work needed for restoration and conservation of these species and habitats.

Problems and threats affecting species are addressed in Chapter 3 (Threats to Wildlife Diversity) and in the Stressors Affecting Wildlife and Habitats section of each regional chapter. The stressors were identified through regional scoping meetings, regional expert consultations, review of wildlife and land conservation plans and documents, and regional peer reviews (see Appendix B for a description of the strategy development). There was little disagreement in workshops, among experts consulted, and in the literature regarding the threats and problems affecting wildlife.

The discussion of priority research and survey needs appears in Section 1 (Resource Assessment) of Chapter 6 (Strengthening California's Conservation Capabilities). Additional research and survey work are important priorities for nearly all aspects of wildlife and conservation efforts throughout the state. With regard to research and survey work, the California Department of Fish and Game chose to focus on wildlife and ecosystems monitoring and on the management of the data that contribute to resource assessment.

The California Department of Fish and Game established a new Resource Assessment Program (RAP) to coordinate and prioritize wildlife and ecosystem monitoring work. (See the RAP description on the Web at http://www.dfg.ca.gov/habitats/RAP/default.html.)

RAP efforts that have contributed to the development of the California Wildlife Action Plan include:

- Conducting an initial survey to identify resource assessment activities of public and private institutions throughout the state (see Appendix I).

- Sponsoring, in partnership with the UC Davis Wildlife Health Center, a workshop on monitoring and assessment priorities. The participants represented various state and federal agencies, universities, and conservation organizations. The workshop goals were: 1) Identify key resource assessment and monitoring priorities in California; 2) Identify top biological issues to address through monitoring; 3) Develop strategies for establishing and collaboratively implementing resource assessment priorities; and 4) Inform participants of the current resource assessment program efforts to increase opportunities for collaboration on future endeavors. (See the workshop results on the Web at http://www.dfg.ca.gov/habitats/index.html.)

4. Descriptions of conservation actions determined to be necessary to conserve the identified species and habitats, and priorities for implementing such actions.

This element is addressed in Chapter 4 (Statewide Conservation Actions) and the Conservation Actions to Restore and Conserve Wildlife section of each regional chapter.

Conservation actions are major efforts, often involving multiple agencies and partners. The conservation actions identify the most appropriate agencies or partners likely to take the lead in the implementation of the actions. The actions are described with enough detail to be clear but in broad enough terms to accommodate flexibility in how they may be implemented.

Developing more specific objectives and performance goals for conservation actions are appropriately done by the agencies and partners, whether statewide, regional, or local, that will be engaged in implementing the conservation actions. Environmental indicators and performance goals will be developed in the early implementation phase of the conservation actions.

Only priority actions are presented in the California Wildlife Action Plan.

Prioritization of conservation actions will continue as the California Plan and its recommended actions are discussed further with agencies and partners that are likely to be involved in implementation.

5. Descriptions of the proposed plans for monitoring species at risk and their habitats for monitoring the effectiveness of the conservation actions proposed in Element 4 and for adapting these conservation actions to respond appropriately to new information or changing conditions.

This element is addressed in Chapter 5 (Monitoring California's Conservation Actions).

Fish and Game and numerous federal, state, and local agencies and private organizations are engaged in various levels of monitoring of species and natural communities throughout the state. Fish and Game's Resource Assessment Program conducted a survey of the wildlife and ecosystem monitoring efforts throughout the state in order to build upon existing efforts and to improve the usefulness of monitoring results from various institutions.

Chapter 5 provides guidance for developing monitoring and adaptive management programs; it identifies existing monitoring efforts and provides a process for designing a monitoring program for each conservation action. Specific monitoring is often best designed by those organizations engaged in implementing a conservation action.

It is not practical to monitor all species at risk and their habitats. It is important to strengthen the state's resource assessment capabilities so that it can better coordinate setting priorities for regional wildlife and habitat monitoring and design and implement efficient monitoring strategies.

Section 1 (Resource Assessment) of Chapter 6 (Strengthening California's Conservation Capabilities) discusses strengthening the state's capacity to monitor and assess habitats and ecosystems across the state.

The California Department of Fish and Game's resource assessment efforts will continue to identify priority regions, habitats, and species for field monitoring and direct resources toward those priorities. Emphasis is given to assessments of natural communities and assessments at a regional scale. For example, the Department has identified oak woodlands in the Sierra Nevada foothills as a high priority for resource assessment; oak woodlands are one of the most biodiverse natural communities, and this area is also experiencing significant development pressures. The results of these coordinated resource assessment efforts will reveal the effectiveness of one or more conservation actions in a given region.

Many of the conservation actions recommended in the California Wildlife Action Plan will be developed further through workshops and public processes. Implementation plans for those actions will include monitoring and adaptive management plans as needed. For example, the California Wildlife Action Plan recommends the completion and implementation of some regional conservation planning efforts, such as the West Mojave Plan. Plans for the monitoring of species and habitats and for monitoring the effectiveness of conservation actions, including procedures for adaptive management, are incorporated into such regional conservation plans.

6. Descriptions of procedures to review the strategy at intervals not to exceed 10 years.

This element is addressed in the Introduction to the California Wildlife Action Plan. The California Department of Fish and Game will establish a Conservation Strategy Special Project Team to monitor and facilitate the implementation of conservation actions recommended in this Plan.

7. Description of the plans for coordinating, to the extent feasible, the development, implementation, review, and revision of the strategy with federal, state, and local agencies and Indian tribes that manage significant land and water areas within the state or administer programs that significantly affect the conservation of identified species and habitats.

This element is addressed in the Introduction to the California Wildlife Action Plan and in Appendix B. The Conservation Strategy Special Project Team, mentioned above, will also coordinate efforts with other agencies and partners to develop updates and revisions to the California Strategy in the years ahead. Coordinating implementation of the California Strategy and revisions to the strategy will involve meetings and workshops with involved agencies and partners.

8. Description of the necessary public participation in the development, revision, and implementation of the strategy.

This element is addressed in Appendix B (Agency Coordination and Public Participation in Plan Development, Review, and Revision) of the California Wildlife Action Plan.

Most of the conservation actions recommended in this report, if implemented, would be reviewed further through well-established public participatory processes such as the California Fish and Game Commission review process, the State Water Resources Control Board hearing process, U.S. Forest Service or BLM resource management planning processes, county planning commission and board of supervisors review processes, or legislative hearings. Conservation actions would also comply with public review requirements pursuant to the California Environmental Quality Act and the National Environmental Protection Act.

Appendix B
Agency Coordination and Public Participation in Plan Development, Review, and Revision

The Department of Fish and Game (DFG) contracted the Wildlife Health Center at the University of California, Davis, to manage the Plan development process and to prepare the report and Web publications. The Wildlife Health Center engaged public agencies, tribes, scientists, technical experts, and the interested public in the following ways to develop the Plan.

Scientific and Technical Input

Regional scoping meetings (November 2003–March 2004)—Regional Fish and Game biologists and managers developed initial lists of major stressors of wildlife habitats and important conservation activities in each region.

Regional consultations (February 2004–March 2005)—In each of the nine regions of the state, authors interviewed about 20 to 30 technical experts (including conservation planners, ecologists, public land managers, representatives of conservation organizations, and other knowledgeable local experts).

Review of conservation plans and scientific literature (February 2004–May 2005)—Authors reviewed relevant wildlife studies, publications, and conservation planning documents pertaining to each region. This review provided background regarding wildlife stressors and past and current conservation activities.

Fish and Game Statewide Review Team (March–April 2005)—Fish and Game scientists from each region of the state reviewed portions of the draft report and provided input regarding wildlife stressors and conservation actions.

Regional peer review groups (April–May 2005)— Regional peer-review groups (each made up of four to six reviewers) reviewed portions of the draft report and commented on the status of species and stressors and on technical, scientific, management, and policy considerations of the conservation actions.

Stakeholder Input

California Legacy Project's bioregional stakeholder workshops (2002–2003)—Some months before the development of this plan, the California Resources Agency initiated the California Legacy Project. This project's goal was to identify the most pressing conservation issues facing the state's biodiversity (both terrestrial and aquatic), recreation, working landscapes, and open space, as well as possible solutions to those issues. The project held nine, two-day-long regional "Spotlight on Conservation" workshops throughout the state to discuss conservation issues, plans, priorities, and monitoring needs. Approximately 3,300 people were invited, and each workshop was attended by approximately 70 to 100 people. Various stakeholder interests were represented by the participants in these workshops, including local, state, and federal agencies, business and building industry representatives, environmental nongovernmental organizations, and farming, ranching, and forestry interests. The similarity between the Legacy Project and this plan was sufficiently close, and the Legacy Project workshop results were sufficiently valuable to the plan's purposes, that it seemed unnecessary to essentially duplicate this extensive outreach effort. The Legacy Project workshop proceedings, including information on regional conservation plans, priorities, strategies, monitoring, management, and stewardship projects, available resource data, and recommended strategies, are available on the Web at http://legacy.ca.gov.

Conservation action workshops (March–May 2005)—Seven conservation action workshops, with participants representing local, state, and federal agencies, nongovernment organizations, and various stakeholder interests, were held to discuss major issues and actions important to conserving and restoring wildlife.

Outreach to California Tribes for Comment on the Draft Plan

The California Legacy Project workshops invited representatives from 136 tribes or bands, as well as 10 intertribal groups or associations. Only five of these groups attended the workshops. While writing the plan, authors interviewed members of four tribes with strong interest in the stressors and actions mentioned in this plan. As part of the review process, DFG contacted 148 tribes or bands by means of letters addressed to tribal chairs with copies sent to tribal administrators and tribal environmental officers. To more readily solicit input from tribes, letters were customized to list the most relevant stressors and actions for each tribe's region. These letters were followed up by personal phone calls to 37 tribes. Tribes were selected to receive personal phone calls based on either their relatively large landholdings (many tribes have fewer than 10 acres of land and others have no landbase) or on their potential interest in wildlife or land use issues as recommended by the California Native American Heritage Commission or regional Fish and Game staff.

Public Comment Period and Public Meetings

Fish and Game's draft Wildlife Action Plan was made available for public review and comment for 75 days, May 5–July 21, 2006. More than 4,000 comments were received during the public comment period.

Fish and Game offered three ways for the public to submit comments on the draft plan:

1) By participating in one of three public comment open meetings (in Sacramento, Redding, and Riverside)
2) By email
3) By regular mail

Review of Public Comments and Preparation of Final Plan

DFG reviewed the 4,000-plus comments and prepared responses to issues that were raised in the comments. Then revisions were made to the draft plan based on the public comments. DFG submitted the final plan to the Fish and Wildlife Service by the Sept. 15, 2006, deadline.

Additional Stakeholder Input and Public Participation

Most of the conservation actions recommended in this report, if implemented, would be reviewed further through well-established public participatory processes such as the California Fish and Game Commission review process, the State Water Resources Control Board hearing process, U.S. Forest Service or BLM resource management planning processes, county planning commission and board of supervisors review processes, or legislative hearings. Conservation actions would also comply with public review requirements pursuant to the California Environmental Quality Act and the National Environmental Protection Act.

Appendix C
Wildlife Information Sources

Terrestrial and Freshwater Species

Multiple Species Groups

- Conservation Planning Program—California Department of Fish and Game
  http://www.dfg.ca.gov/hcpb/conplan/conplan.shtml
  Information about Natural Community Conservation Planning, federal Habitat Conservation
  Planning, and conservation and mitigation banking.

- Recovery and Delisting of Federal Endangered Species
  http://endangered.fws.gov/recovery/index.html
  Information about federally listed endangered species, including online recovery plans;
  Endangered Species Act-related conservation tools, laws and policies; and Federal Register
  notices.

- California Plants and Animals
  http://www.dfg.ca.gov/hcpb/species/species.shtml
  General plant and animal information, lists of special species (threatened and endangered,
  species of concern, etc.), life history and conservation status information, survey standards and
  guidelines, threats to species, and photographs.

- California Wildlife Habitat Relationships—California Department of Fish and Game
  http://www.dfg.ca.gov/bdb/html/cwhr.html
  A state-of-the-art information system for California's wildlife that provides information on life
  history, management, and habitat relationships for 675 species of amphibians, reptiles, birds, and
  mammals known to occur in the state.

- California Natural Diversity Database—California Department of Fish and Game
  http://www.dfg.ca.gov/bdb/html/cnddb.html
  The most comprehensive statewide inventory of locational records of California's most-imperiled species and natural communities.

- UC Berkeley Museum of Vertebrate Zoology
  http://mvz.berkeley.edu
  A university research and education center for the biology of amphibians, reptiles, birds, and mammals. Site provides online data about specimen locations, information about the museum's collections and research activities, and links to other biological databases and specimen collections.

- CalPhotos: Animals
  http:/calphotos.berkeley.edu/
  More than 30,000 online images of California animals.

Bird-specific

- North American Bird Conservation Initiative
  http://www.nabci-us.org/nabci.html
  A continental conservation effort to integrate bird conservation efforts. Site provides online access to existing bird conservation plans, habitat joint ventures, priorities of individual initiatives and programs, species-specific information (assessments, life history, useful identification tips, species lists, population and habitat data), monitoring programs, and mapping tools supporting bird conservation.

- Habitat Joint Ventures in the United States
  http://www.nabci-us.org/jvmap.html
  Directory to the five California Joint Ventures (Central Valley, Intermountain West, Pacific Coast, San Francisco Bay, and Sonoran).

- California Riparian Habitat Joint Venture—Partners in Flight
  http://www.prbo.org/calpif/htmldocs/rhjv
  A collaborative effort by 18 federal, state, and private organizations to protect and enhance habitats for native landbirds throughout California. Site provides access to the California Riparian Conservation Plan.

- Southern Pacific Shorebird Conservation Plan—Partners in Flight
  http://www.prbo.org/cms/index.php?mid=212&module=browse
  A conservation plan that describes species and habitat priorities and goals, threats, recommendations for management, monitoring, research, and education.

- Landbird Conservation Plans—Partners in Flight
  http://www.prbo.org/cms/index.php?mid=3&module=browse
  California-specific plans for bird habitat in coniferous forest, coastal scrub, grassland, oak woodland, shrubsteppe and Sierra Nevada.

- Important Bird Areas of California—Audubon California
  http://ca.audubon.org/IBA.htm
  Information about 150 key areas in California that are most important to birds. Coordinated within the state by Audubon California, this program is part of a worldwide effort coordinated by BirdLife International to identify and protect sites deemed most critical to birds.

- California's Wildlife—Birds
  http://www.dfg.ca.gov/bdb/html/lifehistbirds.html
  Life history descriptions for all native California birds.

- ORNIS (ORNithological Information System
  http://ornisnet.org
  A collaborative network of databases from ornithological collections in 32 North American natural history museums.

Mammal-specific

- California's Wildlife—Mammals
  http://www.dfg.ca.gov/bdb/html/lifehistmammal.html
  Life history descriptions for all native California mammals.

- Mammal Species of Special Concern
  http://www.dfg.ca.gov/hcpb/species/ssc/sscmamml/sscmamml.shtml
  Department of Fish and Game publication *Mammalian Species of Special Concern in California,* by D.F. Williams, 1986. The list of mammalian species of special concern is currently undergoing review. An updated listing and status accounts is expected in 2006.

- Bat Conservation International
  http://www.batcon.org/
  An organization with the mission to protect and restore bats and their habitats worldwide.

- Western Bat Working Group (WBWG)
  http://www.wbwg.org/wbwg.htm/
  A partner in the Coalition of North American Bat Working Groups. The WBWG comprises agencies, organizations, and individuals interested in bat research, management, and conservation from 13 western states and the provinces of British Columbia and Alberta.

- Mammal Networked Information System
  http://elib.cs.berkeley.edu/manis
  A collaborative network of databases from mammal collections in natural history museums, with approximately 10,300 California specimens from 17 institutions.

Reptile- and Amphibian-specific

- California's Wildlife—Amphibians
  http://www.dfg.ca.gov/bdb/html/amphibians.html
  Life history descriptions for all native California amphibians.

- California's Wildlife—Reptiles
  http://www.dfg.ca.gov/bdb/html/reptiles.html
  Life history descriptions for all native California reptiles.

- Amphibian Species of Special Concern
  http://www.dfg.ca.gov/hcpb/species/ssc/sscamphb/sscamphib.shtml
  Species accounts from Jennings and Hayes, *Amphibian and Reptile Species of Special Concern in California,* 1994.

- Reptile Species of Special Concern
  http://www.dfg.ca.gov/hcpb/species/ssc/sscreptl/sscreptl.shtml
  Species accounts from Jennings and Hayes, *Amphibian and Reptile Species of Special Concern in California,* 1994.

- Partners in Amphibian and Reptile Conservation–Southwest
  http://www.parcplace.org/southwest.html
  A partnership dedicated to the conservation of the herpetofauna—reptiles and amphibians—and their habitats. Membership includes state and federal agencies, conservation organizations, museums, pet trade industry, nature centers, zoos, energy industry, universities, herpetological organizations, research laboratories, forest industries, and environmental consultants.

- HerpNET
  http://www.herpnet.org
  A collaborative network of databases from herpetological collections in natural history museums, with approximately 8,900 California specimens from 13 institutions.

Inland Fish-specific

- Ecosystem Restoration Program—California Bay Delta Authority
  http://calwater.ca.gov/Programs/EcosystemRestoration/Ecosystem.shtml
  A joint state-federal effort to initiate and coordinate ecosystem restoration actions for the San Francisco Bay and Sacramento–San Joaquin river system.

- Native Anadromous Fish and Watershed Branch—California Department of Fish and Game
  http://www.dfg.ca.gov/nafwb/index.html
  A program that addresses the health of the state's anadromous fisheries and watersheds. Site provides information on life history, conservation plans, restoration activities and funding, and listing status of species.

- Southwest Region—National Marine Fisheries Service
  http://swr.nmfs.noaa.gov
  A program that addresses the management, regulation, harvesting, conservation, and protection of California's marine resources, including marine fish, invertebrates, and anadromous fish.

- Fish Species of Special Concern
  http://www.dfg.ca.gov/hcpb/species/ssc/sscfish/sscfish.shtml
  Department of Fish and Game publication *Fish Species of Special Concern in California,* second edition, by P.B. Moyle, R.M. Yoshiyama, J.E. Williams, and E.D. Wikramanayake, 1995.

- CalFish
  http://www.calfish.org
  Online access to California fish and aquatic habitat data, including population trends and counts, distributions, migration barriers, hatcheries, habitat restoration projects, genetics, and monitoring.

- FishNet
  http://speciesanalyst.net/fishnet/default.html
  A collaborative network of databases from fish collections in 29 natural history museums.

Inland Invertebrate-specific

- Department of Entomology—California Academy of Sciences
  http://www.calacademy.org/research/entomology
  One of the largest arthropod specimen collections in North America.

- Essig Museum of Entomology—University of California, Berkeley
  http://essig.berkeley.edu/pages/about.htm
  Probably the largest existing specimen collection of California insects.

Plants

- California Native Plant Society
  http://www.cnps.org
  A statewide nonprofit organization focused on California's native plants. Site provides online "Inventory of Rare and Endangered Plants" and information about conservation programs, legislative updates, education, science programs, and related publications.

- Jepson Herbarium—University of California, Berkeley
  http://ucjeps.berkeley.edu
  The only herbarium devoted exclusively to the study of California's native plants. Site provides access to a database of text data and images for over 300,000 California plant specimens.

- The Jepson Manual
  http://ucjeps.berkeley.edu/interchange/I_treat_indexes.html
  The most comprehensive identification guide to nearly 8,000 taxa of native and naturalized California plants. Site provides access to species descriptions and keys to identification.

- CalPhotos: Plants
  http://elib.cs.berkeley.edu/photos/flora
  Approximately 42,000 online images of California plants.

Plant Communities

- Natural Resource Management Program—California State Parks
  http://www.parks.ca.gov/default.asp?page_id=22197
  A program to protect, restore, and maintain natural diversity on state park lands, with special units for prescribed fire, exotic species control, sensitive species management, and biological monitoring.

- California Land Cover Mapping and Monitoring Program. Fire and Resource Assessment Program (FRAP) of the Department of Forestry and Fire Protection.

  http://frap.cdf.ca.gov/projects/land_cover/index.html

  The Fire and Resource Assessment Program (FRAP) of the California Department of Forestry and Fire Protection and the USDA Forest Service coordinate land cover mapping and monitoring within California. Remotely sensed data and GIS (geographic information systems) are used to accomplish the program objectives. This program generates data that describe the extent and condition of various land cover types and the magnitude and cause (e.g. urbanization, natural succession, wildfire, and timber harvest) of land cover changes.

- U.S. Forest Service Research Natural Areas in California

  http://www.fs.fed.us/psw/publications/documents/psw_gtr188/gtr188index.html

  Descriptions of special areas on national forest land that represent both widespread and unique ecosystems and that are protected to maintain biological diversity and provide ecological baseline information, education, and research.

- Natural Reserve System—University of California

  http://nrs.ucop.edu

  The world's largest university-operated system of natural reserves. It broadly represents California's rich ecological diversity and provides relatively undisturbed samples of the state's natural ecosystems and the facilities needed to support teaching and research.

- A Manual of California Vegetation

  http://davisherb.ucdavis.edu/CNPSActiveServer/index.html

  Descriptions and images of 275 vegetation series in California.

- California Wildlife Habitats—California Department of Fish and Game

  http://www.dfg.ca.gov/bdb/html/wildlife_habitats.html

  Descriptions of the major wildlife habitats in California.

- Vegetation Classification and Mapping Program—California Department of Fish and Game

  http://www.dfg.ca.gov/bdb/html/vegcamp.html

  Program to facilitate and oversee efforts to develop accurate and scientifically defensible maps and classifications of vegetation and/or habitat throughout the state. Site provides links to other programs and activities related to California vegetation science.

- Vegetation Program—California Native Plant Society

  http://www.cnps.org/programs/vegetation/index.htm

  Program to coordinate CNPS involvement in improving classification and mapping of California's natural vegetation.

- CalPhotos: Landscapes and Habitats

  http://elib.cs.berkeley.edu/photos/landscape

  Approximately 2,400 online images of California landscapes and habitats.

- Ecological Subregions of California

  http://www.fs.fed.us/r5/projects/ecoregions

  Biophysical descriptions of all 220 geographical sections of the state, each approximately 450,000 acres in size. Descriptions include climate, lithology and stratigraphy, geomorphology, soils, surface water characteristics, vegetation, characteristic fauna, disturbance regimes, land use, and cultural ecology.

- California Biodiversity Council Vegetation Mapping Memorandum of Understanding
  http://www.ceres.ca.gov/biodiversity/vegmou.html
  A cooperative vegetation and habitat mapping initiative which will facilitate statewide joint data collection and processing, establish common mapping and classification standards across all ownerships, and provide timely response to both state and federal information and analytical requirements.

Marine Species

Multiple Species Groups

- California Current Joint Venture
  http://www.prbo.org/cms/index.php?mid=231&module=browse
  An ecosystem-level conservation plan that will define a conservation agenda for the California Current System (CCS), focusing on top predators (including but not limited to seabirds), and their prey.

- Marine Life Protection Act Initiative
  http://www.dfg.ca.gov/mrd/mlpa/index.html
  A cooperative public-private partnership to expand, fund, and manage a system of marine protected areas along the California coast. Site provides MLPA formal documents, species information, and information about scientific activities, public outreach, and existing marine protected areas.

- Priority Conservation Areas—Baja California to the Bering Sea (B2B) Project
  http://www. mcbi.org/marineprotected/Marine.htm#PCA
  Report describing critical marine habitat areas along the Pacific Coast. Prepared by the Marine Conservation Biology Institute as part of the Commission for Environmental Cooperation's North American Marine Protected Area Network.

- Ocean Resources Management Program—California Resources Agency
  http://resources.ca.gov/ocean/index.html
  Statewide program to ensure comprehensive and coordinated management, conservation, and enhancement of California's ocean resources.

- Marine Region—California Department of Fish and Game
  http://www.dfg.ca.gov/mrd
  Program to address marine biodiversity issues along California's coast. Site provides information about marine life management, regulations and enforcements, permits, and reports on identification, biology, and conservation of marine life.

- California Ocean and Coastal Environmental Access Network
  http://ceres.ca.gov/ocean
  A Web-based virtual library for the discovery of and access to data, information, and tools to support ocean and coastal resource management, planning, research, and education. Cal OCEAN is a project of the California Resources Agency's Ocean Resources Management Program.

- Southwest Fisheries Science Center—NOAA Fisheries
  http://swfsc.nmfs.noaa.gov/gen_info.htm
  One of six regional NOAA fisheries research centers. The Center conducts fisheries and marine mammal research at three laboratories in California in support of the Pacific Fishery Management Council.

- Marine Conservation Biology Institute
  http://www.mcbi.org/index.html
  A nonprofit scientific and conservation advocacy organization to protect and restore marine life on the West Coast and other coasts using scientific research and training, integrating science and policy, conducting policy research, educating the public, and building partnerships to solve problems affecting marine life and people.

- California's Living Marine Resources: A Status Report
  http://www.dfg.ca.gov/mrd/status/index.html
  Descriptions of marine ecosystem, including stressors, regulations, human activities in marine ecosystem, and marine law enforcement. Species-specific descriptions (history of fishery, status of scientific knowledge) for marine and estuarine invertebrates, fish, birds, mammals, plants and habitats.

Marine Birds

- Southern Pacific Shorebird Conservation Plan
  http://www.prbo.org/cms/index.php?mid=212&module=browse
  A conservation plan to guide the provision of adequate, high-quality shorebird habitat to restore and maintain California's shorebird populations.

- California Current Marine Bird Conservation Plan
  http://www.prbo.org/cms/index.php?mid=66&module=browse
  A conservation plan that addresses seabird conservation from an ecosystem perspective, synthesizing information on multiple species, multiple habitats, ecological interactions, and the issues and threats that affect the health of seabirds, their prey, and their ocean environments.

- Seabird Conservation Plan—U.S. Fish and Wildlife Service
  http://migratorybirds.pacific.fws.gov/Seabird_Conservation_Plan_Document_pdf_files.htm
  A plan that identifies the USFWS priorities for seabird management, monitoring, outreach, planning, and coordination. It provides profiles of each species (population size and status, ecology, habitats, threats, and recommended conservation actions), and a summary of current management, monitoring, and outreach efforts.

Marine Mammals

- U.S. Pacific Marine Mammal Stock Assessment Reports—NOAA Fisheries
  http://swfsc.nmfs.noaa.gov/PRD/PROGRAMS/CMMP/default.htm
  Information about the distribution, abundance, population trends, human-caused mortality, and the potential biological removal (PBR) of each stock.

- Coastal Marine Mammal Program—NOAA Fisheries
  http://swfsc.nmfs.noaa.gov/PRD/PROGRAMS/CMMP/default.htm
  Program that tracks the abundance and distribution of marine mammals on the U.S. West Coast
  out to 300 nautical miles.

- Southwest Fisheries Science Center—NOAA Fisheries
  http://swfsc.nmfs.noaa.gov/PRD
  Program that conducts applied research on the cetaceans, pinnipeds, and sea turtles of
  the eastern Pacific Ocean.

- Marine Mammals—NOAA Fisheries
  http://www.nmfs.noaa.gov/pr/species/mammals
  Information about marine mammal legal status information, wildlife viewing guidelines,
  and congressional reports.

Marine Nearshore Fish

- Coastal Pelagic Species Fishery Management Plan—Pacific Fishery Management Council
  http://www.pcouncil.org/cps/cpsfmp.html
  Plan that describes management and research actions and harvest policies for the entire coastal
  pelagic species fishery along the U.S. West Coast, including Pacific sardine, Pacific mackerel,
  market squid, and northern anchovy.

- Nearshore Fishery Management Plan—California Department of Fish and Game
  http://www.dfg.ca.gov/mrd/nfmp/index.html
  Management plan for nearshore fisheries on the California coast, including life history, status of
  harvesting, management measures, research needs, and implementation actions.

- Pacific Coast Salmon Plan—Pacific Fishery Management Council
  http://www.pcouncil.org/salmon/salfmp/fmpthrua14.pdf
  Plan provides information about management objectives, harvest goals, and data needs for
  commercial and recreational salmon fisheries off the coasts of Washington, Oregon, and
  California.

- Pacific Fishery Management Council
  http://www.pcouncil.org
  One of eight U.S. regional fishery management councils, with responsibility for fisheries off the
  coasts of California, Oregon, and Washington. Site provides information about Council activities,
  marine reserves, research and data needs, regulatory information and species-specific info such
  as management plans, assessment reports, and life history. Fisheries include ground fish, salmon,
  highly migratory species, coastal pelagic species, and halibut.

- Southwest Region—National Marine Fisheries Service
  http://swr.nmfs.noaa.gov
  Information concerning the management, regulation, harvesting, conservation, and protection of
  California's marine resources, including marine fish, invertebrates, and anadromous fish.

Marine Invertebrates

- Marine Invertebrates and Plants—NOAA Fisheries
  http://www.nmfs.noaa.gov/pr/species/invertebrates
  Information about marine invertebrates and plants listed, candidates for listing, or species of concern under the Endangered Species Act.

- Life History Information for Selected California Marine Invertebrates and Plants
  http://www.dfg.ca.gov/mrd/table_inv_ip.html
  A table with distribution, habitat, life history, and dispersal information for various species of California marine invertebrates.

- San Francisco Bay Marine Invertebrates Bibliography
  http://www.calacademy.org/research/library/biodiv/biblio/sf_marine_invert.htm
  Online summary from California Academy of Sciences of Internet links, books, and articles on marine invertebrates in San Francisco Bay and on the California coast.

- California Abalone Recovery and Management Plan
  http://www.dfg.ca.gov/mrd/armp/index.html
  A plan for all abalone species in California, including the recovery of depleted populations in Southern California and the management of the Northern California populations.

Appendix D
Department of Fish and Game Species and Habitat Information Sources

Further information on California habitats and wildlife species is available on Fish and Game's Web site. This appendix is intended only as a guide for locating additional information, not as a source of the information itself. A general guide to departmental publications can be found at http://www.dfg.ca.gov/coned/publications.html.

A complete list of California's mammals, birds, reptiles, and amphibians can be found at http://www.dfg.ca.gov/bdb/html/cawildlife.html, which includes a link to Species Notes arranged by each major group. (These notes are integrated with Fish and Game's California Habitat Relationship Database software as Wildlife Notes.)

Department of Fish and Game Species Information

Current lists of threatened and endangered animals in the state can be found on Fish and Game's Web site at http://www.dfg.ca.gov/bdb/html/animals.html. Two lists are available: *State and Federally Listed Endangered and Threatened Animals of California* and the more inclusive *Special Animals List*, maintained by Fish and Game's California Natural Diversity Database (CNDDB). The Web site states that:

"Special Animals" is a general term that refers to all of the **taxa** the CNDDB is interested in tracking, regardless of their legal or protection status. These taxa generally fall into one or more of the following categories:

1. Officially listed or proposed for listing under the state and/or federal Endangered Species Acts.

2. State or federal candidate for possible listing.

3. Taxa that meet the criteria for listing, even if not currently included on any list, as described in Section 15380 of the California Environmental Quality Act Guidelines.

4. Taxa considered by Fish and Game to be a Species of Special Concern (CSC).

5. Taxa that are biologically rare, very restricted in **distribution**, declining throughout their range, or have a critical, vulnerable stage in their life cycle that warrants monitoring.

6. Populations in California that may be on the periphery of a taxon's range but are threatened with **extirpation** in California.

7. Taxa closely associated with a **habitat** that is declining in California at an alarming rate (e.g., wetlands, riparian, old growth forests, desert aquatic systems, native grasslands, vernal pools).

8. Taxa designated as a special status, sensitive, or declining species by other state or federal agencies or nongovernmental organization (NGO).

Fish and Game also maintains reports on Species of Special Concern at http://www.dfg.ca.gov/hcpb/species/ssc/ssc.shtml. Species of Special Concern status is defined as:

"Species of Special Concern (SSC)" status applies to animals not listed under the federal Endangered Species Act or the California Endangered Species Act but which nonetheless are declining at a rate that could result in listing or historically occurred in low numbers and known threats to their persistence currently exist. SSC share one or more of the following criteria:

1. occur in small, isolated populations or in fragmented habitat and are threatened by further isolation and population reduction.

2. show marked population declines. Population estimates are unavailable for the vast majority of taxa. Species that show a marked population decline, yet are still abundant, do not meet the Special Concern definition, whereas marked population decline in uncommon or rare species is an inclusion criterion.

3. depend on a habitat that has shown substantial historical or recent declines in size. This criterion infers the population viability of a species based on trends in the habitats upon which it specializes. Coastal wetlands, particularly in the urbanized San Francisco Bay and south-coastal areas, alluvial fan sage scrub and coastal sage scrub in the southern coastal basins, and arid scrub in the San Joaquin Valley, are examples of California habitats that have seen dramatic reductions in size in recent history. Species that specialize in these habitats generally meet the criteria for Threatened or Endangered status or Special Concern status.

4. occur only in or adjacent to an area where habitat is being converted to land uses incompatible with the animal's survival.

5. have few California records, or which historically occurred here but for which there are no recent records.

6. occur largely on public lands but where current management practices are inconsistent with the animal's persistence.

Detailed biological, taxonomic, distribution, range, status, and management information for animals considered Species of Special Concern can be found at http://www.dfg.ca.gov/hcpb/info/info.shtml. The information is presented by major vertebrate groups (fish, mammals, amphibians and reptiles, and birds).

Fish and Game's Habitat Conservation Planning Branch's Web page at http://www.dfg.ca.gov/ hcpb/species/species.shtml contains a Sensitive Species section with links to species accounts for rare, threatened, and endangered species, "fully protected species," and Species of Special Concern.

Species of Special Concern Reports for fishes, birds, mammals, and reptiles and amphibians, and a pdf version of The Status of Rare, Threatened, and Endangered Animals and Plants of California— Annual Report for 2000 (and updates) can be found at http://www.dfg.ca.gov/hcpb/info/info.shtml. This legislatively mandated report contains accounts for state-listed species for which new information on distribution or biology had recently become available at the time of publication.

The California Natural Diversity Database (CNDDB) tracks occurrences of rare, threatened, and endangered plants, animals, and natural communities in the state. Information about the CNDDB can be found at http://www.dfg.ca.gov/bdb/html/cnddb.html. The Animals link on the menu leads to pdf versions of the Special Animals List and the Endangered and Threatened Animals List. Vegetation Mapping and Classification and Natural Communities links lead to pages with information (and future maps) on vegetation maps for the state and a list of Natural Communities, useful for wildlife habitat information.

Rare Find is a subscription-based software product based on the California Natural Diversity Database (CNDDB). It contains text and spatial data on animals contained on Fish and Game's Special Animals List and plants on the Special Vascular Plants, Bryophytes, and Lichens List. A description of Rare Find features and ordering instructions are available on the Wildlife and Habitat Data Analysis Branch Web page, http://www.dfg.ca.gov/bdb/html/rarefind.html.

Also available online is CNDDB's Quick Viewer—a free service at http://www.dfg.ca.gov/bdb/ html/quick_viewer_launch.html—which presents, in table form, CNDDB elements (both individual taxa and natural communities) by USGS 7.5′ quads or by counties.

Various Fish and Game online publications concerned with fish, including freshwater species accounts, as well as individual publications on California trout species and anadromous, freshwater, and warm water fishes, are available at http://www.dfg.ca.gov/fishing/html/Publications/Publications_ 0.htm. Fish identification guides and a life history database can be viewed and downloaded at http://www.dfg.ca.gov/mrd/education.html.

Fish and Game's publication California's Living Marine Resources: A Status Report, which contains biological accounts and population status information for marine and anadromous commercial fisheries species (including invertebrate species as well as fishes) and other resident and migrating marine species such as cetaceans and pinnipeds, is available at http://www.dfg.ca.gov/mrd/status/ index.html.

Species accounts and other information from the Fish and Game Marine Region for selected marine wildlife species can be found at http://www.dfg.ca.gov/mrd/education.html.

Department of Fish and Game Habitat Information

The California Wildlife Habitat Relationship (CWHR) Database is a database application that uses geographic distribution, relationships to habitat types and stages, seasonal use patterns, and presence of habitat elements to predict habitat suitability for 675 terrestrial vertebrates, including all terrestrial species in California and those subspecies included on Fish and Game's Special Animals List. It includes BIOVIEW, an application that translates habitat suitability values for wildlife species into data that can be used with a Geographic Information System. Information and downloading of the CWHR database is available at http://www.dfg.ca.gov/bdb/html/cwhr.html. In 1999, an expansion of the marine and estuarine habitat classification scheme used in the database was begun. Further information on this project is available at http://www.dfgca.gov/bdb/cwhr/pdfs/Preliminary_Marine_Estuarine.pdf.

The California Wildlife Habitat Relationship System provides information and modeling capabilities for California habitat types, with links to descriptions and distribution maps for each type, and is available online at http://www.dfg.ca.gov/bdb/html/wildlife_habitats.html.

Department of Fish and Game GIS Information

BIOS (Biogeographic Information and Observation System) data viewer, http://bios.dfg.ca.gov/, is a collection of distribution maps for Fish and Game and its partners only and contains various data sets from voluntary contributors. A password is necessary to access BIOS but can be obtained by qualified researchers by following the instructions on the Web page.

Marine resource maps, including fish ranges for nearshore fishes and kelp bed distribution, can be found at http://www.dfg.ca.gov/itbweb/gis/mr_nat_res.htm.

CalFish, http://www.calfish.org/DesktopDefault.aspx, is a cooperative project between the Department of Fish and Game and outside collaborators. Included on the Web site are links to species accounts for California freshwater and anadromous fish and an Internet-based map viewer with spatial distribution data for several species.

Appendix E
Off-Highway Vehicles and Wildlife Workshop

Off-highway Vehicles (OHV) and Wildlife Workshop
State Parks' OHV Stakeholders Roundtable, March 24, 2005
Workshop Notes

OHV workshop comments may be summarized under six topics:

- Background
- Provide quality OHV opportunities
- Educate and communicate with OHV community
- OHV rider/driver certification
- Enforcement of the rules
- Major points

Background

- Rapid growth of OHV activity, economy, of all types.
- Double-digit sales growth nationwide, but fewer off-road opportunities.
- No new OHV parks in California in 25 years.
- Not certain wildlife agencies have data showing impacts on wildlife.
- OHV Commission has diverted funds from enforcement and stewardship of facilities to restoration.

Provide quality opportunity for growing demand

- Need to spend more funds on maintaining and rehabilitating OHV facilities.

- If OHV areas are maintained, people will take care of them. If they are a mess, people abuse them.

- Provide quality opportunity, what the OHV enthusiast is looking for.

- Need to include analysis of economics of OHV—takes money to provide opportunity.

- Prevention approach: to prevent illegal OHV activity and damage to natural resources, more should be invested in good facilities and enforcement rather than restoration.

Education and communication

- Give reason (e.g., wildlife conservation) to appreciate and protect or value the resource.

- People must understand and accept the logic of the restrictions or law.

- Must educate youth and adults.

- Need to educate kids on the wise use of OHVs.

- Check education Web site: N2DIRT.

- Threaten closures to get OHV community attention.

- Create incentives to care and partner with agencies.

- Communicate with OHV public about how public can help and how to implement programs.

- Provide the information to the public to distribute and learn from.

Education venues and outreach:

- Meetings between agencies and recreationists.

- On-the-ground canvass effort—distribute materials everywhere an enthusiast might be.

- OHV facility parking lots are very good places to educate people; that is where you can contact most riders.

- Education materials should be in hands of all agencies on the ground to hand out.

- Public Service Announcements—(youth and adult versions) all media outlets.

- Provide rewards for helping to educate (pins, etc.); big with kids, and they will share the information with parents.

- Provide school curriculum for kids under age 10.

- Billboards are good.

- Web site

- Maps

- Need signs at specific areas of concern.

- Need more and better interpretive information.

- Rules and regulations need to be clearly communicated to public.
- Dealers need to actively provide education info.

Education Meetings

- Advantage: face-to-face.
- Disadvantage: Groups generally not the people who are causing the problem and need the message.

Education through schools and with kids

- Advantage: Once changed, it is holistic
- Disadvantage: Takes time and resources.

Need rider certification of some kind

- Need certification on driver license, or certification for youth. Must learn rules to be certified.
- Need mandatory rule card similar to a fishing license.
- Need OHV certificate for young riders. Need booklet and test.

Enforcement

- Commission reducing funding for OHV enforcement.
- Agencies—meet responsibility for enforcement, management, and education.
- Provide patrol and closure signs.
- Some State Parks enforcement officers are excellent. (Example: rangers at Hollister.)
- Make violation consequences severe.
- Enforcement should track violations, so rider gets a couple of warnings then a stiff penalty. (Currently no way to track rider violations.)
- Word-of-mouth of penalty shapes behavior.
- It is more effective to tell what is right than wrong. Positive approaches more effective than negative.
- Most people want to do the right thing; peer pressure to do the right thing is great.

Major Points

- Need to increase quality opportunity.
- Need enforcement and fines.
- Consider OHV certification.
- Need good education effort through many venues.

Roundtable Participants

- **AMADOR, DONALD**, Blue Ribbon Coalition
- **BARNES, GEORGE**, Sierra Club
- **BARNETT, GARY**, U.S. Forest Service, Truckee Ranger District
- **BELL, DANA**, National OHV Conservation Council
- **BUNN, DAVID**, University of California, Davis
- **CORTEZ, ROSARIO**, Department of Parks and Recreation
- **FARRINGTON, RICH**, U.S. Forest Service
- **FISHER, RICK**, California Off Road Vehicle Association
- **GIBSON, JIM**, Snowlands Network
- **GINN, KEITH**, U.S. Forest Service
- **GREENE, DAPHNE**, Department of Parks and Recreation
- **HAAGEN-SMIT, JIM**, International Mountain Bicycling Association
- **HAM, BOB**, Imperial County Executive Office
- **HANSEN, LINDA**, BLM California Desert District
- **HARIS, NICK**, National American Motorcyclist Association
- **HOFMANN, JOHN**, Regional Council of Rural Counties
- **JONES, BECKY**, Department of Fish and Game
- **KEYES, JOHN**, Back Country Horsemen Association
- **KLOCK, BRIAN**, Department of Parks and Recreation
- **KLUSMAN, DON**, California Association of 4WD Clubs
- **McNAY, MARK**, Imperial Country Sheriff's Department
- **MICK, KATHY**, Department of Parks and Recreation
- **OAKLEAF, DAVE**, American Motorcyclist Association—District 37
- **PEREZ, TONY**, Department of Parks and Recreation
- **PICKETT, DAVE**, American Motorcyclist Association—District 36
- **RUGG, BILL**, California-Nevada Snowmobile Association
- **SCHAMBACH, KAREN**, Center for Sierra Nevada Conservation
- **SILVERNAIL, LOIS**, CORVA and Disabled Access Interests
- **SOENS, HAROLD**, American Motorcyclist Association—District 38
- **WALDHEIM, ED**, California Trails User Coalition and OHMVR Commission
- **WARD, TOM**, Department of Parks and Recreation
- **WELCH, VIRGIL**, Planning and Conservation League

Appendix F
Conservation Action Workshop Summaries, Spring 2005

In the course of the regional reviews of stressors affecting wildlife and habitats and the actions needed to restore and conserve wildlife diversity, several key issues repeatedly surfaced. The Wildlife Diversity Project convened workshops, each attended by 15 to 30 experts and stakeholders, to identify challenges and opportunities regarding these issues and to develop recommendations for action. The key issues and their related workshops are:

Integrating Wildlife Conservation into Local Land-Use Decisions (Two workshops) —Local and regional land-use decisions guide growth and development. Preventing the unnecessary loss of wildlife resources requires that conservation be integrated into local and regional land-use and development decision processes.

Restoring and Conserving Riparian Habitat—The regional reviews found that multiple stressors have eliminated or degraded riparian habitat—one of the most important habitat types for maintaining wildlife diversity. A more comprehensive effort is needed to restore and conserve riparian habitats.

Ensuring Water for Wildlife—Water resources are contested throughout the state and the cost of water is increasing. Ensuring water for wildlife through planning and long-term contracts is essential for maintaining wildlife diversity in the future.

Controlling Invasive Species— Invasive species negatively affect wildlife across the state, and it is apparent that more comprehensive statewide solutions are needed to prevent species invasions and to control and eradicate invasive species.

Expanding Wildlife Conservation Education—The future of California's wildlife is dependent on strong public support for public investment in conservation and support for necessary habitat restoration and wildlife conservation projects and programs. Educating California's youth and the public about the state's wildlife and the needs of conservation are essential to build public support.

In spring 2005 the Wildlife Diversity Project facilitated a series of workshops on the key issues listed above. Participants in each workshop discussed one of the issues in depth.

Integrating Wildlife Conservation into Local Land-Use Decisions
May 25 and 26, 2005

Note: The following summary of the results of this workshop reflects the collective discussion and general conclusions of the workshop participants and does not necessarily reflect the views of the Department of Fish and Game, the Wildlife Diversity Project at UC Davis, or any individual participant.

The Issue

Land-use decisions made at the county and municipal levels define the landscape. Without specific policies, regulations, or plans, land-use decisions are often reactive in response to a developer's plans for residential or commercial development. The need for housing, tax revenues that come from commercial development, the desire for recreation and open space, and necessary infrastructure are just some of the pressures on California's lands as its population continues to grow. Short-term, reactive land-use decisions lead to unnecessary loss of California's wildlife resources.

Current Situation

Wildlife conservation is generally not considered in local land-use decisions, and the state lacks policies, funding, or standards for integrating wildlife conservation into local and regional actions. The issues in integrating wildlife conservation into local land-use decisions are planning; regulations and incentives; funding and infrastructure; leadership; and public awareness and support. The overarching context for these issues is the economic pressures confronting local governments. These pressures encourage new commercial development that generates tax revenue for basic public services.

Project-by-project development review does not conserve wildlife.

Local land-use planning is typically done at a project level. But wildlife conservation on a project-by-project basis is not effective; it must be addressed on a broader, landscape scale.

The lack of an integrated planning approach among state, regional, county, and local entities works against a viable wildlife conservation strategy. Moreover, wildlife conservation is not integrated with planning for transportation, floodplain management, and agricultural conversion.

Wildlife conservation has largely had a species-specific, reactive approach, focusing on threatened and endangered species or on a habitat "hot spot," rather than a proactive focus on regional landscapes and ecosystems.

Local land-use decision-makers are not likely to consider wildlife conservation unless they have given the issue consideration in a comprehensive planning process or are required to do so through CEQA.

There are not adequate regulatory requirements or incentives to facilitate integrating wildlife conservation into local land-use decisions.

Statewide policies do not require local agencies to plan for conserving wildlife. Incentives might include local grants, streamlined regulatory processes for addressing wildlife impacts, or flexibility in projects with tools like mitigation banking or the transfer of development rights.

Flexibility is important, whether in regulatory requirements or incentives, to allow for differences between rural and urban landscapes and different situations throughout the state. There is also recognition that existing processes and regulations are obstacles to wildlife conservation; e.g., development ordinances that make it difficult or impossible to build in an environmentally sensitive manner.

Local jurisdictions need either a "carrot" or a "stick" to integrate wildlife conservation into land-use decisions. If they are required to plan for and address wildlife, funding will be necessary.

Local governments generally lack the resources in funds, staff time, data, and information to protect wildlife at the local level.

Funding and attention to green infrastructure (open space, greenways) is inadequate. There is a lack of funding and capacity for integrated, long-term planning, for habitat acquisition, or for wildlife conservation operations and management.

What opportunities there are for funding are limited by a very competitive environment; if competing with health and human services or with housing needs, wildlife will be at the end of the line. If funding does become available, it is typically on a one-time basis or tied to capital investments. There is a lack of dependable funding available over a period of time.

There is a sense that existing data are not sufficient to inform local decision-making. Moreover, there are no state or regional priorities or standards for addressing wildlife conservation on a broader scale.

Leadership at the local level is key to integrating wildlife conservation into local land-use decisions.

Leadership is about local decision-makers and elected officials having a long-term, proactive vision. It is about choosing long-term quality of life over short-term economic gains. It is about demanding and financing research and planning to guide growth and development. Leadership is also about seeing the opportunities and benefits of planning integration and of working across geopolitical boundaries and across agencies. It is seeing the big picture and considering long-term issues.

Elected officials and planning committees are limited by their terms of office and by the nature of the job. They are expected to be experts in everything from waste management to budgets to conservation. They are limited by the pressures of balancing diverse and competing interests. Administrators are limited by institutional inertia and bureaucratic systems that fragment projects and are obstacles to systemic, integrated approaches. And in the absence of guidance for planning, regulation, or policy, they are limited in their ability to impose direction.

The level of public awareness, understanding and support regarding wildlife conservation affects decisions of local elected officials and administrators.

Communities and individuals need to be engaged at all levels to facilitate new approaches to local land use and to bring about individual behavior change. There is considered to be a general lack of knowledge or passion for integrating conservation into local land-use decisions; wildlife conservation is not included in most people's definition of quality of life. And while people may know about biodiversity, endangered species, or specific species, they are less aware of the relationship between wildlife conservation and land use. But without citizen outcry, a long-term vision for wildlife conservation will be neglected, and wildlife will be overlooked.

Needs Identified

Improve conservation planning for wildlife.

- Mandate and fund (or provide incentives for) integrated conservation planning and implementation (like the NCCP) or through the county General Plan process.
- Develop and provide the scientific data and information to the planners and decision-makers.
- Create a biological framework, standards, and priorities for wildlife planning and conservation.
- Create, implement, and fund statewide policies for integrating wildlife conservation into local land-use planning.

Strengthen state and local leadership for conservation planning.

- Define responsibilities at state and local levels for wildlife conservation, and expand Fish and Game's capacity to assist local governments with conservation planning.
- Coordinate wildlife conservation across state agencies.
- Encourage, support, and provide examples of long-term planning, and provide examples of the economic and quality-of-life benefits of wildlife conservation.

Generate public support.

- Provide incentives for private landowners to undertake wildlife conservation.
- Encourage market-based approaches to land stewardship.
- Increase awareness about landscape-scale wildlife conservation.

Ensure adequate funding.

- Secure more program funding for conservation and for operations and maintenance. (See Chapter 6, Strengthening California's Conservation Capabilities.)
- Integrate wildlife conservation into development funding for transportation and other infrastructure.

Workshop Participants (Davis)

BABORN, SHANNON, Sierra Nevada Alliance

BEALE, CHRIS, Resources Law Group

BRITTING, SUSAN, Sierra Nevada Forest Protection Campaign

BURKE, STEVE, Protect Our Water

CAVES, JOE, Conservation Strategy Group

CLARK, LOREN, Placer County Planning Dept

DELFINO, KIM, Defenders of Wildlife

GEYER, BILL, Resource Land Owners Coalition

HOPKINS, JOHN, Institute for Ecological Health

HOSHOVSKY, MARC, Department of Fish and Game

JOHNSON, STEVE, The Nature Conservancy

JOHNSTON, BOB, UC Davis, Dept. of Environmental Science and Policy

KARR, GERALD, Napa-Solano Audubon Society

KELSEY, DEIDRE, Merced County Board of Supervisors

LEE, CHRIS, Solano County Water Agency

LEVIN, JULIA, Audubon California

MARTINI-LAMB, JESSICA, Sonoma County Water Agency

McCAULL, JOHN, Law Offices of John McCaull

MERAL, GERRY, National Wildlife Federation

MILLER, LYDIA, San Joaquin Raptor/Wildlife Rescue Center

MISCZYNSKI, DEAN, California Research Bureau

MULLINS, DENNIS, Tejon Ranch

PRESLEY, GAIL, Department of Fish and Game

SCARBOROUGH, KAREN, California Resources Agency

VINK, ERIK, Trust for Public Land

WILKERSON, CYNTHIA, Defenders of Wildlife

WONG, MARIA, Yolo Habitat

YEATES, BILL, Law Office of J. William Yeates

Workshop Participants (Riverside)

BECK, MICHAEL, Endangered Habitats League

BIRKELAND, JAMES, Natural Resources Defense Council

BOAZ, TRISH, County of San Diego

BUNN, DAVID, UC Davis

DRONGESEN, JEFF, Department of Fish and Game

FRIEDMAN-JOHNSON, LESLIE, Conservation Strategy Group

LaMAR, STEVE, Legisight, LLC

OBERBAUER, TOM, County of San Diego

PRESTON, KRISTINE, Center for Conservation Biology, UC Riverside

REMPEL, RON, Western Riverside County Regional Conservation Center

SCOTT, TOM, University of California

SILVER, DAN, Endangered Habitats League

Controlling Invasive Species That Affect Native Wildlife
May 10, 2005

Note: The following summary of the results of this workshop reflects the collective discussion and general conclusions of the workshop participants and does not necessarily reflect the views of the Department of Fish and Game, the Wildlife Diversity Project at UC Davis, or any individual participant.

The Issue

Invasive species, including animals, plants, and pathogens, are ranked among the major statewide stressors affecting California's native wildlife, but the state does not have an adequate program or legal framework to address their prevention, monitoring, control, and eradication. Currently, Fish and Game has only one position to coordinate the state's invasive species control efforts, and several state agencies have people working on scattered invasive species projects. For invasive species cases that threaten agricultural crops, however, the state has a well-defined program, a powerful legal framework, and funding to aggressively implement control and eradication efforts. California needs a more substantial policy and legal framework with clear direction regarding their prevention, control, and eradication, to reduce the effects of invasive species on wildlife.

With the possible exception of alpine natural communities, California is remarkably vulnerable to species invasions, and almost all of the state's ecosystems are at risk. Riparian systems, estuaries, deserts, grasslands, forests, and Mediterranean ecosystems are all under siege. Freshwater systems and islands are especially susceptible to species extirpations caused by invasive species. Invasive plants like medusahead and French broom harm wildlife directly by producing harmful awns and seeds. Introduced fishes can directly compete with native species, prey on them, or hybridize with them. The invasive pathogen Sudden Oak Death destroys acorn-producing trees, an important food source for native wildlife. In addition to direct harm to wildlife, invasive alien species such as arundo also cause widespread degradation of wildlife habitats.

Current Situation

Although there is significant activity directed toward prevention and management of invasive species, these efforts do not add up to a cohesive, coordinated program.

A substantial amount of invasive-species work is being conducted by diverse groups throughout California. The agencies working on invasive species generally agree on the approach. The problem, however, is that the state's geographic size and diversity of habitats make it difficult to set priorities for such work. There is presently a hodge-podge of policies and procedures concerning invasive species but no overarching policy.

Good lists of invasive species exist for plants and animals, but the data are scattered in various locations.

Invasive plants are well identified in the California Invasive Plant Council database, and life-history and control information is available for many of the 300 species on the list. At present, CAL-IPC is regionalizing the list to make it more relevant to land managers.

Lists of invasive terrestrial animals are located in a few places. The National Park Service manages a database called NP Species that covers terrestrial and aquatic invasive vertebrates in national parks and adjacent lands. The NP Species list is prioritized for management action. The U.S. Geological

Survey has an invasive vertebrates list. Fish and Game maintains a list of animals that are prohibited for import (not necessarily invasive species). A federal list of injurious animal species is maintained by the Department of the Interior.

Some lists cut across species groups. The California Aquatic Invasive Species Management Plan includes aquatic plants and animals in freshwater and marine habitats. Lists of invasive pathogens seem to be less well developed. Most of these lists and databases identify new invaders to watch for, so they can be immediately treated.

Setting priorities for invasive species work is difficult due to California's great size and diversity of habitats.

Some work on risk factors of invasive species is being done at the University of California, Davis, and elsewhere, but a useful framework for prioritizing efforts on ecological and taxonomic criteria is still lacking.

Priorities might include controlling invasive species in California's protected areas like state or national parks or focusing on controlling invasive species in representative habitats of each region of the state through prevention, early detection, and eradication and control of existing invasive species populations. Prioritization of invasive species management should be based on scientifically based strategies.

The Department of Food and Agriculture has a well-managed, comprehensive program and policy framework for preventing and managing invasive species that threaten agriculture. Agricultural inspection stations at state borders, early detection and eradication authority and capacity, and funding sources (even though declining) are all in place to address the threat of invasive agricultural pests, but there is no such system for invasive species that pose threats to wildlife. Several parts of a system exist through executive orders and the individual efforts of some agencies and nongovernmental organizations, but the effort remains less than a coordinated, effective program.

Some existing efforts:

- California Fish and Game Commission is now reviewing its policy regarding the introduction of exotic species to include exclusion of invasive species.

- CALFED's 2000 strategic plan discusses and allocates funding for invasive species.

- State Lands Commission has oversight for aquatic invasive species through ballast water and hull fouling.

- California Department of Water Resources has some educational programs aimed at prevention but no funding to implement them.

- California Division of Forestry considers forest pests and pathogens.

- California Department of Boating and Waterways considers aquatic plant management.

- California Department of Public Health samples for invasive species and human-health pathogens.

- California Water Resources Control Board is addressing non-native amphibians in reservoirs.

- California State Parks manages and conducts research on invasive species.

A current gap in the policy framework is the lack of capability to respond rapidly to new invaders, including funding, prior environmental review, and authority for fast action when the need arises.

Federal fire response now includes invasive species control after the fire, and it is integrated with local efforts through the Burn Area Emergency Rehabilitation and fuel-load control programs. The National Park Service is working to gain authority to work on adjacent lands, and the Department of Defense has a memorandum of understanding with the state of California to work on adjacent lands.

Needs Identified

Create a state coordinating body for invasive species management.

- Create a program with a lead agency at the statewide level, and establish a non-native invasive species advisory council with broad overview and agency representation.

- Compile all the existing invasive species lists, and organize this list on a common data platform as a Web-based decision support system for easy accessibility.

- Identify the leading mechanisms through which invasive species enter the state, and develop the actions to prevent their entry. The various organizations working on invasive species lists are good candidates to do this, beginning with the Department of Agriculture's extensive experience on this topic.

- Develop criteria for prioritizing invasive species projects and funding by geography, stage of invasion, and the cost-benefit of actions.

- Create regional invasive species strategies that outline key species, key constituencies, sources of funding, and an action plan.

- Develop a priorities plan and funding for freshwater systems, beginning with alpine ponds and moving toward more complex systems like valley rivers.

Develop rapid response capacity to identify and eradicate early invaders.

- Develop a rapid response model like the Office of Spill Prevention and Response program, with a rapid response team and emergency fund to tackle new invasions. Cooperative Weed Management Areas groups, watershed groups, and resource conservation districts could be part of the rapid response team.

- Develop early-warning protocols.

- Elevate the priority of research on prevention methods.

- Properly staff existing agricultural check stations.

- Expand emergency eradication provisions from noxious weeds to animals.

- Prepare programmatic environmental reviews under the California Environmental Quality Act and the National Environmental Protection Act, to be completed in advance of the need for emergency response.

- Establish a multidisciplinary research center with dedicated staff to study priority issues.

Engage key audiences and stakeholders on how they can reduce the threat to native wildlife posed by invasive species.

- Conduct a general education program to engage members of the public in prevention and to foster increased support.

- Include invasive species in leadership training for community leaders, including agency leaders, master gardeners, pet store owners, and local elected officials.

- Encourage the use of horticultural species and pet species that are not potentially invasive species in California. Publish lists of preferred species and likely invasive species, such as the one published by the Missouri Botanical Garden, to help consumers choose products. Consider nursery certification and plant labeling. Work with the aquarium industry to prevent releases of invasive aquatic species.

Workshop Participants

ALLEN, SARAH, Point Reyes National Seashore

BRUSATI, ELIZABETH, California Invasive Plants Council

CASSELL, JODI, California Sea Grant

DELFINO, KIM, Defenders of Wildlife

ELLIS, SUSAN, Department of Fish and Game

GARCELON, DAVE, Institute for Wildlife Studies

GEUPEL, GEOFF, PRBO Conservation Science

GOLDSMITH, JAY, National Park Service

GROSHOLZ, TED, UC Davis Cooperative Extension

HEROD, JEFF, U.S. Fish and Wildlife Service

HOSHOVSKY, MARC, Dept of Fish and Game

JOHNSON, DOUG, California Invasive Plants Council

JUREK, RON, Department of Fish and Game

MARTY, JAMIE, Nature Conservancy

MUELLER, MARY ELLEN, USGS Western Ecological Research Center

SCHOENIG, STEVE, California Department of Food and Agriculture

SCHUYLER, PETE, Catalina Conservancy

TERSHY, BERNIE, Island Conservation

Ensuring Water for Wildlife
May 23, 2005

Note: The following summary of the results of this workshop reflects the collective discussion and general conclusions of the workshop participants and does not necessarily reflect the views of the Department of Fish and Game, the Wildlife Diversity Project at UC Davis, or any individual participant.

The Issue

There is increasing urgency to secure water for the long-term benefit of wildlife, particularly in light of the increasing demand for consumptive use of water. Water distribution and management are complex and legally constrained. Water's quality and quantity and the rising cost to supply water are critical for wildlife management throughout California. Integrated planning across agencies, political boundaries, and geographic scales, along with innovative approaches to water finance, storage, and transfers, offer opportunities to secure water for wildlife needs while providing water for agricultural and domestic uses. The relicensing of hydropower projects through the Federal Energy Regulatory Commissions (FERC) process is also an opportunity to improve conditions for aquatic ecosystems and riparian habitats and species.

Most of California's wildlife species depend upon wetlands, lakes, rivers, and riparian habitats at some point in their life cycles. Degradation of habitat is often the consequence of failing to ensure adequate water for wildlife. Habitat and species loss may be due to changes in water quantity or quality, salinity, flow rates, temperature, seasonal flow patterns, or groundwater levels. These changes may also facilitate the establishment of non-native species.

Current Situation

The workshop participants focused on several current conditions, which were especially complex due to the entanglement of public health concerns, water laws and policy, and the ecological requirements of wildlife.

Water quality, quantity, and timing all have an effect on wetlands for wildlife.

Wetlands support hundreds of species, including waterfowl and other birds, fish, amphibians, and invertebrates. The condition and management of wetlands depends on water. The quantity, quality, timing, and cost of water are all important issues for sustaining wetlands. Some wetlands are also integrated into providing ecosystem service to the local community, processing stormwater or sewage drain water. This water may not only be substandard in its quality, but the quantity can be erratic in volume and timing.

Maintaining wetlands also involves other issues, such as mosquito abatement, particularly now with the arrival of West Nile virus in the region. Wetland refuges are charged for mosquito abatement, a substantial expense, and the pesticide spraying causes ecological damage to wetland invertebrates and the aquatic food chain.

Altered stream flows affect wildlife.

Migratory and reproductive behaviors of many species can be affected by changes in a river's seasonal flow patterns. Not only are the cues of rising or falling water volumes disrupted, but necessary habitat may be lost due to excessive or restricted scouring or bank overflow. Water storage for flood control and consumptive uses, as well as out-of-basin water transfers, affect the quantity, quality, and timing of water in California's rivers and streams. Large dams trap sediments, changing the physical nature of downstream habitats. Altered water temperatures and saline intrusions from the Pacific Ocean can also disrupt breeding and animal nursery habitats and changes in species composition. Over the next 10 years, relicensing of hydropower dams through the FERC process will provide opportunities to improve instream flows for wildlife.

Changes in land use and agricultural production can directly affect the water and habitat available for wildlife.

Conversion of agricultural lands to urban centers may change the water flow pattern of an area, as well as the amount of available habitat for wildlife. Rice production in the Central Valley provides significant waterfowl habitat, which is lost when those lands are converted to other crops or are developed. Currently, water transport ditches, as well as adjacent habitat fed by the leaky ditches, can themselves provide food and habitat for wildlife. Water-use efficiencies gained by lining or covering ditches, while increasing the amount of water for use downstream, can also result in a loss of habitat.

Water policy and laws do not adequately consider wildlife values.

California continues to become an increasingly urban state, with water laws and policies that address human needs and limit water use for wildlife conservation purposes. Over-allocation of water resources creates a competitive situation for limited water in a complex legal and institutional framework. The focus currently is on regulation, but future efforts need to add a cooperative, willing-seller approach for long-term solutions. Currently, ungauged water use keeps some water rights holders from participating in transfer discussions under California Water Code section 1707. In addition, conflicting policies and laws must be addressed, such as the spraying for mosquitoes in wetlands with nonspecific pesticides.

Regional integrated planning needs to fully consider wildlife needs.

Wildlife conservation objectives and obligations are not adequately represented in regional integrated planning projects. Out-of-basin water transfers complicate integration of projects within a region, because not all of the available water is being used within the watershed. Additional incentives and adequate staffing from agencies are needed to fully represent wildlife in regional water planning and the FERC hydropower relicensing processes.

Climate change adds long-term uncertainty and the likelihood of seasonal changes in precipitation that must be addressed through changes in storage and distribution systems, and these changes should be considered in the long-term water planning for wildlife conservation and other water demands.

Insufficient funding for supplemental water supplies for wetlands and instream flow is a major concern for wildlife conservation.

The cost of purchasing water for wetlands on the market, especially the spot market, can be very expensive and unpredictable and is becoming more difficult with declining agency budgets. Permanent or long-term water leases for wetlands are needed to replace spot market purchases, but additional public funding is often not available.

Needs Identified

Needs are presented in groups that reflect the major issues identified in the Current Situation Section, with some melding and reorganizing of issues.

Improve water quality, quantity, and timing for wildlife.

- Acquire sufficient water for fish and wildlife resources.
- Effectively implement existing state and federal mandates for environmental flow.
- Create a water transfer clearinghouse for easy reference to facilitate analysis and impact assessment and design sufficient mitigation.
- Have resource agencies collaborate to secure benefits for wildlife through the FERC hydropower project relicensing process.
- Establish a science advisory committee with wildlife conservation expertise to advise water-quality and water-supply agencies statewide.

Support regional integrated planning.

- Planning should be integrated, comprehensive, and strategic, and should involve all stakeholders.
- State and federal agencies and nongovernmental organizations that work at the state and national levels must be trained in how to work with locally and regionally driven planning and funding processes.
- Ensure that qualified science and wildlife expertise is brought into the regional planning efforts through qualified state and federal agency staff and expert contractors.
- Dedicate additional agency staff to work on the FERC process at this critical time.
- Encourage the legislature to monitor and strengthen regional integrated water planning such as that currently occurring with Prop. 50 funding. (Prop. 50 provides project funding to local agencies if the project is consistent with an adopted regional integrated water management plan.)

Develop funding and incentives.

- Develop a water transfer fee or in-kind requirement that all water transfers include an allocation of water for wildlife.

- Assess an acre-foot fee statewide on water use devoted to aquatic ecosystem and wildlife conservation.
- Determine what the implications are for wildlife conservation regarding the "beneficiary pays" approach.
- Develop a water trust.
- Develop a public trust advocate office at the State Water Resources Control Board.
- Ensure that future resource or water bonds pay for proposed enhancements.
- Identify interstate funding opportunities and develop partnerships to lobby Congress; e.g., secure funding for wetlands restoration as has been secured for salmon and steelhead restoration.

Apply sound science to water and wildlife decisions.

- Establish performance criteria and compliance monitoring on water use agreements and for other programs and projects.
- Assess FERC hydropower project effects on aquatic and riparian ecosystems and on wildlife.
- Incorporate adaptive management approaches into policies and projects.
- Develop the information needed to better understand the water needs of wildlife.
- Establish the California equivalent of the National Academy of Sciences to enable rapid development of new information and to resolve scientific disputes.

Workshop Participants

ATKINSON, ANDY, Gray Lodge, Department of Fish and Game

BONHAM, CHUCK, Trout Unlimited

COLBORN, DIANE, California State Assembly

DONLAN, ROB, Ellison, Schneider and Harris, LLP

FELIZ, DAVE, Yolo Wildlife Refuge

FERGUSON, AARON, Northern California Water Association

GREGORY, DAN, U.S. Bureau of Reclamation

HAYDEN, ANN, Environmental Defense

HENLEY, MARK, California Waterfowl Association

HOSHOVSKY, MARC, Department of Fish and Game

INGRAHM, CAMPBELL, U.S Fish and Wildlife Service

KWASNY, DEAN, Department of Fish and Game

MEIER, DAN, U.S. Bureau of Reclamation

MURRAY, NANCEE, Department of Fish and Game

PERRINE, PETER, Wildlife Conservation Board, Wetlands Program

POOLE, RANDY, Sonoma Water Agency

REID, FRITZ, Ducks Unlimited

SPIVY-WEBER, FRANCES, Mono Lake Committee

WEBBER, RENEE, Sonoma Water Agency

WIDELL, DAVE, Ducks Unlimited

ZIRKLE, OLEN, Ducks Unlimited

Restoring and Conserving Riparian Habitats to Maintain Wildlife Diversity
May 12, 2005

Note: The following summary of the results of this workshop reflects the collective discussion and general conclusions of the workshop participants and does not necessarily reflect the views of the Department of Fish and Game, the Wildlife Diversity Project at UC Davis, or any individual participant.

The Issue

Restoring and conserving riparian habitat are essential to conserve wildlife diversity across the state, whether in the desert, the Sierra, or the Central Valley. Perhaps no other habitat type is as demonstrably critical to California wildlife as is riparian habitat. Many studies indicate that riparian habitats are vital to the vast majority of wildlife species.

Riparian habitats have been affected by numerous activities, including, among others, development, water diversions, groundwater overdrafting, grazing, timber harvest, and farming. Though barriers exist that need to be addressed, there are also good opportunities to restore and conserve riparian habitat on both public and private lands. Furthermore, the remaining riparian habitats are so essential for wildlife, they warrant special protection and attention.

Current Situation

At present, riparian areas are in decline in many areas of the state. This workshop focused primarily on flood management, land development, grazing and agricultural use, and water management as the principal factors affecting riparian habitats and wildlife.

Flood Management

In 1907, the *Report of California Debris Commission with Regard to Affording Relief from Floods in the Sacramento Valley and the Adjacent San Joaquin Valley* proposed a comprehensive plan for river rehabilitation, development, and flood control. The final plan, known as the Jackson Report, established the original Sacramento River flood control design, which has set a standard for riparian management in other parts of the state. Its design did not account for the benefits of riparian systems or other ecological functions. Key standards of the Jackson Report include:

- Keeping the river clear of vegetation.

- Minimizing land take, which means maintaining narrow riparian areas.

- Minimizing construction costs.

- Ensuring scour of mining debris. (**Riprap** and levees in the original design have been successful in producing scour but are now encouraging an undesired degree of in-channel erosion.)

In the 1950s, operations and maintenance manuals formalized maintenance practices based on the Jackson Report. These practices typically have negative consequences for riparian habitats. In the 1970s, the Clean Water Act (CWA) and Endangered Species Act (ESA) were enacted but did not result in update of operations and maintenance manuals. The Jackson Report standards and current practices often are in diametric opposition to the complex and conflicting permit requirements of the CWA, ESA, and other conservation laws.

Complicating the current situation are multiple agencies having pieces of authority over riparian areas and floodplains, conflicting missions within and among agencies, and management practices created before present knowledge of conservation values and science was available. Currently, all the liability for compliance with conservation legislation rests with the agencies responsible for flood-control maintenance.

Conflicting missions within and among public resource agencies are common. Large dams are managed for multiple purposes, not just flood control, affecting river flow patterns and timing, and flood-control constraints may limit restoration options. The demands on the water conveyance system levees and canals increase erosion and place stress on the flood control infrastructure.

Where fish weirs are installed at water diversions, large woody debris, usually important for aquatic ecosystems, can pile up and create a flood-flow barrier. Inadequate and disparate funding sources are not conducive to effective integration of flood management and habitat restoration. There is no centralized forum to resolve proactively the fundamental policy issues of floodplain management and habitat restoration. Flood control and restoration are both trying to occur inside the levees, creating areas of conflict.

Management practices in the floodway are based on weak science and outdated rules. Standards and practices are derived from the single focus of the Jackson Report. But neither the mandate of public safety or stewardship of natural resources is met.

Development Issues

Land development presents a host of challenges for riparian habitats and wildlife. In residential development, inadequate setbacks and protection of streams and riparian areas are common, and waterways are often constricted, altering river flow patterns and reshaping waterways. Moreover, without adequate water, new development can lead to excessive demands on surface and ground-water sources. Much of the consumed water in residential developments is returned to river systems through urban runoff, stormwater drains, and sewage treatment outfalls, introducing pollution to the aquatic environment.

Land development frequently causes fragmentation of waterways, impeding their use as wildlife travel corridors. Invasive species, both exotic weeds and animals, are often introduced near developed areas, and they often thrive in disturbed habitats.

In many developed areas, on both public and private lands, stewardship of riparian areas is often neglected. Local agencies may not be informed regarding appropriate, ecologically sound management of riparian areas. Recreational uses of riparian areas can affect wildlife, disrupting their use patterns and chasing them from prime habitats.

Regional coordination of planning and regulation is uncommon at the city and county level, and cities are not consistently included in watershed programs. In rural residential developments, vegetation management for fire prevention and fire recovery has significant consequences for riparian areas.

Agricultural Land Conversion, Grazing, and Agricultural Land-use Issues

California continues to lose agricultural land to other developed uses. As agricultural land disappears, its wildlife value is forever lost.

There are a number of barriers to riparian restoration in an agricultural setting. The agricultural community often has a negative perception of restoration and how it may conflict with agricultural production. Riparian restoration takes both time and money. Private landowners may have inadequate information or experience to design, budget for, and implement riparian restoration projects.

Riparian systems and riparian species are subject to a regulatory process that can deter landowners from engaging in restoration efforts. The burden of long-term management of these restored areas may be daunting. Funding opportunities are not well known among private landowners. The restoration community often has not effectively engaged private landowners.

Successful riparian restoration may have downsides for the agricultural landowner. Restored riparian areas could attract pest species. Restoring habitat that may attract endangered species is a concern for landowners, because it may lead to restrictions on their land or their neighbor's land. Outdated conservation guidelines for threatened and endangered species add to the uncertainty. In addition to the species-related effects of restoration, physical effects can influence landowners. Flood levels, seepage, and buildup of sediments can affect agriculture operations. Overall, better information needs to be provided to landowners regarding habitat restoration.

In addition to those listed above for general agriculture, several riparian issues are specific to ranchland. Riparian restoration may mean a loss of grazing areas. There is a general perception that there can't be a balance between grazing and riparian conservation. Managing grazing on riparian habitats of public lands is difficult, expensive, politically charged, and sometimes unenforceable. Restoration and changes in management of adjacent rangelands are often necessary for successful riparian management.

Water Management Issue

Water is often used in California in ways not consistent with the limits of available water. Acres of residential and commercial lawns, golf courses, and some high water-use crops (such as rice and cotton) are common in the state. The existing legal framework supports this misuse of water. The connection of groundwater to surface water is completely ignored in law. The water allocation and conveyance systems ignore ecosystem values, leading to modified flow regimes and channelization that do not support biodiversity. Instream flow protection laws are weak and almost always aimed at a single endangered species rather than riparian systems.

Making changes in agencies that have functions that affect water for riparian habitat is challenging. Incomplete knowledge of methods to manage for ecosystem benefits exists across all agencies, and agency inertia, fear of change, and existing political structure are hard to alter. Water management is presently approached from an engineering perspective, with little consideration of ecosystem needs, and agencies responsible for maintaining ecosystems are not the decision-makers.

The management of complicated water systems (such as the Sacramento–San Joaquin Delta) for a wide variety of sometimes-conflicting benefits has become enormously complex, which makes changes to benefit riparian habitat more difficult to implement.

Needs Identified

The overall discussion focused on cooperation among the many players in riparian issues: the legal and regulatory environment; funding; and science. Overall, there is so little riparian habitat left that we should be looking to preserve the remaining habitat while creating additional riparian habitat.

We don't have a statewide riparian policy, but we need one. Elements of riparian conservation should involve restoring more natural flow regimes, accommodating over-bank flooding, enlarging levee setbacks, and removing riprap where needed. The public policy need is to figure out how to develop the consensus for restoration and conservation and how to fund it. Education of local decision-makers is key. There is an opportunity to look for situations where goals overlap; e.g., greenways, riparian, and flood control projects. Demonstration projects will be needed to promote best practices and to illustrate the benefits of more natural systems.

Create an ongoing forum of state and federal agencies and nongovernmental organizations to develop a collective vision using present-day conditions that balances conflicting interests of floodplain management.

- Create a process like Cooperative Agreements to prioritize, fund, and implement the vision that's created and to address dispute resolution.
- Use the best-available current science and law to clarify and update operations and maintenance manuals and flood management regulations.
- Update practices relating to sedimentation and erosion repairs and threatened and endangered species concerns.
- Pay more attention to urban creeks, now impacted by rapid and polluted runoff. Consider flood management and riparian conservation in development decisions.
- Develop peer-reviewed guidelines on a regional basis (e.g., Sacramento Valley).
- Include design standards for development to maintain or restore more natural stream flows.
- Investigate the economic benefits of reducing runoff at the source instead of increasing the need for flood control by instituting practices such as establishing local groundwater recharge areas rather than channeling water out of the region.
- Integrate recreation, education, and riparian habitat in greenways, and look at the economic benefits of that integration (e.g., property values).
- Identify mechanisms to fund greenway purchase and maintenance.
- Develop incentives for action by private landowners in restoration and maintenance of riparian areas (e.g., state tax credit).
- Support Weed Management Areas with funding.

Engage grazing and agricultural land users.

- Develop competitive compensation for farm and ranchland through easements or fee title, building on existing programs (e.g., Conservation Reserve Enhancement Program).
- Streamline and consolidate permitting processes for restoration projects.
- Develop Safe Harbor Agreements that encourage landowners to manage lands in ways more beneficial for endangered species and ecosystems.
- Improve the Candidate Conservation Agreement Assurances and provide funds to farmers for preparing Safe Harbor Agreements.

- Encourage programmatic biological opinions and environmental review for large-scale restoration projects.
- Decrease the farmers' cost-share rate for USDA conservation programs.
- Increase funding to programs that include conservation easements with seasonal and use restrictions.

Modernize water management practices.

- Redesign flood control systems to allow for riparian restoration.
- Integrate engineers with conservationists.
- Publicize case studies that are working; e.g., Upper Truckee and the Hamilton City project on the Sacramento River.
- Adjudicate groundwater.
- Inventory and map riparian habitat to provide a baseline for setting goals with regard to water management.

Workshop Participants

ANDERSON, JOHN, Yolo County farmer

BLANKENSHIP, SAM, Department of Fish and Game

CARLON, JOHN, River Partners

CHRISNEY, ANN, Riparian Habitat Joint Venture

CHRISTIAN, BILL, The Nature Conservancy

CLEMONS, SCOTT, Wildlife Conservation Board

GEUPEL, GEOFF, Point Reyes Bird Observatory

GOLET, GREG, The Nature Conservancy

GRECO, STEVE, UC Davis

HUBER, PATRICK, UC Davis

KEELER WOLF, TODD, Department of Fish and Game

KUS, BARBARA, USGS

LIND, AMY, Sierra Nevada Research Center, USFS

LOFT, ERIC, Department of Fish and Game

LORENTZEN, ED, BLM

MOORE, TOM, Natural Resources Conservation Service

NG, MICHELLE, Department of Water Resources

REINER, RICH, The Nature Conservancy

ROBINS, PAUL, Yolo Resource Conservation District

ROBINSON, JOHN, USFS

Russell, Vance, California Audubon

Strachan, Susan, Big Chico Creek Conservancy

Swanson, Keith, Department of Water Resources

Torres, Steve, Department of Fish and Game

Watson, John, Cache Creek Conservancy

Expanding Wildlife Conservation Education
May 23, 2005

Note: The following summary of the results of this workshop reflects the collective discussion and general conclusions of the workshop participants and does not necessarily reflect the views of the Department of Fish and Game, the Wildlife Diversity Project at UC Davis, or any individual participant.

The Issue

Wildlife conservation education seeks to repair the disconnect between people and nature. The goals of wildlife conservation education in California include improving the stewardship of wildlife and their habitat; promoting and facilitating wildlife conservation awareness, appreciation, and knowledge among youth and adults; developing an informed public that understands cause and effect of human activities on wildlife and their habitats; and providing statewide universal access to wildlife conservation education for youth from kindergarten to 12th grade.

Achieving these goals requires increasing the quantity and quality of conservation education programs available to youth and adults and providing sustainable funding for those programs. Pooling of resources, coordinating wildlife education delivery systems, and finding ways to help teachers bring wildlife education into their curricula are necessary parts of breaking down barriers to wildlife education in formal education. In addition, wildlife conservation education must address the misconceptions and lack of correct information regarding science and wildlife. It must also address cultural and demographic changes in the state if it is to be relevant to an urban and increasingly diverse population.

Improving wildlife conservation education throughout the state will create a population that is more informed, engaged, and involved in issues of wildlife conservation and environmental sustainability. This population will be better able to understand and make decisions about the complex interactions among humans, wildlife, and the environment.

Current Situation

Wildlife education has a variety of obstacles to overcome if it is to be broadly available to K-12 youth, as well as to adults.

Several barriers exist to delivering wildlife education in the formal education setting.

There is a shortage of trained, knowledgeable teachers who are willing to teach wildlife education. Teachers typically are overcommitted with their existing work and so may not be eager to teach another program. Many teachers don't see outdoor experiences as relevant, don't understand the importance of wildlife education, and do not know that it is compatible with state standards. In addition, the California content standards above 7th grade don't encourage wildlife education.

The wildlife-education delivery system could be better coordinated.

A variety of outdoor education programs are available to children, youth, and adults—Project WILD and Project Learning Tree are examples—yet only a small percentage of the state's school-aged children are reached. Some programs have expanded their material to reach a broader audience, including curricula for pre-K and college students.

Agency resources are not efficiently used to facilitate wildlife education for a broader audience. Moreover, agencies could improve partnering with the staff of nongovernmental organizations and recreational leaders, who are well-suited to provide nonformal wildlife education.

Misconceptions and lack of correct information abound concerning science and wildlife.

Television is a dominant force in wildlife education, and its focus on single animals or single species ignores landscape concepts and sends the wrong message on wildlife conservation. In school, the testing regime discourages complex thought, and without an adequate knowledge base to build on, exploring more complex ideas is difficult. There is also a growing distrust of science, and government agencies shy away from controversial topics. Linking current research with the solutions to environmental problems will demonstrate the value of sound science.

The public and nature are largely disconnected.

Increasingly, kids are not connected to outdoors and wildlife, whether at home or at school. There is also a disconnect between where students are taught about nature and where they live. Wildlife education should be matched to the setting where people live, not just to wild places. A connection is needed between the day-to-day lives of students and wildlife conservation if we expect students to value wildlife and the environment. Wildlife education programs need problem-solving dilemmas that help students understand the connection between wildlife and themselves. Connecting students to wildlife research-and-monitoring projects in the field and lab and broadly engaging community partnerships to schools for community service–learning partnerships will provide students with real-life experiences.

Cultural and demographic differences and changes require different approaches.

The demographics of the state continue to be more diverse and more urban. Wildlife conservation educators must find a way to reach all kids in a population that is culturally and geographically diverse. Different ethnic groups have different views of wildlife. Unfortunately, there is a distinct lack of cultural diversity among providers, which inhibits the incorporation of wildlife conservation values into all segments of the population. Materials in Spanish and other languages are also needed.

Funding is generally limited for wildlife education.

It is especially difficult to find funding for field trips and transportation. Access to field trip sites can also be difficult. State and federal agencies are not strongly committed to wildlife education, thus it is not prioritized for funding.

Needs Identified

Wildlife conservation educators have an array of challenges to overcome if they are to successfully train the next generation of engaged and informed decision-makers about the environment in which they live. Reconnecting people with nature and providing them with a sense of place, regardless of where they live, is the key challenge but one that can be met. Progress must be made in the following areas to advance wildlife conservation education broadly in the state:

Break down barriers to wildlife education in formal education.

- Ensure that wildlife education remains in the model curriculum (EEI) and in the science content standards test.
- Create an effective marketing approach to inform teachers of free wildlife education training and the California Regional Environmental Education Community (CREEC), and increase travel funding for students.

Pool and coordinate resources into a wildlife education delivery system.

- Develop funding sources for needed programs.
- Establish dedicated contacts within agencies for wildlife education, perhaps through CREEC.
- Create a point position for statewide wildlife education coordination that is connected to the field.
- Develop opportunities for staff from different programs and agencies to meet at conferences and social functions to learn what each is doing and to network on potential opportunities.
- Inventory wildlife education materials and resources, including a gap analysis, and then fill the gap.

Correct misconceptions about science and wildlife education.

- Provide the legislature and media with wildlife mini-trainings.
- Encourage media advocacy among students to address issues, and encourage teachers to use media in critical-thinking activities.
- Develop a "wildlife misconception and myths" Web site/handbook.
- Promote the concept of peer-reviewed science; e.g., via strategic-message campaign and training.
- CREEC should develop awards for the 10-worst and 10-best environmental messages.
- Support efforts by the Association of Environmental and Outdoor Education, the California Science Teachers Association, California Building a Presence for Science, and others to improve training of teachers, naturalists, non-formal educators, et al.

Reconnect people to nature.

- Help children understand their connection with the natural landscape of today and before the onset of human settlement by promoting place-based learning and comparing the built environment to the natural environment.
- Ensure that all students are given an opportunity to participate in outdoor education, a concept that should be part of a "Children's Outdoor Bill of Rights."
- Connect with the school yard, the Internet, and other opportunities, and train teachers to bring the outdoors inside.
- Encourage city redevelopment projects to include parks, open space, and community gardens to give children exposure to urban wildlife.

- Promote connections to environmental justice issues.

Address cultural and demographic differences and population changes.

- Create outreach programs for specific communities with the California Association of Bilingual Educators and train recreational leaders as nonformal educators.
- Educate real estate agencies on the natural environment, economic values of wildlife, living with bears and mountain lions, etc., so that they can provide accurate information to clients.
- Develop a culturally diverse docent- and outdoor-educators pool trained in wildlife education.

Enhance funding for wildlife conservation education.

- Support state bond funding for capital costs of education infrastructure at nature centers, wildlife reserves, open space areas and parks.
- Lobby Congress to amend the State Wildlife Grants program to authorize funding for wildlife conservation education.
- Include wildlife education as part of funding for projects in transportation, habitat restoration, mitigation, water consumption, and other well-funded, environmentally based projects.
- Create incentive funds for schools and others to provide wildlife education.

Workshop Participants

ANDREWS, BILL, EE Program, CDE

BROWN, BRIAN, Water Education Foundation

BRUNS, DEB, YCOE Science Coordinator

CLYMIRE, OLGA, A Child's Place in the Environment

CURLAND, JIM, Defenders of Wildlife

DAVIS, GAIL HICKMAN, Department of Fish and Game

DESAI, LINDA, Project Learning Tree

ENGBRING, TERI, Department of Fish and Game

GUIDA, PATTY, Bureau of Reclamation

JENSEN, DEB, Project Learning Tree

KOEPELE, PATRICK, Tuolumne River Trust

MOORE, DAVID, Department of Fish and Game

PARMER, RICK, Department of Fish and Game

SPARKS, JACK, Outdoor Education

STOKES, MARY, California State Parks

WEBSTER, DAN, Foothill Horizons Outdoor School

WINN, BOBBIE, Department of Fish and Game

Appendix G
Information Sources for Wildlife and Habitat Conservation on Private Lands

With more than 50 percent of California in private ownership, private landowners play an important role in maintaining the state's wildlife diversity. Landowners who are interested in providing wildlife habitat on their lands face a variety of challenges, including inadequate technical knowledge or capacity, funding, or time to take conservation actions.

Depending on their specific situation, landowners may be receptive to different types of assistance. Some landowners prefer minimal or no government involvement. Others may need some financial incentives but prefer market-based approaches, such as conservation banking. Landowners amenable to government assistance may be interested in programs that provide technical assistance, financial assistance, or both.

This appendix lists some of the types of programs and resources that are available for private landowners.

Informational Programs and Documents

The resources below provide information about how to manage agricultural-, range-, and forest-lands in ways that are compatible with wildlife and habitat conservation.

Multiple Land Uses

California Nonpoint Source Encyclopedia
   http://www.swrcb.ca.gov/nps/encyclopedia.html
   Conservation practices to protect land and water from nonpoint sources of pollution.

Natural Resources Conservation Service (NRCS)
Electronic Field Office Technical Guide
http://www.nrcs.usda.gov/technical/efotg/
Recommended practices for the conservation of soil, water, air, and related plant and animal resources.

U.S. Environmental Protection Agency National Management Measures to Control Nonpoint Source Pollution from Agriculture
http://www.epa.gov/owow/nps/agmm/
Information on practices to reduce pollution of surface and groundwater from agriculture.

Best Management Practices Databases
http://swrcb2.swrcb.ca.gov/stormwtr/bmp_database.html
Web links to information about stormwater management.

Salmon Safe Program
http://www.salmonsafe.org
Provides guidance documents, consultation, and a certification process for agricultural management practices that protect aquatic ecosystems.

Dairy Quality Assurance Program
http://www.cdqa.org
Provides guidance documents, consultation, and a certification process for environmental stewardship practices for dairy producers.

Croplands

University of California Conservation Tillage Workgroup
http://groups.ucanr.org/ucct/
Information on research related to conservation tillage production systems in California.

Rangelands

Integrated Hardwood Range Management Program
http://danr.ucop.edu/ihrmp/allpubs.html#2guide
Guidelines for Managing California's Hardwood Rangelands (1996), a report of the University of California, Fish and Game, and California Department of Forestry and Fire Protection.

NRCS Field Office Technical Guides
http://www.nrcs.usda.gov/Technical/efotg/index.html

NRCS National Range and Pasture Handbook
http://www.glti.nrcs.usda.gov/technical/publications/nrph.html
Publications on rangeland management.

Riparian Management Guidance
  http://californiarangeland.ucdavis.edu/Publications%20Web%20Folder/
  Rangeland%20Management%20Series.htm
  Publications from the University of California, Davis, Department of Plant Sciences' rangeland management series.

Rangelands of the Western United States
  http://rangelandswest.org
  A collaborative program comprising land grant universities in the Western U.S. with range extension programs that provides recommendations for management of grazing, invasive species, inventorying and monitoring, fire management, restoration, and wildlife habitat.

University of California Cooperative Extension Rangeland Watershed Program Fact Sheets
  http://danr.ucop.edu/uccelr/htoc.htm

Watershed Resource Guide
  http://www.calcattlemen.org
  (click on "Industry Issues" > "Producer Information" > "Watershed Resources Guide")

Forestlands

NRCS National Forestry Handbook and National Forestry Manual
  http://soils.usda.gov/technical/nfhandbook and http://soils.usda.gov/technical/nfmanual
  Information on forest planning and harvesting on nonpublic lands.

Water Quality Management for Forest System Lands in California: Best Management Practices
  http://www.fs.fed.us/r5/publications/water_resources/waterquality/
  water-best-mgmt.pdf
  Recommended practices to protect water quality for timber management, road construction, mining, recreation, fire management, and range management.

Financial Assistance Programs

A number of programs exist to provide financial assistance, either as direct funding or tax benefits, for management practices that will conserve wildlife and habitat.

Direct Funding

Various state and federal agencies (and private sources) provide direct contributions to private landowners or landowner organizations. These include grants, cost-sharing agreements, debt forgiveness, and reimbursement of expenses. These methods are a way for the government or a private organization to shoulder some of the cost of maintaining habitat or recovering endangered species on private land. Under these types of agreements, a landowner receives financial assistance in carrying out activities intended to benefit wildlife and natural resources.

A relatively comprehensive, regularly updated guide to these programs is available on the Web:

California Department of Forestry and Fire Protection
  http://ceres.ca.gov/foreststeward/html/financial.html
  Cost-share and assistance programs for individual California land owners and Indian tribes.

Tax Benefits

There are several types of tax benefits that can benefit landowners for efforts to conserve natural resources, including deductions based on charitable donations of property and a reduction in capital gains tax on sales of conservation easements or property to a land trust or conservation agency.

Examples of tax incentive programs include:

Department of Conservation—Williamson Act
  http://www.consrv.ca.gov/DLRP/lca/index.htm
  Enables landowners to receive lowered property tax assessments if they enter into contracts with local governments to restrict parcels of their land to agricultural or open-space use.

Wildlife Conservation Board's Natural Heritage Preservation Tax Credit Program
  http://www.wcb.ca.gov/Pages/nhptca_home.htm
  Tax credits are available to private landowners who donate qualified land (fee title or conservation easement), water, or water rights to government agencies or designated nonprofit organizations for conservation purposes.

Reports providing an overview of federal tax benefits and summary of programs in California state government are available on the Web:

Hummon, L., and F. Casey (2005). *Status and trends in federal resource conservation incentive programs: 1996–2001.* http://www.biodiversitypartners.org/pubs

Defenders of Wildlife (2002). *Conservation in America: State government incentives for habitat conservation: A status report.* http://www.biodiversitypartners.org/pubs

Technical Assistance

Technical assistance can include education about available assistance programs, developing conservation plans, or designing on-the-ground habitat improvements.

Three key sources of local technical assistance are:

California Department of Forestry Forest Advisors
  http://www.fire.ca.gov/php/rsrc-mgt_content/downloads/20005_06ForestAdvisorlist.pdf
  Assists individual landowners with land management planning, conservation practices to enhance wildlife habitat, and practices to enhance the productivity of the land. Also assists with prefire fuels treatment, forest health, erosion control, and fisheries issues.

Resource Conservation Districts (RCDs)
  http://www.carcd.org/
  RCDs assist with implementation of resource conservation projects on private and
  public lands.

University of California Cooperative Extension Service
  http://ucanr.org/CES.CEA.shtml
  Provides technical assistance to landowners on farm management and
  environmental protection.

State and Federal Programs

The following programs provide financial and/or technical assistance.

Department of Fish and Game

Fishery Restoration Grants Program
  http://www.dfg.ca.gov/nafwb/fishgrant.html
  Grants to improve or restore salmon and steelhead populations through fishery habitat
  improvement projects, cooperative fish-rearing programs, and public education.

California Landowner Incentive Program
  http://www.dfg.ca.gov/lands/lip/index.html
  Assists with the enhancement of riparian, wetland, and native grassland habitats by providing
  participating landowners with annual incentive payments in return for implementing habitat
  management plans that benefit special status species.

Private Lands Management Program
  http://www.dfg.ca.gov/hunting/deer/plm.html
  Allows landowners to offer fishing and hunting beyond traditional seasons while enhancing and
  safeguarding habitat for wildlife. Also helps develop nonhunting activities such as bird watching,
  photography, camping, and hiking.

Wildlife Conservation Board

  http://www.wcb.ca.gov/index.html
  An independent board within the Department of Fish and Game with authority and funding to
  carry out an acquisition and development program for wildlife conservation. The board offers
  grants for conservation and restoration of oak woodlands, inland wetlands, riparian habitat,
  rangelands, and grasslands.

Department of Conservation

California Farmland Conservancy Program
http://www.consrv.ca.gov/DLRP/cfcp/index.htm
Provides grant funding for projects that use and support agricultural conservation easements for protection of agricultural lands.

California Department of Forestry and Fire Protection

Forest Legacy Program
http://www.fire.ca.gov/php/rsrc-mgt_forestryassistance_legacy.php
Accepts permanent conservation easements from willing landowners on private forestlands that are at risk of being converted to nonforest uses.

California Forest Stewardship Program
http://ceres.ca.gov/foreststeward/index.html
Provides technical and financial assistance to influence positive changes to forestland management.

California Forest Improvement Program
http://www.fire.ca.gov/ResourceManagement/CFIP.asp
Encourages private and public investment in, and improved management of, California's forestlands and resources.

Vegetation Management Program
http://www.fire.ca.gov/php/rsrc-mgt_vegetationmanagement.php
Covers the liability, helps plan for, and conducts prescribed burn on private land to control unwanted brush and other vegetation that create wildfire hazards.

State Water Resources Board

Nonpoint Source Pollution Control Program
http://www.swrcb.ca.gov/nps/
Provide grants to municipalities, local public agencies, and nonprofit organizations for projects to reduce nonpoint source pollution.

State Revolving Loan Program and other funding programs
http://www.swrcb.ca.gov/funding/#funding_programs
Funds projects to reduce pollution loading to surface water or groundwater.

U.S. Fish and Wildlife Service

Partners for Fish and Wildlife
http://www.fws.gov/partners/

Provides technical information and assistance to help landowners improve the quantity and quality of wetlands, riparian habitat, native grasslands, and other important fish and wildlife habitats.

Anadromous Fish Restoration Program
http://www.delta.dfg.ca.gov/afrp/
Assists partners and provides cost-share funding to develop and implement projects that increase natural production of chinook salmon, steelhead, striped bass, American shad, and white and green sturgeon.

U.S. Environmental Protection Agency

Nonpoint Source Implementation Grant (319 Program)
http://www.epa.gov/owow/nps/cwact.html
Provides funding for watershed management and implementation projects to reduce, eliminate, or prevent water pollution and to enhance water quality.

Farm Service Agency (FSA)

Conservation Reserve Program (CRP)
http://www.fsa.usda.gov/dafp/cepd/crp.htm
Provides annual rental payments and cost-share assistance to establish long-term resource-conserving covers on eligible cropland.

Conservation Reserve Enhancement Program (CREP)
http://www.fsa.usda.gov/dafp/cepd/crep.htm
Provides incentive payments for agricultural landowners for instituting specific conservation practices.

Debt for Nature Program (also known as the Debt Cancellation Conservation Contract Program)
http://www.fsa.usda.gov/pas/publications/facts/html/dfn01.htm
Landowners with FSA loans may qualify for cancellation of a portion of their indebtedness in exchange for a conservation contract with a term of 50, 30, or 10 years.

Natural Resources Conservation Service (NRCS)

The NRCS offers 11 programs that provide technical and/or financial assistance. A complete list is available on the Web: http://www.nrcs.usda.gov/programs. Examples are:

Conservation of Private Grazing Lands
http://www.nrcs.usda.gov/programs/cpgl
Technical assistance for grazing land management.

Wildlife Habitat Incentives Program
http://www.nrcs.usda.gov/programs/whip/
Technical assistance and up to 75 percent cost-share assistance to establish and improve fish and wildlife habitat.

Wetlands Reserve Program
http://www.nrcs.usda.gov/programs/wrp
Allows landowners to sell easements to the Department of Agriculture and receive cost-share assistance to restore and protect wetlands.

Environmental Quality Incentives Program
http://www.nrcs.usda.gov/programs/eqip
Provides technical, financial, and educational assistance to address natural resource needs and objectives.

Conservation Security Program
http://www.nrcs.usda.gov/programs/csp
Provides financial and technical assistance to promote the conservation and improvement of soil, water, air, energy, plant and animal life, and other conservation purposes on tribal and private working lands.

Grassland Reserve Program
http://www.nrcs.usda.gov/programs/grp
Assists landowners with protection, restoration, and enhancement of grasslands.

Appendix H
Scientific Names of Species

The common names and scientific names of species and subspecies mentioned in the report are listed below. The species and subspecies are listed alphabetically by common name within each species group.

Amphibians

Common Name	Scientific Name
African clawed frog	*Xenopus laevis*
Arroyo toad	*Bufo californucus*
Bullfrog	*Rana catesbeiana*
California red-legged frog	*Rana aurora draytonii*
California tiger salamander	*Ambystoma californiense*
Cascade frog	*Rana cascadae*
Couch's spadefoot toad	*Scaphiopus couchii*
Foothill yellow-legged frog	*Rana boylii*
Mountain yellow-legged frog	*Rana muscosa*
Northern leopard frog	*Rana pipiens*
Pacific giant salamander	*Dicamptodon tenebrosus*
Red-legged frog	*Rana aurora*
Rough-skinned newt	*Taricha granulosa*
Western spadefoot toad	*Spea hammondii*
Woodhouse's toad	*Bufo woodhousei woodhousei*
Yosemite toad	*Bufo canorus*

Birds

Common Name	Scientific Name
Acorn woodpecker	*Melanerpes formicivorus*
American avocet	*Recurvirostra americana*
American bittern	*Botaurus lentiginosus*
American white pelican	*Pelecanus erythrorhynchos*
Bald eagle	*Haliaeetus leucocephalus*
Band-tailed pigeon	*Patagioenas fasciata*
Bank swallow	*Riparia riparia*
Belding's savannah sparrow	*Passerculus sandwichensis beldingi*
Black oystercatcher	*Haematopus bachmani*
Blue grouse	*Dendragapus obscurus*
Bluebird	*Sialia spp.*
Brewer's sparrow	*Spizella breweri*
Brown pelican	*Pelecanus occidentalis*
Brown-headed cowbird	*Molothrus ater*
Burrowing owl	*Athene cunicularia*
California black rail	*Laterallus jamaicensis coturniculus*
California brown pelican	*Pelecanus occidentalis californicus*
California clapper rail	*Rallus longirostris obsoletus*
California condor	*Gymnogyps californianus*
California gnatcatcher	*Polioptila californica*
California least tern	*Sterna antillarum browni*
California quail	*Callipepla californica*
California spotted owl	*Strix occidentalis occidentalis*
California thrasher	*Toxostoma redivivum*
Cassin's auklet	*Ptychoramphus aleuticus*
Chipping sparrow	*Spizella passerina*
Coastal California gnatcatcher	*Polioptila californica californica*
Common murre	*Uria aalge*
Common raven	*Corvus corax*
Costa's hummingbird	*Calypte costae*
Eared grebe	*Podiceps nigricollis*
European starling	*Sturnus vulgaris*
Ferruginous hawk	*Buteo regalis*
Fox sparrow	*Passerella iliaca*
Gambel's quail	*Callipepla gambelii*
Golden eagle	*Aquila chrysaetos*
Grasshopper sparrow	*Ammodramus savannarum*

Common Name	Scientific Name
Great Basin willow flycatcher	*Empidonax traillii adastus*
Great gray owl	*Strix nebulosa*
Greater sage-grouse	*Centrocercus urophasianus*
Hooded oriole	*Icterus cucullatus*
Inyo California towhee	*Pipilo crissalis eremophilus*
Lawrence's goldfinch	*Carduelis lawrencei*
Least Bell's vireo	*Vireo bellii pusillus*
Light-footed clapper rail	*Rallus longirostris levipes*
Little willow flycatcher	*Empidonax traillii brewsteri*
Long-billed curlew	*Numenius americanus*
MacGillivray's warbler	*Oporornis tolmiei*
Marbled godwit	*Limosa fedoa*
Marbled murrelet	*Brachyramphus marmoratus*
Mountain bluebird	*Sialia currucoides*
Mountain plover	*Charadrius montanus*
Nashville warbler	*Vermivora ruficapilla*
Northern goshawk	*Accipiter gentilis*
Northern harrier	*Circus cyaneus*
Northern spotted owl	*Strix occidentalis caurina*
Olive-sided flycatcher	*Contopus cooperi*
Peregrine falcon	*Falco peregrinus*
Pileated woodpecker	*Dryocopus pileatus*
Prairie falcon	*Falco mexicanus*
Red-tailed hawk	*Buteo jamaicensis*
Ruddy duck	*Oxyura jamaicensis*
Ruddy turnstone	*Arenaria interpres*
Rufous-crowned sparrow	*Aimophila ruficeps*
Sage sparrow	*Amphispiza belli*
Sage thrasher	*Oreoscoptes montanus*
San Diego cactus wren	*Campylorhynchus brunneicapillus sandiegensis*
Sanderling	*Calidris alba*
Sandhill crane	*Grus canadensis*
Sharp-tailed grouse	*Tympanuchus phasianellus*
Short-eared owl	*Asio flammeus*
Snowy plover	*Charadrius alexandrinus*
Southwestern willow flycatcher	*Empidonax traillii extimus*
Steller's jay	*Cyanocitta stelleri*
Surfbird	*Aphriza virgata*
Swainson's hawk	*Buteo swainsoni*

Common Name	Scientific Name
Swainson's thrush	*Catharus ustulatus*
Tricolored blackbird	*Agelaius tricolor*
Varied thrush	*Ixoreus naevius*
Vaux's swift	*Chaetura vauxi*
Western burrowing owl	*Athene cunicularia hypugaea*
Western sandpiper	*Calidris mauri*
Western screech-owl	*Megascops kennicottii*
Western snowy plover	*Charadrius alexandrinus nivosus*
Whimbrel	*Numenius phaeopus*
White-faced ibis	*Plegadis chihi*
Willet	*Catoptrophorus semipalmatus*
Willow flycatcher	*Empidonax traillii*
Xantus's murrelet	*Synthliboramphus hypoleucus*
Yellow rail	*Coturnicops noveboracensis*
Yellow warbler	*Dendroica petechia*
Yellow-billed cuckoo	*Coccyzus americanus*
Yuma clapper rail	*Rallus longirostris yumanensis*

Fishes

Common Name	Scientific Name
American shad	*Alosa sapidissima*
Amargosa pupfish	*Cyprinodon nevadensis*
Arroyo chub	*Gila orcutti*
Black crappie	*Pomoxis nigromaculatus*
Bluegill	*Lepomis macrochirus*
Bonytail	*Gila elegans*
Brook trout	*Salvelinus fontinalis*
Brown trout	*Salmo trutta*
Bullhead catfish	*Ameiurus spp.*
Cabezon	*Scorpaenichthys marmoratus*
California grunion	*Leuresthes tenuis*
California sheephead	*Pimelometopon pulchrum*
Channel catfish	*Ictalurus punctatus*
Chinook, or chinook salmon	*Oncorhynchus tshawytscha*
Coast cutthroat trout	*Oncorhynchus clarkii clarkii*
Coastrange sculpin	*Cottus aleuticus*
Coho salmon	*Oncorhynchus kisutch*
Desert pupfish	*Cyprinodon macularius*

Common Name	Scientific Name
Dorado	*Coryphaena hippurus*
Eagle Lake rainbow trout	*Oncorhynchus mykiss aquilarum*
Flannelmouth sucker	*Catostomus latipinnis*
Golden trout	*Oncorhynchus mykiss ssp.*
Goose Lake redband trout	*Oncorhynchus mykiss ssp.*
Green sturgeon	*Acipenser medirostris*
Hardhead	*Mylopharodon concephalus*
Hitch	*Lavinia exilicauda*
Klamath smallscale sucker	*Catostomus rimiculus*
Klamath River lamprey	*Lampetra similis*
Lahontan cutthroat trout	*Oncorhynchus clarkii henshawi*
Largemouth bass	*Micropterus salmoides*
Lingcod	*Ophiodon elongatus*
Little Kern golden trout	*Oncorhynchus mykiss whitei*
Lost River sucker	*Catostomus luxatus*
Modoc sucker	*Catostomus microps*
Mojave tui chub	*Gila bicolor mohavensis*
Mosquito fish	*Gambusia affinis*
Northern anchovy	*Engraulis mordax*
Owens pupfish	*Cyprinodon radiosus*
Owens speckled dace	*Rhinichthys osculus ssp.*
Owens sucker	*Catostomus fumeiventris*
Owens tui chub	*Gila bicolor snyderi*
Pacific cod	*Gadus macrocephalus*
Pacific lamprey	*Lampetra tridentata*
Pacific mackrel	*Scomber japonicus*
Pacific sardine	*Sardinops sagax caeruleus*
Paiute cutthroat trout	*Oncorhynchus clarkii seleneris*
Pit-Klamath brook lamprey	*Lampetra lethophaga*
Rainbow trout	*Oncorhynchus mykiss ssp.*
Razorback sucker	*Xyrauchen texanus*
Redband trout	*Oncorhynchus mykiss ssp.*
Sacramento perch	*Archoplites interruptus*
Sailfin molly	*Poecilia latipinna*
Santa Ana speckled dace	*Rhinichthys osculus ssp.*
Santa Ana sucker	*Catostomus santaanae*
Shortnose sucker	*Chasmistes brevirostris*
Southern steelhead trout	*Oncorhynchus mykiss ssp.*
Steelhead	*Oncorhynchus mykiss ssp.*

Common Name	Scientific Name
Striped bass	*Morone saxatilis*
Sunfish	*Lepomis spp.*
Tidewater goby	*Eucyclogobius newberryi*
Tui chub	*Gila bicolor*
Tule perch	*Hysterocarpus traksi*
White catfish	*Ameiurus catus*
White seabass	*Cynoscion nobilis*
Yellowfin goby	*Acanthogobius flavimanus*

Invertebrates

Common Name	Scientific Name
Abalone	*Haliotis spp.*
Andrews' dune scarab beetle	*Pseudocotalpa andrewsi*
Argentine ant	*Linepithema humile*
Asian clam	*Corbicula fluminea*
Banana slug	*Ariolimax columbianus*
Barrows' june beetle	*Edrotes barrowsi*
Bay checkerspot butterfly	*Euphydryas editha bayensis*
Beet leafhopper	*Circulifer tenellus*
Black abalone	*Haliotis cracherodii*
Brazilian fire ant	*Solenopsis saevissima*
Brine shrimp	*Artemia spp.*
California freshwater shrimp	*Syncaris pacificus*
Chinese mitten crab	*Eriocheir sinensis*
Coachella giant sand treader cricket	*Macrobaenetes valgum*
Coachella Valley Jerusalem cricket	*Stenopelmatus cahuilaensis*
Dungeness crab	*Cancer magister*
European green crab	*Carcinus maenas*
Fairy shrimp	*Branchinecta and Streptocephalus spp.*
Giant red velvet mite	*Dinothrombium pandorae*
Giant palm-boring beetle	*Dinapate wrightii*
Green abalone	*Haliotis fulgens*
Harvester ant	*Pogonomyrmex spp.*
Hippolyta fritillary	*Speyeria zerene hippolyta*
Japanese mud snail	*Batillaria attramentaria*
Market squid	*Loligo opalescens*
Mysid shrimp	*Mysis mixta*
Opler's longhorn moth	*Adela oplerella*

Common Name	Scientific Name
Pink abalone	*Haliotis corrugata*
Quino checkerspot butterfly	*Euphydryas editha quino*
Red abalone	*Haliotis rufescens*
Riverside fairy shrimp	*Streptocephalus woottoni*
San Diego fairy shrimp	*Branchinecta sandiegonensis*
Shasta crayfish	*Pacifastacus fortis*
Signal crayfish	*Pacifastacus lenuisculus*
Smith's blue butterfly	*Euphilotes enoptes smithi*
Spot prawn	*Pandalus platyceros*
Western pine bark beetle	*Dendroctonus brevicomis*
White abalone	*Haliotis sorensoni*
Zebra mussel	*Dreissena polymorpha*

Mammals

Common Name	Scientific Name
Amargosa vole	*Microtus californicus scirpensis*
American badger	*Taxidea taxus*
Beaver	*Castor canadensis*
Bighorn sheep	*Ovis canadensis*
Black bear	*Ursus americanus*
Black rat	*Rattus rattus*
Black-tailed jackrabbit	*Lepus californicus*
Bobcat	*Lynx rufus*
Buena Vista Lake shrew	*Sorex ornatus relictus*
Burro	*Equus asinus*
Cactus mouse	*Peromyscus eremicus*
California bighorn sheep	*Ovis canadensis californiana*
California ground squirrel	*Spermophilus beecheyi*
California leaf-nosed bat	*Macrotus californicus*
Coachella round-tailed ground squirrel	*Spermophilus tereticaudus chlorus*
Cottontail rabbit	*Sylvilagus spp.*
Coyote	*Canis latrans*
Desert kangaroo rat	*Dipodomys deserti*
Dusky-footed woodrat	*Neotoma fuscipes*
Elk	*Cervus elaphus*
Feral cat	*Felis silvestris*
Feral horse	*Equus caballus*
Feral pig	*Sus scrofa*

Common Name	Scientific Name
Fisher	*Martes pennanti*
Giant kangaroo rat	*Dipodomys ingens*
Gray fox	*Urocyon cinereoargenteus*
Gray whale	*Eschrichtius robustus*
Gray wolf	*Canis lupus*
Grizzly bear	*Ursus arctos*
Humboldt marten	*Martes americana humboldtensis*
Kangaroo rat	*Dipodomys spp.*
Kit fox	*Vulpes macrotis*
Long-eared myotis bat	*Myotis evotis*
Long-legged myotis bat	*Myotis volans*
Marten	*Martes americana*
Marysville kangaroo rat	*Dipodomys californicus eximus*
Mohave River vole	*Microtus californicus mohavensis*
Mojave ground squirrel	*Spermophilus mohavensis*
Monterey dusky-footed woodrat	*Neotoma macrotis luciana*
Morro Bay kangaroo rat	*Dipodomys heermanni morroensis*
Mountain lion	*Puma concolor*
Mule deer	*Odocoileus hemionus*
Nelson's antelope squirrel	*Ammospermophilus nelsoni*
Northern elephant seal	*Mirounga angustirostris*
Norway rat	*Rattus norvegicus*
Pacific fisher	*Martes pennanti pacifica*
Pacific kangaroo rat	*Dipodomys agilis*
Pacific pocket mouse	*Perognathus longimembris pacificus*
Pallid bat	*Antrozous pallidus*
Palm Springs pocket mouse	*Perognathus longimembris bangsi*
Peninsular bighorn sheep	*Ovis canadensis nelsoni dps*
Porcupine	*Erethizon dorsatum*
Pronghorn	*Antilocapra americana*
Pygmy rabbit	*Brachylagus idahoensis*
Raccoon	*Procyon lotor*
Rat (non-native)	*Rattus spp.*
Red fox	*Vulpes vulpes*
Red tree vole	*Arborimus albipes*
Ringtail cat	*Bassariscus astutus*
Rocky Mountain elk	*Cervus canadensis nelsoni*
Roosevelt elk	*Cervus canadensis roosevelti*
San Bernardino flying squirrel	*Glaucomys sabrinus californicus*

Common Name	Scientific Name
San Diego desert woodrat	*Neotoma lepida intermedia*
San Joaquin kangaroo rat	*Dipodomys nitratoides*
San Joaquin kit fox	*Vulpes macrotis mutica*
San Joaquin pocket mouse	*Perognathus inornatus*
San Pablo vole	*Microtus californicus sanpabloensis*
Santa Cruz kangaroo rat	*Dipodomys venustus venustus*
Sea otter	*Enhydra lutris*
Showshoe hare	*Lepus americanus*
Southern sea otter	*Enhydra lutris neries*
Stephens' kangaroo rat	*Dipodomys stephensi*
Striped skunk	*Mephitis mephitis*
Townsend's big-eared bat	*Corynorhinus townsendii*
Tulare grasshopper mouse	*Onychomys torridus tularensis*
Tule elk	*Cervus elaphus nannodes*
Virginia opossum	*Didelphis virginiana*
Western gray squirrel	*Sciurus griseus*
Western yellow bat	*Lasiurus xanthinus*

Plants

Common Name	Scientific Name
A brown alga	*Undaria pinnatifida*
A brown alga	*Undaria spp.*
A green alga	*Caulerpa taxifolia*
Alder	*Alnus spp.*
Algodones Dunes sunflower	*Helianthus niveus*
Antelope bitterbrush	*Purshia tridentata*
Artichoke thistle	*Cynara cardunculus*
Arundo, or Giant reed	*Arundo donax*
Aspen	*Populus spp.*
Barrel cactus	*Ferocactus spp.*
Bay	*Umbellularia californica*
Beach layia	*Layia carnosa*
Big sagebrush	*Artemisia tridentata*
Big-cone Douglas fir	*Pseudotsuga macrocarpa*
Bilberry	*Vaccinium spp.*
Bitterbrush	*Purshia tridentata*
Black cottonwood	*Populus balsamifera subsp. trichocarpa*
Black mustard	*Brassica nigra*
Black oak	*Quercus kelloggii*

Common Name	Scientific Name
Black sage	*Salvia mellifera*
Blue oak	*Quercus douglasii*
Brazilian waterweed	*Egeria densa*
Buckwheat species	*Eriogonum spp.*
Bugseed	*Corispermum sp.*
Bush monkeyflower	*Mimulus aurantiacus*
California juniper	*Juniperus californica*
California lilac	*Ceanothus spp.*
California sagebrush	*Artemisia californica*
Cape ivy	*Delairea odorata*
Castor bean	*Ricinus communis*
Ceanothus	*Ceanothus spp.*
Chamise	*Adenostoma fasciculatum*
Cheatgrass	*Bromus tectorum*
Cholla	*Opuntia spp.*
Coachella Valley milkvetch	*Astragalus lentiginosus var. coachellae*
Coast live oak	*Quercus agrifolia*
Cordgrass (introduced species)	*Spartina alterniflora*
Cottonwood	*Populus spp.*
Coulter pine	*Pinus coulteri*
Cranberry	*Vaccinium spp.*
Deerbrush	*Ceonothus integerrimus*
Dense-flowered cordgrass	*Spartina densiflora*
Desert eriogonum	*Eriogonum deserticola*
Desert saltbush	*Atriplex polycarpa*
Douglas fir	*Pseudotsuga menziesii*
Dune evening primrose	*Oenothera deltoides*
Eelgrass	*Zostera spp.*
Engelmann oak	*Quercus engelmannii*
English ivy	*Hedera helix*
Eucalyptus	*Eucalyptus spp.*
European beach grass	*Ammophila arenaria*
Fennel	*Foeniculum vulgare*
Fescue	*Festuca spp.*
Fig (edible)	*Ficus carica*
Fountain grass	*Pennisetum setaceum*
French broom	*Genista monspessulana*
Giant kelp	*Macrocystis pyrifera*
Giant Spanish needle	*Palafoxia arida var. gigantea*

Common Name	Scientific Name
Gorse	*Ulex europaeus*
Gray pine	*Pinus sabiana*
Himalayan blackberry	*Rubus discolor*
Ice plant	*Carpobrotus edulis*
Incense cedar	*Calocedrus decurrens*
Interior live oak	*Quercus wislizeni*
Iodine bush	*Allenrolfea occidentalis*
Ironwood	*Olneya tesota*
Jeffrey pine	*Pinus jeffreyi*
Joshua tree	*Yucca brevifolia*
Jubata	*Cortaderia jubata*
Juniper	*Juniperus spp.*
Live oak	*Quercus spp.*
Lodgepole pine	*Pinus contorta*
Manzanita	*Arctostaphylos spp.*
Maple	*Acer spp.*
Mediterranean grass	*Schismus spp.*
Medusahead	*Taeniatherum caput-medusae*
Mesquite	*Prosopis spp.*
Monterey Pine	*Pinus radiata*
Mountain heather	*Phyllodoce spp.*
Mountain hemlock	*Tsuga mertensiana*
Mountain mahogany	*Cercocarpus spp.*
Mountain whitethorn	*Ceanothus cordulatus*
Palo verde	*Cercidium spp.*
Pampas grass	*Cortaderia selloana*
Parrotfeather	*Myriophyllum aquaticum*
Peirson's milk vetch	*Astragalus magdalenae var. peirsonii*
Pennyroyal	*Mentha pulegium*
Peppergrass	*Lepidium latifolium*
Pepper weed	*Lepidium latifolium*
Pinyon pine	*Pinus spp.*
Pitcher plant	*Darlingtonia or Sarracenia spp.*
Ponderosa pine	*Pinus ponderosa*
Prickly pear cactus	*Opuntia spp.*
Purple sage	*Salvia leucophylla*
Quaking aspen	*Populus tremuloides*
Red alder	*Alnus rubra*
Red brome grass	*Bromus rubens*

Common Name	Scientific Name
Red fir	*Abies magnifica*
Redwood	*Sequoia sempervirens*
Russian olive	*Elaeagnus angustifolia*
Russian thistle	*Salsola tragus*
Sagebrush	*Artemisia spp.*
Sahara(n) mustard	*Brassica tournefortii*
Saltbush	*Atriplex spp.*
San Diego button celery	*Eryngium aristulatum var. parishii*
San Diego thornmint	*Acanthomintha ilicifolia*
Sand food	*Pholisma sonorae*
Sandmat manzanita	*Arctostaphylos pumila*
Sand verbena	*Abronia spp.*
Santa Lucia fir	*Abies bracteata*
Scotch broom	*Cytisus scoparius*
Scrub oak	*Quercus berberidifolia*
Smoke tree	*Psorothamnus spinosus*
Spectacle pod	*Dithyrea californica*
Spotted knapweed	*Centaurea maculosa*
Starthistle	*Centaurea spp.*
Sugar pine	*Pinus lambertiana*
Sycamore	*Platanus racemosa*
Tamarisk, or Saltcedar	*Tamarix ramosissima*
Tanoak	*Lithocarpus densiflorus*
Tree of heaven	*Ailanthus altissima*
Valley oak	*Quercus lobata*
Veldt grass	*Ehrharta calycina*
Water hyacinth	*Eichhornia crassipes*
Water pennywort	*Hydrocotyle spp.*
Western juniper	*Juniperus occidentalis var. occidentalis*
Western lily	*Lilium occidentale*
Western white pine	*Pinus monticola*
White fir	*Abies concolor*
White sage	*Salvia apiana*
Wiggins' croton	*Croton wigginsii*
Wild oats	*Avena spp.*
Willow	*Salix spp.*
Yellow bush lupine	*Lupinus arboreus*
Yellow starthistle	*Centaurea solstitialis*
Yucca	*Yucca spp.*

Appendix I
Survey of Resource Assessment Activities Statewide

In 2005, Fish and Game's Resource Assessment Program (RAP) initiated a survey of wildlife assessment and monitoring efforts statewide. The survey was designed to provide a summary of current wildlife monitoring efforts in California and to facilitate communication among different individuals, organizations, and agencies.

Surveying wildlife assessment work across the state involves contacting hundreds of researchers and institutions. California is geographically the third-largest and the most biodiverse state in the nation. Given the extensive area, the diversity of species, and the numbers of special-status species, the job of monitoring and assessing California's native wildlife statewide is enormous. There are numerous biologists associated with various public and private institutions studying wildlife and wildlife issues. For this survey, attempts were made to contact biologists at 20 federal, state, and local agencies or branches, including the U.S. Department of the Interior, the U.S. Department of Agriculture, the U.S. Department of Defense, and, in California state government, the Department of Fish and Game, State Parks, Department of Forestry and Fire Protection, Department of Water Resources, and Bay-Delta Authority.

There are 10 campuses within the University of California system, 21 campuses within the California State University system, 25 private colleges and universities, and 103 community colleges that have biological science departments and natural reserves with faculty that may be actively engaged in wildlife research. In addition, there are numerous local biologists employed by city and county governments, nonprofit groups and foundations, and private consulting firms that may be actively involved in wildlife research or may coordinate wildlife monitoring programs. Research projects that actually handle wild animals must have a permit. Fish and Game's License and Revenue Branch issued more than 2,700 scientific collecting permits to individuals from more than 800 different organizations in 2004. (Not all of these permits were issued to individuals involved with wildlife monitoring projects. However, many monitoring activities, such as visual surveys, do not require state permits.) It was beyond the capacity of this project to communicate with all of the active wildlife biologists.

The initial goal of the wildlife monitoring database was to provide a central source of information about all of the wildlife monitoring activities within California. While the information collected to date is far from complete, it is also clear that there is a strong interest in sharing of information about wildlife and wildlife research within California. Examples include:

- The National Park Service has implemented an Inventory and Monitoring Program that organizes national parks and monuments into regional networks based on similar habitats. Within California, examples include the Mojave Network (Joshua Tree National Park, Death Valley National Park, Manzanar National Historic Site, and the Mojave National Preserve), and the Sierra Network (Yosemite National Park, Sequoia and Kings Canyon National Park, and Devils Postpile National Monument).

- The Western Ecological Research Center (WERC) of the U.S. Geological Survey maintains files on all ongoing projects by staff within their jurisdiction. In addition, WERC is working closely with biologists at Fish and Game on the development of a database containing wildlife research data accessible to biologists within the two agencies.

- The California Interagency Wildlife Task Group, created in 1981 to promote improved understanding of the biology of California's wildlife and the application of this information to land management, includes members from 16 federal and state agencies who have met quarterly since 1985. One of the tasks presented to this group is to identify and prioritize the wildlife management, research, and database needs for California. Progress reports on wildlife and wildlife habitat databases indicate that there are a large number of databases available in California, including several extensive lists (Natural Resources Project Inventory, Information Center for the Environment, California Environmental Resources Evaluation System), but none are comprehensive for all wildlife activities statewide. There is also a strong consensus for the development of consistent methodology among agencies and groups for inventory projects.

The survey results are on the Web at http://www.dfg.ca.gov/habitats/wdp/project_search.asp. This initial survey effort identified only a portion of the resource assessment activities in California. Among the individual biologists surveyed, many have indicated an interest in the development of a central database for sharing information within and among agencies, offices, and organizations. If there is continued funding and support for this effort, the initial steps taken as part of the RAP survey, in conjunction with existing databases and cooperative efforts among various agencies, could facilitate the development of a more complete central wildlife database for the state.

Survey Results Summary

The RAP wildlife monitoring database contains 420 responses from 149 individuals, agencies, field offices, and organizations throughout the state. Several agencies and organizations are well represented, including those that conduct multiple studies throughout California and maintain internal project databases, such as the USGS and Point Reyes Bird Observatory offices. In fact, federal agencies and nongovernmental organizations were recognized as the project lead for 46.9 percent and 26.2 percent of the projects, respectively. Others agencies, or units within an agency, indicated an interest in the project but were unable to respond due to low staffing levels or lack of wildlife data that met the parameters of the database. Projects that originated from academic institutions represented 22.9 percent of the responses. However, much of this data was collected from project status reports submitted to third parties, such as the University of California Natural Reserve System. There are few responses from local (city and county) biologists (2.6 percent) or biologists from the private sector (4.0 percent).

Responses vary from studies of individual species to efforts to quantify and identify all wildlife present within a given habitat or area. The majority of the responses (51.9 percent) describe efforts to monitor bird species or include birds within the range of species studied. In contrast, projects addressing reptiles, amphibians, and insects comprised only 9.3 percent, 10.5 percent, and 14.8 percent, respectively. Interest in bird watching, the large number of bird-oriented organizations throughout California, and funding opportunities for avian studies are probably an important factor in the large number of projects collecting avian data. In contrast, monitoring projects that collect invertebrate, amphibian, or reptile data are generally derived from studies of endangered or threatened species.

Results also showed a geographic bias. Data from 37.6 percent of the projects was collected from sites within the Central Valley Region. The North Coast (16.7 percent), Central Coast (14.5 percent), and Sierra (13.1 percent) regions had similar response rates. In contrast, only 6.2 percent of the responses included data from the Colorado or Mojave deserts. While it is likely there are fewer projects and programs in some regions due to the presence of few biologists and regional field offices (such as the Mojave Desert and Colorado Desert), the actual results of the survey are probably more indicative of variation in the availability of time to complete the survey and local biologists' interest in the project.

Survey data were collected and the database updated through August 31, 2005. The database is available on the Web at http://www.dfg.ca.gov/habitats/wdp/project_search.asp. The RAP survey will not be expanded or updated further unless resources are allocated to do so.

Appendix J
Monitoring Needs to Support Conservation Actions

Recommended Conservation Actions	Effectiveness Monitoring Questions	Needed Monitoring	Monitoring Level	Monitoring Collaborators
Statewide Actions				
a. The state should develop policies and incentives to facilitate better integration of wildlife conservation considerations into local and regional planning and land-use decision-making.	Has state adopted regional goals for species and habitat protection? Has DFG staff and resources devoted to assisting local governments to do conservation planning increased? How many local governments have adopted and implemented policies to achieved regional goals?	Monitor county and regional plans for conservation elements. Need long-term regional monitoring.	Management Regional	DFG, FWS, Counties, Cities
b. Permitting agencies, county planners, and land management agencies should work to ensure that infrastructure development projects are designed and sited to avoid harmful effects on sensitive species and habitats.	How many local agencies have adopted policies to ensure that infrastructure development projects avoid effects on sensitive species and habitats?	Monitor infrastructure project plans for elements to avoid sensitive species and habitats.	Management Regional	DFG, FWS, Counties, Cities
c. The state should develop policies and incentives to better integrate wildlife conservation into state and regional transportation planning. Wildlife considerations need to be incorporated early in the transportation planning process.	What new policies and incentives have caused early wildlife conservation to be considered in the planning process for state and regional transportation projects? What transportation retrofits have been completed that reduce impacts on wildlife resources?	Monitor state and regional transportation plans for wildlife conservation elements.	Regional	DFG, FWS, Counties, Cities

479

Recommended Conservation Actions	Effectiveness Monitoring Questions	Needed Monitoring	Monitoring Level	Monitoring Collaborators
d. State and federal agencies should work with cities and counties to secure sensitive habitats and key habitat linkages.	Habitat linkages have been identified for what percentage of the state's landscape? What percentage of identified habitat area of linkages is protected from development?	Identify sensitive habitats and habitat corridors statewide and monitor local government actions to secure them.	Natural Community, Habitat Linkages	DFG, FWS
e. State and local agencies should allocate sufficient water for ecosystem uses and wildlife needs when planning for and meeting regional water supply needs.	What regions have developed a water budget that identifies the needs of wildlife and ecosystems? What number of regional integrated water plans have long-term provisions to adequately ensure water for wildlife and ecosystems? In how many river systems have management changes been made so that flows more closely mimic natural flows? What new long-term contracts for instream flows and wetlands have been secured? What additional water rights have been secured for conservation? What actions have been taken to improve compliance with exisiting water rights?	Monitor state water management decisions and regional integrated water plans for elements to ensure sufficient water for ecosystem uses and wildlife needs.	Natural Community (Riparian, Aquatic)	DFG, FWS. SWRCB, DWR
f. Federal, state, and local agencies should provide greater resources and coordinate efforts to control existing occurrences of invasive species and to prevent new introductions.	What new actions have been implemented to prevent, eradicate or control invasive species? What are the priority invasive species problems in the state, and what are the goals for prevention, eradication, or control of those species?	Monitor the status and trends of the prioritized invasive species.	Species	DFG, FWS, RCDs, CDFA, BLM, USFS, NPS, DPR, CCC
g. Federal, state, and local agencies and nongovernmental conservation organizations, working with private landowners and public land managers, should expand efforts to restore and conserve riparian communities.	To what extent have priority riparian habitats been identified for restoration and conservation? What new policies and incentives have been enacted to increase conservation and restoration of riparian habitats on private lands? Have riparian habitat restoration goals been established on public lands? When riparian goals are established, what area of riparian habitat has been restored or protected?	Map priority areas for restoration and conservation of riparian habitats statewide. Monitor the priority riparian areas for the status and trends of riparian vegetation and associated wildlife species.	Natural Community	See Appendix G

Recommended Conservation Actions	Effectiveness Monitoring Questions	Needed Monitoring	Monitoring Level	Monitoring Collaborators
h. Federal, state, and local agencies and nongovernmental organizations, working with private landowners, should expand efforts to implement agricultural and rangeland management practices that are compatible with wildlife and habitat conservation.	What additional private acreage is managed for improving wildlife habitat and ecosystems?	Establish goals for acres of improved wildlife habitat on agricultural and rangelands. Monitor the numbers of acres that have implemented practices that improve conditions for wildlife.	Natural Community, Ecosystem Function	See Appendix G
i. In their conservation planning and ecosystem restoration work, state and federal wildlife agencies and land managers should consider the most current projections of the effects of global warming.	To what extent have state and federal land management agencies considered future consequences of global warming in their land management planning efforts? To what extent have counties considered the consequences of global warming in county planning?	Prepare a guide and protocol for incorporating climate change considerations into wildlife and land management planning. Monitor wildlife and land management plans for elements regarding climate change.	Regional, Ecosystem Function	CEC
j. The state and federal governments should give greater priority to wildlife and natural resources conservation education.	What percentage of California youth and adults has been exposed to wildlife and conservation education?	Every five years, conduct a survey of grade school children and adults on basic wildlife and natural resources conservation issues.	Management	DFG, CDE, CIWMB
k. The state should strengthen its capacity to implement conservation actions and to assist local agencies and landowners with planning and implementation of wildlife and habitat restoration and conservation efforts.	Has the state expanded its capacity to assist local agencies with conservation planning and implementing wildlife and habitat restoration and conservation efforts?	Assess current staff and resources currently committed to assist local agencies and landowners to develop and implement restoration and conservation plans. Monitor staff and resources committed to this task each year.	Management	DFG
l. Working with the Department of Defense, the state and conservation organizations should expand efforts to secure important wildlife habitat that also serves as development buffer zones around military bases and training grounds.	How much habitat (quantity and quality) surrounds military lands?	Identify habitat quantity and quality around each military base.	Regional, Natural Community	DOD, FWS, DFG, USGS

481

Recommended Conservation Actions	Effectiveness Monitoring Questions	Needed Monitoring	Monitoring Level	Monitoring Collaborators
m. Permitting agencies, county and local planners, and land management agencies should work to ensure that infrastructure development projects are designed and sited to avoid harmful effects on sensitive species and habitats.	How many local agencies have adopted policies to ensure that infrastructure development projects avoid effects on sensitive species and habitats?	Monitor infrastructure project plans for elements to avoid sensitive species and habitats.	Management, Regional	DFG, FWS, Counties, Cities
n. To address habitat fragmentation and avoid the loss of key wildlife corridors, federal, state and local agencies, along with nongovernmental organizations, should support scientific studies to identify key wildlife habitat linkages throughout the state.	Habitat linkages have been identified for what percentage of the state's landscape? What percentage of identified habitat area of linkages is protected from development?	Identify sensitive habitats and habitat corridors statewide, and monitor local government actions to secure them.	Natural Community, Habitat Linkages	DFG, FWS
o. The state should provide scientific and planning assistance and financial incentives to local governments to develop and implement regional multispecies conservation plans for all of the rapidly developing areas.	How many regional multi-species conservation plans have been developed for the rapidly developing areas of the Sierra Nevada and Cascades? To what extent have the conservation goals of those plans been achieved?	Monitoring and adaptive management would be designed and implemented as part of new regional multispecies conservation planning efforts.	Regional, Natural Community, Ecosystem Function, Species	DFG
p. While numerous private landowners are leaders in conservation, Fish and Game, the U.S. Fish and Wildlife Service, the USDA Natural Resources Conservation Service, and local resource conservation districts need to expand efforts to improve conservation and restoration on private lands by assisting private landowners.	What is the status of wildlife and habitats on private lands? How many acres of each habitat are under long-term conservation agreements? Are landowner assistance programs strategically targeting the most important wildlife needs?	Remote sensing of land cover changes; targeted monitoring of indicator species sensitive to private land uses, where agreeable to landowners; regular assessment of landowner incentive programs	Management, Regional, Natural Community	See Appendix G
q. State and federal government should give greater priority to funding and staffing of wildlife and natural resource law enforcement efforts.	To what extent has the Department worked with the Legislature and Fish and Game Commission to develop a long-term strategy for improved laws and regulations and to improve stable funding for law enforcement?	Monitor the status and trends of regulation and law proposals. Develop strategies to hire, deploy, and fund adequate Fish and Game law enforcement officers.	Management	DFG, FGC, Legislature

Recommended Region-Specific Conservation Actions

Mojave Desert Region

Recommended Conservation Actions	Effectiveness Monitoring Questions	Needed Monitoring	Monitoring Level	Monitoring Collaborators
a. Improve stewardship on federally managed lands to protect wildlife diversity.	After resources required to implement federal and state wildlife conservation mandates that apply to federally management lands have been identified, what additional resources have been allocated to improve conservation on federal lands?	Expand existing monitoring efforts to include long-term monitoring of status and trends of sensitive habitats. Expanded monitoring should fill in gaps in existing efforts (i.e., monitoring for recovery of the desert tortoise and other species).	Regional, Natural Community, Species	BLM, DMG
b. Stabilize groundwater levels and recharge depleted sub-basins of the Mojave River Basin, restoring groundwater to levels that support riparian habitat.	What is the trend in groundwater levels in the Mojave River Basin? Riparian habitat has recovered on how many acres along rivers, creeks and wetlands in the basin?	Groundwater monitoring and periodic assessments of riparian habitats in the Mojave River basin by the USGS, DFG, MWA are adequate to assess effectiveness of this action.	Natural Community, Ecosystem Function	MWA, USGS, BLM
c. Stabilize groundwater levels and secure wet habitats in the Amargosa River Basin. This action will help protect the endangered Amargosa vole and the Amargosa pupfish, among other species.	What is the trend in groundwater levels in the Amargosa River Basin? Riparian habitat has recovered on how many acres along rivers, creeks and wetlands in the basin?	Groundwater monitoring and periodic assessments of riparian habitats in the Amargosa River basin by is adequate to assess effectiveness of this action.	Natural Community, Ecosystem Function	BLM, DMG
d. Provide maximum federal and state protection for remaining riparian, spring, seep, and wetland habitats, and restore degraded riparian, spring, seep, and wetland areas.	What policies have been adopted or strengthened or been more fully enforced to protect riparian, spring, seep, and wetland habitats? How many acres of these habitats have been restored?	Expand existing monitoring efforts to include long-term monitoring of sensitive habitats and trends and natural communities. Expanded monitoring should fill in gaps in existing efforts, such as monitoring as part of the desert tortoise recovery efforts.	Natural Community, Ecosystem Function	BLM, FWS, DFG

Recommended Conservation Actions	Effectiveness Monitoring Questions	Needed Monitoring	Monitoring Level	Monitoring Collaborators
e. The Bureau of Land Management should improve and, upon approval, implement the West Mojave Plan with conservation measures to address all special status species and to maintain wildlife diversity.	What is the status of implementation of the West Mojave Plan? What is the status of covered species under the plan? To what extent has the monitoring plan been implemented? Are the plan's goals being met for conserving special status species?	Monitoring and adaptive management is covered by the West Mojave Plan.	Regional, Natural Community, Species	BLM, DWS, DFG
f. Reduce off-road vehicle damage to wildlife habitats.	Have additional OHV parks opened? Have buffer areas around sensitive habitats been expanded? Has compliance with area restrictions improved?	Need quantitative assessment of area damaged by OHVs and a monitoring program (such as use of remote sensing) to assess changes in number acres of habitat restored or damaged.	Regional, Natural Community	BLM, DPR
g. Federal, state, and local agencies should provide greater resources and coordinate efforts to control existing occurrences of invasive species and to prevent new introductions.	In the region, have priority invasive species been reduced?	Need long-term monitoring of priority invasive species.	Species	BLM, DMG
h. Fully implement the recovery plans for the Mojave tui chub, Amargosa vole, and Inyo California towhee.	Have the Mojave tui chub, Amargosa vole, and Inyo California towhee recovery plans been implemented? Have the goals of the plans been met?	Need long-term monitoring of the amargosa vole.	Species	FWS, BLM
i. Fish and Game, BLM, and the three military bases that support the Mohave ground squirrel should develop a collaborative conservation and recovery strategy for the Mohave ground squirrel so that federal listing is not necessary.	Has a conservation and recovery strategy been completed for the Mohave ground squirrel? Have the goals of the plan been met?	Need long-term monitoring of the Mohave ground squirrel.	Species	DFG, BLM, DOD

Colorado Desert Region

Recommended Conservation Actions	Effectiveness Monitoring Questions	Needed Monitoring	Monitoring Level	Monitoring Collaborators
a. Federal, state, and local agencies, along with nongovernmental conservation organizations, should work together to reach agreement upon and fund a restoration plan for the Salton Sea.	Has a restoration plan for the Salton Sea been agreed to by state and federal agencies? Does the plan address the needs of bird species for which the Sea is an important resource? Have state and federal funds been allocated for implementing the restoration plan? To what extent have the plan's restoration goals been met?	Need comprehensive monitoring and adaptive management element incorporated into the Salton Sea Restoration Plan that meets the standards of NCCP.	Natural Community, Ecosystem Function, Species	DOI, FWS, DFG, SWRCB
b. Federal and state wildlife agencies should work to ensure that environmental impacts resulting from water transfers (both those permitted under the Quantification Settlement Agreement [QSA] and any future transfers) are mitigated.	To what extent have the Salton Sea and Imperial Valley Habitat Conservation Plan and the provisions of the related Biological Opinion been implemented? Have the goals of the HCP been achieved?	Covered by the Salton Sea and Imperial Valley Habitat Conservation Plan.	Natural Community, Ecosystem Function, Species	DOI, FWS, DFG, SWRCB
c. Federal and state wildlife agencies, water management agencies, and nongovernmental conservation organizations should develop and invest in restoration and protection efforts for the Salton Sea, the Colorado River delta, and other regional wildlife habitats.	What restoration has been achieved at the Salton Sea, Colorado River delta, and other wetland habitats in the region?	Need a monitoring and adaptive management element for restoration plans established for the Colorado River delta.	Regional, Natural Community, Species	DOI, FWS, DFG, SWRCB
d. Wildlife agency staff developing the Imperial Valley Habitat Conservation Plan, working with Imperial County planners and nongovernmental conservation organizations, should identify and protect critical avian habitats in southern Imperial County.	Have priority bird habitats been identified in the Imperial Valley? To what extent have these habitats been protected?	Need long-term monitoring program for critical avian habitats in southern Imperial County.	Natural Community	DFG, FWS, Imperial County

Recommended Conservation Actions	Effectiveness Monitoring Questions	Needed Monitoring	Monitoring Level	Monitoring Collaborators
e. The Bureau of Land Management, working with state and federal wildlife agencies and nongovernmental conservation organizations, should protect and restore biologically significant habitats in the Algodones Dunes.	Are habitat values improving in the Algodones Dunes? Are key species populations increasing or maintaining their numbers?	Need long-term monitoring of the dune natural community.	Natural Community	BLM, FWS, DFG
f. State and federal agencies and nongovernmental partners should collaborate to develop a comprehensive Southern California Outdoor Recreation Program (for the South Coast and Colorado Desert regions) to provide recreational opportunities and access that do not conflict with wildlife habitat needs. Areas for intensive recreational access and off-road vehicle use should be developed on the least-sensitive public lands in order to direct pressures away from sensitive habitats.	Has a comprehensive Southern California Outdoor Recreation Program been developed? To what extent have the wildlife conservation goals of the plan been achieved?	Need quantitative assessment of area damaged by OHVs and a monitoring program (such as use of remote sensing) to assess changes in number acres of habitat restored or damaged.	Regional	DPR, BLM, DFG, FWS
g. Federal, state, and local agencies and nongovernmental conservation organizations should work to protect and restore biologically significant habitats in the Coachella Valley.	Has the Coachella Valley Multispecies Conservation Plan been finalized? To what extent have the goals of the plan been achieved?	Covered by the CVMCP.	Regional, Natural Community, Species	BLM, FWS, DFG
h. Nongovernmental conservation organizations should continue to work to protect important wildlife habitat areas.	What additional lands in the important wildlife areas have protected status?	Establishment of new protected habitats should include monitoring and adaptive management as part of the management plans for those lands.	Natural Community	DFG, FWS

486

Recommended Conservation Actions	Effectiveness Monitoring Questions	Needed Monitoring	Monitoring Level	Monitoring Collaborators
i. Permitting agencies, county and local planners, and land management agencies should work to ensure that infrastructure development projects are designed and sited to avoid harmful effects on sensitive species and habitats.	Have sensitive habitats of the region been identified and prioritized? Have policies been adopted that ensure infrastructure projects approved by land management agencies and local agencies do not harm theses habitats? What is the status of the identified sensitive habitats?	Need long-term regional monitoring.	Regional, Natural Community	DFG, FWS, Counties, Cities
j. Federal, state, and local agencies should work with nongovernmental organizations to provide greater resources to control and limit introductions of invasive species in the region.	In the region, have priority invasive species been reduced? (See statewide action f.)	Need long-term monitoring of priority invasive species. (See Statewide Action f.)	Species	See Statewide Action f.

South Coast Region

Recommended Conservation Actions	Effectiveness Monitoring Questions	Needed Monitoring	Monitoring Level	Monitoring Collaborators
a. Wildlife agencies and local governments should work to improve the development and implementation of regional Natural Community Conservation Plans (NCCPs), which is the primary process to conserve habitat and species in the region's rapidly urbanizing areas.	To what extent have the goals of the NCCPs of the region been achieved?	Covered by NCCPs.	Regional, Natural Community, Species	DFG, FWS, Counties, Cities
b. Wildlife agencies should establish regional goals for species and habitat protection and work with city, county, and state agency land-use planning processes to accomplish those goals.	Have wildlife agencies established regional goals for species and habitat conservation? To what extent have the regional conservation goals been adopted by local planning efforts? To what extent have those regional goals been achieved?	Need long-term regional monitoring.	Regional	DFG, FWS
c. Safeguard and build upon Camp Pendleton's contribution to the regional network of conservation lands.	What additional lands adjacent to Camp Pendleton have been protected?	Covered by existing efforts.	Natural Community	DFG, FWS, DOD
d. To address regional habitat fragmentation, federal, state, and local agencies, along with nongovernmental conservation organizations, should support the protection of the priority wildlands linkages identified by the South Coast Missing Linkages project.	What percentage of 15 areas identified as important wildlands linkages by the South Coast Missing Linkages project have been protected?	Need long-term monitoring program for habitat values of wildlands linkage areas identified by the South Coast Missing Linkages project.	Regional, Habitat Linkages, Species (wide-ranging)	SCW, DFG, FWS
e. Federal, state, and local agencies, along with nongovernmental conservation organizations, should protect and restore the best remaining examples of coastal wetlands that provide important wildlife habitat.	What additional acreages of coastal wetlands have been restored or protected?	Covered by existing efforts.	Natural Community	CCC, DFG, FWS, NMFS, SCWRP
f. Public agencies and nongovernmental conservation organizations should invest in efforts to protect and restore the best remaining regional examples of ecologically intact river systems.	What additional areas of ecologically intact river systems have been protected or restored?	Need to expand long-term monitoring of priority river systems.	Natural Community, Ecosystem Function	DFG, FWS, CCC, USFS

Recommended Conservation Actions	Effectiveness Monitoring Questions	Needed Monitoring	Monitoring Level	Monitoring Collaborators
g. Federal, state, and local agencies should provide greater resources and coordinate efforts to control existing occurrences of invasive species and to prevent new introductions.	In the region, have priority invasive species been reduced?	Need to expand long-term monitoring of priority invasive species.	Species	See: Statewide Action f.
h. Federal, state, and local public agencies should sufficiently protect sensitive species and important wildlife habitats on their lands and should be adequately funded and staffed to do so.	After identifying resources required to implement federal and state wildlife conservation mandates that apply to federally management lands. What additional resources have been allocated to improve conservation on federal lands?	Need to expand long-term monitoring on public lands.	Natural Community, Species	DFG, FWS, CCC, USFS, Counties
i. Federal and state agencies and nongovernmental partners should collaborate to institute appropriate fire management policies and practices to restore the ecological integrity of the region's ecosystems while minimizing loss of property and life.	To what extent have fire management policies been implemented to restore the ecological integrity of forests? How many additional forested acres have improved ecological conditions?	Covered by land and resource management plans of the state and federal agencies.	Natural Community	USFS, CDF, DFG, FWS, DPR
j. The state should coordinate the development of a model ordinance and building codes for new or expanding communities in fire-adapted landscapes to make those communities more fire compatible and reduce the state's liability for fire suppression.	Has a model ordinance been adopted by counties for building codes to make new construction more tolerant in fire-adapted landscapes?	Covered by monitoring pursuant to forest management plans.	Management, Natural Community	CDF, DFG, USFS, FWS, Counties
k. State and federal wildlife agencies, the U.S. Forest Service, state and county parks, BLM, and nongovernmental partners should collaborate to develop a comprehensive Southern California Outdoor Recreation Program to provide recreational opportunities and access that do not conflict with wildlife habitat needs.	Has a comprehensive Southern California Outdoor Recreation Program been developed? To what extent have the wildlife conservation goals of the plan been achieved?	Need quantitative assessment of area damaged by OHVs and a monitoring program (such as use of remote sensing) to assess changes in number acres of habitat restored or damaged.	Regional	DPR, BLM, DFG, FWS

Recommended Conservation Actions	Effectiveness Monitoring Questions	Needed Monitoring	Monitoring Level	Monitoring Collaborators
Central Coast Region				
a. Wildlife agencies should establish regional goals for species and habitat protection and work with city, county, and state agency land-use planning processes to accomplish those goals.	Have wildlife agencies established regional goals for species and habitat conservation? To what extent have the regional conservation goals been adopted by local planning efforts? To what extent have those regional goals been achieved?	Monitoring and adaptive management should be developed in conjunction with the development of regional conservation goals.	Regional	DFG, FWS
b. Federal, state, and local agencies, along with nongovernmental organizations, should work with private landowners and land managers to implement agricultural- and rangeland management practices that are compatible with wildlife and habitat conservation.	What additional private acreage are managed for improving wildlife habitat and ecosystems?	Establish goals for acres of improved wildlife habitat on agricultural and rangelands. Monitor the numbers of acres that have implemented practices that improve conditions for wildlife.	Regional, Natural Community	See Appendix G
c. Federal, state, and local agencies, along with nongovernmental organizations, should work with private landowners to both continue and develop programs that help keep grazing land uses profitable.	What is the status and trends of conversion of rangelands for development of other land uses less compatible with wildlife conservation?	Need monitoring of land conversion of rangelands in important wildlife areas, including migratory corridors.	Management, Habitat Linkages	See Appendix G
d. Federal, state, and local agencies, along with nongovernmental conservation organizations, should work to protect large, relatively unfragmented habitat areas, wildlife corridors, and underprotected ecological community types.	What percent of large habitat areas, wildlife corridors, and underprotected ecological communities are protected from land conversion or development?	Need a long-term monitoring program for large habitat, wildlife corridors, and priority ecological community types. This program should coordinate with and build upon existing monitoring in the region.	Regional, Habitat Linkages	DFG, WCB, FWS, CCC
e. Federal, state, and local public agencies should sufficiently protect sensitive species and important wildlife habitats on their lands.	To what extent have sensitive species and wildlife habitats been identified and prioritized on public lands? What percent of these priority areas are restored or adequately managed to conserve species at risk?	Expand wildlife and natural community monitoring on public lands to levels adequate to assess the status and trends of identified sensitive species and priority wildlife habitats.	Natural Community, Species	DFG, FWS, USFS, BLM, CCC, DPR, DOD, Counties
f. Federal, state, and local agencies should work to restore fish passage in aquatic systems important for anadromous and wide-ranging fish populations.	How many fish barriers have been removed, and how many miles of rivers and streams have restored fish passage for anadromous and wide-ranging fish populations?	Covered by periodic fish barrier monitoring conducted by DFG, the Coastal Conservancy, and NGOs.	Species	DFG, NMFS, CCC, Caltrans

Recommended Conservation Actions	Effectiveness Monitoring Questions	Needed Monitoring	Monitoring Level	Monitoring Collaborators
g. State and local agencies should allocate sufficient water for ecosystem uses when planning for and meeting regional water supply needs. Providing adequate water for wildlife and instream uses is particularly important in systems that support sensitive species or important habitat areas.	Have instream flow needs been met for anadromous fish and other fauna for the rivers and streams of the region? In how many river systems have management changes been made so that flows more closely mimic natural flows? What new long-term contracts for instream flows have been secured?	Many existing efforts collect data on the status of aquatic ecosystems. However, monitoring of aquatic ecosystems needs to be expanded in the region.	Ecosystem Function, Species	SWRCB, DFG
h. State and federal agencies should work to protect and restore biologically significant regional river systems.	Have watershed restoration and conservation plans been developed for biologically important regional river systems in the region? To what extent have the goals of those plans been met?	Covered by Department of Water Resources river flow monitoring programs.	Natural Community, Ecosystem Function	RWQCBs, USEPA, Army Corps, DFG, CCC, NMFS
i. Federal, state, and local agencies should provide greater resources and coordinate efforts to control existing occurrences of invasive species and prevent new introductions.	In the region, have priority invasive species been reduced? (See Statewide Action f.)	Need long-term monitoring of priority invasive species. (See Statewide Action f.)	Species	See Statewide Action f.

North Coast–Klamath Region

Recommended Conservation Actions	Effectiveness Monitoring Questions	Needed Monitoring	Monitoring Level	Monitoring Collaborators
a. For regional river systems where insufficient or altered flow regimes limit populations of salmon, steelhead, and other sensitive aquatic species, federal and state agencies and other stakeholders should work to increase instream flows and to replicate natural seasonal flow regimes.	Have actions increased instream flows and restored flow regimes to improve conditions for salmon, steelhead and other sensitive aquatic species?	Covered by Department of Water Resources river flow monitoring programs.	Ecosystem Function, Species	SWRCB, DWR, DFG, Watershed Councils, RCDs, NMFS
b. Federal, state, and local agencies and private landowners should work to restore fish passage in aquatic systems important for anadromous and wide-ranging fish populations.	How many fish barriers have been removed, and how many miles of rivers and streams have restored fish passage for anadromous and wide-ranging fish populations?	Covered by periodic fish barrier monitoring conducted by DFG, the Coastal Conservancy, and NGOs.	Species	SWRCB, DFG, Caltrans, NMFS, CCC, FERC
c. Through the Federal Energy Regulatory Commission (FERC) relicensing process, the state should pursue changes in operations of hydropower projects to provide more water for aquatic species and ecosystems and require that flows be managed to approximate natural flow regime.	Have aquatic ecosystems been restored due to conservation measures adopted in new FERC license agreements?	Covered by FERC agreement.	Ecosystem Function, Species	FERC, DFG, NMFS, SWRCB
d. Fish and Game should continue fisheries restoration and watershed assessment efforts.	Have fish populations recovered and aquatic ecosystems been restored due to utilization of watershed assessment information and fisheries restoration projects?	Generally covered by existing fish monitoring efforts.	Regional, Ecosystem Function	DFG
e. Fish and Game should develop future state- or regionwide recovery plans to benefit multiple species.	How many species at risk and how many acres of wildlands have benefited from multi-species conservation plans?	Covered by multispecies recovery plans.	Species	DFG

Recommended Conservation Actions	Effectiveness Monitoring Questions	Needed Monitoring	Monitoring Level	Monitoring Collaborators
f. Where historical or active gravel mining has had substantial effects on river systems that are important for sensitive aquatic species, federal, state, and local agencies should continue monitoring and restoration efforts to minimize the negative effects of mining. Active mining operations should employ the most ecologically sensitive practices possible.	Is monitoring adequate to assess the impacts of gravel mining on sensitive aquatic species?	Need long-term monitoring of aquatic ecosystems.	Ecosystem Function, Species	DFG, NMFS
g. Public forest lands should be managed to maintain healthy ecosystems and wildlife diversity. State and federal forest and wildlife managers should work cooperatively to develop a vision for future forest conditions.	Have wildlife conservation and ecological restoration goals been established for public forest lands? To what extent have those goals been achieved?	Need to amend forest management plans to include adequate monitoring and adaptive management plans to assess general improvements in ecosystem health and wildlife diversity.	Natural Community	PSRS–USFS, DFG, FWS, USGS, DPR
h. On public lands, post-fire and post-harvest treatments and forest management should be designed to achieve the principles listed in Action g, above.	Are post-fire practices and post-harvest forest management practices on public lands consistent with wildlife conservation and ecological restoration goals?	Covered by existing forest management monitoring efforts.	Natural Community	USFS, FWS, DFG
i. Federal and state agencies should work to understand the natural fire regimes of different ecosystems and how the ecological role of wildfire can be replicated with prescribed fire and other forest management practices.	To what extent have forest management practices been implemented to restore natural fire regimes or otherwise restore wildlife diversity and healthy ecosystems?	Covered by existing forest management monitoring efforts.	Natural Community, Ecosystem Function	PSRS–USFS, DFG, FWS, USGS, DPR
j. State and federal forest and wildlife managers should work cooperatively with private landowners and timber companies to develop timber-harvest cumulative-impact standards for watersheds in the North Coast–Klamath Region to protect ecosystem health and wildlife habitat.	Have cumulative impact standards been established for watersheds? Have those standards been achieved?	Need regional long-term forest monitoring to assess cumulative impacts. Additional monitoring should be build upon existing monitoring and address gaps in current efforts.	Regional, Ecosystem Function	DFG, CDF, FWS, NMFS, See Appendix G

Recommended Conservation Actions	Effectiveness Monitoring Questions	Needed Monitoring	Monitoring Level	Monitoring Collaborators
k. State and federal agencies should work with private forestry operators and landowners to implement forest management practices that are compatible with wildlife and habitat conservation.	On how many additional acres of private forest lands have management practices been implemented to improve conditions wildlife?	Covered by monitoring pursuant to forest management plans.	Natural Community, Species	DFG, CDF, FWS, NMFS, See Appendix G
l. The state should coordinate the development of a model ordinance and building codes for new or expanding communities in fire-adapted landscapes to make those communities more fire compatible and reduce the state's liability for fire suppression.	Has the state established a model ordinance and building codes for fire-adapted communities? How many counties have adopted such ordinances to make their communities fire-tolerant?	Covered by monitoring pursuant to forest management plans.	Natural Community	CDF, DFG, USFS, FWS, Counties
m. Federal, state, and local agencies and nongovernmental organizations should work with regional landowners to develop and implement agricultural and rangeland management practices that are compatible with wildlife and habitat conservation.	On how many additional acres of private agricultural and range lands have management practices been implemented to improve conditions wildlife?	Establish goals for acres of improved wildlife habitat on agricultural and rangelands. Monitor the numbers of acres that have implemented practices that improve conditions for wildlife.	Regional, Natural Community	See Appendix G
n. Federal, state, and local agencies should provide greater resources and coordinate efforts to control existing occurrences of invasive species and to prevent new introductions.	In the region, have priority invasive species been reduced? (See Statewide Action f.)	Need long-term monitoring of priority invasive species. (See Statewide Action f.)	Species	See Statewide Action f.
o. Federal, state, and local agencies, nongovernmental conservation organizations, and private landowners should protect and restore underprotected and sensitive habitat types like riparian forests and coastal dunes.	Have sensitive habitats been identified and prioritized for the region? How additional acres of sensitive habitats have been restored or protected?	Need to expand long-term monitoring of sensitive habitats.	Natural Community	DFG, FWS, RCDs, USGS, PSRS-USFS

Modoc Plateau Region

Recommended Conservation Actions	Effectiveness Monitoring Questions	Needed Monitoring	Monitoring Level	Monitoring Collaborators
a. Federal land management agencies should more effectively manage forest, shrub, aspen, meadow, and riparian habitat to enhance ecosystems and conditions for wildlife.	How many acres of forest, shrub, aspen, meadow, and riparian habitats have been restored to improve conditions for wildlife?	Need to expand natural community and ecosystem monitoring on public lands to assess the effects of land and natural resources management actions.	Natural Community, Ecosystem Function	USFS, BLM, DFG, FWS
b. Federal land management agencies should implement modifications to grazing management on public lands that are conducive to recovery of key habitats for restoring and conserving wildlife.	How many acres of key wildlife habitat have been restored due to changes in grazing management practices on public lands?	Need to expand natural community and ecosystem monitoring on public lands to assess the effects of land and natural resources management actions.	Natural Community, Ecosystem Function	USFS, BLM, DFG, FWS
c. The Bureau of Land Management should update the Resource Management Plans (RMPs) to include provisions to restore and conserve wildlife diversity.	Have the Resource Management Plans been updated to include stronger wildlife restoration and conservation elements? To what extent have those elements been implemented?	Need to expand natural community and ecosystem monitoring on public lands to assess the effects of land and natural resources management actions.	Natural Community, Ecosystem Function	BLM, FWS, DFG
d. Feral horse numbers should be maintained at levels that meet the constraints imposed by law, and funds should be provided for BLM and the Forest Service to meet the standards in place for the protection of meadows and riparian areas.	Have feral horse numbers been reduced to levels that do not cause damage to sensitive meadows and riparian areas?	Need to monitor meadow and riparian habitats.	Natural Community, Ecosystem Function	BLM, USFS, FWS, DFG
e. The Cooperative Sagebrush Steppe Restoration Initiative and the National Resource Conservation Service (NRCS) should design juniper-removal projects to benefit wildlife diversity and ecosystem health.	Are juniper-removal projects being implemented in a way that is conducive to the recovery of native wildlife species?	Long-term monitoring of juniper-removal projects is needed to assess whether the removal strategies are conducive to restoration of native wildlife and ecosystem health.	Natural Community, Ecosystem Function	NRCS, BLM, USFS

Recommended Conservation Actions	Effectiveness Monitoring Questions	Needed Monitoring	Monitoring Level	Monitoring Collaborators
f. Public forest lands should be managed to maintain healthy ecosystems and wildlife diversity, including thinning to restore diverse habitats and reducing the risk of catastrophic wildfire. State and federal forest managers and wildlife agencies should work cooperatively to develop a vision for the future forest condition.	Have ideal forest conditions been identified to benefit wildlife and ecosystems? To what extent have practices been implemented to achieve the goals set for forest conditions?	Need to monitor for species and ecological indicators designed to assess progress toward achieving desired forest conditions.	Natural Community, Ecosystem Function, Species	PSRS-USFS, DFG, FWS
g. Regarding forest management conservation actions, see Conservation Actions d, e, f, and g in Chapter 13, Sierra Nevada and Cascades Region.	In the region, to what extent have forest conservation actions been implemented?	Need to monitor for species and ecological indicators designed to assess progress toward achieving desired forest conditions.	Natural Community, Ecosystem Function, Species	BLM, USFS, FWS, DFG
h. Land management and wildlife agencies and conservation NGOs should develop an aquatic multispecies conservation plan for the Pit River watershed.	Has an aquatic multispecies conservation plan been established for the Pit River watershed? To what extent have the conservation goals of the plan been achieved?	Need to implement monitoring to support adaptive management element of the plan.	Natural Community, Ecosystem Function, Species	PRWA, DFG, FWS, RCD's

Sierra Nevada and Cascades Region

Recommended Conservation Actions	Effectiveness Monitoring Questions	Needed Monitoring	Monitoring Level	Monitoring Collaborators
a. The state should provide scientific and planning assistance and financial incentives to local governments to develop and implement regional multispecies conservation plans for all of the rapidly developing areas of the Sierra Nevada and Cascades.	How many regional multi-species conservation plans have been developed for the rapidly developing areas of the Sierra Nevada and Cascades? To what extent have the conservation goals of those plans been achieved?	Monitoring and adaptive management would be designed and implemented as part of new regional multispecies conservation planning efforts.	Regional, Natural Community, Ecosystem Function, Species	DFG
b. The Sierra Nevada Conservancy should develop a program, closely coordinated with federal, state, and local wildlife conservation planning efforts, that prioritizes areas for acquisition and easements based on the needs of wildlife.	Have wildlands important for wildlife conservation been prioritized throughout the Sierra and Cascades? What percent of the identified priority lands have been protected through easements or acquisitions?	Need long-term monitoring program of status and trends of wildlife habitats region-wide.	Management, Regional, Habitat Linkages	SNC
c. In areas where substantial development is projected, the state and federal land management and wildlife agencies should identify and protect from development those critical wildlife migration or dispersal corridors that cross ownership boundaries and county jurisdictions.	Have wildlife migration or dispersal corridors been identifed throughout the region? To what extent have those corridors been protected from development?	Need long-term monitoring of priority wildlife migration and dispersal corridors.	Regional, Habitat Linkages	USFS, BLM, DFG, FWS, SNC, NPS
d. Public forest lands should be managed to maintain healthy ecosystems and wildlife diversity, including thinning to restore diverse habitats and reducing the risk of catastrophic wildfire. State and federal forest managers and wildlife agencies should work cooperatively to develop a vision for the future forest condition.	Have forest plans for public lands adopted principles for maintaining healthy ecosystems and wildlife diversity? What percent of public lands are managed according to such principles?	Need to monitor for species and ecological indicators designed to assess progress toward achieving desired forest conditions.	Natural Community, Ecosystem Function, Species	USFS, CDF, DFG, FWS, NPS, DPR
e. On public lands, post-fire and post-harvest treatments and forest management should be designed to achieve the principles listed in Action d.	What percent of post-fire and post-harvest treatments on public lands are designed according to the principles for maintaining ecosystem health and wildlife diversity?	Need to monitor for species and ecological indicators designed to assess progress toward achieving desired forest conditions.	Natural Community, Ecosystem Function	USFS, NPS, CDF, BLM, DFG, FWS

Recommended Conservation Actions	Effectiveness Monitoring Questions	Needed Monitoring	Monitoring Level	Monitoring Collaborators
f. State and federal forest managers and state and federal wildlife managers should cooperatively develop timber-harvest cumulative-impact standards for each watershed or group of adjacent watersheds of the Sierra, Cascades, and Modoc regions to protect aquatic ecosystems and conserve wildlife habitat.	Have cumulative impact standards been established for watersheds? Have those standards been achieved?	Monitoring and adaptive management plans should be designed and implemented with implementation of cumulative impact standards.	Natural Community, Ecosystem Function	USFS, NPS, CDF, BLM, DFG, FWS, SWRCB
g. The California Resources Agency should coordinate the development of a model ordinance and building codes for new or expanding communities in fire-adapted landscapes to make those communities more fire compatible and reduce the state's liability for fire suppression.	Has the state established a model ordinance and building codes for fire-adapted communities? How many counties have adopted such ordinances to make their communities fire-tolerant?	None needed.	Management	CRA
h. Federal, state, and local agencies and fire-safe councils should work cooperatively to expand the use of prescribed fire and natural-burn programs.	Prescribed fire and natural burn programs have been successfully implemented on how many acres of forest lands in the last year?	None needed.	Management	USFS, BLM, NPS, FSCs
i. State and federal wildlife agencies and federal land managers should jointly develop and implement grazing strategies for the Sierra Nevada and Cascades Region to reduce or eliminate livestock grazing on sensitive habitats to restore the condition of meadow, riparian, aspen, and aquatic habitats.	How many acres of key wildlife habitat have been restored due to changes in grazing management practices on public and private lands?	Need expanded monitoring of sensitive habitats such as meadows and riparian habitats.	Natural Community, Ecosytem Function	USFS, BLM, FWS, DFG
j. Federal, state, and local agencies should provide greater resources and coordinate efforts to control existing occurrences of invasive species and to prevent new introductions.	In the region, have priority invasive species been reduced? (See Statewide Action f.)	Need long-term monitoring of priority invasive species. (See Statewide Action f.)	Species	See Statewide Action f.
k. In their conservation planning and ecosystem restoration work, state and federal wildlife agencies and land managers should consider the most current projections of the effects of global warming.	To what extent have global climate changes projections been incorporated into wildlife and land management plans?	None needed.	Management	CEC, DFG, FWS, SWRCB

Recommended Conservation Actions	Effectiveness Monitoring Questions	Needed Monitoring	Monitoring Level	Monitoring Collaborators
l. Fish and Game should be allocated the resources to monitor the distribution of sensitive fish and other aquatic species populations and to engage effectively in water-rights decision processes, water diversion issues, land-management planning, and conservation planning actions to restore and enhance aquatic systems.	What improvements in the status of sensitive fish and aquatic species may be attributed to changes in water rights, water diversions, and other water management issues?	Expand monitoring of sensitive fish and aquatic species.	Ecosystem Function, Species	DFG
m. Through the FERC relicensing process, the state should pursue changes in operations of hydropower projects that will provide more water for wildlife, mandate that water flows be managed as close to natural flow regimes as possible, and ensure that the new license agreements provide the best possible conditions for ecosystems and wildlife.	Have aquatic ecosystems been restored due to conservation measures adopted in new FERC license agreements?	Monitoring needs should be covered as part of FERC agreements.	Ecosystem Function, Species	DFG, SWRCB, CHRC
n. The state, Inyo County, and the city of Los Angeles should fully implement the Lower Owens River Project (LORP), restoring riparian and aquatic habitat along 62 miles of the lower Owens River.	To what extent have the goals of the Lower Owens River Project been achieved?	Covered by existing monitoring efforts.	Natural Community	LADWP, DFG
o. The city of Los Angeles should reach long-term agreement with Inyo County and the state to use shallow flooding to control dust on the Owens Lake lakebed.	Has agreement been reached and implemented to use shallow flooding to control dust on the Owens Lake lakebed?	None needed.	Management	LADWP, DFG
p. Fish and Game should establish trout-free sub-basins and lakes across the high Sierra and Cascades to restore amphibians and other native species while concurrently improving trout fisheries in other lakes.	In how many basins have native amphibians and other fauna been restored due to the establishment of trout-free sub-basins?	Monitoring of high mountain aquatic ecosystems should continue to inform adaptive management.	Ecosystem Function, Species	DFG

Recommended Conservation Actions	Effectiveness Monitoring Questions	Needed Monitoring	Monitoring Level	Monitoring Collaborators
q. Fish and Game and the U.S. Fish and Wildlife Service should seek an agreement with the Los Angeles Department of Water and Power (LADWP) to establish Owens pupfish and Owens tui chub in springs and creeks of the Owens Valley on LADWP lands as part of a strategy to recover these two endangered fish and ensure their long-term survival.	Has an agreement been reach and implemented to establish Owens pupfish and Owens tui chub in springs and creeks of the Owens Valley on LADWP lands?	Need to monitor the status of Owens pupfish and Owens tui chub in springs and creeks where they are established.	Species	FWS, DFG, LADWP

Central Valley and Bay-Delta Region

Recommended Conservation Actions	Effectiveness Monitoring Questions	Needed Monitoring	Monitoring Level	Monitoring Collaborators
a. The California Resources Agency, Fish and Game, the U.S. Fish and Wildlife Service, public land managing agencies, and local governments need to develop multicounty regional habitat conservation and restoration plans.	Have regional habitat conservation and restoration plans been developed and implemented? Have the conservation goals of the regional conservation and restoration plans been achieved? Are adjoining regional plans compatible with each other? Are they integrated with other regional plans (housing, transportation, infrastructure, etc.)? Do plans collectively address cumulative impacts and needs of all habitats and species?	Monitoring and adaptive management would be designed and implemented as part of new regional multispecies conservation planning efforts.	Regional, Natural Community, Ecosystem Function, Species	CRA, DFG, FWS, Counties
b. Fish and Game, the U.S. Fish and Wildlife Service, the USDA Natural Resources Conservation Service, and local resource conservation districts need to improve conservation and restoration on private lands by assisting private landowners.	What is the status of wildlife and habitats on private lands? How many acres of each habitat are under long-term conservation agreements? Are landowner assistance programs strategically targeting the most important wildlife needs?	Remote sensing of land cover changes; targeted monitoring of indicator species sensitive to private land uses, where agreeable to landowners; regular assessment of landowner incentive programs.	Management, Regional, Natural Community	See Appendix G
c. Public land managers need to continue improving wildlife habitat for a variety of species on public lands.	What is the status of wildlife and habitats on public lands? What are the trends in funding for wildlife management on public lands? Are all wildlife species addressed in land and habitat management plans?	Remote sensing of land cover changes; targeted monitoring of indicator species sensitive to public land uses; regular assessment of public land management plans, including funding and achievement of goals.	Management, Regional, Natural Community	CBDA, DFG
d. Public agencies and private organizations need to work with the San Francisco Bay Joint Venture to protect and restore tidal habitats and baylands in San Francisco Bay.	How many acres of tidal habitats and baylands have been restored? How many acres are under long-term conservation management (including fee-title, easements, and private land options)? What are the status and trends of water quality and invasive species in these habitats? What are the trends in funding for wildlife management on public lands? Are all wildlife species addressed in land and habitat management plans? Are goals of the San Francisco Bay Joint Venture's strategic plan and the San Francisco Bay Estuary Project's Comprehensive Conservation and Management Plan being achieved? Is implementation of both plans integrated with the other?	Remote sensing of land cover changes; targeted monitoring of indicator species; assessment of land management status; trends in water quality and invasive species; regular assessment of conservation and public land management plans, including funding and achievement of goals.	Natural Community	SFEI, SFBJV, DFG

Recommended Conservation Actions	Effectiveness Monitoring Questions	Needed Monitoring	Monitoring Level	Monitoring Collaborators
e. Public agencies and private organizations need to collaboratively protect and restore habitat connectivity along major rivers in the Central Valley.	How many contiguous acres of riparian habitat along major rivers of the Central Valley have been restored and protected? Do water supply and flood management practices and structures allow for long-term persistence of riparian habitat?	Remote sensing of land cover changes; assessment of land management status; trends in invasive species;regular assessment of water supply and flood management practices and structures.	Habitat Linkages	CVHJV, RHJV, CBDA, DFG, FWS
f. Public agencies and private organizations need to collaboratively protect and restore upland linkages among protected areas in the San Joaquin Valley.	What are the extent and condition of key upland habitat linkages in San Joaquin Valley? Do regional conservation plans identify key habitat linkages for a variety of wildlife species? How much of each key habitat linkage is under long-term conservation management? What are trends in habitat connectivity and fragmentation?	Remote sensing of land cover changes; assessment of land management status; assessment of regional plans, including goals, funding and implementation success.	Habitat Linkages	CVHJV, RHJV, CBDA, DFG, FWS
g. Public agencies and private organizations need to collaboratively protect and restore lowland linkages in San Francisco Bay.	What are the extent and condition of key lowland habitat linkages in San Francisco Bay area? Do regional conservation plans identify key habitat linkages for a variety of wildlife species? How much of each key habitat linkage is under long-term conservation management? What are trends in habitat connectivity and fragmentation?	Remote sensing of land cover changes; assessment of land management status; assessment of regional plans, including goals, funding and implementation success.	Habitat Linkages	SFEI, SFBJV, DFG
h. Public agencies and private organizations need to collaboratively protect upland linkages and reduce the risk of habitat isolation in the eastern and northern San Francisco Bay area.	What are the extent and condition of key upland habitat linkages in eastern and northern San Francisco Bay area? Do regional conservation plans identify key habitat linkages for a variety of wildlife species? How much of each key habitat linkage is under long-term conservation management? What are trends in habitat connectivity and fragmentation?	Remote sensing of land cover changes; assessment of land management status; assessment of regional plans, including goals, funding and implementation success.	Habitat Linkages	SFEI, SFBJV, DFG
i. Water management agencies need to secure dependable and adequate amounts and quality of water for wildlife.	How many long-term agreements exist that assure wildlife areas with adequate amounts of water, at the appropriate seasons, to meet the needs of all species that use these areas? How many water-banking projects are established to provide water for wildlife?	Water supply to wildlife areas, compared to the needs of species on those wildlife areas; assessment of water-bank success.	Natural Community, Ecosystem Function	CVHJV, RHJV, CBDA, DFG, FWS

Recommended Conservation Actions	Effectiveness Monitoring Questions	Needed Monitoring	Monitoring Level	Monitoring Collaborators
j. Water management agencies need to reestablish and maintain more natural river flows, flooding patterns, water temperatures, and salinity conditions to support wildlife species and habitats.	Do water supply and flood management practices and structures allow for long-term persistence of riparian habitat? Are river flows, particularly in the major rivers of the Central Valley, of sufficient frequency, timing, duration, and magnitude to restore and maintain functional natural floodplain, riparian, and riverine habitats? What are seasonal and year-to-year patterns of variability in estuary salinity?	Remote sensing of land cover changes; regular assessment of water flows and flood management practices and structures; regular assessment of aquatic species populations and habitat conditions; water quality monitoring.	Ecosystem Function	SWRCB, DWR
k. Water management agencies need to restore gravel supply in sediment-starved rivers downstream of reservoirs to maintain functional riverine habitats.	Is there adequate gravel supply in rivers for spawning salmon and other anadromous fish? What is the condition and trends of natural or artificial sediment sources? Can river banks and floodplains provide adequate sediment supply to rivers? What are the status and trends in sediment deposition and erosion processes along rivers? Does each watershed have a comprehensive sediment management plan and an ecologically based stream-flow regulation plan that is adequately funded?	Disturbances to natural sediment sources; changes in flood and water management that reduce gravel supply; changes in sediment deposition and erosion.	Ecosystem Function	SWRCB, DWR

Recommended Conservation Actions	Effectiveness Monitoring Questions	Needed Monitoring	Monitoring Level	Monitoring Collaborators
l. Public agencies and private organizations should protect, restore, and improve water-dependent habitats (including wetland, riparian, and estuarine) throughout the region. Design of these actions should factor in the likely effects of accelerated climate change.	Have priority areas of water-dependent habitats been identified throughout the region? To what extent have these priority areas been protected or restored? Are runoff, sediment and contaminant loading from upland areas increasing due to changes in land use?	Nonpoint source pollution from upland areas. Vegetation and land cover mapping. Assessment of land use plans. Assessment of floodplain and bypass management. Assess functioning of hydrological connections.	Natural Community, Ecosystem Function	DWR, SWRCB, CBDA
	Are habitats decreasing in extent and distribution due to climate change?			
	How many acres of wetland, riverine, and aquatic habitats have been restored?			
	Is up-to-date information about flood-prone areas (not just FEMA flood zones) incorporated into land use plans?			
	Is urban and residential expansion precluding opportunities to conserve wetlands that may shift due to climate change?			
	Are floodplains and bypasses managed to maximize ecosystem protection, habitat restoration, and wildlife use while still providing for public safety and flood-damage reduction?			
	Are functional hydrological connections between upper watersheds and downstream habitats being maintained, restored, and improved?			
m. Water management agencies, state and federal wildlife agencies, and other public agencies and private organizations need to collaboratively improve fish passage by removing or modifying barriers to upstream habitat.	How many fish passage barriers have been removed? How many additional miles of aquatic habitats are now accessible for anadromous or wide-ranging fish species due to removal of fish barriers?	Locations and numbers of barriers and their relative abilities to block fish passage.	Ecosystem Function, Species	CBDA, DFG, Caltrans

Recommended Conservation Actions	Effectiveness Monitoring Questions	Needed Monitoring	Monitoring Level	Monitoring Collaborators
n. To support healthy aquatic ecosystems, public agencies and private organizations, in collaboration with the California Bay-Delta Authority, need to improve and maintain water quality in the major river systems of this region.	What are the status and trends of water quality in the major rivers of the region? Are the goals of the Bay Delta Authority's Drinking Water Quality Program and the Ecosystem Restoration Program being met?	Water quality.	Ecosystem Function	SWRCB, RWQCB, CBDA
o. Regional water quality boards, in collaboration with other public agencies and private organizations, need to improve and maintain water quality in streams and tidal waters of San Francisco Bay.	What are the status and trends of water quality in the streams and tidal waters of San Francisco Bay? Are the goals of the San Francisco Estuary Project's Comprehensive Conservation and Management Plan being achieved?	Water quality.	Ecosystem Function	RWQCBs, USEPA, Army Corps, DFG, CCC, NMFS
p. Fish and Game should expand funding and coordinate efforts to prevent the establishment of invasive species and to reduce the damage of established invasive species.	In the region, have priority invasive species been reduced? (See Statewide Action f.)	Need long-term monitoring of priority invasive species. (See Statewide Action f.)	Species	See Statewide Action f.
q. State and federal agencies should expand law enforcement funding and staffing and coordinate efforts to enforce regulations to prevent the degradation of rivers and streams and to detect, prevent and take actions to protect water quality.	In the region, have priority riverine systems been identified and classified for specific protective/ enforcement measures? What ate the status and trends of water quality in rivers and streams? What is the department doing to provide for more enforcement officers and a stable enforcement branch funding base?	Riverine quality, water / riparian habitat.	Management, Ecosystem Function	DFG

Marine Region

Recommended Conservation Actions	Effectiveness Monitoring Questions	Needed Monitoring	Monitoring Level	Monitoring Collaborators
a. The state should fully implement the Marine Life Management Act to ensure that marine fisheries and the marine ecosystem are managed sustainably.	For how many major fisheries are management plans completed and implemented? To what extent are the management goals of those plans being achieved?	Monitoring and adaptive management should be an element of each fishery management plan. Species and ecosystems affected by the management plans should be monitored.	Natural Community, Ecosystem Function, Species	DFG
b. The state should move forward in implementing the Marine Life Protection Act by establishing a network of marine protected areas.	For what percent of the coast have marine protected areas been designated pursuant to the MLPA? To what extent have the goals of the marine protected areas been achieved?	Monitoring and adaptive management should be an element of MPA management plans.	Natural Community, Ecosystem Function, Species	DFG
c. The state should secure Tidelands Revenues for implementation of the California Ocean Protection Act.	Have Tideland Revenues been secured for the implementation of the California Ocean Protection Act? To what extent have these critical marine habitats been protected in marine protected areas or by other means?	None needed.	Management	DFG, SLC
d. The state should increase efforts to restore coastal watersheds.	For how many coastal watersheds have restoration plans been developed? To what extent have the conservation goals of those plans been achieved?	Additional monitoring of coastal watersheds.	Regional, Natural Community, Ecosystem Function	DFG, CCC
e. The state should adopt a "no net loss" policy for critical marine habitat.	Have critical marine habitats been identified and mapped along the coast? To what extent have those key habitats been protected?	Need long-term monitoring of critical marine habitats.	Natural Community	DFG
f. The federal and state resource agencies should expand efforts to eradicate introduced predators from all seabird colonies.	Introduced predators have been eradicated from how many additional seabird colonies?	Covered by existing monitoring.	Species	FWS, NPS, DFG
g. The state should systematically review and monitor the distribution and abundance of nonharvested marine fish and invertebrates.	What additional efforts have been established to monitor and assess the status and trends of nonharvested marine fish and invertebrates?	Need long-term monitoring of nonharvested marine fish and invertebrates.	Species	DFG

Recommended Conservation Actions	Effectiveness Monitoring Questions	Needed Monitoring	Monitoring Level	Monitoring Collaborators
h. Federal and state resource agencies and institutions should foster and facilitate interstate collaborative research on marine species whose ranges cross jurisdictional boundaries.	To what extent have interstate and transnational research efforts been established to assess marine species whose ranges cross jurisdictional boundaries?	Need long-term monitoring of marine species and ecosystem indicators that are relevant across boundary water with Mexico and Oregon.	Regional, Natural Community, Ecosystem Function, Species	DFG, NMFS, NOAA Fisheries, CCC
i. Federal and state resource agencies should foster and facilitate interstate collaborative enforcement efforts on marine species whose ranges cross jurisdictional boundaries.	To what extent has interstate collaborative enforcement efforts been implemented for marine species whose range cross jurisdictional boundaries?	Need long-term marine species monitoring and appropriate methodology to access the effectiveness of law enforcement actions to protect and conserve these marine species.	Regional, species	DFG, DPR, NMFS, BLM

Abbreviations Used in Monitoring Needs to Support Conservation Actions

CDE, California Department of Education, http://www.cde.ca.gov/pd/ca/sc/oeeintrod.asp

CDF, California Department of Fire Protection and Prevention, http://www.fire.ca.gov/php/rsrc-mgt.php

CDHCD, California Department of Housing and Community Development

CEC, California Energy Commission, http://www.energy.ca.gov/

CHRC, California Hydropower Reform Coalition, http://www.calhrc.org/

Cities, http://www.igs.berkeley.edu/library/localweb.html

CIWMB, California Waste Management Board, http://www.ciwmb.ca.gov/

Counties, http://www.csac.counties.org/default.asp?id=7

CRA, California Resources Agency, http://resources.ca.gov/

CVHJV, Central Valley Habitat Joint Venture, http://www.centralvalleyjointventure.org/pages/1/index.htm

DFG, California Department of Fish and Game, www.dfg.ca.gov

DMG, Desert Managers Group, http://www.dmg.gov/

DOD, U.S. Department of Defense

DOI, U.S. Department of Interior, http://www.interior.gov/subject.html

DPR, California Department of Parks and Recreation, http://www.parks.ca.gov/

DWR, Department of Water Resources, http://www.water.ca.gov/

FERC, Federal Energy Regulatory Commission, http://www.ferc.gov/industries/hydropower.asp

FSC, Fire Safe Councils, http://www.firesafecouncil.org/about/index.cfm

FWS, U.S. Fish and Wildlife Service, http://www.fws.gov/offices/directory/ListOffices.cfm?statecode=6

Imperial County, http://www.co.imperial.ca.us/

LADWP, Los Angeles Department of Water and Power, http://www.ladwp.com/ladwp/cms/ladwp004409.jsp

MWA, Mojave Water Agency, http://www.mojavewater.org/

NMFS, National Marine Fisheries Service, http://swr.nmfs.noaa.gov/

NPS, National Park Service, http://www.nature.nps.gov/nnl/Registry/USA_Map/States/California/california.cfm

PRWA, Pit River Watershed Alliance, http://www.pitriveralliance.net/

PSRS-USFS, Pacific Southwest Research Station, http://www.fs.fed.us/psw/

RCDs, Resource Conservation Districts, http://www.carcd.org/yourdistrict/rcdabout.htm

NOAA Fisheries Service, http://www.nmfs.noaa.gov/

NRCS, Natural Resources Conservation Service, http://www.ca.nrcs.usda.gov/

RHJV, Riparian Habitat Joint Venture, http://www.prbo.org/calpif/htmldocs/rhjv/

RWQCBs, Regional Water Quality Control Boards, http://www.swrcb.ca.gov/regions.html

SCW, South Coast Wildlands, http://www.scwildlands.org/

SCWRP, Southern California Wetlands Recovery Project, http://www.scwrp.org/index.htm

SFBJV, San Francisco Bay Joint Venture, http://www.sfbayjv.org/

SFEI, San Francisco Estuary Institute, http://www.sfei.org/progprojhome.html

SLC, State Lands Commission, http://www.slc.ca.gov/

SNC, Sierra Nevada Conservancy, http://sierranevadaconservancy.ca.gov/

SWRCB, State Water Resources Control Board, http://www.swrcb.ca.gov/

USACE, US Army Corps of Engineers, http://www.usace.army.mil/where/where.html#States

USEPA, U.S. Environmental Protection Agency, http://www.epa.gov/region9/

USFS, U.S. Forest Service, http://www.fs.fed.us/r5/

USGS (Mojave), US Geological Survey, http://mojave.usgs.gov/rvde/

Watershed Councils, http://cwp.resources.ca.gov/cwc_about.html

WCB, Wildlife Conservation Board, http://www.wcb.ca.gov/

Appendix K
Regional Consultations

Mojave Desert Region

AARDAHL, JEFF. Wildlife Biologist, BLM, Ridgecrest

AXELSON, KEITH. Naturalist, Onyx

BERRY, KRISTIN. Wildlife Biologist, USGS, Riverside

BILHORN, THOMAS. Hydrologist, Consultant to Department of Fish and Game, San Diego

BLACK, GLENN. Senior Environmental Scientist, Department of Fish and Game, Eastern Sierra–Inland Deserts Region, Ontario

BRILL, KIRBY. General Manager, Mojave Water Agency, Apple Valley

CHRISTIAN, BILL. Project Director, Amargosa River, The Nature Conservancy, California

CAOULETTE, NORMAN. Assistant General Manager, Mojave Water Agency, Apple Valley

EVERLY, CLARENCE. Department of Defense, Barstow

HAMILL, JOHN. Coordinator of Desert Managers Group, Department of Interior, Barstow

HANSON, LINDA. Desert District Manager, BLM, Barstow

HASTEY, ED. Conservation Consultant, Resources Law Group, Sacramento

JONES, REBECCA. Environmental Scientist, Department of Fish and Game, South Coast Region, Palmdale

KEELER-WOLF, TODD. Vegetation Ecologist, Department of Fish and Game, Sacramento

LaPRE, LARRY. Wildlife Biologist, BLM, Barstow

LEITNER, PHIL. Adjunct Professor, Department of Biological Science, Endangered Species Recovery Program, California State University, Stanislaus, Fresno

Lovich, Jeffrey E. Deputy Director, Southwest Biological Science Center, USGS, Flagstaff, Ariz.

Lynn, Neil. Wildlife Biologist, Charis Corp., Fort Irwin

Moore, Jim. Mojave Desert Ecologist and Amargosa River Project Manager, The Nature Conservancy, California

Patterson, Daniel R. Desert Ecologist, Center for Biodiversity, Tucson, Ariz.

Presley, Gail. Program Manager, Conservation Planning Program, Department of Fish and Game, Sacramento

Scott, Randy. Natural Resources Chief, San Bernardino County, San Bernardino

Spitler, Paul. Conservation Consultant, Resources Law Group, Sacramento

Steele, Dale. Wildlife Biologist, Department of Fish and Game, Sacramento

Whalon, Larry. Chief of Resources, Mojave National Preserve, National Park Service, Barstow

Colorado Desert Region

Anderson, Tom. Avian Biologist, U.S. Fish and Wildlife Service, Sonny Bono Wildlife Refuge, Calipatria

Barnum, Doug. Research Scientist, U.S. Geological Survey, Salton Sea Science Office, La Quinta

Barrows, Cameron. Southern California Regional Director, Center for Natural Lands Management, Coachella Valley Dunes Preserve, Thousand Palms

Black, Glenn. Senior Environmental Scientist, Department of Fish and Game, Eastern Sierra–Inland Deserts Region, Ontario

Bolster, Betsy. Staff Environmental Scientist, Habitat Conservation Planning Branch, Department of Fish and Game, Sacramento

Boyce, Walter. Executive Director, Wildlife Health Center, University of California, Davis

Cooper, Dan. Director of Bird Conservation, Audubon California, Sacramento

Crayon, Jack. Associate Biologist, Department of Fish and Game, Bermuda Dunes

Crowe, Dick. Biologist; Coordinator of Northern and Eastern Colorado Desert Coordinated Management Plan, Bureau of Land Management, Moreno Valley office

Delfino, Kim. California Director, Defenders of Wildlife, Sacramento

Dillard, Lester. Biologist, U.S. Fish and Wildlife Service, Sonny Bono Wildlife Refuge, La Quinta

Gross, Howard. California Desert Field Manager, National Parks Conservation Association

Hayes, Chris. Senior Environmental Scientist, Department of Fish and Game, Blythe

Jones, Bryn. Desert Program Director, California Wilderness Coalition, Riverside

Jones, Jeanine. Chief, Colorado River and Salton Sea Office, California Dept. of Water Resources, Sacramento

Kirk, Tom. Executive Director, Salton Sea Authority, La Quinta

Knauf, Chris. Natural Resource Specialist, Bureau of Land Management, El Centro

Konno, Eddy. Associate Biologist, Department of Fish and Game, Bermuda Dunes

Lesicka, Leon. Desert Wildlife Unlimited/New River Wetlands Construction, Brawley

Levin, Julia. State Policy Director, Audubon California, Sacramento

Nicol, Kimberly. Senior Environmental Scientist, Department of Fish and Game, Bermuda Dunes

Pitt, Jennifer. Senior Policy Analyst, Environmental Defense, Boulder, Colo.

Schonam, Chris. Biologist, U.S. Fish and Wildlife Service, Sonny Bono Wildlife Refuge, La Quinta

Smith, Paul. Member, Board of Directors, Mojave Desert Land Trust, and Public at Large Representative, District Advisory Council, Desert District, Bureau of Land Management, Twentynine Palms

Thomas, Willadeena. Environmental Protection Office, Cocopah Tribe, Somerton, Ariz.

South Coast Region

Berry, Bill. Wildlife Biologist, Marine Corps Base, Camp Pendleton

Bond, Monica. Biologist, Center for Biological Diversity, San Francisco

Chapman, Trish. Project Manager, California State Coastal Conservancy, Oakland

Fisher, Robert. Research Zoologist, USGS, San Diego

Larson, Mary. Senior Fisheries Biologist Specialist, Department of Fish and Game, South Coast Region, Los Alamitos

Loe, Steve. Forest Biologist, San Bernardino National Forest, San Bernardino

Luke, Claudia. Linkage Manager for Santa Ana–Palomar Linkage, Santa Margarita Ecological Reserve, Temecula

Miller, Becky. Environmental Scientist, Department of Fish and Game, Habitat Conservation Planning Branch, Sacramento

Morrison, Scott. Senior Ecologist, The Nature Conservancy, San Diego

Penrod, Kristeen. Executive Director, South Coast Wildlands and Missing Linkages Project, Idyllwild

Presley, Gail. Program Manager, Conservation Planning Program, Department of Fish and Game, Sacramento

Quigley, Ken. Strategic/Regional Environmental Planner, Planning Branch, Marine Corps Base, Camp Pendleton

Silver, Dan. Executive Director, Endangered Habitats League, Los Angeles

Spencer, Wayne. Conservation Biologist and Conservation Planner, Conservation Biology Institute, San Diego

Stewart, Terri. Senior Biologist, Supervisor, Department of Fish and Game, Land Management and Monitoring Program, South Coast Region, San Diego

Swift, Camm C. Senior Project Scientist, ENTRIX, Inc., Ventura, and Emeritus, Section of Fishes, Natural History Museum of Los Angeles County

Tippets, Bill. Principal Water Resources Specialist, San Diego County Water Authority (formerly Assistant Regional Manager with Department of Fish and Game), San Diego

Wynn, Susan. Fish and Wildlife Biologist, San Diego County NCCP/U.S. Fish and Wildlife Service, Carlsbad

Central Coast Region

Baumgartner, Jo Ann. Wild Farms Alliance, Watsonville

Bolster, Betsy. Staff Environmental Scientist, Department of Fish and Game, Habitat Conservation Planning Branch, Sacramento

Clark, Liz. Wildlife Biologist, Fort Hunter Liggett

Collins, Paul. Curator of Vertebrate Zoology, Santa Barbara Museum of Natural History

Cox, Robin. Senior Conservation Planner, The Nature Conservancy, San Francisco

Curry, Bob, Adjunct Professor, Earth Systems Science and Policy Institute, and Director of the Watershed Institute, California State University, Monterey Bay

Delgado, Bruce. Botanist, BLM, Fort Ord

Delgado, Julie. Botanist, BLM, Hollister District

Duffy, Erin. California Wilderness Coalition, Santa Barbara

Fischer, Chris. Monterey County Project Director, The Nature Conservancy, Monterey County

Hillyard, Deb. Staff Environmental Scientist, Department of Fish and Game, Central Coast Region, San Luis Obispo County

Kearns, Dennis. Botanist, BLM, Bakersfield

Kuyper, Jeff. Director, Los Padres Forest Watch, Santa Barbara

Moonijan, Jennifer. Wildlife Biologist, Camp Roberts

Page, Gary. Biologist, Point Reyes Bird Observatory, Stinson Beach

Patton, Gary. Director, Land Watch Monterey, Monterey

Perry, Katie. Senior Biologist, Specialist, Department of Fish and Game, Native Anadromous Fish and Watershed Branch, Sacramento

Rayburn, Richard. Chief, Natural Resources Division, California State Parks, Sacramento

Shaffer, Kevin. Environmental Scientist, Department Fish and Game, Native Anadromous Fish and Watershed Branch, Sacramento

Shallcross, Gary. Member, Regional Water Quality Control Board, Monterey

Stafford, Bob. Associate Biologist, Department of Fish and Game, Central Coast Region, San Luis Obispo County

Sweet, Sam. Professor, Ecology and Evolution, University of California, Santa Barbara

WATT, TERRY. AICP (American Institute Certified Planner), Terrell Watt Planning Consultants, San Francisco

WEIGAND, JIM. Ecologist, BLM, California State Office, Sacramento

WILCOX, CARL. Habitat Conservation Manager, Department of Fish and Game, Central Coast Region, Yountville

WILSON, SCOTT. Conservation Planning Supervisor, Department of Fish and Game, Central Coast Region, Yountville

North Coast Region

ALEXANDER, JOHN. Executive Director, Klamath Bird Observatory, Ashland, Ore.

BARR, BRIAN. Program Officer, World Wildlife Fund, Klamath-Siskiyou Program, Ashland, Ore.

BLEIER, CATHY. Deputy Assistant Secretary, Resources Agency, Sacramento

BROWN, RANDY. Deputy Field Supervisor, U.S. Fish and Wildlife Service, Arcata

CALLAS, RICHARD. Senior Wildlife Biologist, Supervisor, Department Fish and Game, Northern California–North Coast Region, Yreka

CREASY, MAX. Ecologist, U.S. Forest Service, Happy Camp

DellaSALA, DOMINICK. Program Director, World Wildlife Fund, Klamath-Siskiyou Program, Ashland, Oregon

DILLER, LOWELL. Senior Biologist, Green Diamond Resource Company, Korbel

DOWNIE, SCOTT. Senior Biologist Supervisor, Department of Fish and Game, Coastal Watershed Planning and Assessment Program, Northern California–North Coast Region, Fortuna

JACOBS, DIANA. Deputy Director, Department of Fish and Game, Sacramento

KOVACS, KAREN. Senior Wildlife Biologist, Supervisor, Department Fish and Game, Northern California–North Coast Region, Eureka

McALLISTER, BOB. Coastal Watershed Supervisor, Department of Fish and Game, Northern California–North Coast Region, Redding

MILLET, WENDY. North Coast Project Director, The Nature Conservancy, North Coast and Klamath Ecoregion

MOORE, MARK. Staff Environmental Scientist, Department of Fish and Game Coastal Timberland Planning Program, Northern California–North Coast Region, Eureka

NEWTON, GAIL. Environmental Scientist, Department of Fish and Game, Native Anadromous Fish and Watershed Branch, Sacramento

SAWYER, JOHN O. JR. Professor of Botany, Emeritus, Humboldt State University, Arcata

SCHAFFER, KEVIN. Environmental Scientist, Department of Fish and Game, Native Anadromous Fish and Watershed Branch, Sacramento

SIPEREK, JOHN. Wildlife Program Manager, Department of Fish and Game, Northern California–North Coast Region, Redding

WILLIAMS, JACK. Senior Scientist, Trout Unlimited, Ashland, Ore.

YOLLES, PETER. Aquatic Biologist, The Nature Conservancy, North Coast and Klamath Ecoregion

Modoc Plateau Region

ARMENTROUT, DON. Resource Ecologist, BLM, Eagle Lake Resource Area, Susanville

BLEICH, VERN. Supervising Biologist, Department of Fish and Game, Eastern Sierra–Inland Deserts Region, Bishop

CALLAS, RICHARD. Senior Wildlife Biologist, Department of Fish and Game, Northern California–North Coast Region, Yreka

FLORES, MARY. Wildlife Biologist, Warner Mountains Ranger District, Modoc National Forest, Alturas

HALL, FRANK. Wildlife Biologist, Department of Fish and Game, Northern California–North Coast Region, Susanville

KEELER-WOLF, TODD. Vegetation Ecologist, Department of Fish and Game, Sacramento

HOLMES, AARON. Biologist, Point Reyes Bird Observatory, Shrub-Steppe Project

LAUDENSLAYER, BILL. Forest Ecologist, Pacific Southwest Research, U.S. Forest Service, Fresno

LOFT, ERIC. Environmental Scientist, Department of Fish and Game, Sacramento

MENKE, JOHN. Professor of Agronomy and Range Science (retired), Fort Jones

MILLER, RICHARD. Range Scientist, Eastern Oregon Agricultural Research Center, Burns, Ore.

MOYLE, PETER. Professor of Fisheries and Conservation Biology, University of California, Davis

NELSON, MELISSA. Wildlife Management Biologist, BLM, Susanville

PASERO, KC. Supervisor, Horse and Burro Program, BLM, Susanville

RICKMAN, TOM. Forest Ecologist, Forest Service, Eagle Lake District, Lassen National Forest, Susanville

ROUSH, PAUL. Wildlife Biologist, BLM, Northern California Support Team, Arcata

SCHAEFFER, BOB. Wildlife Biologist, Department of Fish and Game, Northern California–North Coast Region, Yreka

SHINN, RICHARD. Biologist, Department of Fish and Game, Northern California–North Coast Region, Alturas

SIPEREK, JOHN. Wildlife Program Manager, Department of Fish and Game, Northern California–North Coast Region, Redding

SMITH, DAVID. Wildlife Biologist, Department of Fish and Game (retired), Northern California–North Coast Region, Redding

SMITH, SYDNEY. Zone Ecologist, Modoc National Forest, Alturas

WOODBRIDGE, BRIAN. Endangered Species Forest Resource Supervisor, U.S. Fish and Wildlife Service, Yreka

YAMAGIWA, MARTY. Forest Biologist, Modoc National Forest, Alturas

Sierra Nevada and Cascades Region

ARMENTROUT, DON. Resource Ecologist. Bureau of Land Management, Eagle Lake Resource Area, Susanville

BLANKENSHIP, SAM. Wildlife Biologist, Department of Fish and Game, Sacramento

BLEICH, VERN C. Supervising Biologist, Department of Fish and Game, Eastern Sierra–Inland Deserts Region, Bishop

BLUMBERG, LOUIS. Forestry Policy Director, The Nature Conservancy, San Francisco

BOYCE, WALTER. Professor of Veterinary Medicine, Co-Director of the Wildlife Health Center, University of California, Davis

BRITTING, SUSAN. Forest Science and Policy Analyst, Coloma

BUCKLEY, JOHN. Executive Director, Central Sierra Environmental Resource Center, Twain Harte

BURTON, DAVID. Consultant, Aspen Delineation Project (multiagency), Penryn

CALLAS, RICHARD. Senior Wildlife Biologist, Department of Fish and Game, Northern California–North Coast Region, Yreka

COLTON, LAURA. Wildlife Biologist, Department of Fish and Game, San Joaquin Valley–Southern Sierra Region, Fresno

COTTER, CLU. Wildlife Biologist, Department of Fish and Game, San Joaquin Valley–Southern Sierra Region, Fresno

DAVIS, FRANK W. Professor, Donald Bren School of Environmental Science and Management, University of California, Santa Barbara

FURNAS, BRETT. Wildlife Biologist, Timber Harvest Review, Department of Fish and Game, Northern California–North Coast Region, Redding

GRABER, DAVE. Senior Science Adviser, Sequoia and Kings Canyon National Parks

HEATH, SACHA. Point Reyes Bird Observatory, Lee Vining

HUNSAKER, CAROLYN. Aquatic Ecologist, Pacific Southwest Research Station, Forestry Sciences Laboratory, U.S. Forest Service, Fresno

PURCELL, KATHRYN. Research Wildlife Biologist, Pacific Southwest Research Station, Forestry Sciences Laboratory, U.S. Forest Service, Fresno

KNAPP, ROLAND. Aquatic Ecologist, Sierra Nevada Aquatic Research Laboratory, University of California

LAUDENSLAYER, WILLIAM. Research Wildlife Biologist, Pacific Southwest Research Station, Forestry Sciences Laboratory, U.S. Forest Service, Fresno

LOFT, ERIC. Environmental Scientist, Department of Fish and Game, Sacramento

MANGELS, FRANCIS. District Biologist, Shasta McCloud Management Unit, U.S. Forest Service, McCloud

McCRARY, MARY ANN. Plant Ecologist, Department of Fish and Game, San Joaquin Valley–Southern Sierra Region, Fresno

McFARLAND, PAUL. Executive Director, Friends of the Inyo, Bishop

McKINNEY, JIM. Environmental Policy Specialist, California Energy Commission

MILLIRON, CURTIS. Wildlife Biologist, Department of Fish and Game, Eastern Sierra–Inland Deserts Region, Bishop

MOYLE, PETER. Professor of Fisheries Biology, University of California, Davis

O'CONNER, KEVIN. Environmental Scientist, Department of Fish and Game, San Joaquin Valley–Southern Sierra Region, Fresno

PARMENTER, STEVE. Fisheries Biologist, Department of Fish and Game, Eastern Sierra–Inland Deserts Region, Bishop

RICKMAN, TOM. District Wildlife Biologist, Lassen National Forest, Eagle Lake District, Susanville

ROBY, KEN. Aquatic Ecologist, Plumas National Forest, Chester

SINGLE, JEFF. Environmental Program Manager, Department of Fish and Game, San Joaquin Valley–Southern Sierra Region, Fresno

SIPEREK, JOHN. Wildlife Program Manager, Department of Fish and Game, Northern California–North Coast Region, Redding

SMITH, DAVID O. Wildlife Biologist, Department of Fish and Game, retired, Northern California–North Coast Region, Redding

STEPHENS, STAN. Senior Fisheries Biologist, Department of Fish and Game, San Joaquin Valley–Southern Sierra Region, Fresno

STINE, PETER. Program Manager, Principal Research Scientist, Pacific Southwest Research Station, Sierra Nevada Research Center, U.S. Forest Service, Davis

TIBSTRA, ROBB. Fish Biologist, Department of Fish and Game, Fresno

Central Valley and Bay-Delta Region

ARMOR, CHUCK. Operations Manager, Department of Fish and Game, Central Valley Bay-Delta Branch, Stockton

BAXTER, RANDY. Senior Biologist (Fisheries), Department of Fish and Game, Central Valley Bay-Delta Branch, Stockton

BLOOM, ROGER. Associate Fisheries Biologist, Department of Fish and Game, Sacramento

BOLSTER, BETSY. Senior Wildlife Biologist, Department of Fish and Game, Sacramento

BRIDEN, LAURIE. Senior Wildlife Biologist Supervisor, Department of Fish and Game, Central Valley Bay-Delta Branch, Stockton

BROWN, JULIE. Staff Environmental Scientist, Department of Fish and Game, Sacramento

CHAMBERLIN, JAY. Working Landscapes Coordinator, California Bay-Delta Authority, Sacramento

CHRISNEY, ANN. Coordinator, Riparian Habitat Joint Venture, Sacramento

COLLINS, JOSHUA. Environmental Scientist, San Francisco Estuary Institute, Oakland

COULSTON, PAT. Supervising Biologist, Department of Fish and Game, Central Valley Bay-Delta Branch, Stockton

EDMONDSON, STEVE. Northern California Supervisor, Habitat Conservation Division, National Marine Fisheries Service, Santa Rosa

FLEMING, KEVIN. Environmental Scientist, Department of Fish and Game, Central Valley Bay-Delta Branch, Stockton

GERSTENBERG, GREG. Associate Wildlife Biologist, Department of Fish and Game, San Joaquin Valley–Southern Sierra Region, Fresno

GEUPEL, GEOFFREY. Terrestrial Ecology Division Director, PRBO Conservation Science, Stinson Beach

GIFFORD, DAN. Associate Wildlife Biologist, Department of Fish and Game, Sacramento Valley–Central Sierra Region, Rancho Cordova

GONZALES, ARMAND. Supervising Biologist, Department of Fish and Game, Sacramento Valley–Central Sierra Region, Rancho Cordova

HANSEN, ROB. Vice President, Sequoia Riverlands Trust, Visalia

HARRISON, WAYNE. Senior State Park Resource Ecologist, Central Valley, California Parks and Recreation, Arnold

HOLBROOK, ROB. Science Coordinator, Central Valley Habitat Joint Venture, Sacramento

JACOBS, DIANA. Deputy Director, California Department of Fish and Game, Sacramento

JOHNSON, DOUG. Executive Director, California Invasive Plant Council, Berkeley

JUAREZ, STEVE. Habitat Conservation Planning Supervisor, Department of Fish and Game, San Joaquin Valley–Southern Sierra Region, Fresno

KELLY, PATRICK. Coordinator and Director, Endangered Species Recovery Program, California State University, Fresno

KIMMERER, WIM. Research Professor, Romberg Tiburon Center, San Francisco State University, Tiburon

KLEINFELTER, ERIC. Associate Wildlife Biologist, Department of Fish and Game, San Joaquin Valley–Southern Sierra Region, Fresno

KROEKER, TIM. Associate Wildlife Biologist, Department of Fish and Game, San Joaquin Valley–Southern Sierra Region, Fresno

LOW, ALICE. Senior Fishery Biologist, Department of Fish and Game, Native Anadromous Fish and Watershed Branch, Sacramento

MARR, JENNY. Staff Environmental Scientist, Department of Fish and Game, Sacramento Valley–Central Sierra Region, Chico

McEWAN, DENNIS. Senior Environmental Scientist, Department of Fish and Game, Native Anadromous Fish and Watershed Branch, Sacramento

MITCHELL, DALE. Environmental Program Manager, Department of Fish and Game, San Joaquin Valley–Southern Sierra Region, Fresno

MOYLE, PETER. Professor, Wildlife, Fish, and Conservation Biology, University of California, Davis

MULLIGAN, MIKE. Staff Environmental Scientist, Department of Fish and Game, San Joaquin Valley–Southern Sierra Region, Fresno

PALMISANO, TERRY. Senior Wildlife Biologist, Department of Fish and Game, Central Coast Region, Monterey

PHILLIPS, SCOTT. GIS Analyst and Network Administrator, Endangered Species Recovery Program, California State University, Fresno

RAYBURN, RICK. Chief, Natural Resources Division, California Department of Parks and Recreation, Sacramento

SASLAW, LARRY. Wildlife Biologist, Bureau of Land Management, Bakersfield

SCHAUB, DAVID. Program Manager, California Department of Parks and Recreation, Sacramento

SELMON, MICHELLE. Associate Wildlife Biologist, Department of Fish and Game, San Joaquin Valley–Southern Sierra Region, Fresno

SHAFFER, BOB. Coordinator, Central Valley Habitat Joint Venture, Sacramento

SINGLE, JEFF. Manager, Terrestrial Conservation Programs, Department of Fish and Game, San Joaquin Valley–Southern Sierra Region, Fresno

TAKEKAWA, JOHN. Research Wildlife Biologist, San Francisco Bay Estuary Field Station, U.S. Geological Survey, Vallejo

UPTAIN, CURT. Coordinator of the Land Retirement Demonstration Project and Project Supervisor, Endangered Species Recovery Program, California State University, Fresno

WERNETTE, FRANK. Program Manager, Department of Fish and Game, Central Valley Bay-Delta Branch, Stockton

WOODWARD, ROY. Manager, Inventory, Monitoring, and Assessment Program, California Department of Parks and Recreation, Sacramento

ZELEKE, DAWIT, Sacramento River Project Director, The Nature Conservancy, Chico

ZEZULAK, DAVE. Environmental Scientist, Department of Fish and Game, Central Valley Bay-Delta Branch, Stockton

Marine Region

ALLEN, JAMES. Principal Scientist, Southern California Coastal Water Research Project, Westminster

ALLEN, LARRY. Professor, Dept. of Biology, California State University, Northridge

BECK, MIKE. Senior Scientist, The Nature Conservancy, Santa Cruz

BEDFORD, DENNIS. Associate Marine Fisheries Biologist, California Dept. of Fish and Game Marine Region, Los Alamitos

BERGEN, MARY. Environmental Specialist IV, Department of Fish and Game, Marine Region, Santa Barbara

CROOKE, STEVE. Senior Biologist, Department of Fish and Game, Marine Region, Los Alamitos

DAVIS, GARY. Senior Scientist, Channel Islands National Park, Ventura

DAYTON, PAUL. Professor, Scripps Institution of Oceanography, University of California, San Diego

FAULKNER, KATE. Chief of Natural Resource Management, Channel Islands National Park, Ventura

FUJITA, ROD. Scientist, Environmental Defense, Oakland

GRADER, ZEKE. Executive Director, Pacific Coast Federation of Fishermen's Associations, San Francisco

GLEASON, MARY. Senior Conservation Planner, The Nature Conservancy, San Francisco

GROSHOLZ, EDWIN. Cooperative Extension Specialist, University of California, Davis

HAAKER, PETE. Senior Marine Biology Specialist, Department of Fish and Game, Marine Region, Los Alamitos

HASTINGS, SEAN. Resource Protection Coordinator, Channel Islands NMS, Santa Barbara

HENNEMAN, BURR. Director, Commonweal Ocean Policy Program, Bolinas

KARPOV, KONSTANTIN. Senior Biologist, Department of Fish and Game, Marine Region, Ft. Bragg

LANGABEER, BRENNA. Program Coordinator, PRBO Conservation Science, Stinson Beach

MARTIN, KAREN. Frank R. Seaver Chair of Biology, Pepperdine University, Malibu

McWILLIAMS, SARAH. Management Plan Specialist, Channel Islands NMS, Santa Barbara

MOORE, JAMES. Senior Fisheries Biologist, Department of Fish and Game, Marine Region, Bodega Bay

PARKER, DAVE. Senior Biologist, Department of Fish and Game, Marine Region, Los Alamitos

PERDUE, MITCHELL. Senior Biologist, United States Navy, San Diego

REILLY, PAUL. Senior Biologist, Department of Fish and Game, Marine Region, Monterey

SCHUCHAT, SAM. Executive Director, California Coastal Conservancy

TANAGUCHI, IAN. Associate Marine Fisheries Biologist, Department of Fish and Game, Marine Region, Los Alamitos

UGORETZ, JOHN. Nearshore Ecosystem Manager, Department of Fish and Game, Marine Region, Santa Barbara

VOJKOVICH, MARIJA. Offshore Ecosystem Manager, Department of Fish and Game, Marine Region, Santa Barbara

WALTON, ANNE. Management Plan Coordinator, Gulf of Farallones/Cordell Bank National Marine Sanctuaries, San Francisco

WANG, GUANG-YU. Senior Scientist, Santa Monica Bay Restoration Commission, Los Angeles

WEBER, MICHAEL. Marine Resource Conservation Consultant and Writer, Redondo Beach

YOCHEM, PAMELA. Vice President, Hubbs–SeaWorld Research Institute, San Diego

Glossary

adaptive management: the process of adjusting management actions and/or directions as new and better information emerges about an ecosystem.

alluvium: clay, silt, sand, gravel, or similar detrital material deposited by flowing water

anadromous: refers to fish **species** that spend most of their lives in the ocean but **migrate** to freshwater rivers and streams to spawn.

animal unit month (AUM): the amount of forage needed by an "animal unit" (AU) grazing for one month. The animal unit in turn is defined as one mature 1,000-pound cow and calf, one horse, five sheep, or one steer.

anthropogenic: resulting from the influence of humans on nature.

aquatic: growing, living in, or frequenting water, usually open water; compare with **wetland.**

aquifer: an underground reservoir of water.

AUM: See animal unit month.

benthic: living on or near the bottom of a body of water.

bioaccumulation: The uptake and concentration of chemicals by living systems.

biodiversity: the full array of living things.

biological diversity: the variety of life over some spatial unit, used to describe all aspects of the broadly diverse forms into which organisms have evolved, especially including species richness, ecosystem complexity, and genetic variation.

biomes: areas on the earth with similar climate, plants, and animals, classified according to the predominant vegetation and characterized by adaptations of organisms to that particular environment.

bioregion: an area that includes a rational ecological community with characteristic physical (climate, geology), biological (vegetation, animal), and environmental conditions.

BLM: Bureau of Land Management.

browse: 1. tender shoots, twigs, and leaves of trees and shrubs and grass that are available and acceptable to grazing animals (see also **forage**); 2. to feed on browse, graze.

California Legacy Project: an initiative that involves a broad range of government agencies and citizen organizations working together to develop a suite of tools and maps to help Californians make important decisions about conserving and protecting the state's working lands and natural resources.

California Wildlife Habitat Relationships System (CWHR): an information system and predictive model for California's wildlife containing range maps and habitat relationship information on all of the state's regularly occurring amphibians, reptiles, birds, and mammals.

canopy: the cover provided by a layer of vegetation, such as **overstory** trees in a forest.

cavity nesting: a type of bird species that nests in holes (cavities) in trees. They are divided into two groups. Primary cavity nesters excavate their own holes in trees and snags, while secondary cavity nesters are dependent upon natural cavities or abandoned sites excavated by primary cavity nesters.

clearcutting: a **silvicultural** method in which all trees in a designated area are removed in one operation.

commensal: having benefit for one member of a two-species association but neither positive nor negative effect on the other.

competition: occurs when two or more organisms have the potential for using the same resource. Competition may be between individuals of the same **species** or between two or more different species.

conifer: trees belonging to the order *Gymnospermae*, comprising a wide range of trees that are mostly evergreens. Conifers bear cones and have needle-shaped or scalelike leaves. In the wood products industry, the term "softwoods" refers to conifers.

conservation: the use of natural resources in ways such that they may remain **viable** for future generations. Compare with **preservation.**

conservation bank: privately or publicly owned land that is permanently protected and managed for its natural resource values. A conservation bank operator may sell habitat credits to developers who need to satisfy legal requirements for mitigating environmental impacts of development projects. Conservation banks must be approved by such wildlife agencies as the Department of Fish and Game and the U.S. Fish and Wildlife Service.

distribution: the pattern of occurrences for a **species** or **habitat** throughout the state; generally more precise than range.

disturbance regime: the characteristic pattern of natural- or human-caused events that disrupts the current physical and biological conditions of an area, such as floods, fires, storms, and human activity.

down logs: trees, limbs, or trunks that have fallen and are at least 10 feet long and at least 10 inches in diameter as measured on the large end.

ecological integrity: the degree to which the components (types of species, soil, etc.), structures (arrangement of components), and processes (flows of energy and nutrients) of an ecosystem or natural community are present and functioning intact. Lands with high ecological integrity generally have not been subjected to significant human influences or disruption of natural processes, such as fire, floods, or nutrient and hydrological cycling.

Ecological Reserve: designation given to certain lands owned or managed by the Department of Fish and Game as a way of regulating appropriate use. This designation is usually reserved for land with special status plants, animals, or vegetation types. Compare with **Wildlife Area.**

ecosystem: a natural unit defined by both its living and non-living components; a balanced system for the exchange of nutrients and energy. Compare with **habitat.**

ecosystem function: the operational role of ecosystem components, structure, and processes.

ecosystem health: the degree to which a biological community and its nonliving environmental surroundings function within a normal range of variability; the capacity to maintain ecosystems structures, functions, and capabilities to provide for human need.

ecosystem processes: the flow or cycling of energy, materials, and nutrients through space and time.

ecosystem services: the beneficial outcomes for the natural environment or for people that result from ecosystem functions. Some examples of ecosystem services are support of the food chain, harvesting of animals or plants, clean water, or scenic views. In order for an ecosystem to provide services to humans, some interaction with, or at least some appreciation by, humans is required.

ecosystem structure: spatial distribution or pattern of ecosystem components.

endangered species: any species, including subspecies or qualifying distinct population segment, which is in danger of extinction throughout all or a significant portion of its range.

endemic: found only in a specified geographic region.

endemism: used here as a measure of distribution for those **taxa** that are found only in one specific area, such as one region or the state itself. A region of high endemism has many taxa restricted to it.

estuary: an area in which salt water from the ocean mixes with flowing fresh water, usually at the wide mouth of a river.

evolutionarily significant unit (ESU): refers to a genetically distinct population segment of a species. An ESU is protected under the federal Endangered Species Act, which defines species to include "any subspecies of fish or wildlife or plants, and any distinct population segment of any species of vertebrate fish or wildlife, which interbreeds when mature."

Excessive livestock grazing: livestock grazing at a frequency or intensity that causes degradation of native plant communities, reduces habitat values for native wildlife species, degrades aquatic or other ecosystems, or impairs ecosystem functions. (The term "overgrazing" has a different meaning; it is usually used in referring to the productivity of the forage crop and range condition).

exotic species: a species of plant or animal introduced from another country or geographic region outside its natural range; non-native.

extinct: refers to a plant or animal or vegetation type that no longer exists anywhere.

extirpated: refers to a plant or animal or vegetation type that has been locally eliminated but is not **extinct**.

fauna: refers to all of the animal **taxa** in a given area.

fen: low land covered wholly or partly with water.

fire frequency: a broad measure of the rate of fire occurrence in a particular area.

fire regime: a measure of the general pattern of fire frequency and severity typical to a particular area or type of landscape.

flagship species: popular species that appeal to the general public and have interesting or notable features that make them suitable for communicating conservation concerns.

flora: refers to all of the plant taxa in a given area.

fluvial: pertaining to rivers.

forage: browse and herbage that is available and acceptable to grazing animals (see also **browse**).

forb: a broad-leaved herb, such as clover, as distinguished from a grass or a woody plant.

forest health: capacity of a forest for renewal, for recovery from a wide range of disturbances, and for retention of ecological function, while meeting the current and future needs of people for desired levels of values, uses, products, and services.

forest structure: the horizontal and vertical distribution of components of a forest stand, including height, diameter, crown layers, and stems of trees, shrubs, herbaceous understory, and down woods' debris.

fragmentation: the process by which a contiguous land cover, vegetative community, or habitat is broken into smaller patches within a mosaic of other forms of land use/land cover; e.g., islands of an older forest age class immersed within areas of younger-aged forest, or patches of oak woodlands surrounded by housing development.

FRAP: Fire and Resource Assessment Program.

FSC: Fire Safe Council.

fyke: a long bag fishing net kept open by hoops.

FWS: U.S. Fish and Wildlife Service.

GAP: Gap Analysis Program. It identifies gaps between land areas that are rich in biodiversity and areas that are managed for conservation.

genus: the level of biological classification above **species**. Closely related species belong to the same genus.

geographic information system (GIS): an organized assembly of people, data, techniques, computers, and programs for acquiring, analyzing, storing, retrieving, and displaying spatial information about the real world.

GIS: See Geographic Information System.

grazing permit: land lease offering written permission to graze a specific number, kind, and class of livestock for a specified defined allotment.

habitat: where a given plant or animal species meets its requirements for food, cover, and water in both space and time; may or may not coincide with a single vegetation type. Compare with **ecosystem.**

habitat quality: the capacity of a habitat to support a species.

HCP: Habitat Conservation Plan.

herbaceous: having characteristics of an herb; i.e., a nonwoody stem such as forbs, grasses, and ferns, or the nonwoody tissues of a branch or stem.

hybridization: refers here to the crossbreeding of two animals or plants of different species or subspecies.

impaired: condition of the quality of an ecosystem or habitat that has been adversely affected for a specific use by contamination or pollution.

Inland Empire: Riverside and San Bernardino Counties in Southern California.

introduced: refers to any **species** intentionally or accidentally transported and released into an environment outside its **native** range.

invasive: an **introduced species** which spreads rapidly once established and has the potential to cause environmental or economic harm. Not all introduced species are invasive.

invertebrate: an animal without an internal skeleton. Examples are insects, spiders, clams, shrimp, and snails.

keystone species: A species whose loss from an ecosystem would cause a greater than average change in other species populations or ecosystem processes and whose continued well-being is vital for the functioning of a whole community.

land cover: predominant vegetation life forms, natural features, or land uses of an area.

landscape: The traits, patterns, and structure of a specific geographic area, including its biological composition, its physical environment, and its anthropogenic or social patterns. An area where interacting ecosystems are grouped and repeated in similar form.

late succession forest: stands of dominant and predominant trees with open, moderate, or dense canopy, often with multiple canopies, and at least 20 acres in size. Characteristics include large decadent trees, snags, and large **down logs**.

late successional: the latter developmental stages of a plant community where vegetation structures are in a stable state and slow to change, reflective of increased age.

listed: general term used for a taxon protected under the federal Endangered Species Act, the California Endangered Species Act, or the California Native Plant Protection Act.

mesic: neither wet (hydric) nor dry (xeric); intermediate in moisture, without extremes.

metapopulation: A group of populations, usually of the same species, that exist at the same time but in different places.

migrate; migratory: referring to animals that travel seasonally. Migrations may be local or over long distances.

monitoring: collecting and analyzing observations of a species, habitat, or vegetation type over time. Monitoring also includes collecting data on other ecosystem components such as water and soil.

morphology: The form and structure of organisms.

native: naturally occurring in a specified geographic region.

natural community: general term often used synonymously with **habitat** or vegetation type.

NatureServe: a non-profit conservation organization that hosts a network of natural heritage programs providing information about rare and endangered species and threatened ecosystems.

non-native species: *See* **exotic species.**

nonpoint: pollution whose source cannot be ascertained, including runoff from storm water and agricultural, range, and forestry operations, as well as dust and air pollution that contaminate waterbodies.

OHV: off-highway vehicles.

old growth forest: a stand or stands of forest trees that exhibit large tree sizes, relatively old age, and decay characteristics common with over-mature trees.

overdraft: The pumping of water from a groundwater basin or aquifer in excess of the supply flowing into the basin; results in a depletion or "mining" of the groundwater in the basin.

overstory: The uppermost canopy (treetops) in a stand of trees.

Pacific Flyway: the westernmost migratory bird flyway in North America, which begins in Alaska and runs south through California. It consists of several parallel routes linked together by several branches and follows the coast of North America and the valleys of the major mountain ranges.

pelagic: Living on the open ocean rather than coastal or inland bodies of water.

piscivore: an animal whose primary food source is fish.

plant alliance: a level of classification for vegetation types generally based upon the dominant plant species in the uppermost or dominant layer of vegetation.

plant association: a level of classification for vegetation types below **plant alliance** and defined by the most characteristic species associated with a plant alliance. Many plant associations may be nested within a single plant alliance, just like many species may be nested within a single **genus**.

population: the number of individuals of a particular **taxon** in a defined area.

predation: the act of killing and eating other animals.

prescribed fire: a deliberate burn of wildland fuels in either their natural or modified setting and under specific environmental conditions that allow the fire to be confined to a predetermined area and intensity to attain a planned resource management objective.

preservation: generally, the nonuse of natural resources. Compare with **conservation.**

private: lands not publicly owned, including private conservancy lands.

public: lands owned by local, state, or federal government or special districts.

Ramsar Convention: an international treaty providing the framework for national action and international cooperation for the conservation and wise use of wetlands and their resources.

range: defined here as the maximum geographic extent of a **taxon** or **habitat**; does not imply that suitable conditions exist throughout the defined limits. Compare with **distribution**.

rangelands: any expanse of land not fertilized, cultivated, or irrigated that is suitable and pre-dominately used for grazing domestic livestock and wildlife.

rare: one of several **special status** listing designations in state law; it applies only to plants. Under California law, a plant is rare when, although it is not in immediate danger of **extinction**, it occurs in such low numbers that it may become **endangered** if its environment worsens. The word rare is also commonly applied to non-listed plants and animals whose populations are low in number and therefore at risk.

rarity: used here as a measure of sensitivity for those **taxa** that have special status due to very limited **distribution**, low population levels, or immediate threat. An area high in rarity has many taxa that meet this definition.

recruitment: the influx of new members into a population by reproduction or immigration.

redd: nesting site for salmonids and other fish.

refugia: areas where species can take refuge during times of climatic upheaval or biological stress. Places of past refugium are sometimes areas that still harbor high biological diversity.

regime: A regular pattern of occurrence or action.

resident: refers to animal **taxa** that remain in a given location throughout the year.

richness: used here as a measure of diversity; the total number of plant **taxa**, animal species, or vegetation types in a given area.

riparian: of or relating to rivers or streams.

riprap: gabions, stones, blocks of concrete, or other protective covering material of like nature deposited upon river and stream beds and banks, lake, tidal, or other shores to prevent erosion and scour by water flow, wave, or other movement.

salmonids: collective term for a family of fish that includes salmon and trout.

sensitive species: Those plant and animal species for which population viability is a concern.

seral, from **sere:** A series of stages in community transformation during ecological succession

silviculture: generally, the science and art of cultivating forest crops.

snags: standing dead trees with a minimum diameter of 10 inches and a height of 10 feet.

Special Animals List: a list compiled by Fish and Game containing **threatened, endangered,** and unlisted, but **sensitive** or declining, vertebrate and invertebrate **taxa**; taxa on this list are included in the California Natural Diversity Database.

species at risk: candidate, **threatened,** or **endangered** species pursuant to state and federal Endangered Species Acts, and **species of special concern.**

Species of Special Concern (SSC): an administrative designation given to animals that were not **listed** under the federal Endangered Species Act or the California Endangered Species Act at the time of designation but are declining at a rate that could, and sometimes does, result in listing.

substrate: the base or material on which an organism lives; subsoil.

succession: the gradual transformation of one ecological community to another, either in response to an environmental change or induced by the organisms themselves.

successional stage: a particular state of ecological development.

tailwater: Irrigation runoff water from agriculture.

take: to hunt, pursue, catch, capture, or kill, or attempt to hunt, pursue, catch, capture, or kill.

taxa: plural of **taxon.**

taxon: the name that is applied to a group in biological classification, for example, species, subspecies, variety, or evolutionarily significant unit (ESU). The plural is **taxa.**

threatened species: any species that is likely to become endangered within the foreseeable future throughout all or a significant portion of its range.

threatened: one of several special status listing designations of plant and animal **taxa**. Under the California and federal Endangered Species Acts, threatened refers to a **taxon** that is likely to become endangered in the foreseeable future. The word threatened is also commonly applied to non-listed taxa in danger of extinction.

TMDL: See Total Maximum Daily Load.

Total Maximum Daily Load (TMDL): a calculation of the maximum amount of a pollutant that a waterbody can receive and still meet water quality standards, as well as an estimation of the percentage originating from each pollution source. A TMDL is the sum of the allowable loads of a single pollutant from all contributing point and nonpoint sources. The calculation must include a margin of safety to ensure that the waterbody can be used for state-designated purposes. The calculation must also account for seasonal variation in water quality.

turbidity: reduced water clarity resulting from the presence of suspended matter.

umbrella species: a species whose conservation protects a wide range of co-existing species in the same habitat, which may be lesser-known and difficult to protect otherwise.

understory: the trees and other woody species growing under a relatively continuous cover of branches and foliage formed by the overstory trees.

uneven-aged: a silvicultural system in which individual trees originate at different times and result in a forest with trees of many ages and sizes.

upland: a general term referring to species, habitats, or vegetation types in nonflooded or non-saturated areas.

vernal pools: seasonal **wetlands** that form in depressions on the soil surface above a water-re-stricting layer of soil or rock. Plant and animal **taxa endemic** to vernal pools are those which can adapt to a unique cycle of flooding, temporary ponding, and drying.

vertebrate: an animal with an internal skeleton. Examples are birds, mammals, reptiles, amphibians, and fish.

viable: able to persist over time; self-sustaining.

watershed: defined here as a stream or river basin and the adjacent hills and peaks which "shed," or drain, water into it.

wetland: a general term referring to the transitional zone between **aquatic** and **upland** areas. Some wetlands are flooded or saturated only during certain seasons of the year. **Vernal pools** are one example of a seasonal wetland.

wildfire: any fire occurring on undeveloped land; the term specifies a fire occurring on a wild-land area that does not meet management objectives and thus requires a suppression response. Wildland fire protection agencies use this term generally to indicate a vegetation fire. Wildfire often replaces such terms as forest fire, brush fire, range fire, and grass fire.

wildlands: collective term for public or private lands largely undeveloped and in their natural state.

wildlife: all species of free-ranging animals, including but not limited to mammals, birds, fishes, reptiles, amphibians, and invertebrates.

Wildlife Area: designation given to certain lands owned or managed by the Department of Fish and Game as a way of regulating appropriate use. This designation is usually given to land with potential for multiple wildlife- dependent public uses such as waterfowl hunting, fishing, or wildlife viewing. Compare with **Ecological Reserve**.

woody debris: fallen dead wood or large branches. Woody debris is an important source of nutrients and habitat as well as a source of fuel for fire.

xeric: dry or desert-like.

zooplankton: minute, often microscopic, animal life that drift or swim in water bodies such as the ocean.

References ~~~~~~~~~~~~~~~~~~~~~~~~~~~~~~~

ACIA (Arctic Climate Impact Assessment). 2004. *Impacts of a warming Arctic.* Arctic Climate Impact Assessment Team, Arctic Council and International Arctic Science Committee. New York: Cambridge University Press. http://amap.no/acia/.

Allen, L.G., M.M. Yoklavich, G.M. Cailliet, and M.H. Horn. In prep. Bays and estuaries. In Allen, L.G., D.J. Pondella II, and M.H. Horn, eds. *Ecology of marine fishes: California and adjacent waters.* University of California Press, Berkeley.

Ally, J.R. 2001. *Potential impacts to biological resources by recreational users in a 3.6 mile stretch of the San Gabriel River, East Fork.* Unpublished report of Calif. Dept. of Fish and Game, South Coast Region, Northern Unit, Los Alamitos.

Alonzo, S.H., M. Key, T. Ish, and A. McCall. 2004. *Status of California sheephead* (Semicossyphus pulcher) *stock (2004).* Report to Calif. Dept. of Fish and Game. http://www.dfg.ca.gov/mrd/sheephead2004/index.html.

Alverson, W.S., W. Kuhlman, and D.A. Waller. 1994. *Wild forests: Conservation biology and public policy.* Washington, D.C.: Island Press.

Anderson, M.A., and C. Amrhein. 2002. *Nutrient cycling in the Salton Sea.* Final Report to the Salton Sea Authority. La Quinta, Calif.

Andrews, R.N.L., and P.F. Nowak, eds. 1980. *Off-road vehicle use: A management challenge.* Office of Environmental Quality of the U.S. Dept. of Agriculture.

Aplet, G.H., and W.S. Keeton. 1999. Application of historical range of variability concepts to biodiversity conservation. In *Practical approaches to the conservation of biological diversity,* Richard K. Baydack et al., eds. Washington, D.C.: Island Press.

Armour, C.L., D.A. Duff, and W. Elmore. 1991. The effects of livestock grazing on riparian and stream ecosystems. *Fisheries* 16:7-11.

Armsworth, P.R., G.C. Daily, P. Kareiva, and J.N. Sanchirico. 2004. *Land market feedbacks undermine biodiversity conservation*. (draft). Sheffield: University of Sheffield, United Kingdom.

Arno, S.F., and C.E. Fiedler. 2005. *Mimicking nature's fire: Restoring fire-prone forests in the West.* Washington, D.C.: Island Press.

Atkinson, A.J., P.C. Trenham, R.N. Fisher, S.A. Hathaway, B.S. Johnson, S.G. Torres, and Y.C. Moore. 2004. Designing monitoring programs in an adaptive management context for regional multiple species conservation plans. U.S. Geological Survey Technical Report. USGS Western Ecological Research Center, Sacramento, Calif. 69 pages. http://www/dfg/ca/gov/nccp/pups/monframewk10-04.pdf.

Avery, H.W. 1999. *Livestock grazing in the Mojave desert in relation to the desert tortoise.* Presentation at the Mojave Desert Science Symposium. U.S. Geological Survey, Western Ecological Research Center.

Backer, D.M., S.E. Jensen, and G.R. McPherson. 2004. Impacts of fire-suppression activities on natural communities. *Conservation Biology* 18(4):937–946.

Bainbridge, D.A., and R.A. Virginia. 1995. Desert soils and soil biota. In *The California desert: An introduction to natural resources and man's impact.* J. Latting and P.G. Rowlands, eds. June Latting Books. Printed by University of California, Riverside, Press.

Baker, W.L., and D.J. Shinneman. 2004. Fire and restoration of pinyon-juniper woodlands in the western United States: A review. *Forest Ecology and Management* 189:1–21.

Barbour, M., B. Pavlik, F. Drysdale, and S. Lindstrom. 1993. *California's changing landscapes: Diversity and conservation of California vegetation.* Sacramento: California Native Plant Society.

Barrows, C.W. 1996. An ecological model for the protection of a dune ecosystem. *Conservation Biology* 10(3):888–891.

Barrows, C.W. 1997. Habitat relationships of the Coachella Valley fringe-toed lizard (*Uma inornata*). *Southwestern Naturalist* 42(2):218–223.

Barrows, C.W., M.B. Swartz, W.L. Hodges, M.F. Allen, J.T. Rotenberry, B. Li, T.A. Scott, and X. Chen. 2005. A framework for monitoring multiple species conservation plans. *Journal of Wildlife Management.* In press.

Bartos, D., and W. Sheppard. 2003. *Aspen restoration in the western United States.* USDA Forest Service RMRS. http://www.fs.fed.us/rm/aspen.

Bay Area Open Space Council 2004. [cited December 2004]. *Program description.* http://www.openspacecouncil.org/Documents/OSC/ProgramDescription2004.03.28.pdf.

Beck, M.W., K.L. Heck, K.W. Able, D.L. Childers, D.B Eggleston, B.M. Gillanders, B.S Halpern, C.G. Hays, K.Hoshino, T.J. Minello, R.J. Orth, P.F. Sheridan, and M.P. Weinstein. 2003. The role of nearshore ecosystems as fish and shellfish nurseries. *Issues in Ecology* 11:1–12.

Beever, E.A. 2003. Management implications of the ecology of free-roaming horses in semiarid ecosystems of the western United States. *Wildlife Society Bulletin* 31:887–895.

Behnke, R.J. 1992. *Native trout of western North America.* American Fisheries Society Monograph 6.

———. 2002. *Trout and salmon of North America.* New York: The Free Press.

Beier, P., K. Penrod, C. Luke, W. Spencer, and C. Cabanero. In press. South Coast Missing Linkages: Restoring connectivity to wildlands in the largest metropolitan area in the United States. In *Connectivity Conservation,* K. Crooks and M. Sanjayan, eds.

Belnap, J. 2002. Impacts of off-road vehicles on nitrogen cycles in biological soil crusts: Resistance in different U.S. deserts. *Journal of Arid Environments* 52:155–165.

Belsky, A.J. 1996. Viewpoint: Western juniper expansion: Is it a threat to arid northwestern ecosystems? *Journal of Range Management* 49(1):53–59.

Belsky, A.J., and J.L. Gelbard. 2000. *Livestock grazing and weed invasions in the arid West.* A scientific report published by the Oregon Natural Desert Association.

Belsky, A.J., A. Matzke, and S. Uselman. 1999. Survey of livestock influences on stream and riparian ecosystems in the western United States. *Journal of Soil and Water Conservation* 54:419–431.

Bennett, A.F. 1999. *Linkages in the landscape: The role of corridors and connectivity in wildlife conservation.* Gland, Switzerland: IUCN The World Conservation Union.

Berry, K. 1997. The desert tortoise recovery plan: An ambitious effort to conserve biodiversity in the Mojave and Colorado deserts of the United States. In *Proceedings: Conservation, Restoration, and Management of Tortoises and Turtles—an International Conference.* New York Turtle and Tortoise Society.

———. 1999. *Desert tortoise research projects in the Mojave and Colorado deserts of California: Status, trends, demography, and habitats.* Presentation at the Mojave Desert Science Symposium. U.S. Geological Survey, Western Ecological Research Center.

Berry, K. 2003. *Declining trends in desert tortoise populations at long-term study plots in California between 1979 and 2002: Multiple issues.* 28th Annual Meeting and Symposium of the Desert Tortoise Council.

Best, C. 2004. Forest loss and fragmentation. In *California Forests* 8(2):8–9.

Bisbal, G. A. 2001. Conceptual design of monitoring and evaluation plans for fish and wildlife in the Columbia River ecosystem. *Environmental Management* 28:433-453.

Biswell, H. 1989. *Prescribed burning in California wildlands vegetation management.* Berkeley: University of California Press.

Bleich, V.C., S.G. Torres, J.D. Wehausen, and T.A. Swank. 1996. History of transplanting mountain sheep—California. *Biennial Symposium on North American Wild Sheep and Goat Council* 10:164–166.

BLM (Bureau of Land Management). 1980. *California Desert Conservation Area Final Environmental Impact Statement and Proposed Plan.*

———. 1995. *West Mojave Coordinated Management Plan, Draft Environmental Impact Statement. Administrative Review Draft.*

———. 1999. *California Desert Strategic Plan for the management of wild burros. California Desert interagency burro strategy.*

———. 2000. *Greater sage-grouse and sage-steppe ecosystems management guidelines.* Product of the interagency, interdisciplinary sage-grouse planning team.

———. 2002a. Proposed California Desert Conservation Area Plan Amendment for the Coachella Valley and Final Environmental Impact Statement. Palm Springs, Calif.

———. 2002b. *Record of Decision for approved Northern and Eastern Mojave Desert Management Plan, an amendment to the California Desert Conservation Area Plan 1980.*

———. 2003a. *Annual report.*

———. 2003b. *Draft Imperial Sand Dunes Recreation Management Plan.* El Centro, Calif. http://www.ca.blm.gov/pdfs/elcentro_pdfs/FinalEISandRAMP/finalRAMP.pdf.

———. 2004a. BLM data regarding wild horse AMLs for California and Nevada herd management units. Available at BLM's Susanville office.

———. 2004b. *California Desert District wild horse and burro data on population estimates, excess animals and removals.*

———. 2004c. *Draft Resource Management Plan/Draft Environmental Impact Statement for the California Coastal National Monument.* U.S. Dept. of the Interior, Bureau of Land Management, California State Office.

———. 2004d. *Western juniper management strategy.* http://www.ca.blm.gov/alturas/juniper_concept_paper1.htm.

———. 2005a. *BLM grazing allotments in California.* Unpublished data, available from BLM, California State Office, Sacramento.

———. 2005b. *West Mojave, a Habitat Conservation Plan and California Desert Conservation Area Plan Amendment, Draft Environmental Impact Report.* January.

———. [cited July 2004]. *National Wild Horse and Burro Program, the Wild Free-Roaming Horses and Burros Act of 1971 (Public Law 92–195).* http://www.wildhorseandburro.blm.gov/92–195.htm.

BLM (Bureau of Land Management), California Desert District and CDFG (California Department of Fish and Game), Inland, Deserts, and Eastern Sierra Region. 2002. *Proposed*

Northern and Eastern Colorado Desert Coordinated Management Plan and Final Environmental Impact Statement. Riverside, Calif.

Boarman, W.I., and K. Berry. 1995. Common ravens in the southwestern United States, 1968–92. In *Our living resources: A report to the nation on the distribution, abundance, and health of U.S. plants, animals, and ecosystems,* E.T. Laroe, ed. U.S. Dept. of Interior. National Biological Service. Washington, D.C.

Boarman, W.I., and S.J. Coe. 2002. An evaluation of the distribution and abundance of common ravens at Joshua Tree National Park. *Southern California Academy of Sciences Bulletin* 101(2):86–102.

Bombay, H. L., M. L. Morrison, and L. S. Hall. 2003. Scale perspectives in habitat selection and animal performance for willow flycatchers *(Empidonax traillii)* in the central Sierra Nevada, California. *Studies in Avian Biology* 26:60–72.

Boone, J., and W.C. Krueger. 1984. Livestock impacts on riparian ecosystems and streamside management implication, a review. *Journal of Range Management* 37(5):430–437.

Bossard, C., J.M. Randall, and M. Hoshovsky, eds. 2000. *Invasive plants of California's wildlands.* Berkeley: University of California Press. http://groups.ucanr.org/ceppc/Invasive_Plants_of_California's_Wildlands/.

Bowling, A.T., and R.W. Touchberry. 1990. Parentage of Great Basin USA feral horses. *Journal of Wildlife Management* 54(3):424–429.

Briggs, K.T., W.B. Tyler, D.B. Lewis, and D.R. Carlson. 1987. Bird communities at sea off California, 1975–1983. *Studies in Avian Biology* 11:1–74.

Briggs, M.K., and S. Cornelius. 1998. Opportunities for ecological improvement along the lower Colorado River and delta. *Wetlands* 18(4):513–529.

Brooks, M.L., C.M. D'Antonio, D.M. Richardson, J.B. Grace, J.E. Keeley, J.M. DiTomaso, R.J. Hobbs, M. Pellent, and D. Pyke. 2004. Effects of invasive alien plants on fire regimes. *BioScience* 54(7):677–688.

Brooks, M.L. and T.C. Esque. 2003. *Nonnative grass invasions and fire in the Mojave Desert.* USGS, Western Ecological Research Center. http://www.werc.usgs.gov/invasivespecies/mojavegrassfire.html.

Brooks, M.L., and J. R. Matchett. 2002. Sampling methods and trapping success trends for the Mohave ground squirrel, *Spermophilus mohavensis. California Fish and Game* 88(4):165–177.

Brooks, M.L., and D.A. Pyke. 2001. Invasive plants and fire in the deserts of North America. In *Proceedings of the Invasive Species Workshop: the Role of Fire in the Control and Spread of Invasive Species.* K.E.M. Galley and T.P. Wilson, eds. Fire Conference 2000: the First National Congress on Fire Ecology, Prevention, and Management. Miscellaneous Publication No. 11. Tall Timbers Research Station, Tallahassee, Fla.

Brown, R.T., J.K. Agee, and J.F. Franklin. 2004. Forest restoration and fire: Principles in the context of place. *Conservation Biology* 18(4):903–912.

Bruehler, G., and A. de Peyster. 1999. Selinium and other trace metals in pelicans dying at the Salton Sea. *Bulletin of Environmental Contamination and Toxicology* 63:590–597.

Bryant, E. 1848. *What I saw in California: Being the journal of a tour by the emigrant route and south pass of the rocky mountains, across the continent of North America, the Great Desert Basin, and through California in the years 1846, 1847.* New York: Appleton and Co Press. http://www.authorama.com/book/what-i-saw-in-california.html.

Burcham, L.T. 1982. *California range land.* Center for Archaeological Research. Publication Number 7. University of California, Davis.

Burton, D. 2002. Aspen in California: Assessment and management. In *The changing California, forest and range 2002 assessment.* California Department of Forestry and Fire Protection.

Busch, D.C., and S.D. Smith. 1995. Mechanisms associated with decline of woody species in riparian ecosystems of the southwest U.S. *Ecological Monographs* 65(3):347–371.

Byers, J.A. 2003. *Built for speed, a year in the life of pronghorn.* Harvard University Press.

CAANG (California Army National Guard). 2001. *Final Draft Integrated Natural Resources Management Plan for Camp Roberts Training Center.* Sacramento.

Caffrey, J., M. Brown, W.B. Tyler, and M. Silberstein, eds. 2002. *Changes in a California estuary: A profile of Elkhorn Slough.* Moss Landing, Calif.: Elkhorn Slough Foundation.

Cahill, T.A., J.J. Carroll, D. Campbell, and T.E. Gill. 1996. *Air Quality.* Sierra Nevada Ecosystem Project: Final Report to Congress. Vol II. Davis: University of California, Centers for Water and Wildland Resources.

Cain, J.W. III, and M.L. Morrison. 2003. Reproductive ecology of dusky flycatchers in montane meadows of the central Sierra Nevada. *Western North American Naturalist* 63(4):507–512.

CALFED (California Bay-Delta Authority). 2000. *Ecosystem restoration program plan: Volume 1: Ecological attributes of the San Francisco Bay-Delta watershed.* Final Programmatic EIS/EIR Technical Appendix. Sacramento. http://calwater.ca.gov/Programs/EcosystemRestoration/EcosystemVol1RestorationPlan.shtml.

———. 2003. *CALFED Mercury Project—Final project reports,* Sacramento. http://loer.tamug.tamu.edu/calfed/FinalReports.htm.

———. 2004a. *Ecosystem restoration multi-year program plan (Years 5-8).* Sacramento. http://calwater.ca.gov/ProgramPlans_2004/Ecosystem_Restoration_Program_Plan_7-04.pdf.

———. 2004b. *Drinking water quality program multi-year program plan (Years 5-8).* Sacramento. http://calwater.ca.gov/ProgramPlans_2004/Drinking_Water_Quality_Program_Plan_7-04.pdf.

CALFED Bay-Delta Program. 2000b. Recommendations for the implementation and continued refinement of a comprehensive monitoring, assessment, and research program.

Final Programmatic EIS/EIR Technical Appendix. July 2000. http://calwater.ca.gov/CALFEDDocuments/Final_EIS_EIR.shtml

Calfish 2005. *California fish passage assessment database project.* [cited January 2005]. http://www.calfish.org/DesktopDefault.aspx?tabId=69.

California Labor Workforce Development Agency. 2003a. *Regional economic base reports: Northern Sacramento Valley.* Sacramento. http://www.labor.ca.gov/panel/NorthernSacramentoValleyReport.pdf.

————. 2003b. *Regional economic base reports: San Joaquin Valley.* Sacramento. http://www.labor.ca.gov/panel/SanJoaquinValleyReport.pdf.

California Legacy Project, California Resources Agency. 2003. *Spotlight on conservation.* South Coast Workshop, July 24–25, 2002. Unpublished report. Sacramento. http://legacy.ca.gov/workshop_reports.epl.

California Legacy Project (California Resources Agency)/UC Davis ICE (University of California, Davis, Information Center for the Environment). 2004. GIS Dataset: General Plan Map.

California Resources Agency and California Environmental Protection Agency. 2004. *Protecting our ocean: California's action strategy: final report to Gov. Arnold Schwarzenegger.* September 2004.

California State Lands Commission. 1993. *California's rivers: A public trust report.* http://elib.cs.berkeley.edu/cgi-bin/doc_home?elib_id=1446.

California State Parks (California Department of Parks and Recreation). 2004. *California state parks and the Great Central Valley.* Sacramento. http://www.parks.ca.gov/pages/21491/files/cvreport.pdf.

CalIPC (California Invasive Plant Council). 1999. *Exotic pest plants of greatest ecological concern in California.* Berkeley. http://groups.ucanr.org/ceppc/1999_Cal-IPC_list.

CalPIF (California Partners in Flight). 2000. *The draft grassland bird conservation plan: A strategy for protecting and managing grassland habitats and associated birds in California.* (B. Allen, lead author). Version 1.0. Stinson Beach: Point Reyes Bird Observatory. http://www.prbo.org/CPIF/Consplan.html.

————. 2002. *The oak woodland bird conservation plan: A strategy for protecting and managing oak woodland habitats and associated birds in California.* (S. Zack, lead author). Version 2.0. Stinson Beach. Point Reyes Bird Observatory. http://www.prbo.org/calpif/plans.html.

————. 2004. *The coastal scrub and chaparral bird conservation plan: A strategy for protecting and managing coastal scrub and chaparral habitats and associated birds in California.* (J. Lovio, lead author). Version 2.0. Stinson Beach: Point Reyes Bird Observatory. http://www.prbo.org/calpif/plans.html.

Campbell, L.A., W.J. Zielinski, and D.C. Macfarlane. 2000. *A risk assessment for four forest carnivores in the Sierra Nevada under proposed Forest Service management activities.* Unpublished report of the Sierra Nevada Framework Project.

Caprio, A.C., and D.M. Graber. 2000. Returning fire to the mountains: Can we successfully restore the ecological role of pre-Euroamerican fire regimes to the Sierra Nevada? *Proceedings: Wilderness Science in the Time of Change.* Ogden, Utah.

Caprio, A.C., and T.W. Swetnam. 1993. Historical fire regimes along an elevational gradient on the west slope of the Sierra Nevada, California. *Proceedings: Symposium on Fire in Wilderness and Park Management: Past Lessons and Future Opportunities,* March 30–April 1, 1993.

CASS (California Agricultural Statistics Service). 2003. *Agricultural overview.* Sacramento. ftp://www.nass.usda.gov/pub/nass/ca/AgStats/2003cas-ovw.pdf.

Caughey, J.W. 1970. *California, a remarkable state's life history.* Prentice-Hall.

CBD (Center for Biological Diversity). 2002. *A conservation alternative for the management of the four southern California National Forests.* A report submitted by the Center for Biological Diversity to the U.S. Forest Service. Idyllwild.

CBI (Conservation Biology Institute). 2003. *Conservation significance of Tejon Ranch: A biogeographic assessment.* A report to Environment Now. San Diego. http://www.savetejonranch.org/doclibrary/index.html.

CBI (Conservation Biology Institute). 2004. *Conservation assessment of Tejon Ranch.* A report to Preserving Wild California and Resources Legacy Fund. San Diego. http://www.savetejonranch.org/doclibrary/index.html.

CCC (California Coastal Conservancy). 2001. *Southern California Wetlands Recovery Project Regional Strategy.* A report of the California Coastal Conservancy. Oakland. http://www.scwrp.org/regional_strategy.htm.

CDC (California Department of Conservation). 2002. Farmland Mapping and Monitoring Program. GIS dataset: Farmland Mapping (Agricultural Land Use).

CDF (California Department of Forestry and Fire Protection). 2002. GIS dataset: Multi-source land cover data 2002 v.2.

———. [updated June 2004]. *CDF 2003 fire season summary.* http://www.fire.ca.gov/php/about_factsheets.php.

———. 2003. *The changing California forest and range assessment.* Fire and Resource Assessment Program.

CDFA (California Department of Food and Agriculture). [Cited January 2005]. *Weed management areas.* http://www.cdfa.ca.gov/phpps/ipc/weedmgtareas/wma_index_hp.htm.

CDFG (California Department of Fish and Game). 1988-1990. *California's wildlife.* California Wildlife Habitat Relationships System. http://www.dfg.ca.gov/bdb/html/cawildlife.html.

————. 1991a. *Operation and Management Plan for lands managed by the Department of Fish and Game.*

————. 1991b. *A vision for the future.* Sacramento.

————. 1993. *Restoring Central Valley streams: A plan for action.* Sacramento. http://www.dfg.ca.gov/nafwb/pubs/1993/RCVS.pdf.

————. 1995. *Strategic plan.* Sacramento.

————. 1996. *Steelhead restoration and management plan.* Sacramento. http://www.dfg.ca.gov/nafwb/pubs/swshplan.pdf.

————. 1997. *California's wild gardens.* California Native Plant Society.

————. 1998a. *California salmonid stream habitat restoration manual.* Third edition. Sacramento.

————. 1998b. *Living with California mountain lions.* http://www.dfg.ca.gov/lion/index.html.

————. 1998c. *A status review of the spring-run chinook salmon* (Oncorhynchus tshawytscha) in *the Sacramento River drainage.* Candidate Species Status Report (98-01) to the California Fish and Game Commission. Sacramento. http://www.dfg.ca.gov/nafwb/pubs/1998/chinook_status.pdf.

————. [Web site updated 1999]. *California's plants and animals, marbled murrelet.* http://www.dfg.ca.gov/hcpb/cgi-bin/read_one.asp?specy=birds&idNum=59.

————. 2000. *Giant and bull kelp commercial and sport fishing regulations, draft final environmental document.* California Dept. of Fish and Game, Marine Region.

————. 2001. *The master plan: A guide for the development of fishery management plans as directed by the Marine Life Management Act of 1998.* Resources Agency, California Dept. of Fish and Game, Marine Region.

————. 2002a. *Draft abalone recovery and management plan.* California Dept. of Fish and Game Marine Region. http://www.dfg.ca.gov/mrd/armp/index.html.

————. 2002b. *Condition and historical trends of aspen in the Warner Mountains.* Resource Assessment Program.

————. 2002c. *Nearshore fishery management plan.* http://www.dfg.ca.gov/mrd/nfmp.

————. 2002d. *Status review of California coho salmon north of San Francisco.* Report to the California Fish and Game Commission. Sacramento.

————. 2003a. *Atlas of the biodiversity of California.* http://atlas.dfg.ca.gov.

————. 2003b. *Lessons learned from regional conservation planning efforts.* Sacramento. http://www.dfg.ca.gov/nccp/pubs/lessonslearned.pdf.

————. 2003c. *September 2002 Klamath River fish-kill: Preliminary analysis of contributing factors.* Northern California–North Coast Region. http://www.pcffa.org/KlamFishKillFactorsDFGReport.pdf.

————. 2003d. *White seabass fishery management plan* http://www.dfg.ca.gov/mrd/wsfmp.

————. 2004a. *Budget Fact Book.* 2004–2005 Proposed Governor's Budget.

————. 2004b. *Channel Islands Marine Protected Areas Monitoring Plan* http://www.dfg.ca.gov/mrd/channel_islands/monitoring.html.

————. 2004c. *Elk Hunting Final Environmental Document.*

————. 2004d. *Final California commercial landings for 2003.* http://www.dfg.ca.gov/mrd.

————. 2004e. *Habitat Water Supply Management Plan for the adjudicated area of the Mojave River Basin, San Bernardino, California.*

————. 2004f. *Pronghorn Antelope Hunting Final Environmental Document.*

————. 2004g. *Recovery strategy for California coho salmon* (Oncorhynchus kisutch). A report to the California Fish and Game Commission. Species Recovery Strategy 2004-1. Sacramento. http://www.dfg.ca.gov/nafwb/CohoRecovery/RecoveryStrategy.html.

————. 2004h. *Sacramento River spring-run chinook salmon. 2002-2003 biennial report.* Prepared for the Fish and Game Commission by California Department of Fish and Game. Sacramento. http://www.dfg.ca.gov/nafwb/pubs/2004/ChinookSR0203.pdf.

————. 2005a. *California Wildlife Habitat Relationships database.* http://www.dfg.ca.gov/bdb/html/cwhr.html.

————. 2005b. *The status of rare, threatened, and endangered plants and animals of California 2000–2004.* Sacramento.

CDFG (California Department of Fish and Game), Habitat Conservation Planning Branch. [cited August 2004]. *Species accounts.* http://www.dfg.ca.gov/hcpb/species/search_species.shtml.

CDFG (California Department of Fish and Game) and NMFS (National Marine Fisheries Service). 2002. *Guidelines for maintaining instream flows to protect fisheries resources downstream of water diversions in mid-California coastal streams.* Sacramento and Santa Rosa. http://swr.nmfs.noaa.gov/hcd/policies/Waterdiversion%20guidelines.pdf.

CDOF (California Department of Finance). 2000. *E-5 city/county population and housing estimates, 1991–2000, with 1990 census counts.* Sacramento. http://www.dof.ca.gov/HTML/DEMOGRAP/E-5text.htm.

————. 2003. *E-2 California county population estimates and components of change,* July 1, 2000–2003. Sacramento. http://www.dof.ca.gov/html/demograp/e-2text.htm.

———. 2004. *P3 population projections by race/ethnicity, gender and age for California and its counties 2000–2050.* Sacramento. http://www.dof.ca.gov/html/demograp/dru_Publications/ Projections/P3/P3.htm.

———. [cited June 2004]. *Demographic information. Population change 1990–2000.* http://www.dof.ca.gov/html/demograp/table1.xls.

———. [updated February 2005]. *California population estimates, with components of change and crude rates, July 1, 1941-2004.* http://www.dof.ca.gov/html/demograp/e-7_Jul04.xls.

CDPAR (California Department of Parks and Recreation). 2004. *Anza Borrego Desert State Park Preliminary General Plan/Final Environmental Impact Report.* SCH #2002021060. Sacramento. http://www.parks.ca.gov/?page_id=21314.

CDPR (California Department of Pesticide Regulation). 2001. *2001 annual pesticide use report.* Indexed by commodity for Monterey County. http://www.cdpr.ca.gov/docs/pur/pur01rep/ comrpt01.pdf.

CEC (California Energy Commission). 1995. *Avian collision and electrocution: An annotated bibliography.* California Energy Commission Publication Number: P700-95-001 Sacramento. http://www.energy.ca.gov/reports/avian_bibliography.html.

———. 2002a. *A roadmap for PIER research on avian collisions with power lines in California.* Sacramento. http://www.energy.ca.gov/reports/2002-12-24_500-02-070F.PDF.

———. 2002b. *A roadmap for PIER research on avian collisions with power lines in California.* Sacramento. http://www.energy.ca.gov/reports/2002-12-24_500-02-071F.PDF.

———. 2005. [Cited January 2005]. *Climate change and California.* Sacramento. http://www.energy.ca.gov/global_climate_change/index.html.

CERES (California Environmental Resources Evaluation System). [cited June 2004]. *CERES California Bioregions.* http://ceres.ca.gov/geo_area/bioregions/Colorado_Desert.

———. [cited October 2004]. *CERES California bioregions.* http://ceres.ca.gov/geo_area/bioregions/South_Coast.

———. [cited March 2005]. *CERES California bioregions.* http://ceres.ca.gov/geo_area/bioregions/North_Coast.

Chambers, J.C., and J.R. Miller. 2004. Restoring and maintaining riparian ecosystems: The Great Basin ecosystem management project. In *Great Basin riparian ecosystems.* Washington, D.C.: Island Press.

Chandler, W.J., and H. Gillelan. 2004. The history and evolution of the National Marine Sanctuaries Act. *Environmental Law Reporter* 6-2004 (34 ELR 10505).

Chang, C. 1996. *Ecosystem responses to fire and variations in fire regime.* Sierra Nevada Ecosystem Project: Final Report to Congress. Vol II. Davis: University of California, Centers for Water and Wildland Resources.

Charnley, S. 2005. *Northwest Forest Plan: The first ten years, socioeconomic monitoring results. Volume II: Timber and non-timber resources.* A report of the Interagency Regional Monitoring Program in the Pacific Northwest. http://www.reo.gov/monitoring/10yr-report/social-economic.

City of Arcata. 2005. *The Arcata marsh.* http://www.arcatacityhall.org/arcata_marsh.html.

Cleverly, J.R., S.D. Smith, A. Sala, and D.A. Devitt. 1997. Invasive capacity of *Tamarix ramosissima* in a Mojave Desert floodplain: The role of drought. *Oecologia* 111:12–18.

CNDDB (California's Natural Diversity Data Base) [cited May 2005]. California Department of Fish and Game's Wildlife and Habitat Data Analysis Branch. http://www.dfg.ca.gov/bdb/html/cnddb.html.

CNPS (California Native Plant Society). 2001. *Inventory of rare and endangered plants of California,* sixth edition, D.P. Tibor, ed. Rare Plant Scientific Advisory Committee, Sacramento.

Cody, M. 2000. Slow-motion population dynamics in Mojave Desert perennial plants. *Journal of Vegetation Science.* 11(3):351–358.

Cohen, M.J., and C. Henges-Jeck. 2001. *Missing water: The uses and flows of water in the Colorado River delta region.* A report of the Pacific Institute for Studies in Development, Environment and Security. Oakland, Calif.

Cohen, M.J., J.I. Morrison, and E. P. Glenn. 1999. *Haven or hazard: The ecology and future of the Salton Sea.* A report of the Pacific Institute for Studies in Development, Environment and Security. Oakland, Calif.

Cohn, J.P. 2000. Saving the Salton Sea. *Bioscience* 50(4):295–319.

Collins, P.W., E.D. Pierson, W.E. Rainey, and T.E. Kucera. 2004. *Terrestrial mammal species of special concern in California.* Draft final report to the California Department of Fish and Game. Sacramento.

Connelly, J.W., S.T. Knick, M.A. Schroeder, and S.J. Stiver. 2004. *Conservation assessment of greater sage-grouse and sagebrush habitats.* Unpublished report of the Western Asscociation of Fish and Wildlife Agencies, Cheyenne, Wyo.

Connelly, J.W., M.A. Schroeder, A.R. Sands, and C.E. Braun. 2000. Guidelines to manage sage-grouse populations and their habitats. *Wildlife Society Bulletin* 28(4):967–985.

Conservation International. 2005. *Biodiversity hotspots: California floristic province.*

Cooper, D.S. 2003. [updated 2003]. *Audubon California. Introduction to the Salton Sea.* http://www.audubon-ca.org/salton_sea.html.

Cordell Bank National Marine Sanctuary. 2003. *Joint Management Plan Review (JMPR): Recommendations of the JMPR working groups and internal team to the Cordell Bank Sanctuary Advisory Council.*

Cowles, R.B. 1977. *Desert journal: A naturalist reflects on arid California.* Berkeley: University of California Press.

Cox, G.W. 1981. The yucca with the big bang. *Environment Southwest* 493:12–16.

Cox, R.D., and V.J. Anderson. 2004. Increasing native diversity of cheatgrass-dominated range-land through assisted succession. *Journal of Range Management* 57(2):203–210.

CRA (California Resources Agency). 1998. *Preserving California's natural heritage.*

———. 2003. *California Legacy Project spotlight on conservation, Sierra Nevada Regional Workshop.* June 11–12, 2003.

———. 2004. *Conservation and Trust Lands dataset.*

CVAG (Coachella Valley Association of Governments). 2004. *Coachella Valley Multiple Species Habitat Conservation Plan and Natural Community Conservation Plan.* Public Review Draft. October 15, 2004.

CVHJV (Central Valley Habitat Joint Venture). 1990. *Implementation plan: A component of the North American Waterfowl Management Plan.* Sacramento. http://www.usbr.gov/mp/cvhjv/.

CWC (California Wilderness Coalition). [updated 2004]. *California's ten most threatened wild places, 2004.* http://www.calwild.org/resources/pubs/10Most04.pdf.

Cypher, B.L., M.E. Koopman, and D.R. McCullough. 2001. Space use and movements by kit fox family members. *Transactions of the Western Section of the Wildlife Society* 37:84–87.

D'Antonio, C.M. 2000. Fire, plant invasions and global changes. In *Invasive species in a changing world,* H.A. Mooney and R.J Hobbs, eds. Washington, D.C.: Island Press.

Daels, P.F., and J.P. Hughes. 1995. Fertility control using intrauterine devices: An alternative for population control in wild horses. *Theriogenology.* 44(5):629–639.

Dailey, M.D., D.J. Reish, and J.W. Anderson. 1993. *The ecology of the Southern California bight.* University of California Press, Berkeley and Los Angeles.

Davis, F.W., D.M. Stoms, A.D. Hollander, K.A. Thomas, P.A. Stine, D. Odion, M.I. Borchert, J.H. Thorne, M.V. Gray, R.E. Walker, K. Warner, and J. Graae. 1998. *The California Gap Analysis Project—final report.* University of California, Santa Barbara. http://www.biogeog.ucsb.edu/projects/gap/gap_rep.html.

Davis, F.W., D.M. Stoms, R.L. Church, W.J. Orkin, and K.N. Johnson. 1996. *Selecting Biodiversity Management Areas.* Sierra Nevada Ecosystem Project: Final Report to Congress, Vol II. Davis: University of California, Centers for Water and Wildland Resources.

Dayton, P.K., S. Thrush, and F.C. Coleman. 2002. *Ecological effects of fishing in marine ecosystems of the United States.* Pew Oceans Commission, Arlington, Va.

DeFalco, L.A., and M. Brooks. 1999. *Ecology and management of exotic annual plant species.* Presentation at the Mojave Desert Science Symposium. U.S. Geological Survey, Western Ecological Research Center.

Defenders of Wildlife. 2002. *Conservation in America: State government incentives for habitat conservation: A status report.* West Linn, Ore. http://www.biodiversitypartners.org/pubs/ CinAReport/Intro.shtml.

DellaSala, D.A., J.E. Williams, C.D. Williams, and J.E. Franklin. 2004. Beyond smoke and mirrors: A synthesis of fire policy and science. *Conservation Biology* 18(4):976–86.

DeLoach, J.C., R.I. Carruthers, J.E. Lovich, T.L. Dudley, and S.D. Smith. 2000. Ecological interactions in the biological control of saltcedar (*Tamarix* spp.) in the United States: Toward a new understanding. In *Proceedings of the XI International Symposium on Biological Control of Weeds.* Bozeman, Mont.

Di Orio, A.P., R. Callas, and R.J. Schaefer. 2005. Forty-eight year decline and fragmentation of aspen (*Populus tremuloides*) in the South Warner Mountains of California. *Forest Ecology and Management* 206:307–313.

DiTomaso, J.M., and J.D. Gerlach Jr. 2000. Centaurea solstitialis. In *Invasive plants of California's wildlands.* C.C. Bossard, J.M. Randall, and M.C. Hoshovsky, eds. Berkeley: University of California Press.

DMG (Desert Managers Group). 2002a. *Memorandum of Understanding, Mojave Weed Management Area.*

———. 2002b. *Summary of the Desert Tortoise Recovery Actions, Western Mojave Recovery Unit.* Prepared by the Redlands Institute, University of Redlands.

———. 2002c. *Summary of the Desert Tortoise Recovery Actions, Eastern Mojave Management Unit.* Prepared by the Redlands Institute, University of Redlands.

———. 2004. *Desert Tortoise Recovery Program Assessment Committee Report.*

———. [cited October 2004]. *Draft California Desert Riparian Restoration Strategy.* http://www.dmg.gov/documents/CDRRS2ndDraft.pdf.

———. 2005. *FY04 Accomplishment Report & FY05 Five Year Plan.* http://www.dmg.gov.

Doak, D., P. Kareiva, and B. Klepetka. 1994. Modelling population viability for the desert tortoise in the western Mojave Desert. *Ecological Applications* 4:446–460.

Dobkin, D.S. 1995. *Management and conservation of sage grouse, denominative species for the ecological health of shrubsteppe ecosystems.* Report of the Bureau of Land Management, Portland, Ore.

Dobkin, D.S., A.C. Rich and W.H. Pyle. 1998. Habitat and avifaunal recovery from livestock grazing in a riparian meadow system of the northwestern Great Basin. *Conservation Biology* 12(1):209–221.

Dombeck, M.P., J.E. Williams, and C.A. Wood. 2004. Wildfire policy and public lands: Integrating scientific understanding with social concerns across landscapes. *Conservation Biology* 18(4):883–889.

Dotson, R.C., and R.L. Charter. 2003. Trends in the Southern California sport fishery. *CalCOFI Reports* 44:94–106.

Duane, T.P. 1998. *Shaping the Sierra: Nature, culture and conflict in the changing West.* Berkeley: University of California Press.

Ducks Unlimited. 2004. *Ducks Unlimited's conservation plan.* Memphis, Tenn. http://www.ducks.org/conservation/conservation_plan.asp.

duVair, P. 2003. *Climate change and California.* Staff report of the California Energy Commission. http://www.energy.ca.gov/reports/2003-11-26_100-03-017F.pdf

DWR (Department of Water Resources). 1993. California Water Plan Update. Volume 2. *Bulletin* 160-93. http://rubicon.water.ca.gov/v2index.html.

———. 1996. GIS dataset: Land Use Data.

———. 1998. The California Water Plan Update. *Bulletin* 160-98.

———. 2002. *California floodplain management report: Recommendations of the California Floodplain Management Task Force.* December 12, 2002. Sacramento. http://fpmtaskforce.water.ca.gov/.

———. 2003a. California's groundwater. *Bulletin* 118. 2003 update.

———. 2003b. *Fish passage improvement.* California Department of Water Resources Bulletin 250-2002. Public Review Draft, V. 2. Sacramento. http://www.watershedrestoration.water.ca.gov/fishpassage/b250/index.cfm.

———. 2004. *California water plan* (Draft) Update 2004. Sacramento. http://www.waterplan.water.ca.gov/b160/workgroups/chapterreviewgroup.htm.

———. 2005a. *California Water Plan Update 2005.* Public review draft. http://www.waterplan.water.ca.gov/cwpu2005/index.cfm.

———. 2005b. *Flood warnings: Responding to California's flood crisis.* Sacramento. http://www.publicaffairs.water.ca.gov/newsreleases/2005/01-10-05flood_warnings.pdf.

ELI (Environmental Law Institute). 2003. *Conservation thresholds for land use planners.* Washington DC: The Environmental Law Institute. http://www.elistore.org/reports_detail.asp?ID=10839.

Ellis, M.J., and J.D. Cook. 2001. Recovery efforts for the shasta crayfish (*Pacifastucus fortis*): Lessons in progress. *Proceedings of the 2001 conference on California riparian systems: Processes and floodplains management, ecology, and restoration.* March 12–15.

Elzinga, C. L., D. W. Salzer, J. W. Willoughby, and J. P. Gibbs. 2001. Monitoring Plant and Animal Populations. Blackwell Science, Inc., Malden, Mass.

Environmental Defense. 2000. *Progress on the back forty: An analysis of three incentive-based approaches to endangered species conservation on private land.* New York. http://www.environmentaldefense.org/documents/150_BackForty.pdf.

EOARC (Eastern Oregon Agricultural Research Center). [cited August 2004]. *Western Juniper woodland management.* http://oregonstate.edu/dept/EOARC/researchhome/currentresearch/ecology/jonjuniper.html.

Esque, T.C. 1999. *Managing fire and invasive plants in the Mojave desert: Defining an integrated research program to address knowledge gaps.* Presentation at the Mojave Desert Science Symposium. U.S. Geological Survey, Western Ecological Research Center.

Evans, R.A., and J.A. Young. 1978. Effectiveness of rehabilitation practices following wildfire in degraded big sagebrush-downy brome community. *Journal of Range Management* 31(3):185–188.

Fellers, G.M. and Freel, K.L. 1995. A standardized protocol for surveying aquatic amphibians. United States Department of the Interior, National Park Service. Technical Report, NPS/WRUC/NRTR-95-01

Field, C.B., G.C. Daily, F.W. Davis, S. Gaines, P.A. Matson, J. Melack, and N.L. Miller. 1999. *Confronting climate change in California: Ecological impacts on the Golden State.* Cambridge, Mass: The Union of Concerned Scientists and the Ecological Society of America. http://www.ucsusa.org/documents/calclimate.pdf.

Fischer, P. 2004. *Landowner perspectives in conservation and assistance programs in Oregon's Willamette Valley.* West Linn, Ore.: Defenders of Wildlife. http://www.biodiversitypartners.org/incentives/case01.shtml.

Flat-tailed Horned Lizard Interagency Coordinating Committee. 2003. *Flat-tailed horned lizard rangewide management strategy.* 2003 revision. Phoenix, Arizona.

Fleicshner, T.L. 1999. Keeping the cows off: Conservation of riparian areas in the American West. In *Terrestrial ecoregions of North America, a conservation assessment.* Washington, D.C.: Island Press.

Ford, L.S., and D.C. Cannatella. 1993. The major clades of frogs. *Herpetological Monographs* 7:94–117.

Franklin, J.F., and J.A. Fites-Kaufman. 1996. *Assessment of late-successional forests of the Sierra Nevada.* Sierra Nevada Ecosystem Project: Final Report to Congress, vol. II, Assessments and Scientific Basis for Management Options. Davis: University of California, Centers for Water and Wildland Resources.

FRAP (California Department of Forestry and Fire Protection, Fire and Resource Assessment Program). 1997. *Bioregional demographic trends and implications for biodiversity.* A report to the California Biodiversity Council. Sacramento. http://frap.cdf.ca.gov/projects/bioregional_trends/bioreg_pop.html.

FRAP (California Department of Forestry and Fire Protection, Fire and Resource Assessment Program). 2003. *The changing California. Forest and range 2003 assessment.* Sacramento. http://www.frap.cdf.ca.gov/assessment2003.

Freilich, J.E., K.P Burnham, C.M. Collins, and C.A. Garry. 2000. Factors affecting population assessments of desert tortoises. *Conservation Biology* 14(5):1479–1489.

FSEEE (Forest Service Employees for Environmental Ethics). 1999. *Restoring our forest legacy, blueprint for Sierra Nevada National Forests.* Eugene, Ore.

Fujimori, T. 2001. *Ecological and silvicultural strategies for sustainable forest management.* Elsevier.

Gallos, J. [cited June 2005]. *The Conception Coast Project.* http://www.conceptioncoast.org.

George, T.L. 2000. Varied thrush (*Ixoreus naevius*). In *The Birds of North America*, No. 541. A. Poole and F. Gill, eds. Philadelphia: The Birds of North America, Inc.

Germano, D.J., G.B. Rathbun, and L.R. Saslaw. 2001. Managing exotic grasses and conserving declining species. *Wildlife Society Bulletin* 29(2):551–559.

Gibbs, J. P., H. L. Snell, and C. E. Causton. 1999. Effective monitoring for adaptive wildlife management: Lessons from the Galapagos Islands. *Journal of Wildlife Management* 63:1055–1065.

Gillilan, D.M., and T.C. Brown. 1997. *Instream flow protection.* Washington, D.C.: Island Press.

Ginsberg, J., R. Mintz, and W.S. Walter. 1976. *The fragile balance: Environmental problems of the California desert.* Stanford Environmental Law Society.

Glenn, E.P., P.L. Zamora-Arroyo, M.B. Nagler, W. Shaw, and K. Flessa. 2001. Ecology and conservation biology of the Colorado River delta, Mexico. *Journal of Arid Environments* 49:5–15.

Goals Project. 1999. *Baylands ecosystem habitat goals. A report of habitat recommendations prepared by the San Francisco Bay Area Wetlands Ecosystem Goals Project.* San Francisco and Oakland: U.S. Environmental Protection Agency and San Francisco Bay Regional Water Quality Control Board. http://www.abag.ca.gov/bayarea/sfep/pdf/habitat_goals/Habitat_Goals.pdf.

Graber, D.M. 1996. *Status of terrestrial vertebrates.* Sierra Nevada Ecosystem Project: Final Report to Congress, Vol. II. Davis: University of California, Centers for Water and Wildland Resources.

Green, G.A., H.L. Bombay, and M.L. Morrison. 2003. *Conservation assessment of the willow flycatcher in the Sierra Nevada.* U.S. Forest Service, Vallejo.

Grenfell, W.E., M.D. Parisi, and D. McGriff. 2003. *Complete list of amphibians, reptiles, birds and mammals in California.* Wildlife Habitat Relationships Program. Sacramento. http://www.dfg.ca.gov/bdb/pdfs/species_list.pdf.

Griffs-Kyle, K.L., and P. Beier. 2003. Small isolated aspen stands enrich bird communities in southwestern ponderosa pine forests. *Biological Conservation* 110(3):375–385.

Grissino-Mayer, H.D., and T.W. Swetnam. 2000. Century-scale climate forcing of fire regimes in the American southwest. *The Holocene* 10:213–220.

Grosholz, E. 2002. Ecological and evolutionary consequences of coastal invasions. *Trends in Ecology and Evolution* 17(1):22–27.

Grosholz, E.D., G.M. Ruiz, C.A. Dean, K.A. Shirley, J.L. Maron, and P.G. Connors. 2000. The impacts of a nonindigenous marine predator in a California bay. *Ecology* 81(5):1206–1224.

Grubbs, D. 2001. *Study team tracks foraging and nesting habits of invasive bird species. Agricultural research initiative research report.* Fresno: California State University. http://ari.calstate.edu/FundedProjects/pdf/Grubbs-Startings.pdf.

Gulf of the Farallones National Marine Sanctuary. 2003. *Joint management plan review (JMPR): Recommendations of the JMPR working groups and internal team to the Gulf of the Farallones Sanctuary Advisory Council.* July 2003.

Gutierrez, R.J., J. Verner, K.S. McKelvey, B.R. Noon, G.S. Steger, D.R. Call, W.S. LaHaye, B.B. Bingham, and J.S. Senser. 1992. *Habitat relations of the California spotted owl.* Chapter 5. U.S. Forest Service Gen. Tech. Rep. PSW-GTR-133.

Haley, J., and D. Bainbridge. 1999. *Desert restoration: Do something or wait a thousand years.* Presentation at the Mojave Desert Science Symposium. U.S. Geological Survey, Western Ecological Research Center.

Hall, F. 2002. Sage grouse on Modoc's Devil's Garden. *Tracks.* California Department of Fish and Game.

Hall, J.A. 1980. Direct impacts of off-road vehicles on vegetation. In *Effects of disturbance on desert soils, vegetation, and community processes, with emphasis on off-road vehicles—a critical review.* Unpublished report, Bureau of Land Management. Riverside, Calif.

Halsey, R.W. 2004. *Fire, chaparral, and survival in southern California.* Sunbelt Publications: San Diego.

Hamilton, J.B., G.L. Curtis, S.M. Snedaker, and D.K. White. 2005. Distribution of anadromous fishes in the upper Klamath River watershed prior to hydropower dams—a synthesis of historical evidence. *Fisheries* 30(4):10–20.

Hampton, S., R.G. Ford, H.R. Carter, C. Abraham, and D. Humple. 2003a. Chronic oiling and seabird mortality from the sunken vessel *SS Jacob Luckenbach* in central California. *Marine Ornithology* 31:35-41.

Hampton, S., P.R. Kelly, and H.R. Carter. 2003b. Tank vessel operations, seabirds and chronic oil pollution in California. *Marine Ornithology* 31(1):29–34.

Hansen, R.M., R.C. Clark, and W. Lawhorn. 1977. Foods of wild horses, deer, and cattle in the Douglas Mountain Area, Colorado. *Journal of Range Management* 30(2):116–118.

Hayhoe, K., D. Cayan, C.B. Field, P.C. Frumhoff, E.P. Maurer, N.L. Miller, S.C. Moser, S.H. Schneider, K.N. Cahill, E.E. Cleland, L. Dale, R. Drapek, R.M. Hanemann, L.S. Kalkstein, J. Lenihan, C.K. Lunch, R.P. Neilson, S.C. Sheridan, and J.H. Verville. 2004. Emissions pathways, climate change, and impacts on California. *Proceedings of the National Academy of Sciences* 101(34):12422–12427.
http://www.pnas.org_cgi_doi_10.1073_pnas.0404500101.

Heath, S. 2003. Mono's tributary streams as songbird habitat. *Mono Lake Newsletter.* Spring.

Heath, S., and G. Ballard. 2003. Patterns of breeding songbird diversity and occurrence in riparian habitats of the eastern Sierra Nevada. In *California riparian systems: Processes and floodplain management, ecology, and restoration.* Riparian Habitat Joint Venture.

Henson, B. 2004. *Increasing agricultural community involvement in regional conservation planning: Lessons from landowners, non-profit organizations, local governments, and agency staff.* Prepared for California Department of Fish and Game. Sacramento.
http://www.dfg.ca.gov/nccp/pubs/ag_involvement_rec.pdf.

Henstrom, M.A., M.J. Wisdom, W.J. Hann, M.M. Rowland, B.C. Wales, and R.A. Gravenmier. 2002. Sagebrush-steppe vegetation dynamics and restoration potential in the interior Columbia Basin, U.S.A. *Conservation Biology* 16:1242–1255.

Hickey, C., W.D. Shuford, G.W. Page, and S. Warnock. 2003. *The Southern pacific shorebird conservation plan: A strategy for supporting California's Central Valley and coastal shorebird populations.* Version 1.1. Stinson Beach: Point Reyes Bird Observatory.
http://www.prbo.org/cms/docs/wetlands/SPSCPlan_010904.pdf.

Hobbs, R.J. 2000. Land-use changes and invasions. In *Invasive species in a changing world,* H.A. Mooney and R.J. Hobbs, eds. Washington, D.C.: Island Press.

Holliday, J.S. 1999. *Rush for riches: Gold fever and the making of California.* Berkeley: University of California Press.

Holmes, A.L., M.E. Flannery, and G.R. Geupel. 2001. The effects of saltcedar (*Tamarix* spp.) on resident songbirds in riparian habitats of the Salton Sea. In *Proceedings of the 2001 conference on California riparian systems: Processes and floodplains management, ecology, and restoration.*

Huff, M. 2002. *Marbled murrelet effectiveness monitoring, Northwest Forest Plan. Annual Summary Report 2002.* (v.2.) A report of the Interagency Regional Monitoring Program in the Pacific Northwest. Portland, Ore.

Hummon, L., and F. Casey. 2004. *Status and trends in federal resource conservation incentive programs: 1996–2001.* Washington, DC: Defenders of Wildlife.
http://www.biodiversitypartners.org/pubs/NSI/01.shtml.

Hunt, R.J., and I.H. Christiansen. 2000. *Dissolved oxygen information kit.* Australia Cooperative Research Center For Sustainable Sugar Production Technical Publication, November 2000. Townsville, Australia.
http://www-sugar.jcu.edu.au/images/publications/technical/dissolved%20oxygen%20in%20streams.pdf.

Hunter, L.M., M.J. Gonzalez G., M. Stevenson, K.S. Karish, R. Toth, T.C. Edwards Jr., R.J. Lilieholm, and M Cablk. 2003. Population and land use change in the California Mojave: Natural habitat implications of alternative futures. *Population Research and Policy Review* 22:373–397.

Hunter, M.L., ed. 1999. *Maintaining biodiversity in forest ecosystems.* Cambridge University Press.

Hunter, R. 1999. *South Coast regional report: California Wildlands Project vision for wild California.* A report of the California Wilderness Coalition. Davis.

Hunting, K.W., and S. Fitton. 1999. *Winter distribution and habitat use by the mountain plover* (Charadrius montanus) *in California.* Transactions of the Western Section of the Wildlife Society 34:37–42.

Husari, S., and K.S. McKelvey. 1996. *Fire-management policies and programs.* Sierra Nevada Ecosystem Project: Final Report to Congress, Vol. II. Davis: University of California, Centers for Water and Wildland Resources.

IPCC (Intergovernmental Panel on Climate Change). 2001. *Climate change 2001: The science of climate change. Contribution of working group I to the Intergovernmental Panel On Climate Change third assessment report.* J. T. Houghton, Y. Ding, D.J. Griggs, M. Noguer, P.J. van der Linden, X. Dai, K. Maskell, and C.A. Johnson, eds. Cambridge University Press, Cambridge, UK. http://www.grida.no/climate/ipcc_tar/wg1/408.htm.

Jackson, J.B.C., M.X. Kirby, W.H. Berger, K.A. Bjorndal, L.W. Botsford, B.J. Bourque, R.H. Bradbury, R. Cooke, J. Erlandson, J.A. Estes, T.P. Hughes, S. Kidwell, C.B. Lange, H.S. Lenihan, J.M. Pandolfi, C.H. Peterson, R.S. Steneck, M.J. Tegner, and R.R. Warner. 2001. Historical over-fishing and the recent collapse of coastal ecosystems. *Science* 293:629–638.

Jasny, M., J. Reynolds, and A. Notthoff. 1997. *Leap of faith: Southern California's experiment in natural community planning.* A report of the Natural Resources Defense Council. New York.

Jayco, A.S., and C.I. Millar. 2000. *Impacts of climate change on landscapes of the eastern Sierra Nevada and western Great Basin.* Workshop Summary. U.S. Geological Survey Open-File Report 01-202.

Jennings, M.R. 1996. *Status of amphibians.* Sierra Nevada Ecosystem Project: Final Report to Congress, Vol. II. Davis: University of California, Centers for Water and Wildland Resources.

Jennings, M.R., and M.P. Hayes. 1994. *Amphibian and reptile species of special concern in California.* A report to the California Department of Fish and Game, Inland Fisheries Division, Rancho Cordova.

Jepson Flora Project. 2002. *Online interchange for California floristics.* Jepson Herbarium, Berkeley.

Johnson, D.W. 1999. *Biogeography of quaking aspen* (Populus tremuloides). Project paper. San Franciso State University, Department of Geography.

Johnson, P.T.J., and J.M. Chase. 2004. Parasites in the food web: Linking amphibian malformations and aquatic eutrophication. *Ecology Letters* 7(7):521–526.

Johnston, V.R. 1994. *California forests and woodlands, a natural history.* Berkeley: University of California Press.

Johnston, V.R. 1998. *Sierra Nevada, the naturalist's companion.* Berkeley: University of California Press.

Jurek, R. 1994. *A bibliography of feral, stray, and free-roaming domestic cats in relation to wildlife conservation.* California Department of Fish and Game Nongame Bird and Mammal Program Report No. 94-5. Sacramento. http://www.dfg.ca.gov/hcpb/species/nuis_exo/dom_cat/cats_wildlife.shtml.

Kaiser, J. 1999. Battle over a dying sea. *Science* 284(5411):28–32.

Karpov, K.A., P.L. Haaker, D. Albin, I.K. Tanaguchi, and D. Kushner. 1998. The red abalone (*Haliotus rufescens*) in California: Importance of depth refuge to abalone management. *Journal of Shellfish Research* 17(3):863–870.

Karpov, K.A., P.L. Haaker, I.K. Tanaguchi, and L. Rogers-Bennett. 2000. Serial depletion and the collapse of the California abalone (*Haliotis* spp.) fishery. In: Workshop on rebuilding abalone stocks in British Columbia. A. Campbell, ed. *Can. Spec. Publ. Fish. Aquat. Sci.* 130:11–24.

Kattelman, R. 2000. Riparian vegetation loss in the Sierra Nevada. *Proceedings of the International Conference on Riparian Ecology and Management in Multi-Land Use Watersheds.* American Water Resources Association.

Kattleman, R., and M. Embury. 1996. Riparian areas and wetlands. Sierra Nevada Ecosystem Project: Final Report to Congress, Vol III. Davis: University of California, Centers for Water and Wildland Resources.

Kauffman, B.J. 2004. Death rides the forest: Perceptions of fire, land use, and ecological restoration of western forests. *Conservation Biology* 18(4):878–882.

Keeley, J.E. 2001. Historic fire regime in Southern California shrublands. *Conservation Biology* 15(6):1536–1548.

Keeley, J.E. 2004. Invasive plants and fire management in California Mediterranean climate ecosystems. In *Proceedings 10th MEDECOS Conference, April 25–May 1, 2004.* Rhodes, Greese, Arianoutsou, and Papanastasis, eds.

Keeley, J.E., D. Lubin, and C.J. Fotheringham. 2003. Fire and grazing impacts on plant diversity and alien plant invasions in the southern Sierra Nevada. *Ecological Applications* 13(5):1355-1374.

Keifer, M.B., N.L. Stephenson, and J. Manley. 2000. *Prescribed fire as the mininum tool for wilderness forest and fire regime restoration: A case study from the Sierra Nevada, California.* USDA Forest Service Proceedings RMRS-P Vol. 5.

Kelleher, K. 2004. Discards in the world's marine fisheries: An update (draft). *FAO Fisheries Technical Paper* No. 470.

Kelly, P.A., S.E. Phillips, and D.F. Williams. 2005 in press. Documenting ecological change in time and space: The San Joaquin Valley of California. In Lacey, E.A., and P. Myers, eds. *Mammalian diversification: From chromosomes to phylogeography.* Publications in Zoology Series. University of California Press, Berkeley. 383 pp. http://esrpweb.csustan.edu/publications/pubhtml.php?doc=mvz2003&file=mvzmss.html.

Kie, J.G., C.J. Evans, E.J. Loft, and J.W. Menke. 1991. Foraging behavior by mule deer, the influence of cattle grazing. *Journal of Wildlife Management* 55(4):665–674.

Kilgore, B.M. 1973. The ecological role of fire in Sierran conifer forests, its application to national park management. *Journal of Quaternary Research* 3(3):496–513.

Kiparsky, M., and P.H. Gleick. 2003. *Climate change and California water resources: A survey and summary of the literature.* Oakland: Pacific Institute for Studies in Development, Environment, and Security. http://www.energy.ca.gov/reports/CEC-500-2004-073/CEC-500-2004-073.PDF.

Knapp, R.A. 1996. *Non-native trout in natural lakes of the Sierra Nevada: An analysis of their distribution and impacts on native aquatic biota.* Sierra Nevada Ecosystem Project: Final Report to Congress, Vol. II. Davis: University of California, Centers for Water and Wildland Resources.

Knapp, R.A., and K.R. Mathews. 1996. Livestock grazing, Golden Trout, and streams in the Golden Trout Wilderness, California: Impacts and management implications. *North American Journal of Fisheries Management* 16:805–820.

Knapp, R.A., and K.R. Mathews. 2000. Non-native fish introductions and the decline of the mountain yellow-legged frog from within protected areas. *Conservation Biology* 14:428–438.

Koch, D. 2003. December 9th letter to U.S Bureau of Land Management regarding Resource Management Plans for Alturas, Eagle Lake, and Surprise Valley field offices. Department of Fish and Game, Redding.

Koehler, P.A., R.S. Scott, and W.G. Spaulding. Development of vegetation in the central Mojave Desert of California during the late Quarternary. 2005. *Palaeogeography, Palaeoclimatology, Palaeoecology* 215:297–311.

Koenig, W. D. 2003. European starlings and their effect on native cavity-nesting birds. *Conservation Biology* 17(4):1134.

Kondolf, G. M., R. Kettelman, M. Embury, and D.C. Erman. 1996. *Status of riparian habitat.* Sierra Nevada Ecosystem Project: Final Report to Congress, Vol. II. Davis: University of California, Centers for Water and Wildland Resources.

Kostow K. 2002. *Oregon lampreys: Natural history status and analysis of management issues.* A report of the Oregon Department of Fish and Wildlife. http://rainbow.dfw.state.or.us/nrimp/information/docs/fishreports/FinalOregonLampreysReport.pdf.

Krausman, P.R., R. Valdez, and J.A. Bissonette. 1996. Bighorn sheep and livestock. In *Rangeland Wildlife*, P.R. Krausman, ed. The Society for Range Management, Denver, Colo.

Krebs, C. J. 1999. *Ecological Methodology*, 2nd Edition. Addison-Welsey Educational Publishers, Inc., Menlo Park, Calif.

Kreuder, C., M.A. Miller, D.A. Jessup, L.J. Lowenstine, M.D. Harris, J.A. Ames, T.E. Carpenter, P.A. Conrad, and J.A.K. Mazet. 2003. Patterns of mortality in southern sea otters (*Enhydra lutris nereis*) from 1998–2001. *Journal of Wildlife Diseases* 39(3):495–509.

Kristan, W.B. III, and W.I. Boarman. 2003. Spatial pattern of risk of common raven predation on desert tortoises. *Ecology* 84(9):2432–2482.

Lamberson, R.H., R.L. Truex, W.J. Zielinski, and D. Macfarlane. 2000. *Preliminary analysis of fisher population viability in the southern Sierra Nevada.* Unpublished report.

Landis, J.D., and M. Reilly. 2003. *How we will grow: Baseline projections of the growth of California's urban footprint through the year 2100.* Institute of Urban and Regional Development Working Paper 2003–04. Berkeley: University of California.

LAO (Legislative Analyst's Office). 1991. *A review of the Department of Fish and Game, issues and options for improving performance.*

LaRue, E. 2000. *Fort Irwin National Training Center proposed southwestern expansion, Fort Irwin Tortoise Panel report.* BLM, Barstow.

Latting, J. and P.G. Rowlands, eds. 1995. *The California desert: An introduction to natural resources and man's impact.* June Latting Books. Printed by University of California, Riverside, Press.

Leet, W.S., C.M. Dewees, R. Klingbeil, and E.J. Larson, eds. 2001. *California's living marine resources: A status report.* California Dept. of Fish and Game, and University of California Division of Agriculture and Natural Resources. Publication No. SG01-11.

Leung, Y., and J.L. Marion. 2000. *Recreation impacts and management in wilderness: A state-of-knowledge review.* USDA Forest Service Proceedings RMRS-P-15-Vol. 5.

Levin, J., and D. Cooper. [updated 2003]. *Audubon California. Criteria and Goals for Restoration of the Salton Sea.* http://www.ca.audubon.org/Restoration_Goals.pdf.

Lewis, J.C., K.L. Sallee, and R.T. Golightly Jr. 1993. *Introduced red fox in California.* California Department of Fish and Game Nongame Bird and Mammal Section Report 93-10. Sacramento. http://www.dfg.ca.gov/hcpb/info/bm_research/bm_pdfrpts/93_10.pdf.

Liebezeit, J.R., and T.L. George. 2002. *A summary of predation by corvids on threatened and endangered species in California and management recommendations to reduce corvid predation.* California Dept. of Fish and Game, Species Conservation and Recovery Program Report.

Light, T., D. Erman, C. Myrick, and J. Clark. 1995. Decline of the Shasta crayfish of northeastern California. *Conservation Biology* 9(6):1567–1577.

Ligon, F., A. Rich, G. Rynearson, D. Thornburg, and W. Trush. 1999. *Report of the scientific review panel on California forest practice rules and salmonid habitat.* A report prepared for The Resources Agency of California and the National Marine Fisheries Service, Sacramento. http://resources.ca.gov/SRP_Rept.pdf.

Lindenmayer, D.B., and J.F. Franklin. 2002. *Conserving forest biodiversity, a comprehensive multi-scaled approach.* Washington, D.C.: Island Press.

Lines, G.C. 1996a. Ground-water and surface-water relations along the Mojave River, southern California. U.S. Geological Survey, *Water-resources investigations report 95-4189.*

————. 1996b. Riparian vegetation and its water use during 1995 along the Mojave River, southern California. U.S. Geological Survey, *Water-resources investigations report 96-4241.*

————. 1999a. Health of native riparian vegetation and its relation to hydrologic conditions along the Mojave River, southern California. U.S. Geological Survey, *Water-resources investigations report 99-4112.*

————. 1999b. *Riparian vegetation along the Mojave River.* Presentation at the Mojave Desert Science Symposium. U.S. Geological Survey, Western Ecological Research Center.

Loft, E.R. 1998. Economic contribution of deer, pronghorn antelope, and sage grouse hunting to northeastern California and implications to the overall "value" of wildlife. *California Wildlife Conservation Bulletin* No. 11:42.

Loft, E.R., D. Armentrout, G. Smith, D. Craig, M. Chapel, J. Willoughby, C. Rountree, T. Mansfield, S. Mastrup, and F. Hall. 1998. *An assessment of mule and black-tailed deer habitats and populations in California.* Report to the Fish and Game Commission, Joint Report of the California Department of Fish and Game, the U.S. Bureau of Land Management, and the U.S. Forest Service.

Loft, E.R., J.W. Menke, J.G. Kie, and R.C. Bertram. 1987. Influence of cattle stocking rate on the structural profile of deer hiding cover. *Journal of Wildlife Management.* 51(3):655–663.

LACDPW (Los Angeles County Department of Public Works). [Web site copyright 2005]. *Los Angeles River watershed.* http://ladpw.org/wmd/watershed/LA.

Love, M.S., M. Yoklavich, and L. Thorsteinson. 2002. *The rockfishes of the northeast Pacific.* Berkeley: University of California Press.

Lovich, J.E., 2000. *Tamarix ramosissima Lebed, Tamarix chinensis, Tamarix gallica, Tamarix parviflora.* In *Invasive plants of California's wildlands*, C.C. Bossard, J.M. Randall, and M.C. Hoshovsky, eds. Berkeley: University of California Press.

Lovich, J.E., and D. Bainbridge. 1999. Anthropogenic degradation of the Southern California desert ecosystem and prospects for natural recovery and restoration. *Environmental Management* (24)3:309–326.

Lovich, J.E., and K. Meyer. 2002. The western pond turtle (*Clemmys marmorata*) in the Mojave River, California, USA: Highly adapted survivor or tenuous relict? *Journal of Zoology* (London) 256:537–545.

Lovio, J., lead author. 2004. *The Coastal Scrub and Chaparral Bird Conservation Plan.* Version 2.0. A report of California Partners in Flight (CalPIF). Stinson Beach: Point Reyes Bird Observatory Conservation Science. http://www.prbo.org/calpif/plans.html.

Luckenbach, R.A., and R.B. Bury. 1983. Effects of off-road vehicles on the biota of the Algodones Dunes, Imperial County, California. *The Journal of Applied Ecology* 20(1):265–86.

Luecke, D.F., J. Pitt, C. Congdon, E. Glenn, C. Valdes-Casillas, and M. Briggs. 1999. *A delta once more: Restoring riparian and wetland habitat in the Colorado River delta.* A report of the Environmental Defense Fund. Boulder, Colo.

MacDonald, L. H., and A. Smart. 1992. Beyond the guidelines: practical lessons for monitoring. Invited paper presented at the Workshop on Improving Natural Resource Management through Monitoring, Oregon State University, Corvallis, Ore., March 10-11, 1992.

MAGTF (Marine Air Ground Task Force) 2002. *Integrated Natural Resources Management Plan and Environmental Assessment.* Twentynine Palms, Calif.

Manuwal, D.A., H.R. Carter, T.S. Zimmerman, and D.L. Orthmeyer. 2001. *Biology and conservation of the common murre in California, Oregon, Washington, and British Columbia. Volume 1: Natural history and population trends.* U.S. Geological Survey, Biological Resources Division, Information and Technology Report USGS/BRD/ITR-2000-0012, Washington, D.C.

Margoluis, R., N. Salafsky, and A. Balla. 1998. *Measures of Success: Designing, Managing, and Monitoring Conservation and Development Projects.* Washington, D.C.: Island Press.

Martin, G.. 2001. U.S. shifts policy on Sierra—trees, wildlife protected. *San Francisco Chronicle,* January 13, 2001.

Marty, J.T. 2005. Effects of cattle grazing on diversity in ephemeral wetlands. *Conservation Biology* 19:1626-1632.

Mathews, K.R., R.A. Knapp, and K.L. Pope. 2002. Garter snake distributions in high-elevation aquatic ecosystems: Is there a link with declining amphibian populations and nonnative trout introductions? *Journal of Herpetology* 36:16–22.

Mathews, K.R., K.L. Pope, R.A. Knapp, and H.K. Preisler. 2001. Effects of non-native trout on Pacific treefrogs (*Hyla regilla*) in the Sierra Nevada. *Copeia* 101:1130–1137.

Mayer, C., P. Weiant, L. Serpa, C. Tam, R. Cox, and J. Gaither. 1999. *Sierra Nevada ecoregional plan.* The Nature Conservancy.

MBAWM (Mojave Basin Area Water Master). *Tenth annual report of the Mojave Basin Area Watermaster, water year 2002–03.*

McAdoo, J.K., S.R. Swanson, B. Schultz, and P.F. Brussard. 2002. Habitat requirements of sagebrush-associated species and implications for management. *Proceedings of the Restoration and Management of Sagebrush/grass Communities Workshop.* Elko, Nev.

McArdle, D., ed. 1997. *California Marine Protected Areas.* California Sea Grant College System. Publication No. T-039, La Jolla.

McArdle, D. 2002. *California Marine Protected Areas past & present.* California Sea Grant College System. Publication No. T-050, La Jolla.

MCB/MCAS Camp Pendleton (Marine Corps Base and Marine Corps Air Station Camp Pendleton). 2001. *Integrated Natural Resources Management Plan.* http://www.cpp.usmc.mil/base/environmental/inrmp.htm.

McCreary, D.D. 2001. *Regenerating rangeland oaks in California.* University of California, Agriculture and Natural Resources, Publication 21601.

McKelvey, K.S., C.N. Skinner, C. Chang, D.C. Erman, S.J. Husari, D.J. Parsons, J.W. van Wagtendonk, and C.P. Weatherspoon. 1996. *An overview of fire in the Sierra Nevada.* Sierra Nevada Ecosystem Project: Final Report to Congress. Vol II. Davis: University of California, Centers for Water and Wildland Resources.

McKenzie, D., Z. Gedalof, D.L. Peterson, and P. Mote. 2004. Climatic change, wildfire, and conservation. *Conservation Biology* 18(4):890–902.

McKinney, C., L. Ris, H. Rorer, and S. Williams. 2005. *Investing in wildlife, state wildlife funding campaigns.* Report by the International Association of Fish and Wildlife Agencies and the Ecosystem Management Initiative at the University of Michigan.

McKinney, J. 2003. California hydropower system: Energy and environment. *Appendix D, 2003 Environmental Performance Report.* California Energy Commission. Staff Report, October, 100-03-018.

McKnight, T.L. 1958. The feral burro in the United States: Distribution and problems. *Journal of Wildlife Management* 22:163–179.

McMahon, E.T. 2003. *Better models for development in California: Ideas for enhancing small towns and suburban communities.* Sacramento: The Conservation Fund and Local Government Commission.

Menke, J.W., C. Davis, and P. Beesley. 1996. *Rangeland assessment.* Sierra Nevada Ecosystem Project: Final Report to Congress. Vol III. Davis: University of California, Centers for Water and Wildland Resources.

Miller, C., and D.L. Urban. 1999. Forest pattern, fire, and climatic change in the Sierra Nevada. *Ecosystems* 2(1):76–87.

Miller, P.R. 1996. *Biological effects of air pollution in the Sierra Nevada.* Sierra Nevada Ecosystem Project: Final Report to Congress. Vol III. Davis: University of California, Centers for Water and Wildland Resources.

Miller, R.F. 2001. *Managing western juniper for wildlife.* Woodland Fish and Wildlife. Publication number misc0286.

Miller, R.F., E. Heyerdahl, and K. Hopkins. 2003. *Fire regimes, pre-and post-settlement vegetation, and the modern expansion of western juniper at Lava Beds National Monument.* Final Report to the USDI Lava Beds National Monument.

Miller, R.F., and J.A. Rose. 1999. Fire history and western juniper encroachment in sagebrush steppe. *Journal of Range Management* 52(6):550–559.

Miller, R.F., T.J. Svejcar, and J.A. Rose. 2000. Impacts of western juniper on plant community composition and structure. *Journal of Range Management* 53(6):574–585.

Miller, R.F., T.J. Svejcar, and N.E. West. 1994. Implications of livestock grazing in the intermountain sagebrush region: Plant composition. In *Ecological implications of livestock herbivory in the West.* Society for Range Management.

Milliron, C. 1999. *Aquatic biodiversity management plan for the Big Pine Creek Wilderness Basin of the Sierra Nevada, Inyo County.* California Department of Fish and Game.

Milliron, C., P.L. Kiddo, M. Lockhart, J. Lane, and R. Ziegler. 2004. *Aquatic biodiversity management plan for the Bishop Creek High Country Management Unit of the Sierra Nevada, Inyo County California.* California Department of Fish and Game.

Mills, K.L., and W.J. Sydeman, eds. 2004. *Draft California Current marine bird conservation plan, version 2.1.* September 2004. PRBO Conservation Science, Stinson Beach, Calif.

Minckley, W.L., P.C. Marsh, J.E. Deacon, T.E. Dowling, P.W. Hedrick, W.J. Matthews, J. William, and G. Mueller. 2003. A conservation plan for native fishes of the lower Colorado River. *Bioscience* 53(3):219–234.

Missouri Botanical Garden. 2005. *Phytoremediation: Biological remediation of environmental problems using plants.* http://www.mobot.org/jwcross/phytoremediation.

Monsen, S.B., and N.L. Shaw. 2000. *Big sagebrush* (Artemisia tridentata) *communities—ecology, importance and restoration potential.* In Billings Land Reclamation Symposium 2000. Montana State University, Reclamation Res. Unit 00-01, Bozeman, Mont.

Monterey Bay National Marine Sanctuary. 2000. *Sanctuary Integrated Monitoring Network (SIMoN).* October 2000. Monterey Bay National Marine Sanctuary, Monterey.

Morey, S.C. 2003. Comment letter regarding the West Mojave Plan on behalf of the California Department of Fish and Game. December 22.

———. 2005. Comment letter regarding the West Mojave Plan on behalf of the California Department of Fish and Game. May 2.

Morrison, J.I., S.L. Postel, and P.H. Gleick. 1996. *The sustainable use of water in the lower Colorado River basin.* A joint report of the Pacific Institute for Studies in Development, Environment and Security, and the Global Water Policy Project. Oakland, Calif.

Morrison, M. L., W. M. Block, M. D. Strickland, and W. L. Kendall. 2001. *Wildlife Study Design.* New York: Springer-Verlag.

Mount, J.F. 1995. *California rivers and streams.* Berkeley: University of California Press.

Mount, J.F., and R. Twiss. 2005. Subsidence, sea level rise, and seismicity in the Sacramento–San Joaquin Delta. *San Francisco Estuary and Watershed Science* 3(1), Article 5. http://repositories. cdlib.org/jmie/sfews/vol3/iss1/art5.

Moyle, P.B. 1996a. *Potential Aquatic Diversity Management Areas.* Sierra Nevada Ecosystem Project: Final Report to Congress, Vol II. Davis: University of California, Centers for Water and Wildland Resources.

———. 1996b. *Status of aquatic habitat types.* Sierra Nevada Ecosystem Project: Final Report to Congress, Vol. II. Davis: University of California, Centers for Water and Wildland Resources.

———. 2002. *Inland fishes of California.* Berkeley: University of California Press.

Moyle, P.B., R. Kattelmann, R. Zomer, and P.J. Randall. 1996. *Management of riparian areas in the Sierra Nevada.* Sierra Nevada Ecosystem Project: Final Report to Congress, Vol III. Davis: University of California, Centers for Water and Wildland Resources.

Moyle, P.B., and P.J. Randall. 1998. Evaluating the biotic integrity of watersheds in the Sierra Nevada, California. *Conservation Biology* 12(6):1318–1326.

Moyle, P.B., and R.M. Yoshiyama. 1994. Protection of aquatic biodiversity in California: A five-tiered approach. *Fisheries* 19:6–18.

Mozingo, H. 1984. *Shrubs of the Great Basin, a natural history.* Reno and Las Vegas: University of Nevada Press.

MWA (Mojave Water Agency). 1994. Regional Water Management Plan.

———. [cited June 2004]. Regional Water Management Plan Articles. http://www.mojavewater.org/articles.

Naiman, R.J., H. Decamps, and M. Polluck. 1993. The role of riparian corridors in maintaining regional biodiversity. *Ecological Applications* 3(2):209–212.

NASS (USDA National Agricultural Statistics Service). 2002. *2002 census of agriculture. Volume 1: Geographic area series, census, state-county data.* Washington, D.C. http://www.nass.usda.gov/census/.

———. 2004. *Annual report to Congress on the status of U.S. fisheries, 2003.* U.S. Dept. of Commerce, NOAA, National Marine Fisheries Service, Silver Spring, Md.

National Park Service. 2002. *Mojave National Preserve General Plan.*

National Research Council. 1990. *Managing Troubled Waters: The Role of Marine Environmental Monitoring.* Washington, D.C.: National Academy Press.

————. 1995. *Understanding marine biodiversity: A research agenda for the nation.* National Academy Press.

————. 2000. *Ecological Indicators for the Nation.* National Academy Press

————. 2002. *Riparian areas, functions and strategies for management.* National Academy Press.

Natural Resources Project Inventory. 2005. [Cited April 15, 2005]. Information Center for the Environment, University of California, Davis. http://www.ice.ucdavis.edu/nrpi/.

NCBSIAG (Northeastern California Bighorn Sheep Interagency Advisory Group). 1991. *California bighorn sheep recovery and conservation guidelines for northeastern California.*

NDOW (Nevada Department of Wildlife). 2004. *Greater sage-grouse conservation plan for Nevada and Eastern California.*

Neel, L., ed. 1999. *Nevada Partners in Flight bird conservation plan.* Nevada Partners in Flight Working Group. Reno.

Nelle, P.J., K.P. Reese, and J.W. Connelly. 2000. The long-term effect of fire on sage grouse nesting and brood-rearing habitats on the Upper Snake River Plain. *Journal of Range Management* 53(6):586–591.

Newman, W., F. Watson, M. Angelo, J. Casagrande, and B. Fiekert. 2003. *Land use history and mapping in California's Central Coast region.* Report No. WI-2003-03. Watershed Institute, California State University Monterey Bay. http://science.csumb.edu/%7Eccows/pubs/reports, see http://CCoWS_LandUseMappingRegion3_WI-2003-03_030512.pdf.

NMFS (National Marine Fisheries Service). 1991. *Southern California eelgrass mitigation policy.* http://swr.nmfs.noaa.gov/hcd/eelpol.htm.

————. Proposed threatened status for three contiguous ESUs of coho salmon ranging from Oregon through central California. *Federal Register* 60(142):38011–38030.

————. 1997. Designated Critical Habitat; central California coast and southern Oregon/Northern California coast coho salmon. *Federal Register* 62(227):62741–62751.

NOAA National Center for Coastal Ocean Studies. 2003. *A biogeographic assessment of North/ Central California to support the Joint Management Plan Review for Cordell Bank, Gulf of the Farallones, and Monterey Bay National Marine Sanctuaries, phase —marine fishes, birds, and mammals.* Silver Spring, Md.

————. 2005. *Sea level data.* http://www.nodc.noaa.gov/General/sealevel.html.

Noon, B. R. 2003. Conceptual issues in monitoring ecological resources. In: *Monitoring Ecosystems: Interdisciplinary Approaches for Evaluating Ecoregional Initiatives.* Edited by D. E. Busch and J. C. Trexler. Washington, D.C: Island Press, 27–72.

Norton, J.B., T.A. Monaco, J.M. Norton, D.A. Johnson, and T. Jones. 2004. Soil morphology and organic matter dynamics under cheatgrass and sage-steppe plant communities. *Journal of Arid Environments* 57:445–466.

Noss, R. F., and A. Y. Cooperrider. 1994. *Saving Nature's Legacy: Protecting and Restoring Biodiversity.*

Noss, R. F., M. A. O'Connell, and D. D. Murphy. 1997. *The Science of Conservation Planning: Habitat Conservation under the Endangered Species Act.* Washington, D.C.: Island Press.

Nowakowski, N.A., P.F. Folliott, and D.R. Patton. 1982. Livestock-wildlife interactions in the Southwest. In *Wildlife technical report of the Forest Service, Southwest Region.*

NPS (National Park Service). [updated 2002]. *Joshua Tree National Park, Nature and Science, Natural Features and Ecosystems: Fan Palm Oases.* http://www.nps.gov/jotr/nature/features/oases/oases.html.

———. [cited 2005]. *Final General Management Plan Amendment, Environmental Impact Statement, Backcountry and Wilderness Management Plan, Joshua Tree National Park.* http://www.nps.gov/jotr/pphtml/documents.html.

NRC (National Research Council). 2002. *Riparian areas, functions and strategies for management.* National Academy Press.

———. 2003. *Endangered and threatened fishes in the Klamath River basin: Causes of decline and strategies for recovery.* Washington, D.C.: National Academies Press.

Nyberg, J. B. 1998. Statistics and the practice of adaptive management. In: *Statistical Methods for Adaptive Management Studies*, V. Sit. and B. Taylor (editors). Res. Br.,B.C. Min. For., Res. Br., Victoria, BC, Land Management Handbook. No. 42. pp. 1-8.

Nystrom, E.C. 2003. *From neglected space to protected place: An administrative history of Mojave National Preserve.* National Park Service.

Odion, D.C., E.J. Frost, J.R. Strittholt, H. Jiang, D.A. Dellasala, and M.A. Moritz. 2004. Patterns of fire severity and forest conditions in the western Klamath Mountains, California. *Conservation Biology* 18(4):927–936.

Ogden, J. C., S. M. Davis, and L. A. Brandt. 2003. Science strategy for a regional ecosystem monitoring and assessment program: The Florida Everglades example. In: *Monitoring Ecosystems: Interdisciplinary Approaches for Evaluating Ecoregional Initiatives.* Edited by D. E. Busch and J. C. Trexler. Washington, D.C.: Island Press. pp. 135-163.

Olin, P.A., and J.L. Cassell, eds. 1996. *Marine and aquatic nonindigenous species in California: An assessment of current status and research needs.* California Sea Grant College System. Report No. T-043, La Jolla.

Omart, R.D. 1996. Historical and present impacts of livestock grazing on fish and wildlife resources in western riparian habitats. In *Rangeland Wildlife*, P.R. Krausman, ed. The Society for Range Management, Denver, Colo.

Pacific Fishery Management Council. 2004. *Pacific Coast groundfish fishery management plan for the California, Oregon, and Washington groundfish fishery, as amended through Amendment 17.* PFMC, National Ocean and Atmospheric Administration.

Page, G.W., and W.D. Shuford. 2000. *Southern Pacific Coast Regional Shorebird Plan.* Version 1. A report of California Partners in Flight (CalPIF). Stinson Beach: Point Reyes Bird Observatory Conservation Science. http://www.prbo.org/calpif/plans.html.

Parmesan, C., and H. Galbraith. 2004. *Observed impacts of global climate change in the U.S.* Arlington, Va.: Pew Center on Global Climate Change. http://www.pewclimate.org/docUploads/final%5FObsImpact%2Epdf.

Pawley, A. 2000. Program performance indicators for the CALFED Bay-Delta Ecosystem Restoration Program. Technical report prepared by The Bay Institute of San Francisco for the CALFED Science Program. http://www.bay.org/science/Indrpt02.pdf

Pelagic Working Group. 2002. *Pelagic predators, prey and processes: Exploring the scientific basis for offshore marine reserves.* Proceedings of the First Pelagic Working Group Workshop. Santa Cruz, Calif.

Pellent, M. 1996. *Cheatgrass: The invader that won the West.* Interior Columbia Basin Ecosystem Project.

Pellent, M. 2002. Cheatgrass: Invasion, occurrence, biological/competitive features and control measures. *Proceedings of the Restoration and Management of Sagrebrush/Grass Communities Workshop.* Elko, Nev.

Penrod, K., C. Cabanero, C. Luke, P. Beier, W. Spencer, and E. Rubin. 2003. *South Coast missing linkages: A linkage design for the Tehachapi connection.* Unpublished report, South Coast Wildlands Project. Monrovia. http://www.savetejonranch.org/doclibrary/index.html.

Penrod, K., R. Hunter, and M. Merrifield. 2000. *Missing linkages: Restoring connectivity to the California landscape.* South Coast Wildlands Project, Talon Associates, and The Nature Conservancy.

Perry, D.A. 1994. *Forest ecosystems.* Johns Hopkins University Press, Baltimore, Md.

Peterson, D.H, D.R. Cayan, M.D. Dettinger, J.S. DiLeo, S.E. Hager, N. Knowles, F.H. Nichols, L.E. Schemel, R.E. Smith, and R.E. Uncles. 2005. *Seasonal/yearly salinity variations in San Francisco Bay.* US Geological Fact Sheet. http://sfbay.wr.usgs.gov/access/factsheets/sal_fact_sheet.html.

Pew Oceans Commission. 2003. *America's living oceans—charting a course for sea change.* Pew Oceans Commission, Arlington, Va.

Piner, K.R., E.J., Dick, and J. Field. 2005. Stock Status of Cowcod in the Southern California Bight and future prospects. Appendix in *Pacific Fishery Management Council. Status of the Pacific Coast groundfish fishery through 2005 and recommended acceptable biological catches for 2007: stock assessments and fishery evaluation.* Pacific Fishery Management Council, Portland, Ore.

Pitt, J. 2001. Can we restore the Colorado River delta? *Journal of Arid Environments* 49:211–220.

Poff, N.L., J.D. Allan, M.B. Bain, J.R. Karr, K.L. Prestegaard, B.D. Richter, and J.C. Stromberg. 1997. The natural flow regime: A paradigm for river conservation and restoration. *Bioscience* 47:769–84.

Pollak, D. 2001a. *The future of habitat conservation? The NCCP experience in Southern California.* A report to the California Research Bureau, California State Library.

———. 2001b. *Natural Community Conservation Planning (NCCP): The origins of an ambitious experiment to protect ecosystems.* A report to the California Research Bureau, California State Library.

Poole, A. and F. Gill, eds. 2002. *The birds of North America,* No. 610. Philadelphia: The Academy of Natural Sciences.

PRBO (Point Reyes Bird Observatory). 2003. *Developing and implementing an adaptive conservation strategy: A guide for improving adaptive management and sharing the learning among conservation practitioners.* Developed By PRBO Conservation Science with Resource Management Partners. Stinson Beach. http://www.prbo.org/cms/docs/consplans/ACSGUIDEweb.pdf.

———. 2004a. *California Current marine bird conservation plan.* http://www.prbo.org/cms/index.php?mid=66&module=browse

———. 2004b. Spartina *effects on shorebirds.* http://www.prbo.org/cms/index.php?mid=287.

QSA JPA (Quantification Settlement Agreement Joint Powers Authority Creation and Funding Agreement). 2003a.

———. 2003b. Exhibit B–Environmental Cost Sharing Agreement.

RECOVER. 2004. CERP Monitoring and Assessment Plan, Part 1: Monitoring and Supporting Research. Technical report available from U.S. Army Corps of Engineers, Jacksonville District, Jacksonville, FL and South Florida Water Management District, West Palm Beach, Fla. http://www.evergladesplan.org/pm/recover/recover_map_2004.cfm#2004.

Resources Agency. 2003a. *California Legacy project spotlight on conservation: Bay Area workshop.* Held in Oakland Oct 16–17, 2002. Sacramento. http://www.legacy.ca.gov/pub_docs/Bay_Area_interim_report.pdf.

———. 2003b. *California Legacy Project spotlight on conservation: Sacramento Valley workshop.* Held in Chico April 8–9, 2003. Sacramento. http://www.legacy.ca.gov/pub_docs//Sac_Valley_Wkshp_interim_report.pdf.

———. 2003c. *California Legacy Project spotlight on conservation: San Joaquin Valley workshop.* Held in Fresno March 12–13, 2003. Sacramento. http://www.legacy.ca.gov/pub_docs/San_Joaquin_interim_report.pdf.

RHJV (Riparian Habitat Joint Venture). 2004. *The riparian bird conservation plan: A strategy for reversing the decline of riparian associated birds in California.* Version 2.0. California Partners in Flight. http://www.prbo.org/calpif/pdfs/riparian_v-2.pdf.

RI (Redlands Institute). 2002a. *Summary of desert tortoise recovery actions, Eastern Mojave Recovery Unit.* Prepared for the Desert Managers Group.

————. 2002b. *Summary of the desert tortoise recovery actions, Western Mojave Recovery Unit.* Prepared for the Desert Managers Group.

Richins, P. 2005. *Coastal power plants using once-through cooling.* Presentation to the California Ocean Protection Council, June 10, 2005, San Francisco, Calif. California Energy Commission.

Richter, B.D., J.V. Baumgartner, R. Wigington, and D.P. Braun. 1997. How much water does a river need? *Freshwater Biology* 37(1):231–249.

Ricketts, T.H., E. Dinerstein, D.M. Olson, and C.J. Louks. 1999. *Terrestrial ecoregions of North America, a conservation assessment.* Washington, D.C.: Island Press.

Rickman, T. 2004. *Draft Champs/Gooch environmental analysis, historical assessment and reference condition.* Lassen National Forest, Eagle Lake District, Susanville.

Riedel, R., L. Caskey, and B.A. Costa-Pierce. 2002. Fish biology and fisheries ecology of the Salton Sea, California. *Hydrobiologia* 473(1–3):229–44.

Rindle, F R. 1949. A revision of the geometrid moths formerly assigned to *Drepanulatrix* (Lepidoptera). *Bulletin of the American Museum of Natural History.* 94(5):231-298.

Riverside Superior Court. 2003. City of Barstow, et al. v. City of Adelanto, et al. Case No. 208568, Judgment After Trial.

Robinson, J., and J. Alexander, lead authors. 2002. *Draft coniferous forest bird conservation plan.* Version 1.0. A report of California Partners in Flight. Stinson Beach: Point Reyes Bird Observatory Conservation Science. http://www.prbo.org/calpif/plans.html.

Romsos, J.S. 2000. Ecologically significant area: Aspen. In *Lake Tahoe Watershed Assessment,* Vol. I, Appendix C. Pacific Southwest Research Station, U.S. Forest Service.

Rutledge, D. 2003. *Landscape indices as measures of the effects of fragmentation: can pattern reflect process?* DOC Science Internal Series 98. Department of Conservation, P.O. Box 10-420, Wellington, New Zealand. http://www.doc.govt.nz.

RWQCB (California Environmental Protection Agency, Regional Water Quality Control Board), Colorado River Basin Region. 2003. Staff report: *Water quality issues in the Salton Sea transboundary watershed.* Palm Desert.

Sacramento River Conservation Area Forum. 2005. Web site. [Cited January 2005] http://www.sacramentoriver.ca.gov/.

Salafsky, N., R. Margoluis and K. Redford. 2001. *Adaptive management: A tool for conservation practitioners.* Washington, D.C.: Biodiversity Support Program, World Wildlife Fund. http://www.worldwildlife.org/bsp/publications/aam/112/about.pdf.

San Francisco Estuary Invasive Spartina Project. 2005. Web site. [Cited January 2005] http://www.spartina.org/control.

San Joaquin River Conservancy. 2005. Web site hosted by San Joaquin River Parkway and Conservation Trust, Inc. [Cited March 2005]. http://www.riverparkway.org/html/consagen.html.

Sanders, S. 2004. *Growth trends and challenges in California.* Coral Gables, Fla.: Funders' Network for Smart Growth and Livable Communities. http://www.calregions.org/pdf/growthTrendsChallenges.pdf.

Saracino-Kirby-Snow. 2002. *Regional Water Management Plan Update.* Report prepared for the Mojave Water Agency.

Save Tejon Ranch Working Group. [Cited August 2004]. *Save Tejon Ranch: What's at stake?* http://www.savetejonranch.org.

Save-the-Redwoods League and BLM (Bureau of Land Management). 2001. *North coastal California: A stewardship report.* San Francisco and Arcata. http://www.savetheredwoods.org/protecting/pdf/mp_northcoast_report.pdf.

SB 654 (Senate Bill 654). (Machado, Chapter 613, Statutes of 2003.)

SCAG (Southern California Association of Governments). [Cited August 2004]. *Census data.* http://www.scag.ca.gov/census.

Schaefer, R.J., D.J. Thayer, and T.S. Burton. 2003. Forty-one years of vegetation change on permanent transects in northeastern California: Implications for wildlife. *California Fish and Game* 89(2):55–71.

Schneider, S.H., and K. Kuntz-Duriseti. 2002. Uncertainty and climate change policy. In *Climate change policy.* S.H. Schneider, A. Rosencranz, and J.O. Niles, eds. Washington D.C.: Island Press.

Schneider, S.H., A. Rosencranz, and J.O. Niles, eds. 2002. *Climate change policy.* Washington D.C.: Island Press.

Schoenherr, A.A. 1992. *A natural history of California.* Berkeley: University of California Press.

Schwartz, M.W., D.J.Porter, J.M. Randall, and K.E. Lyons. 1996. *Impacts of nonindigenous plants.* Sierra Nevada Ecosystem Project: Final Report to Congress. Vol II. Davis: University of California, Centers for Water and Wildland Resources.

Schwartz, W. 1969. *Voices for the wilderness.* New York: Ballantine Books.

Sequoia Riverlands Trust 2005. *Homer Ranch: Community and conservation working together: A Sequoia Riverlands Trust success story* [cited June 2005] http://www.sequoiariverlands.org/success_homer.html.

SFEI (San Francisco Estuary Institute). 2004. The pulse of the estuary 2004: Monitoring and managing water quality in the San Francisco Estuary. *SFEI Contribution* No. 78, San Francisco Estuary Institute, Oakland.

SFEP (San Francisco Estuary Project). 1993. *Comprehensive conservation and management plan.* Oakland. http://www.abag.ca.gov/bayarea/sfep/reports/ccmp/ccmp-index.html.

Shaw, R. 2002. *Ecological impacts of a changing climate.* Prepared for Public Interest Energy Research Program. Sacramento: California Energy Commission. http://www.energy.ca.gov/reports/2003-04-16_500-03-025FA-III.PDF.

Shevock, J.R. 1996. *Status of rare and endemic plants.* Sierra Nevada Ecosystem Project: Final Report to Congress. Vol II. Davis: University of California, Centers for Water and Wildland Resources.

Shilling, F., E. Girvetz, C. Erichsen, B. Johnson, and P.C. Nichols. 2002. *A guide to wildlands conservation in the greater Sierra Nevada bioregion.* California Wilderness Coalition.

Shirley, D.M., and V. Erickson. 2001. *Aspen restoration in the Blue Mountains of northeastern Oregon.* USDA Forest Service Proceedings RMRS-P-18.

Shuford, W.D., N. Warnock, K.C. Molina, and K.K. Sturm. 2002. The Salton Sea as critical habitat to migratory and resident waterbirds. *Hydrobiologia* 473:255–274.

Skinner, C.N., and C. Chang. 1996. *Fire regimes, past and present.* Sierra Nevada Ecosystem Project: Final Report to Congress. Vol II. Davis: University of California, Centers for Water and Wildland Resources.

SLO Co. Ag. Comm. (San Luis Obispo County Agriculture Commission). 2004. GIS dataset: Crop data derived from Dept. of Pesticide Regulation.

Smith, D.O. 2001. *Closing canopies and changing trophic energy pathways in western conifer forests: Where do we go from here?* Presented at the 2001 meeting of the Western Section of the Wildlife Society.

Smith, G., ed. 2000. *Sierra East, edge of the Great Basin.* California Natural History Guides. Berkeley: University of California Press.

Smith, S.D. 1999. *Structure and function of riparian ecosystems in the Mojave Desert.* Presentation at the Mojave Desert Science Symposium. U.S. Geological Survey, Western Ecological Research Center.

SNEP (Sierra Nevada Ecosystem Project). 1996. *Status of the Sierra Nevada, Final Report to Congress, Vol. I, Assessment Summaries and Management Strategies.* Davis: University of California, Centers for Wildland and Water Resources.

Sommer, T., B. Harrell, M. Nobriga, R. Brown, P. Moyle, W. Kimmerer, and L. Schemel. 2001. California's Yolo Bypass: Evidence that flood control can be compatible with fisheries, wetlands, wildlife, and agriculture. *Fisheries* 26(8):6–16. http://wfcb.ucdavis.edu/www/Faculty/Peter/petermoyle/publications/YoloFisheries.pdf.

Soule, M.E., and J. Terborgh, eds. 1999. *Continental conservation: Scientific foundations of regional reserve networks.* Washington, D.C.: Island Press.

Stamos, C.L., T. Nishikawa, and P. Martin. 2001. *Water supply in the Mojave River ground-water basin, 1931–1999, and benefits of artificial recharge.* U.S. Geological Survey *Water Fact Sheet* 122-01.

Stanford, J.A., J.V. Ward, W.J. Liss, C.A. Frissell, R.N. Williams, J.A. Lichatowich, and C.C. Coutant. 1996. A general protocol for restoration of regulated rivers. *Regulated Rivers: Research and Management* 12:391–413.

State Lands Commission. 1993. *California rivers: A public trust report.* Sacramento. http://elib.cs.berkeley.edu/cgi-bin/doc_home?elib_id=1446.

State of California. 2004. Permit number 2081-2003-024-006. For the project: Imperial Irrigation District/San Diego County Water Authority Transfer Project—Quantification Settlement Agreement; issued to permittee: Imperial Irrigation District.

———. 2005. Permit number 2081-2005-008-06. For the project: Lower Colorado River Multi-Species Conservation Program; issued to permittees: California Water and Power Agencies.

Stebbins, R.C. 2003. *A field guide to western reptiles and amphibians.* 3d ed. Boston: Houghton Mifflin.

Stebbins, R.C., T.J. Papenfuss, and F.D. Amamoto. 1978. *Teaching and research in the California desert.* Institute of Government Studies, University of California, Berkeley, *Research Report* 78-1.

Steere, J.T., and N. Schaefer. 2001. *Restoring the estuary: An implementation strategy for the San Francisco Bay Joint Venture.* Oakland: San Francisco Bay Joint Venture. http://www.sfbayjv.org/strategy.html.

Stein, B.A. 2002. *States of the union: Ranking America's biodiversity.* Arlington, Virginia: NatureServe. http://www.natureserve.org/Reports/stateofunions.pdf

Stein, B.A., L.S. Kutner, and J.S. Adams. 2000. *Precious heritage: The status of biodiversity in the United States.* A joint project of The Nature Conservancy and Association for Biodiversity Information. New York: Oxford University Press.

Steinitz, C., ed. 1996. *Biodiversity and landscape planning: Alternative futures for the region of Camp Pendleton, California.* A report of the Harvard University Graduate School of Design. Cambridge, Mass.

Stephenson, J.R., and G.M. Calcarone. 1999. *Southern California mountains and foothills assessment: Habitat and species conservation issues.* General Technical Report GTR-PSW-175. A report of the Pacific Southwest Research Station, U.S. Forest Service and U.S. Department of Agriculture. Albany.

Stevens, L. E., and B. D. Gold. 2003. Monitoring for adaptive management of the Colorado River ecosystem in Glen and Grand Canyons. In: *Monitoring Ecosystems: Interdisciplinary Approaches for Evaluating Ecoregional Initiatives.* Edited by D. E. Busch and J. C. Trexler. Washington, D.C.: Island Press. pp. 101-134.

Stewart, I.T., D.R. Cayan, and M.D. Dettinger. 2004. Changes in snowmelt runoff timing in western North America under "business as usual" climate change scenario. *Climate Change* 62:217–232.

Strittholt, J.R., and D.A. DellaSala. 2001. Importance of roadless areas in forested ecosystems: Case study of the Klamath-Siskiyou ecoregion of the U.S. *Conservation Biology* 15(6):1742–1754.

Sustainable Conservation 2004. [Cited December 2004]. *Partners in Restoration Project overview.* http://www.suscon.org/pir/index.asp.

Sutinen, J.G., and R.J. Johnston. 2003. Angling Management Organizations: Integrating the recreational sector into fishery management. *Marine Policy* 27:471–487.

SWRCB (State Water Resources Control Board). 2002a. *California's 2002 section 303(d) list of water quality limited segments (approved by US EPA July 2003).* http://www.swrcb.ca.gov/tmdl/303d_lists.html.

————. 2002b. *State of the watershed report, Pit River sub-watershed.*

————. [cited October 2004]. *California's rivers and streams: Working toward solutions.* http://www.swrcb.ca.gov/general/publications/pubs/riversst.htm.

Takemoto, B.K., A. Bytnerowicz, and M.E. Fenn. 2001. Current and future effects of ozone and atmospheric nitrogen deposition on California's mixed conifer forests. *Forest Ecology and Management* 144:159–173.

Tallent-Halsell, N.G., and L.R. Walker. 2002. Responses of *Salix gooddingii* and *Tamarix ramosissima* to flooding. *Wetlands* 22(4):776–85.

Tappeiner, J.C., and P.M. McDonald. 1996. *Regeneration of Sierra Nevada forests.* Sierra Nevada Ecosystem Project: Final Report to Congress. Vol II. Davis: University of California, Centers for Water and Wildland Resources.

Thorne, J., D. Cameron, and V. Jigour. 2002. *A guide to wildlands conservation in the Central Coast region of California.* A report of the California Wilderness Coalition. Oakland.

TNC (The Nature Conservancy). 1987. *Sliding toward extinction: The state of California's natural heritage 1987.* Prepared at the request of the California Senate Committee on Natural Resources and Wildlife by Jones and Stokes Associates. Sacramento.

————. 1995. *Sacramento Valley and foothill bioregion: Biological scoping project.* San Francisco.

————. 1997. *Central Coast ecoregion: Ecoregional Planning Project.* San Francisco.

————. 1998. *San Joaquin Valley and foothill ecoregional plan.* San Francisco.

————. 2000a. *An ecological analysis of conservation priorities in the Sonoran Desert ecoregion.* Tuscon, Ariz.

————. 2000b. *Ecoregion-based conservation in the Mojave desert.* Las Vegas, Nev.

————. 2001. *Great Basin: An ecoregion-based conservation blueprint.* Reno, Nev.

————. 2004. *Klamath mountains ecoregional assessment.* Portland, Ore.

————. 2005. *Central Coast ecoregional assessment.* San Francisco.

TPL (Trust for Public Land). 2001. *California rivers report: The state of California rivers.* Oakland: The Trust for Public Land. http://www.tpl.org/tier3_cdl.cfm?content_item_id=6501&folder_id=1685.

Tracy, C.R., R. Averill-Murray, W.I. Boarman, D. Delehanty, J. Heaton, E. McCoy, D. Morafka, K. Nussear, B. Hagerty, and P. Medica. 2004. *Desert tortoise recovery plan assessment.* Report to the U.S. Fish and Wildlife Service.

Trombulak, S.C., and C.A. Frissell. 2000. Review of ecological effects of roads on terrestrial and aquatic communities. *Conservation Biology* 14:18–30.

Turman, E.G. 2002. Regional impact assessments: A case study of California. In *Climate change policy*, S.H. Schneider, A. Rosencranz, and J.O. Niles, eds. Washington, D.C.: Island Press.

USBOR (U.S. Bureau of Reclamation), Lower Colorado Region. 2003. *Salton Sea study: Status report.* Boulder City, Nev.

———. 2005. Lower Colorado River Multi-Species Conservation Program Implementing Agreement. http://www.usbr.gov/lc/lcrmscp/documents.html.

U.S. Commission on Ocean Policy. 2004. *Preliminary report of the U.S. Commission on Ocean Policy.* Governor's Draft; Washington, D.C.

US DOD (Department of Defense). 2001. Marine Corps Base Camp Pendleton Integrated Natural Resource Management Plan, Marine Corps Base, Camp Pendleton. http://www.cpp.usmc.mil/base/environmental/inrmp.htm

US DOI. (U.S. Department of the Interior). 2005. Record of Decision, Lower Colorado River Multi-Species Conservation Program. Final Environmental Impact Statement.

USFS (U.S. Forest Service). 1991a. *Forest Plan, Analysis of the Management Situation.* Modoc National Forest.

———. 1991b. *Modoc National Forest Land and Resource Management Plan.* Modoc National Forest.

———. 2001a. Final Rule and Record of Decision Special Areas; Roadless Area Conservation. January 12, 2001. *Federal Register* 66(9):3244–3273.

———. 2001b. *Sierra Nevada forest plan amendment, final impact statement.* Pacific Southwest Region. Volumes 1–6.

———. 2001c. *Sierra Nevada forest plan amendment, final impact statement, Record of Decision.* Pacific Southwest Region.

———. 2003. *A strategic assessment of forest biomass and fuel reduction treatments in western states.*

———. 2004a. Forest Service Launches Action Campaign to Protect Old Growth Forests, Wildlife, and Communities with New Decision. News release. January 22, 2004.

———. 2004b. *Sierra Nevada forest plan amendment, final impact statement, Record of Decision.* Pacific Southwest Region.

———. 2005a. Special Areas; State Petitions for Inventoried Roadless Area Management. May 13, 2005. *Federal Register* 70(92):25653–25662.

———. 2005b. Grazing allotments on national forest lands. Unpublished data, available from the offices of the Mendocino, Shasta-Trinity, Klamath, and Six Rivers national forests.

———. [cited July 2004]. *Modoc National Forest wild horses.* http://www:fs.fed/us/r5/modoc/resources/wildhorses.shtml.

USFS (U.S. Forest Service). Modoc National Forest. 2000a. *Upper Pit River watershed restoration project business plan.*

———. 2000b. *Warner Mountain rangeland project environmental assessment.* Warner Mountain Ranger District.

USFS (U.S. Forest Service), Pacific Southwest Region. 2003a. *Business plan for the Angeles National Forest.* R5-MB-020. http://www.fs.fed.us/r5/business-plans.

———. 2003b. *Business plan for the Cleveland National Forest.* R5-MB-021. http://www.fs.fed.us/r5/business-plans.

———. 2004a. *Business plan for the San Bernardino National Forest.* R5-MB-023. http://www.fs.fed.us/r5/business-plans.

———. 2004b. *Southern California Land Management Plan revisions, draft.* R5-MB-052. Vallejo. http://www.fs.fed.us/r5/scfpr/draft/publication/index.htm.

———. 2003c. *Business plan for the Los Padres National Forest.* R5-MB-022. Vallejo. http://www.fs.fed.us/r5/business-plans.

USFS (U.S. Forest Service), Plumas National Forest. 1988. *Record of Decision, Land and Resource Management Plan.*

USFS (U.S. Department of Agriculture Forest Service) and BLM (U.S. Department of the Interior Bureau of Land Management). 1994. *Record of Decision for amendments to Forest Service and Bureau of Land Management planning documents within the range of the northern spotted owl.* Portland, Ore.

———. 2004a. *Record of Decision amending resources management plans for seven Bureau of Land Management districts and nineteen national forests within the range of the northern spotted owl; Decision to clarify provisions relating to the Aquatic Conservation Strategy.* Portland, Ore. http://www.reo.gov/library/acs/FinalROD03_17_04.pdf.

———. 2004b. *Record of Decision to remove or modify the survey and manage mitigation measure standards and guidelines in Forest Service and Bureau of Land Management planning documents within the range of the northern spotted owl.* Portland, Ore. http://www.fs.fed.us/r6/SMROD.pdf.

———. 1989. *Restoring degraded riparian areas on western rangelands.* Testimony of James Duffus III, Associate Director, Resources, Community and Economic Development Division, before the Subcommittee on National Parks and Public Lands, Committee on Interior and Insular Affairs, House of Representatives.

————. 1991. *Public land management, attention to wildlife is limited.* Report to the Honorable Alan Cranston, U.S. Senate.

————. 1991a. *Rangeland management, BLM's hot desert grazing program merits reconsideration.* Report to the Chairman, Subcommittee on National Parks and Public Lands, Committee on Interior and Insular Affairs, House of Representatives.

————. 1992b. *Rangeland management, profile of the Bureau of Land Management's grazing allotments and permits.* Fact sheet for House of Representatives.

————. 1992. *Rangeland management, results of recent work addressing the performance of land management agencies.* Testimony of J. Dexter Peach, Asst. Controller General, before the Subcommittee on National Parks and Public Lands, Committee on Interior and Insular Affairs, House of Representatives.

————. 2002. *Endangered species, research strategy and long-term monitoring needed for the Mojave desert tortoise recovery program.* Report to Congress.

USFWS (U.S. Fish and Wildlife Service). 1984a. *Recovery Plan for the Mohave tui chub,* Gila bicolor mohavensis. Portland, Ore.

————. 1984b. *Recovery plan for the valley elderberry longhorn beetle.* Portland, Ore.

————. 1985. *Recovery plan for the light-footed clapper rail.* Portland, Ore.

————. 1993a. *Desert pupfish Recovery Plan.* Pheonix, Ariz.

————. 1993b. Special rule concerning take of the threatened coastal California gnatcatcher. *Federal Register* 58:236. December 10, 1993.

————. 1994a. *Biological Opinion for cattle grazing on 25 allotments in the Mojave Desert, Riverside and San Bernardino Counties, California.* U.S. Fish and Wildlife Service (1-8-94-F-17). March 14.

————. 1994b. *Desert tortoise (Mojave population) Recovery Plan.* Portland, Ore.

————. 1994c. *Proposed Desert Wildlife Management Areas for recovery of the Mojave population of the desert tortoise.* Portland, Ore.

————. 1997a. *Amargosa vole* (Microtus californicus scirpensis) *Recovery Plan.* Portland, Ore.

————. 1997b. *Recovery plan for the marbled murrelet* (Brachyramphus marmoratus) *in Washington, Oregon, and California.* Portland, Ore.

————. 1998a. *Draft recovery plan for the least Bell's vireo.* Portland, Ore.

————. 1998b. *Owens Basin wetland and aquatic species recovery plan, Inyo and Mono Counties, California. Owens pupfish, Owens tui chub and Fish Slough milk-vetch and selected species of concern.* Portland, Ore.

———. 1998c. *Point Arena mountain beaver* (Aplodontia rufa nigra) *recovery plan.* Portland, Ore.

———. 1998d. Recovery plan for insect and plant taxa from the Santa Cruz Mountains in California. Portland, Ore.

———. 1998e. Recovery plan for serpentine soil species of the San Francisco Bay Area. Portland, Ore.

———. 1998f. *Recovery Plan for the Inyo California towhee.* Portland, Ore.

———. 1998g. *Recovery plan for vernal pools of Southern California.* Portland, Ore.

———. 1998h. *Recovery plan for upland species of the San Joaquin Valley, California.* Region 1, Portland, Ore. http://sacramento.fws.gov/es/recovery_plans/upland_species.htm.

———. 1999. *Arroyo southwestern toad recovery plan.* Portland, Ore.

———. 2000a. Emergency rule to list the Santa Barbara County distinct population of the California tiger salamander as endangered. *Federal Register* 65(12):3096–3109.

———. 2000b. Final rule to list the Santa Barbara County distinct population of the California tiger salamander as endangered. *Federal Register* 65(184):57242–57264.

———. 2000c. *Recovery Plan for bighorn sheep in the Peninsular Ranges, California.* Portland, Ore.

———. [updated 2001]. *The California red-legged frog.* http://endangered.fws.gov/features/rl_frog/rlfrog.html.

———. 2002a. *Biological opinion on the Bureau of Reclamation's voluntary fish and wildlife conservation measures and associated conservation agreements with the California water agencies.* December 18, 2002.

———. 2002b. *Candidate conservation agreements with assurances for non-federal property owners.* Portland, Ore. http://endangered.fws.gov/listing/cca.pdf.

———. 2002c. *Draft recovery plan for chaparral and scrub community species east of San Francisco Bay, California.* Portland, Ore. http://sacramento.fws.gov/ea/Documents/Chaparral%20Draft%20Recovery%20Plan%20web.pdf.

———. 2002d. *Final Recovery Plan for southwestern willow flycatcher* (Empidonax trailii extimus). Albuquerque, New Mexico.

———. 2002e. *Recovery plan for California red-legged frog.* Portland, Ore.

———. 2002f. *Safe harbor agreements for private landowners.* Portland, Ore. http://endangered.fws.gov/recovery/harborqa.pdf.

———. 2003a. Proposed designation of critical habitat for *Astragalus magdalenae* var. *peirsonii* (Peirson's milk-vetch). *Federal Register* 68(150). Proposed Rules. Carlsbad, Calif.

———. 2003b. *Recovery Plan for the Quino checkerspot butterfly* (Euphydryas editha quino). Portland, Ore.

———. 2004a. *Conservation plans and agreements database.* Portland, Ore. http://ecos.fws.gov/conserv_plans/public.jsp.

———. 2004b. *Draft recovery plan for the tidewater goby.* Portland, Ore.

———. 2004c. *Draft recovery plan for vernal pool ecosystems of California and southern Oregon.* Portland, Ore. http://pacific.fws.gov/ecoservices/endangered/recovery/Vernal_pool/.

———. 2004d. *Draft regional seabird conservation plan.* U.S. Fish and Wildlife Service, Migratory Birds and Habitats Program, Pacific Region, Portland, Ore.

———. 2004e. Notice of 12-month Petition Finding. *Federal Register,* April 8, 2004, Vol. 69, Number 68.

———. 2005. *Biological and conference opinion for the Lower Colorado Multi-Species Conservation Program (LCR MSCP), Arizona, California, and Nevada.* March 4, 2005.

———. [Accessed June 2005]. *Threatened and Endangered Species System* (TESS). http://ecos.fws.gov/tess_public/TESSWebpage.

———. [Accessed September 2005]. GIS dataset: Private landownership–Northwest California. Unpublished data, available from USFWS, Arcata office. http://www.fws.gov/cno/arcata/irm/gisdata.html.

———. Sacramento Fish and Wildlife Office. [cited October 2004]. *Species account: San Joaquin kit fox.* http://sacramento.fws.gov/es/animal_spp_acct/sj_kit_fox.htm.

———. Designation of critical habitat for the California red-legged frog, and special rule exemption associated with final listing for existing routine ranching activities. *Federal Register* 71(71): 19243-19346.

USGAO (U.S. General Accounting Office). 1989. *Restoring degraded riparian areas on western rangelands.* Testimony of James Duffus III, Associate Director, Resources, Community and Economic Development Division, before the Subcommittee on National Parks and Public Lands, Committee on Interior and Insular Affairs, House of Representatives.

———. 1991a. *Public land management, attention to wildlife is limited.* Report to the Honorable Alan Cranston, U.S. Senate.

———. 1991b. *Rangeland management, BLM's hot desert grazing program merits reconsideration.* Report to the Chairman, Subcommittee on National Parks and Public Lands, Committee on Interior and Insular Affairs, House of Representatives.

———. 1992a. *Rangeland management, results of recent work addressing the performance of land management agencies.* Testimony of J. Dexter Peach, Assistant Controller General, before the Subcommittee on National Parks and Public Lands, Committee on Interior and Insular Affairs, House of Representatives.

———. 1992b. *Rangeland management, profile of the Bureau of Land Management's grazing allotments and permits.* Fact sheet for House of Representatives.

———. 2002. Endangered species, research strategy and long-term monitoring needed for the Mojave desert tortoise recovery program. Report to Congress.

USGS (U.S. Geological Survey). 2003. Impact of fire and grazing on plant diversity and invasion in Sierran forests. Fact Sheet. http://www.werc.usgs.gov.

———. 2004. *Status and trends of the nation's biological resources, human-induced changes in the Mojave and Colorado desert ecosystems: Recovery and restoration potential.*

USGS (U.S. Geological Survey), Western Ecological Research Center. 2003. *Development of a comprehensive ecological monitoring strategy in support of the coastal sage scrub NCCP program in southern California and analysis of the existing monitoring efforts.* http://www.werc.usgs.gov/sandiego/pdfs/hcpsocal.pdf.

Van Devender, T.R. 1999. *Deep history of the Mojave Desert.* Presentation at the Mojave Desert Science Symposium. U.S. Geological Survey, Western Ecological Research Center.

van Wagtendonk, J.W. 1995. Dr. Biswell's influence on the development of prescribed burning in California. From *Biswell Symposium: Fire issues and solutions in urban interface and wildland ecosystems.* U.S. Forest Service Gen. Tech. Rep. PSW-GTR-158.

Vanrheenen, N.T., A.W. Wood, R.N. Palmer, and D.P. Lettenmaier. 2004. Potential implications of PCM climate change scenarios for Sacramento-San Joaquin river basin hydrology and water resources. *Climate Change* 62:257–281.

Vasek, F. 1995. Ancient creosote rings and yucca rings. In *The California desert: An introduction to natural resources and man's impact,* Latting, J., and P.G. Rowlands, eds. June Latting Books. Printed by University of California, Riverside, Press.

Vasek, F.C., and M.G. Barbour. 1988. Mojave Desert scrub vegetation. In *Terrestrial Vegetation of California*, M.G. Barbour and J. Major, eds. New York: John Wiley and Sons.

Vredenburg, V.T. 2004. Reversing introduced species effects: Experimental removal of introduced fish leads to rapid recovery of a declining frog. *Proceedings of the National Academy of Sciences* 101(20):7646–7650.

W. Riverside MSHCP (Western Riverside County Multiple Species Habitat Conservation Plan), Integrated Hardwood Range Management Program, University of California, Berkeley, Center for Conservation Biology, and University of California, Riverside. [cited August 2004]. *Understanding the plants and animals of the Western Riverside County Multiple Species Habitat Conservation Plan.* http://ecoregion.ucr.edu/search/dudek_search.asp.

Wall, T. and R. Miller. 2001. Juniper encroachment into aspen in the northwest Great Basin. *Journal of Range Management.* 54(6):691–698.

Walters, C. 1986. *Adaptive management of renewable resources.* Caldwell, N.J.: Blackburn Press.

Warner, R.E., and K.M Hendrix, eds. 1984. *California riparian systems, ecology, conservation, and productive management.* Berkeley: University of California Press.

Watson, F., L. Pierce, M. Mulitsch, W. Newman, A. Rocha, M. Fain, and J. Nelson. 1999. *Water resources and land use change in the Salinas Valley.* Report No. WI-1999-01. Watershed Institute, California State University, Monterey Bay. http://science.csumb.edu/%7Efwatson/publications/ SV2020_SummaryPaper_020530.pdf.

Weatherspoon, C.P., and C.N. Skinner. 1996. *Landscape-level strategies for forest fuel management.* In Sierra Nevada Ecosystem Project: Final Report to Congress, Vol. II. Davis: University of California, Centers for Water and Wildland Resources.

Webb, R.H., and H. Wilshire, eds. 1983. *Environmental effects of off-road vehicles: Impacts and management in arid regions.* New York: Springer-Verlag.

Weber, M.L., and B. Heneman. 2000. *Guide to California's Marine Life Management Act.* Common Knowledge Press, Berkeley.

Weiss, S.B. 1999. Cars, Cows, and Checkerspot Butterflies: Nitrogen Deposition and Management of Nutrient-poor Grasslands for a Threatened Species. *Conservation Biology* 13(6): 1476-1486.

West Mojave Planning Team. 1999. *Current management situation of special status species in the West Mojave Planning Area.*

Whitford, W.G., ed. 1986. *Pattern and process in desert ecosystems.* Albuquerque: University of New Mexico Press.

Wilhere, G. F. 2002. Adaptive management in habitat conservation plans. *Conservation Biology* 16:20–29.

Williams, D. F. 1986. *Mammalian species of special concern in California.* California Department of Fish and Game, Wildlife Management Report, Division Administration Report 86-1.

Wills, R.D., and J.D. Stuart. 1994. Fire history and stand development of a Douglas-fir/hardwood forest in Northern California. *Northwest Science* 68(3):205–212.

Wisdom, M.J., M.M Rowland, B.C. Wales, M.A. Hemstrom, W.J. Hann, M.G. Raphael, R.S. Holthausen, R.A. Gravenmier, and T.D. Rich. 2001. Modeled effects of sagebrush-steppe on greater sage-grouse in the interior Columbia Basin, U.S.A. *Conservation Biology* 16(5):1223–1231.

Woodbridge, B. 1998. *Swainson's hawk* (Buteo swainsoni*). Technical supplement to the riparian bird conservation plan: A strategy for reversing the decline of riparian-associated birds in California.* Stinson Beach: California Partners in Flight. http://www.prbo.org/calpif/htmldocs/ species/riparian/swainsons_hawk.htm.

Woodhouse, C.W. Hobson, and C. Wilder. 2002. *Upper Lost River and Clear Lake Reservoir watershed, total maximum daily load analysis, water temperature and nutrients.* California Regional Water Quality Control Board, North Coast.

Wrobleski, D.W., and J.B. Kauffman. 2003. Initial effects of prescribed fire on morphology, abundance, and phenology of forbs in big sagebrush communities in southeastern Oregon. *Restoration Ecology* 11(1):82–90.

Wuerthner, G. 1997. *California's wilderness areas.* Vol. 1. *Mountains and coastal ranges.* Westcliffe Publishers.

Wunder, M.B., and F.L. Knopf. 2003. The Imperial Valley of California is critical to wintering mountain plovers. *Journal of Field Ornithology* 74(1):74–80.

Young, J. 2000. *Bromus tetorum.* In *Invasive Plants of California's Wildlands.* C.C. Bossard, J.M. Randall, and M.C. Hoshovsky, eds. Berkeley: University of California Press.

Young, J.A., and C.D. Clements. 2002a. Purshia: *The wild and bitter roses.* Reno and Las Vegas: University of Nevada Press.

Young, J.A., and C.D. Clements. 2002b. Weed problems on Great Basin rangelands. *Proceedings of the Restoration and Management of Sagrebrush/Grass Communities Workshop.* Elko, Nevada.

Young, J.A., and B.A. Sparks. 2002. *Cattle in the cold desert* (expanded edition). Reno and Las Vegas: University of Nevada Press.

Young, J.A., R.A. Evans, and J. Major. 1988. Sagebrush steppe. In *Terrestrial vegetation of California.* M.G. Barbour and J. Major, eds. Hoboken, N.J.: John Wiley & Sons.

Yuskavitch, J. 2001. Vanishing aspen. *Forest Magazine.* January/February.

Zack, S. 2002. *The oak woodland bird conservation plan.* Version 2.0. A report of California Partners in Flight (CalPIF). Point Reyes Bird Observatory Conservation Science. http://www.prbo.org/calpif/plans.html.

Zeiner, D.C., W.F. Laudenslayer Jr., K.E. Mayer, and M. White, eds. 1990. *California's wildlife, volume III: Mammals.* California Department of Fish and Game, Wildlife Habitat Relationships System. http://www.dfg.ca.gov/bdb/html/M183.html.

Zielinkski, W.J., T.E. Kucera, and R.H. Barrett. 1995. Current distribution of the fisher, *Martes pennanti,* in California. *California Fish and Game* 81:104–112.

Index 〰〰〰〰〰〰〰〰〰〰〰〰〰〰〰〰〰〰〰

M

mammals. *See also specific* mammals
    information sources, 415, 423–425
    names, scientific, 469–471
management. *See* adaptive management, monitoring and; land management, general needs; military land management
maps
    Central Coast Region
        agricultural lands, 209
        fish passage barriers, 216
        land ownership, 196
        vineyard expansion, San Luis Obispo County, 212
    Central Valley and Bay-Delta Region
        agricultural land conversion in the San Joaquin Valley, 348
        elevation, 358
        fish passages and barriers, 352
        housing density, 350
        impaired water quality, 355
        land ownership, 332
    Colorado Desert Region
        Algodones Dunes management zones, 145
        Coachella Valley Preserve lands, 146
        Colorado desert aquatic habitat and canals, 141
        land ownership, 129
    Marine Region
        general region, 372
        marine protected areas, 377
    Modoc Plateau Region
        grazing allotments, 278
        greater sage-grouse, 274
        juniper cover, 284
        land ownership, 268
    Mojave Desert Region
        desert tortoise habitat, 104
        Jawbone Canyon and Dove Springs, 117
        land ownership, 96
        multiple use conflicts in Jawbone-Butterbredt ACEC, 109
        projected urban development, 112
        riparian vegetation, 114
    North Coast–Klamath Region
        coho salmon ranges, 246
        fish passage barriers, 250
        land ownership, 236
        Trinity Dam, 252
    range maps, Wildlife Species Matrix and, 22
    Sierra Nevada and Cascades Region
        development along upland highway corridors, 305
        Federal Energy Regulatory Commission projects, 323

        land ownership, 290
        road network, 320
        Sierra Nevada Bighorn Sheep Recovery Program, 315
    South Coast Region
        conservation planning, 182
        Huntington Beach and Newport Bay wetlands, 176
        land ownership, 162
        Santa Clara and Los Angeles Rivers, 174
marbled murrelet, 57–58, 243
Marine Corps Air Station Miramar, 184–185, 189
marine life. *See also* fish; salmon
    information sources, 419–422
    invasive species monitoring program, 58–59
    Marine Life Management Act (MLMA), 89, 375, 392–393
    Marine Life Protection Act, 89, 375–376, 392–393, 394
    multi-agency fish barrier monitoring, 56
Marine Region, 373–399
    Caulerpa taxifolia eradication, 388
    conservation actions, 392–399
        implementation of California Ocean Protection Act, 396
        implementation of Marine Life Protection Act, 394–395
        management of marine fisheries and ecosystem, 392–394
    description of, 373–374
    maps
        general region, 372
        Marine Protected Areas (MPAs), 377
    monitoring needs of, 506–507
    regional consultations, 520–521
    species at risk, 376–382
        abalone, 380–381
        common murre, 381–382
        special status invertebrates, 379
        special status vertebrates, 378
    stressors affecting wildlife and habitats, 382–392
        degradation of marine habitats, 386–388
        human disturbance, 391–392
        invasive species, 388–390
        overfishing, 384–386
        overview of challenges, 382–383
        pollution, 390–391
Mattole River, 263
meadows, monitoring, 54–55
mercury contamination, 354
military land management
    Central Coast Region, 227
    Mojave Desert Region, 122–123
    South Coast Region, 35, 184–185, 189, 195